# MILITARY AIRCRAFT MARKINGS 2006

PETER R. MARCH &
HOWARD J. CURTIS

## MIDLAND

An imprint of
Ian Allan Publishing

# Contents

Photographs by Peter R. March (PRM) unless otherwise credited

This twenty-seventh edition published 2006

ISBN (10) 1 85780 227 6
ISBN (13) 978 1 85780 227 6

Published by Midland Publishing

an imprint of Ian Allan Publishing Ltd,
Hersham, Surrey KT12 4RG.

Printed in England by Ian Allan Printing Ltd,
Hersham, Surrey KT12 4RG

Code: 0603/D2

*Front cover:* Lockheed Martin F-16 Fighting Falcon. *Richard Cooper*

# Introduction

Jointly edited by Howard J Curtis and Peter R. March, this twenty-seventh annual edition of abc Military Aircraft Markings, follows the pattern of previous years and lists in alphabetical and numerical order the aircraft that carry a United Kingdom military serial, and which are normally based, or might be seen, in the UK. It also includes airworthy and current RAF/RN/Army aircraft that are based permanently or temporarily overseas. The term 'aircraft' used here covers powered, manned aeroplanes, helicopters, airships and gliders. Included are all the current Royal Air Force, Royal Navy, Army Air Corps, Defence Procurement Agency, QinetiQ operated, manufacturers' test aircraft and civilian-owned aircraft with military markings or operated for the Ministry of Defence.

Aircraft withdrawn from operational use but which are retained in the UK for ground training purposes or otherwise preserved by the Services and in the numerous museums and collections are listed. The serials of some incomplete aircraft have been included, such as the cockpit sections of machines displayed by the RAF, aircraft used by airfield fire sections and for service battle damage repair training (BDRT), together with significant parts of aircraft held by preservation groups and societies. Where only part of the aircraft fuselage remains the abbreviation <ff> for front fuselage/cockpit section or <rf> for rear fuselage is shown after the type. Many of these aircraft are allocated, and sometimes wear, a secondary identity, such as an RAF 'M' maintenance number. These numbers are listed against those aircraft to which they have been allocated.

A serial 'missing' from a sequence is either because it was never issued as it formed part of a 'black-out block' or because the aircraft has been written off, scrapped, sold abroad or allocated an alternative marking. Aircraft used as targets on MoD ranges to which access is restricted, and UK military aircraft that have been permanently grounded and are based overseas and unlikely to return to Britain have generally been omitted. With the appearance of some military registered UAVs, drones and small target aircraft at public events and ground displays, these have now been included if they are likely to be seen.

In the main, the serials listed are those markings presently displayed on the aircraft. Where an aircraft carries a false serial it is quoted in italic type. Very often these serials are carried by replicas, that are denoted by <R> after the type. The manufacturer and aircraft type are given, together with recent alternative, previous, secondary or civil identity shown in round brackets. Complete records of multiple previous identities are only included where space permits. The operating unit and its based location, along with any known unit and base code markings in square brackets, are given as accurately as possible. The unit markings are normally carried boldly on the sides of the fuselage or on the aircraft's fin. In the case of RAF and AAC machines currently in service, they are usually one or two letters or numbers, while the RN continues to use a well-established system of three-figure codes between 000 and 999 together with a tail letter code denoting the aircraft's operational base. RN squadrons, units and bases are allocated blocks of numbers from which individual aircraft codes are issued. To help identification of RN bases and landing platforms on ships, a list of tail-letter codes with their appropriate name, helicopter code number, ship pennant number and type of vessel, is included; as is a helicopter code number/ships' tail-letter code grid cross-reference.

Code changes, for example when aircraft move between units and therefore the markings currently painted on a particular aircraft, might not be those shown in this edition because of subsequent events. Aircraft still under manufacture or not yet delivered to the Service, such as Eurofighter Typhoons, Hawk 128s and Airbus A400Ms are listed under their allocated serial numbers. Likewise there are a number of newly built aircraft for overseas air arms that carry British serials for their UK test and delivery flights. The airframes which will not appear in the next edition because of sale, accident, etc, have their fates, where known, shown in italic type in the locations column.

The Irish Army Air Corps fleet is listed, together with the serials of other overseas air arms whose aircraft might be seen visiting the UK from time to time. The serial numbers are as usually presented on the individual machine or as they are normally identified. Where possible, the aircraft's base and operating unit have been shown.

USAF, US Army and US Navy aircraft based in the UK and in Western Europe, and types that regularly visit the UK from the USA, are each listed in separate sections by aircraft type. The serial number actually displayed on the aircraft is shown in full, with additional Fiscal Year (FY) or full serial information also provided. Where appropriate, details of the operating wing, squadron allocation and base are added. The USAF is, like the RAF, in a continuing period of change, resulting in the adoption of new unit titles, squadron and equipment changes and the closure of bases. Only details that concern changes effected by January 2006 are shown.

Veteran and vintage aircraft which carry overseas military markings but which are based in the UK or regularly visit mainland Europe, have been separately listed showing their principal means of identification. The growing list of aircraft in government or military service, often under contract to private operating companies, that carry civil registrations has again been included at the end of the respective country.

With the use of the Internet now very well established as a rich source of information, the section listing a selection of military aviation 'world wide web' sites, has again been expanded and up-dated this year. Although only a few of these provide details of aircraft serials and markings, they do give interesting insights into air arms and their operating units, aircraft, museums and a broad range of associated topics. Information shown is believed to be correct at 31 January 2006, and significant changes can be downloaded from The Airnet web site, http://fly.to/AirNet/.

# Acknowledgements

The compilers wish to thank the many people who have taken the trouble to send comments, additions, deletions and other useful information since the publication of the previous edition of abc Military Aircraft Markings. In particular the following individuals: Alan Allen, Allan Barley, Richard Cawsey, Glyn Coney, Mike Cubitt, Patrick Dirksen, Ben Dunnell, John Dyer, Bob Elliott, Andy Gabriel, Wal Gandy, Alan Gray, Kev Hart, Ray F. Hill, Bill Hodges, Geoff Hooper, Lee Howard, Paul van den Hurk, Phil Jones, Terry Lee, Rob Leigh, Andrew March, Tony McCarthy, Tom McGhee, Gavin McLean, Gary Parsons, Martin Pole, Jummi Richmond-Cole, Colin Rossiter, Roger Smith, Kev Storer, David Stretton, David Symington, Len Taylor, Jurgen van Toor and Bob Turner.

The 2006 edition has also relied upon the printed publications and/or associated internet web-sites as follows: Aerodata Quantum+, Air-Britain Information Exchange,'Air-Britain News', Airfields e-mail group, Airliners.net web site, BAEG e-mail group, Graham Gaff/East London Aviation Society, Fighter Control, JetPhotos.net web site, Joe Baugher's Home Page, Brian Pickering/'Military Aviation Review', Military Spotter's Forum, NAMAR e-mail group, P-3 Orion Research Group, Pacific Database, RAF Leeming e-mail group, RAF Shawbury web site, Andrew & Mervyn Thomas/St Athan Aviation Group, SAAB Viggen E-mail group, Mark Walton/'Scottish Air News', 'Scramble', Spotter's Nest web site, UK Serials Resource Centre, Keith Preen/Wales Aviation Research Centre, Geoff Goodall/Warbirds Directory 4 and Mick Boulanger/Wolverhampton Aviation Group.

PRM & HJC                                                                                    January 2006

# Abbreviations

| Abbrev | Meaning |
|---|---|
| AAC | Army Air Corps |
| AACS | Airborne Air Control Squadron |
| AACTS | Airborne Air Control Training Squadron |
| ACC | Air Combat Command |
| ACCGS | Air Cadets Central Gliding School |
| ACW | Airborne Control Wing |
| AD&StA | Aberdeen, Dundee & St Andrews |
| AEF | Air Experience Flight |
| AESS | Air Engineering & Survival School |
| AEW | Airborne Early Warning |
| AF | Arméflyget (Army Air Battalion) |
| AFB | Air Force Base |
| AFD | Air Fleet Department |
| AFRC | Air Force Reserve Command |
| AFSC | Air Force Systems Command |
| AFSK | Armeflygskolan (Army Flying School) |
| AFWF | Advanced Fixed Wing Flight |
| AG | Airlift Group |
| AGA | Academia General del Aire (General Air Academy) |
| AkG | Aufklärungsgeschwader (Reconnaissance Wing) |
| AMC | Air Mobility Command |
| AMD-BA | Avions Marcel Dassault-Breguet Aviation |
| AMF | Aircraft Maintenance Flight |
| AMG | Aircraft Maintenance Group |
| AMIF | Aircraft Maintenance Instruction Flight |
| AMW | Air Mobility Wing |
| ANG | Air National Guard |
| APS | Aircraft Preservation Society |
| ARS | Air Refuelling Squadron |
| ARW | Air Refuelling Wing |
| ARWS | Advanced Rotary Wing Squadron |
| AS | Airlift Squadron/Air Squadron |
| ASF | Aircraft Servicing Flight |
| AS&RU | Aircraft Salvage and Repair Unit |
| ATC | Air Training Corps |
| ATCC | Air Traffic Control Centre |
| AVDEF | Aviation Defence Service |
| Avn | Aviation |
| AW | Airlift Wing/Armstrong Whitworth Aircraft |
| AWC | Air Warfare Centre |
| BAC | British Aircraft Corporation |
| BAe | British Aerospace PLC |
| BAPC | British Aviation Preservation Council |
| BATSUB | British Army Training Support Unit Belize |
| BATUS | British Army Training Unit Suffield |
| BBMF | Battle of Britain Memorial Flight |
| BDRF | Battle Damage Repair Flight |
| BDRT | Battle Damage Repair Training |
| Be | Beech |
| Bf | Bayerische Flugzeugwerke |
| BG | Bomber Group |
| BGA | British Gliding & Soaring Association |
| bk | black (squadron colours and markings) |
| bl | blue (squadron colours and markings) |
| BNFL | British Nuclear Fuels Ltd |
| BP | Boulton & Paul |
| br | brown (squadron colours and markings) |
| BS | Bomber Squadron |
| B-V | Boeing-Vertol |
| BW | Bomber Wing |
| CAARP | Co-operative des Ateliers Air de la Région Parisienne |
| CAC | Commonwealth Aircraft Corporation |
| CARG | Cotswold Aircraft Restoration Group |
| CASA | Construcciones Aeronautics SA |
| Cav | Cavalry |
| CC | County Council |
| CCF | Combined Cadet Force/Canadian Car & Foundry Company |
| CDE | Chemical Defence Establishment |
| CEAM | Centre d'Expérimentation Aériennes Militaires (Military Air Experimental Centre) |
| CEPA | Centre d'Expérimentation Pratique de l'Aéronautique Navale |
| CEV | Centre d'Essais en Vol (Flight Test Centre) |
| CFS | Central Flying School |
| CGMF | Central Glider Maintenance Flight |
| CIFAS | Centre d'Instruction des Forces Aériennes Stratégiques (Air Strategic Training Centre) |
| CinC | Commander in Chief |
| CinCLANT | Commander in Chief Atlantic |
| CITac | Centre d'Instruction Tactique (Tactical Training Centre) |
| CLV | Centrum Leteckeho Vycviku (Air Training Centre) |
| Co | Company |
| Comp | Composite with |
| CT | College of Technology |
| CTE | Central Training Establishment |
| CV | Chance-Vought |
| D-BA | Daimler-Benz Aerospace |
| D-BD | Dassault-Breguet Dornier |
| D&G | Dumfries and Galloway |
| DARA | Defence Aviation Repair Agency |
| DCAE | Defence College of Aeronautical Engineering |
| DEFTS | Defence Elementary Flying Training School |
| DEODS | Defence Explosives Ordnance Disposal School |
| Det | Detachment |
| DH | de Havilland |
| DHC | de Havilland Canada |
| DHFS | Defence Helicopter Flying School |
| DLMW | Dywizjon Lotniczy Marynarki Wojennej |
| DLO | Defence Logistics Organisation |
| DMS | Defence Movements School |
| DPA | Defence Procurement Agency |
| DS&DC | Defence Storage & Disposition Centre |
| DS&TL | Defence Science & Technology Laboratory |
| DTI | Department of Trade and Industry |
| EA | Escadron Aérien (Air Squadron) |
| EAAT | Escadrille Avions de l'Armée de Terre |
| EAC | Ecole de l'Aviation de Chasse (Fighter Aviation School) |
| EAP | European Aircraft Project |
| EAT | Ecole de l'Aviation de Transport (Transport Aviation School) |
| EC | Escadre de Chasse (Fighter Wing) |
| ECM | Electronic Counter Measures |
| ECS | Electronic Countermeasures Squadron |
| EDA | Escadre de Detection Aéroportée (Air Detection Wing) |
| EdC | Escadron de Convoyage |
| EDCA | Escadron de Détection et de Control Aéroportée (Airborne Detection & Control Sqn) |
| EE | English Electric/Escadrille Electronique |
| EET | Escadron Electronique Tactique (Tactical Electronics Flight) |
| EFTS | Elementary Flying Training School |
| EH | Escadron d'Helicoptères (Helicopter Flight) |
| EHI | European Helicopter Industries |
| EKW | Eidgenössiches Konstruktionswerkstätte |
| EL | Escadre de Liaison (Liaison Wing) |
| EL | Eskadra Lotnicza |
| ELT | Eskadra Lotnictwa Taktycznego (Tactical Air Squadron) |
| ELTR | Eskadra Lotnictwa Transportowego (Air Transport Squadron) |
| EMA | East Midlands Airport |
| EMVO | Elementaire Militaire Vlieg Opleiding (Elementary Flying Training) |
| ENOSA | Ecole des Navigateurs Operationales Systemes d'Armees (Navigation School) |
| EoN | Elliot's of Newbury |
| EPAA | Ecole de Pilotage Elementaire de l'Armée de l'Air (Air Force Elementary Flying School) |

9

| | |
|---|---|
| **EPE** | Ecole de Pilotage Elementaire (Elementary Flying School) |
| **EPNER** | Ecole du Personnel Navigant d'Essais et de Reception |
| **ER** | Escadre de Reconnaissance (Reconnaissance Wing) |
| **ERS** | Escadron de Reconnaissance Stratégique (Strategic Reconnaissance Squadron) |
| **ES** | Escadrille de Servitude |
| **Esc** | Escuadron (Squadron) |
| **Esk** | Eskadrille (Squadron) |
| **Eslla** | Escuadrilla (Squadron) |
| **Esq** | Esquadra (Squadron) |
| **ET** | Escadre de Transport (Transport Squadron) |
| **ETE** | Escadron de Transport et Entrainement (Transport Training Squadron) |
| **ETEC** | Escadron de Transport d'Entrainement et de Calibration (Transport Training & Calibration Sqn) |
| **ETL** | Escadron de Transport Légère (Light Transport Squadron) |
| **ETO** | Escadron de Transition Operationnelle |
| **ETOM** | Escadron de Transport Outre Mer (Overseas Transport Squadron) |
| **ETPS** | Empire Test Pilots' School |
| **ETS** | Engineering Training School |
| **FAA** | Fleet Air Arm/Federal Aviation Administration |
| **FBS** | Flugbereitschaftstaffel |
| **FBW** | Fly-by-wire |
| **FC** | Forskokcentralen (Flight Centre) |
| **FE** | Further Education |
| **FETC** | Fire and Emergency Training Centre |
| **ff** | Front fuselage |
| **FG** | Fighter Group |
| **FH** | Fairchild-Hiller |
| **FI** | Falkland Islands |
| **FJWOEU** | Fast Jet & Guided Weapon Operational Evaluation Unit |
| **FISt** | Flieger Staffel (Flight Squadron) |
| **Flt** | Flight |
| **FMA** | Fabrica Militar de Aviones |
| **FMT** | Flotila Militara de Transport (Transport Regiment) |
| **FMV** | Forsvarets Materielwerk |
| **FONA** | Flag Officer Naval Aviation |
| **FRADU** | Fleet Requirements and Air Direction Unit |
| **FRA** | FR Aviation |
| **FS** | Fighter Squadron |
| **FSAIU** | Flight Safety & Accident Investigation Unit |
| **FSCTE** | Fire Services Central Training Establishment |
| **FTS** | Flying Training School |
| **FTW** | Flying Training Wing |
| **Fw** | Focke Wulf |
| **FW** | Fighter Wing/Foster Wickner |
| **FWTS** | Fixed Wing Test Squadron |
| **FY** | Fiscal Year |
| **F3 OCU** | Tornado F3 Operational Conversion Unit |
| **GAF** | Government Aircraft Factory |
| **GAL** | General Aircraft Ltd |
| **GAM** | Groupe Aerien Mixte (Composite Air Group) |
| **gd** | gold (squadron colours and markings) |
| **GD** | General Dynamics |
| **GHL** | Groupe d'Helicopteres Legeres (Light Helicopter Group) |
| **GI** | Ground Instruction/Groupement d'Instruction (Instructional Group) |
| **gn** | green (squadron colours and markings) |
| **GRD** | Gruppe fur Rustunggdienste (Group for Service Preparation) |
| **GRV** | Groupe de Ravitaillement en Vol (Air Refuelling Group) |
| **GT** | Grupo de Transporte (Transport Wing) |
| **GTT** | Grupo de Transporte de Tropos (Troop Carrier Wing) |
| **gy** | grey (squadron colours and markings) |
| **H&W** | Hereford and Worcester |
| **HAF** | Historic Aircraft Flight |
| **HC** | Helicopter Combat Support Squadron |
| **HCS** | Hunting Contract Services |
| **HF** | Historic Flying Ltd |
| **HFUS** | Heeresfliegerunterstützungsstaffel |
| **HFVAS** | Heeresfliegerverbindungs/Aufklärungsstaffel |
| **HFVS** | Heeresfliegerversuchstaffel |
| **HFWS** | Heeresflieger Waffenschule (Army Air Weapons School) |
| **Hkp.Bat** | Helikopter Bataljon (Helicopter Battalion) |
| **HMA** | Helicopter Maritime Attack |
| **HMF** | Harrier Maintenance Flight/Helicopter Maintenance Flight |
| **HMS** | Her Majesty's Ship |
| **HOCU** | Harrier OCU |
| **HP** | Handley-Page |
| **HQ** | Headquarters |
| **HRO** | Harc1szati Repülő Ezred |
| **HS** | Hawker Siddeley |
| **IAF** | Israeli Air Force |
| **IAP** | International Airport |
| **INTA** | Instituto Nacional de Tecnica Aerospacial |
| **IOW** | Isle Of Wight |
| **IWM** | Imperial War Museum |
| **JATE** | Joint Air Transport Establishment |
| **JbG** | Jagdbombergeschwader (Fighter Bomber Wing) |
| **JFACTSU** | Joint Forward Air Control Training & Standards Unit |
| **JG** | Jagdgeschwader (Fighter Wing) |
| **JHF** | Joint Helicopter Force |
| **KHR** | Kampfhubschrauberregiment |
| **Kridlo** | Wing |
| **lbvr** | letka Bitevnich Vrtulníkü (Attack Helicopter Squadron) |
| **Letka** | Squadron |
| **LTG** | Lufttransportgeschwader (Air Transport Wing) |
| **LTV** | Ling-Temco-Vought |
| **LVG** | Luftwaffen Versorgungs Geschwader (Air Force Maintenance Wing)/Luft Verkehrs Gesellschaft |
| **LZO** | Letecky Zku ební Odbor (Aviation Test Department) |
| **m** | multi-coloured (squadron colours and markings) |
| **MAPK** | Mira Anachestistis Pantos Kerou (All Weather Interception Sqn) |
| **MASD** | Marine Air Support Detachment |
| **MASU** | Mobile Aircraft Support Unit |
| **MBB** | Messerschmitt Bolkow-Blohm |
| **MCAS** | Marine Corps Air Station |
| **McD** | McDonnell Douglas |
| **MDMF** | Merlin Depth Maintenance Facilities |
| **Med** | Medical |
| **MFG** | Marine Flieger Geschwader (Naval Air Wing) |
| **MH** | Max Holste |
| **MIB** | Military Intelligence Battalion |
| **MiG** | Mikoyan — Gurevich |
| **Mod** | Modified |
| **MR** | Maritime Reconnaissance |
| **MRH** | Multi-role Helikopters |
| **MS** | Morane-Saulnier |
| **MTHR** | Mittlerer Transporthubschrauber Regiment (Medium Transport Helicopter Regiment) |
| **MTM** | Mira Taktikis Metaforon (Tactical Transport Sqn) |
| **NA** | North American |
| **NACDS** | Naval Air Command Driving School |
| **NAEW&CF** | NATO Airborne Early Warning & Control Force |
| **NAF** | Naval Air Facility |
| **NAS** | Naval Air Station |
| **NASU** | Naval Air Support Unit |
| **NATO** | North Atlantic Treaty Organisation |
| **NAWC** | Naval Air Warfare Center |
| **NAWC-AD** | Naval Air Warfare Center Aircraft Division |
| **NBC** | Nuclear, Biological and Chemical |
| **NE** | North-East |
| **NFATS** | Naval Force Aircraft Test Squadron |
| **NI** | Northern Ireland |
| **NMSU** | Nimrod Major Servicing Unit |

| | |
|---|---|
| **NOCU** | Nimrod Operational Conversion Unit |
| **NTOCU** | National Tornado Operational Conversion Unit |
| **NYARC** | North Yorks Aircraft Restoration Centre |
| **OCU** | Operational Conversion Unit |
| **OEU** | Operation Evaluation Unit |
| **OFMC** | Old Flying Machine Company |
| **OGMA** | Oficinas Gerais de Material Aeronautico |
| **or** | orange (squadron colours and markings) |
| **OSAC** | Operational Support Airlift Command |
| **OVH Kmp** | Observations-Helicopter Kompagni |
| **PAT** | Priority Air Transport Detachment |
| **PBN** | Pilatus Britten-Norman |
| **PLM** | Pulk Lotnictwa Mysliwskiego (Fighter Regiment) |
| **pr** | purple (squadron colours and markings) |
| **PRU** | Photographic Reconnaissance Unit |
| **PVH Kmp** | Panservaerns-Helicopter Kompagni |
| **r** | red (squadron colours and markings) |
| **R** | Replica |
| **RAeS** | Royal Aeronautical Society |
| **RAF** | Royal Aircraft Factory/Royal Air Force |
| **RAFC** | Royal Air Force College |
| **RAFM** | Royal Air Force Museum |
| **RAFGSA** | Royal Air Force Gliding and Soaring Association |
| **RE** | Royal Engineers |
| **Regt** | Regiment |
| **REME** | Royal Electrical & Mechanical Engineers |
| **rf** | Rear fuselage |
| **RFA** | Royal Fleet Auxiliary |
| **RJAF** | Royal Jordanian Air Force |
| **RM** | Royal Marines |
| **RMB** | Royal Marines Base |
| **RMC of S** | Royal Military College of Science |
| **RN** | Royal Navy |
| **RNAS** | Royal Naval Air Station |
| **RNGSA** | Royal Navy Gliding and Soaring Association |
| **ROF** | Royal Ordnance Factory |
| **RQS** | Rescue Squadron |
| **R-R** | Rolls-Royce |
| **RS** | Reid & Sigrist/Reconnaissance Squadron |
| **RSV** | Reparto Sperimentale Volo (Experimental Flight School) |
| **RW** | Reconnaissance Wing |
| **SA** | Scottish Aviation |
| **SAAB** | Svenska Aeroplan Aktieboleg |
| **SAH** | School of Air Handling |
| **SAL** | Scottish Aviation Limited |
| **SAR** | Search and Rescue |
| **Saro** | Saunders-Roe |
| **SARTU** | Search and Rescue Training Unit |
| **SCW** | Strategic Communications Wing |
| **SDoLt** | Samostatna Dopravniho Letka (Independent Transport Squadron) |
| **SEAE** | School of Electrical & Aeronautical Engineering |
| **SEPECAT** | Société Européenne de Production de l'avion Ecole de Combat et d'Appui Tactique |
| **SFDO** | School of Flight Deck Operations |
| **SHAPE** | Supreme Headquarters Allied Forces Europe |
| **SHOPS** | Sea Harrier Operational Support Unit |
| **si** | silver (squadron colours and markings) |
| **SIET** | Section d'Instruction et d'Etude du Tir |
| **SKTU** | Sea King Training Unit |
| **Skv** | Skvadron (Squadron) |
| **SLK** | Stihacie Letecké Kridlo (Fighter Air Wing) |
| **slt** | stíhací letka (Fighter Squadron) |
| **SLV** | School Licht Vliegwezen (Flying School) |
| **Sm** | Smaldeel (Squadron) |
| **smdl** | Smisena Dopravní Letka |
| **SNCAN** | Société Nationale de Constructions Aéronautiques du Nord |
| **SOG** | Special Operations Group |
| **SOS** | Special Operations Squadron |
| **SoTT** | School of Technical Training |
| **SOW** | Special Operations Wing |
| **SPAD** | Société Pour les Appareils Deperdussin |
| **SPP** | Strojirny Prvni Petilesky |
| **Sqn** | Squadron |
| **SWWAPS** | Second World War Aircraft Preservation Society |
| **TA** | Territorial Army |
| **TAP** | Transporten Avio Polk (Air Transport Regiment) |
| **TFC** | The Fighter Collection |
| **TGp** | Test Groep |
| **TIARA** | Tornado Integrated Avionics Research Aircraft |
| **TL** | Taktická Letka (Tactical Squadron) |
| **tlt** | taktická letka (Tactical Squadron) |
| **TMF** | Tornado Maintenance Flight |
| **TMTS** | Trade Management Training School |
| **TOCU** | Typhoon Operational Conversion Unit |
| **tpzlt** | taktická a prùzkumná letka (Tactical & Reconnaissance Squadron) |
| **TS** | Test Squadron |
| **TsAGI** | Tsentral'ny Aerogidrodinamicheski Instut (Central Aero & Hydrodynamics Institute) |
| **TsLw** | Technische Schule der Luftwaffe (Luftwaffe Technical School) |
| **TW** | Test Wing |
| **UAS** | University Air Squadron |
| **UAV** | Unmanned Air Vehicle |
| **Uberwg** | Uberwachunggeschwader (Surveillance Wing) |
| **UK** | United Kingdom |
| **UKAEA** | United Kingdom Atomic Energy Authority |
| **UNFICYP** | United Nations' Forces in Cyprus |
| **US** | United States |
| **USAF** | United States Air Force |
| **USAFE** | United States Air Forces in Europe |
| **USAREUR** | US Army Europe |
| **USCGS** | US Coast Guard Station |
| **USEUCOM** | United States European Command |
| **USMC** | United States Marine Corps |
| **USN** | United States Navy |
| **NWTSPM** | United States Navy Test Pilots School |
| **VAAC** | Vectored thrust Advanced Aircraft flight Control |
| **VFW** | Vereinigte Flugtechnische Werke |
| **VGS** | Volunteer Gliding Squadron |
| **VLA** | Vojenska Letecka Akademia |
| **vlt** | vycviková letka (Training Squadron) |
| **VMGR** | Marine Aerial Refuelling/Transport Squadron |
| **VMGRT** | Marine Aerial Refuelling/Transport Training Squadron |
| **VQ** | Fleet Air Reconnaissance Squadron |
| **VR** | Fleet Logistic Support Squadron |
| **VrK** | Vrtulnikové Letecké Kridlo |
| **VS** | Vickers-Supermarine |
| **VSD** | Vegyes Sz1llitorepülö Dand1r (Aircraft Transport Brigade) |
| **w** | white (squadron colours and markings) |
| **Wg** | Wing |
| **WHL** | Westland Helicopters Ltd |
| **WLT** | Weapons Loading Training |
| **WRS** | Weather Reconnaissance Squadron |
| **WS** | Westland |
| **WSK** | Wytwornia Sprzetu Kominikacyjnego |
| **WTD** | Wehrtechnische Dienstelle (Technical Support Unit) |
| **WW2** | World War II |
| **y** | yellow (squadron colours and markings) |
| **zDL** | základna Dopravního Letectva (Air Transport Base) |
| **zL** | základna Letectva |
| **ZmDK** | Zmie any Dopravny Kridlo (Mixed Transport Wing) |
| **zSL** | základna Speciálního Letectva (Training Air Base) |
| **zTL** | základna Taktického Letectva (Tactical Air Base) |
| **zVrL** | základna Vrtulníkového Letectva (Helicopter Air Base) |

# A Guide to the Location of Operational Military Bases in the UK

This section is to assist the reader to locate the places in the United Kingdom where operational military aircraft (including helicopters and gliders) are based.

The alphabetical order listing gives each location in relation to its county and to its nearest classified road(s) (*by* means adjoining; *of* means proximate to), together with its approximate direction and mileage from the centre of a nearby major town or city. Some civil airports are included where active military units are also based, but **excluded** are MoD sites with non-operational aircraft (eg *gate guardians*), the bases of privately-owned civil aircraft that wear military markings and museums.

| User | Base name | County/Region | Location | Distance/direction from (town) |
|------|-----------|---------------|----------|-------------------------------|
| Army | Abingdon | Oxfordshire | W by B4017, W of A34 | 5m SSW of Oxford |
| RAF | Aldergrove/Belfast Airport | Co Antrim | W by A26 | 13m W of Belfast |
| RM | Arbroath | Angus | E of A933 | 2m NW of Arbroath |
| RAF/HCS | Barkston Heath | Lincolnshire | W by B6404, S of A153 | 5m NNE of Grantham |
| RAF | Benson | Oxfordshire | E by A423 | 1m NE of Wallingford |
| QinetiQ/ RAF | Boscombe Down | Wiltshire | S by A303, W of A338 | 6m N of Salisbury |
| RAF | Boulmer | Northumberland | E of B1339 | 4m E of Alnwick |
| RAF | Brize Norton | Oxfordshire | W of A4095 | 5m SW of Witney |
| Marshall | Cambridge Airport/ Teversham | Cambridgeshire | S by A1303 | 2m E of Cambridge |
| RM/RAF | Chivenor | Devon | S of A361 | 4m WNW of Barnstaple |
| RAF | Church Fenton | Yorkshire North | S of B1223 | 7m WNW of Selby |
| Army | Colerne | Wiltshire | S of A420, E of Fosse Way | 5m NE of Bath |
| RAF | Coltishall | Norfolk | W of B1150 | 9m NNE of Norwich |
| RAF | Coningsby | Lincolnshire | S of A153, W by B1192 | 10m NW of Boston |
| RAF | Cosford | Shropshire | W of A41, N of A464 | 9m WNW of Wolverhampton |
| RAF | Cottesmore | Rutland | W of A1, N of B668 | 9m NW of Stamford |
| RAF | Cranwell | Lincolnshire | N by A17, S by B1429 | 5m WNW of Sleaford |
| RN | Culdrose | Cornwall | E by A3083 | 1m SE of Helston |
| Army | Dishforth | Yorkshire North | E by A1 | 4m E of Ripon |
| USAF | Fairford | Gloucestershire | S of A417 | 9m ESE of Cirencester |
| RN | Fleetlands | Hampshire | E by A32 | 2m SE of Fareham |
| RAF | Halton | Buckinghamshire | N of A4011, S of B4544 | 4m ESE of Aylesbury |
| RAF | Henlow | Bedfordshire | E of A600, W of A6001 | 1m SW of Henlow |
| RAF | Honington | Suffolk | E of A134, W of A1088 | 6m S of Thetford |
| Army | Hullavington | Wiltshire | W of A429 | 1m N of M4 jn 17 |
| RAF | Kenley | Greater London | W of A22 | 1m W of Warlingham |
| RAF | Kinloss | Grampian | E of B9011, N of B9089 | 3m NE of Forres |
| RAF | Kirknewton | Lothian | E by B7031, N by A70 | 8m SW of Edinburgh |
| USAF | Lakenheath | Suffolk | W by A1065 | 8m W of Thetford |
| RAF | Leeming | Yorkshire North | E by A1 | 5m SW of Northallerton |
| RAF | Leuchars | Fife | E of A919 | 7m SE of Dundee |
| RAF | Linton-on-Ouse | Yorkshire North | E of B6265 | 10m NW of York |
| RAF | Lossiemouth | Grampian | W of B9135, S of B9040 | 4m N of Elgin |
| RAF | Lyneham | Wiltshire | W of A3102, S of A420 | 10m WSW of Swindon |
| RAF | Marham | Norfolk | N by A1122 | 6m W of Swaffham |
| Army | Middle Wallop | Hampshire | S by A343 | 6m SW of Andover |
| USAF | Mildenhall | Suffolk | S by A1101 | 9m NNE of Newmarket |
| RAF | Northolt | Greater London | N by A40 | 3m E of M40 jn 1 |
| RAF | Odiham | Hampshire | E of A32 | 2m S of M3 jn 5 |
| RN | Predannack | Cornwall | W by A3083 | 7m S of Helston |
| RAF | St Athan | South Glamorgan | N of B4265 | 13m WSW of Cardiff |
| RAF | St Mawgan/Newquay | Cornwall | N of A3059 | 4m ENE of Newquay |
| RAF | Scampton | Lincolnshire | W by A15 | 6m N of Lincoln |
| RAF | Sealand | Flint | W by A550 | 6m WNW of Chester |
| RAF | Shawbury | Shropshire | W of B5063 | 7m NNE of Shrewsbury |
| RAF | Syerston | Nottinghamshire | W by A46 | 5m SW of Newark |
| RAF | Ternhill | Shropshire | SW by A41 | 3m SW of Market Drayton |
| RAF/Army | Topcliffe | Yorkshire North | E of A167, W of A168 | 3m SW of Thirsk |

| User | Base name | County/Region | Location | Distance/direction from (town) |
|------|-----------|---------------|----------|-------------------------------|
| RAF | Valley | Gwynedd | S of A5 on Anglesey | 5m SE of Holyhead |
| RAF | Waddington | Lincolnshire | E by A607, W by A15 | 5m S of Lincoln |
| Army | Wattisham | Suffolk | N of B1078 | 5m SSW of Stowmarket |
| RAF | Weston-on-the-Green | Oxfordshire | E by A43 | 9m N of Oxford |
| RAF | Wittering | Cambridgeshire | W by A1, N of A47 | 3m S of Stamford |
| RAF | Woodvale | Merseyside | W by A565 | 5m SSW of Southport |
| RAF | Wyton | Cambridgeshire | E of A141, N of B1090 | 3m NE of Huntingdon |
| RN | Yeovilton | Somerset | S by B3151, S of A303 | 5m N of Yeovil |

13

# British Military Aircraft Serials

The Committee of Imperial Defence through its Air Committee introduced a standardised system of numbering aircraft in November 1912. The Air Department of the Admiralty was allocated the first batch 1-200 and used these to cover aircraft already in use and those on order. The Army was issued with the next block from 201-800, which included the number 304 which was given to the Cody Biplane now preserved in the Science Museum. By the outbreak of World War 1 the Royal Navy was on its second batch of serials 801-1600 and this system continued with alternating allocations between the Army and Navy until 1916 when number 10000, a Royal Flying Corps BE2C, was reached.

It was decided not to continue with five digit numbers but instead to start again from 1, prefixing RFC aircraft with the letter A and RNAS aircraft with the prefix N. The RFC allocations commenced with A1 an FE2D and before the end of the year had reached A9999 an Armstrong Whitworth FK8. The next group commenced with B1 and continued in logical sequence through the C, D, E and F prefixes. G was used on a limited basis to identify captured German aircraft, while H was the last block of wartime-ordered aircraft. To avoid confusion I was not used, so the new postwar machines were allocated serials in the J range. A further minor change was made in the serial numbering system in August 1929 when it was decided to maintain four numerals after the prefix letter, thus omitting numbers 1 to 999. The new K series therefore commenced at K1000, which was allocated to an AW Atlas.

The Naval N prefix was not used in such a logical way. Blocks of numbers were allocated for specific types of aircraft such as seaplanes or flying-boats. By the late 1920s the sequence had largely been used up and a new series using the prefix S was commenced. In 1930 separate naval allocations were stopped and subsequent serials were issued in the 'military' range which had by this time reached the K series. A further change in the pattern of allocations came in the L range. Commencing with L7272 numbers were issued in blocks with smaller blocks of serials between not used. These were known as blackout blocks. As M had already been used as a suffix for Maintenance Command instructional airframes it was not used as a prefix. Although N had previously been used for naval aircraft it was used again for serials allocated from 1937.

With the build-up to World War 2 the rate of allocations quickly accelerated and the prefix R was being used when war was declared. The letters O and Q were not allotted, and nor was S which had been used up to S1865 for naval aircraft before integration into the RAF series. By 1940 the serial Z9999 had been reached, as part of a blackout block, with the letters U and Y not used to avoid confusion. The option to recommence serial allocation at A1000 was not taken up; instead it was decided to use an alphabetical two-letter prefix with three numerals running from 100 to 999. Thus AA100 was allocated to a Blenheim IV.

This two-letter, three-numeral serial system which started in 1940 continues today. The letters C, I, O, Q, U and Y were, with the exception of NC, not used. For various reasons the following letter combinations were not issued: DA, DB, DH, EA, GA to GZ, HA, HT, JE, JH, JJ, KR to KT, MR, NW, NZ, SA to SK, SV, TN, TR and VE. The first postwar serials issued were in the VP range while the end of the WZs had been reached by the Korean War. In January 1952 a civil servant at the then Air Ministry penned a memo to his superiors alerting them to the fact that a new military aircraft serial system would soon have to be devised. With allocations accelerating to accommodate a NATO response to the Korean War and a perceived Soviet threat building, he estimated that the end of the ZZs would quickly be reached. However, over five decades later the allocations are only at the start of the ZKs and at the present rate are unlikely to reach ZZ999 until the end of this century!

Military aircraft serials are allocated by the Defence Procurement Agency, where the Military Aircraft Register is maintained. A change in policy in 2003 has resulted in the use of the first 99 digits in the ZK sequence (ZK001 to ZK099), following on from ZJ999. There is also a growing trend for 'out-of-sequence' serial numbers to be issued. At first this was to a manufacturer's prototype or development aircraft. However, following the Boeing C-17 Globemasters leased from Boeing (ZZ171-ZZ174), more allocations have been noted, including the reservation of ZM400 to ZM424 for the RAF's prospective Airbus A400Ms and ZR321 to ZR323 for a trio of new Agusta A.109Es for No 32 (The Royal) Squadron.

Since 2002 there has also been a new official policy concerning the use of military serial numbers on some types of UAV. 'Where a UAV is of modular construction the nationality and registration mark shall be applied to the fuselage of the vehicle or on the assembly forming the main part of the fuselage. To prevent the high usage of numbers for target drones which are eventually destroyed, a single registration mark (prefix) should be issued relating to the UAV type. The agency or service operating the target drone will be responsible for the identification of each individual UAV covered by that registration mark by adding a suffix.' This has resulted in the use of the same serial on a number of UAVs with a letter following it. Hence the appearance of ZK201A, ZK201B, ZK201C et seq on Army Meggitt Banshee drones. UAVs using this system are denoted in the text by an asterisk (*).

**Note:** The compilers will be pleased to receive comments, corrections and further information for inclusion in subsequent editions of *Military Aircraft Markings* and the monthly up-date of additions and amendments. Please send your information to Military Aircraft Markings, 25 Sabrina Way, Stoke Bishop, Bristol BS9 1ST or e-mail to HJCurtis@aol.com.

A serial in *italics* denotes that it is not the genuine marking for that airframe.

| Serial | Type (code other identity) | Owner/operator, location or fate | Notes |
|---|---|---|---|
| *168* | Sopwith Tabloid Scout <R> (G-BFDE) | RAF Museum, Hendon | |
| 304 | Cody Biplane (BAPC 62) | Science Museum, South Kensington | |
| 687 | RAF BE2b <R> (BAPC 181) | RAF Museum, Hendon | |
| *2345* | Vickers FB5 Gunbus <R> (G-ATVP) | RAF Museum, Hendon | |
| 2699 | RAF BE2c | Imperial War Museum, Lambeth | |
| *3066* | Caudron GIII (G-AETA/9203M) | RAF Museum, Hendon | |
| *5964* | DH2 <R> (BAPC 112) | Privately owned, Stretton on Dunsmore | |
| *5964* | DH2 <R> (G-BFVH) | Privately owned, Withybush | |
| 6232 | RAF BE2c <R> (BAPC 41) | Yorkshire Air Museum, stored Elvington | |
| 8359 | Short 184 <ff> | FAA Museum, RNAS Yeovilton | |
| *9917* | Sopwith Pup (G-EBKY/N5180) | The Shuttleworth Collection, Old Warden | |
| | | | |
| A301 | Morane BB (frame) | RAF Museum Reserve Collection, Stafford | |
| *A1742* | Bristol Scout D <R> (BAPC 38) | Bristol Aero Collection, Kemble | |
| *A7317* | Sopwith Pup <R> (BAPC 179) | Midland Air Museum, Coventry | |
| *A8226* | Sopwith 1? Strutter <R> (G-BIDW) | RAF Museum, Hendon | |
| | | | |
| *B595* | RAF SE5a <R> (G-BUOD) [W] | Privately owned, Kemble | |
| B2458 | Sopwith 1F.1 Camel <R> (G-BPOB/*F542*) [R] | Flying Aces Museum, Compton Abbas | |
| *B3459* | Nieuport Scout 17/23 <R> (G-BWMJ) [21] | *Repainted as N1723, 2005* | |
| B5539 | Sopwith 1F.1 Camel <R> | Flying Aces Museum, Compton Abbas | |
| B5577 | Sopwith 1F.1 Camel <R> (*D3419*/BAPC 59) [W] | Royal Scottish Mus'm of Flight, E Fortune | |
| *B6401* | Sopwith 1F.1 Camel <R> (G-AWYY/C1701) | FAA Museum, RNAS Yeovilton | |
| B7270 | Sopwith 1F.1 Camel <R> (G-BFCZ) | Brooklands Museum, Weybridge | |
| | | | |
| *C1904* | RAF SE5a <R> (G-PFAP) [Z] | Privately owned, Castle Bytham, Leics | |
| *C3011* | Phoenix Currie Super Wot (G-SWOT) [S] | Privately owned, Sibson | |
| *C4451* | Avro 504J <R> (BAPC 210) | Solent Sky, Southampton | |
| *C4918* | Bristol M1C <R> (G-BWJM) | The Shuttleworth Collection, Old Warden | |
| *C4994* | Bristol M1C <R> (G-BLWM) | RAF Museum, Hendon | |
| *C9533* | RAF SE5a <R> (G-BUWE) [M] | Privately owned, Boscombe Down | |
| | | | |
| *D276* | RAF SE5a <R> (BAPC 208) [A] | Prince's Mead Shopping Centre, Farnborough | |
| D5329 | Sopwith 5F.1 Dolphin RAF Museum | Restoration Centre, Cosford | |
| D5649 | Airco DH9 | Aero Vintage, St Leonards-on-Sea | |
| D7560 | Avro 504K | Science Museum, South Kensington | |
| *D7889* | Bristol F2b Fighter (G-AANM/BAPC 166) | Privately owned, Old Warden | |
| *D8084* | Bristol F2b Fighter (G-ACAA/*F4516*) [S] | The Fighter Collection, Duxford | |
| D8096 | Bristol F2b Fighter (G-AEPH) [D] | The Shuttleworth Collection, Old Warden | |
| | | | |
| *E373* | Avro 504K <R> (BAPC 178) | *Currently not known* | |
| E449 | Avro 504K (G-EBJE/9205M) | RAF Museum, Hendon | |
| *E2466* | Bristol F2b Fighter (BAPC 165) [I] | RAF Museum, Hendon | |
| E2581 | Bristol F2b Fighter [13] | Imperial War Museum, Duxford | |
| E8894 | Airco DH9 (G-CDLI) | Aero Vintage, St Leonards-on-Sea | |
| | | | |
| *F141* | RAF SE5a <R> (G-SEVA) [G] | Privately owned, Boscombe Down | |
| *F235* | RAF SE5a <R> (G-BMDB) [B] | Privately owned, Boscombe Down | |
| F904 | RAF SE5a (G-EBIA) | The Shuttleworth Collection, Old Warden | |
| F938 | RAF SE5a (G-EBIC/9208M) | RAF Museum, Hendon | |
| *F943* | RAF SE5a <R> (G-BIHF) [S] | Museum of Army Flying, Middle Wallop | |
| *F943* | RAF SE5a <R> (G-BKDT) | Yorkshire Air Museum, Elvington | |
| F1010 | Airco DH9A [C] | RAF Museum, Hendon | |
| F3556 | RAF RE8 | Imperial War Museum, Duxford | |
| *F5447* | RAF SE5a <R> (G-BKER) [N] | Privately owned, Bridge of Weir | |

| Notes | Serial | Type (other identity) [code] | Owner/operator, location or fate |
|---|---|---|---|
| | F5459 | RAF SE5a <R> (G-INNY) [Y] | Privately owned, North Coates |
| | F5475 | RAF SE5a <R> (BAPC 250) | Brooklands Museum, Weybridge |
| | F6314 | Sopwith 1F.1 Camel (9206M) [B] | RAF Museum Restoration Centre, Cosford |
| | F8010 | RAF SE5a <R> (G-BDWJ) [Z] | Privately owned, Langport, Somerset |
| | F8614 | Vickers FB27A Vimy IV <R> (G-AWAU) | RAF Museum, Hendon |
| | H1968 | Avro 504K <R> (BAPC 42) | Yorkshire Air Museum, stored Elvington |
| | H2311 | Avro 504K (G-ABAA) | Gr Manchester Mus of Science & Industry |
| | H3426 | Hawker Hurricane <R> (BAPC 68) | NW Aviation Heritage Group, Hooton Park |
| | H5199 | Avro 504K (BK892/3118M/ G-ACNB/G-ADEV) | The Shuttleworth Collection, Old Warden |
| | J7326 | DH53 Humming Bird (G-EBQP) | Mosquito Aircraft Museum, London Colney |
| | J8067 | Westland Pterodactyl 1a | Science Museum, South Kensington |
| | J9941 | Hawker Hart 2 (G-ABMR) | RAF Museum, Hendon |
| | K1786 | Hawker Tomtit (G-AFTA) | The Shuttleworth Collection, Old Warden |
| | K1930 | Hawker Fury <R> (G-BKBB/OO-HFU) | Privately owned, Wevelgem, Belgium |
| | K2048 | Isaacs Fury II (G-BZNW) | Privately owned, Fishburn |
| | K2050 | Isaacs Fury II (G-ASCM) | Privately owned, English Bicknor |
| | K2059 | Isaacs Fury II (G-PFAR) | Privately owned, Netherthorpe |
| | K2060 | Isaacs Fury II (G-BKZM) | Privately owned, Haverfordwest |
| | K2075 | Isaacs Fury II (G-BEER) | Privately owned, Shennington |
| | K2227 | Bristol 105 Bulldog IIA (G-ABBB) | RAF Museum, Hendon |
| | K2567 | DH82A Tiger Moth (DE306/7035M/G-MOTH) | Privately owned, Tadlow |
| | K2572 | DH82A Tiger Moth (NM129/G-AOZH) | Privately owned, Redhill |
| | K2587 | DH82A Tiger Moth <R> (G-BJAP) | Privately owned, Shobdon |
| | K3241 | Avro 621 Tutor (K3215/G-AHSA) | The Shuttleworth Collection, Old Warden |
| | K3661 | Hawker Nimrod II (G-BURZ) | Aero Vintage, St Leonards-on-Sea |
| | K3731 | Isaacs Fury <R> (G-RODI) | Privately owned, Hailsham |
| | K4232 | Avro 671 Rota I (SE-AZB) | RAF Museum, Hendon |
| | K4259 | DH82A Tiger Moth (G-ANMO) [71] | Privately owned, White Waltham |
| | K4672 | Hawker Hind (BAPC 82) | RAF Museum, Cosford |
| | K4972 | Hawker Hart Trainer IIA (1764M) | RAF Museum, Hendon |
| | K5054 | Supermarine Spitfire <R> (BAPC 190/EN398) | Privately owned, Hawkinge |
| | K5054 | Supermarine Spitfire <R> (BAPC 214) | Tangmere Military Aviation Museum |
| | K5054 | Supermarine Spitfire <R> (G-BRDV) | Solent Sky, stored |
| | K5054 | Supermarine Spitfire <R> | Kent Battle of Britain Museum, Hawkinge |
| | K5054 | Supermarine Spitfire <R> | Southampton Airport, on display |
| | K5414 | Hawker Hind (G-AENP/BAPC 78) [XV] | The Shuttleworth Collection, Old Warden |
| | K5600 | Hawker Audax I (2015M/G-BVVI) | Aero Vintage, St Leonards-on-Sea |
| | K5673 | Isaacs Fury II (G-BZAS) | Bournemouth Aviation Museum |
| | K5673 | Hawker Fury I <R> (BAPC 249) | Brooklands Museum, Weybridge |
| | K5674 | Hawker Fury I (G-CBZP) | Aero Vintage, St Leonards-on-Sea |
| | K6035 | Westland Wallace II (2361M) | RAF Museum, Hendon |
| | K7271 | Hawker Fury II <R> (BAPC 148) | Shropshire Wartime Aircraft Recovery Grp Mus, Sleap |
| | K8042 | Gloster Gladiator II (8372M) | RAF Museum, Hendon |
| | K8203 | Hawker Demon I (G-BTVE/2292M) | Demon Displays, Hatch |
| | K8303 | Isaacs Fury II (G-BWWN) [D] | Privately owned, Wisbech St Mary |
| | K9926 | VS300 Spitfire I <R> (BAPC 217) [JH-C] | RAF Bentley Priory, on display |
| | K9942 | VS300 Spitfire I (8383M) [SD-D] | RAF Museum Restoration Centre, Cosford |
| | K9962 | VS300 Spitfire I <R> [JH-C] | Privately owned, |
| | L1070 | VS300 Spitfire I <R> (BAPC 227) [XT-A] | Edinburgh airport, on display |
| | L1592 | Hawker Hurricane I [KW-Z] | Science Museum, South Kensington |
| | L1639 | Hawker Hurricane I | Cambridge Fighter & Bomber Society |
| | L1679 | Hawker Hurricane I <R> (BAPC 241) [JX-G] | Tangmere Military Aviation Museum |
| | L1710 | Hawker Hurricane I <R> (BAPC 219) [AL-D] | RAF Biggin Hill, on display |
| | L2301 | VS Walrus I (G-AIZG) | FAA Museum, RNAS Yeovilton |
| | L2940 | Blackburn Skua I | FAA Museum, RNAS Yeovilton |

| Serial | Type (other identity) [code] | Owner/operator, location or fate | Notes |
|---|---|---|---|
| L5343 | Fairey Battle I [VO-S] | RAF Museum, Hendon | |
| L6906 | Miles M14A Magister I (G-AKKY/ T9841/BAPC 44) | Museum of Berkshire Aviation, Woodley | |
| L7005 | Boulton Paul P82 Defiant I <R> [PS-B] | Boulton Paul Association, Wolverhampton | |
| L7181 | Hawker Hind (G-CBLK) | Aero Vintage, Duxford | |
| L8756 | Bristol 149 Bolingbroke IVT (RCAF 10001) [XD-E] | RAF Museum, Hendon | |
| N248 | Supermarine S6A (S1596) | Solent Sky, Southampton | |
| N500 | Sopwith LC-1T Triplane <R> (G-PENY/G-BWRA) | Privately owned, Yarcombe/RNAS Yeovilton | |
| N546 | Wright Quadruplane 1 <R> (BAPC 164) | Solent Sky, Southampton | |
| N1671 | Boulton Paul P82 Defiant I (8370M) [EW-D] | RAF Museum, Hendon | |
| N1723 | Nieuport Scout 17/23 <R> (G-BWMJ) | Privately owned, Popham | |
| N1854 | Fairey Fulmar II (G-AIBE) | FAA Museum, RNAS Yeovilton | |
| N2078 | Sopwith Baby (8214/8215) | FAA Museum, RNAS Yeovilton | |
| N2532 | Hawker Hurricane I <R> (BAPC 272) [GZ-H] | Kent Battle of Britain Museum, Hawkinge | |
| N2980 | Vickers Wellington IA [R] | Brooklands Museum, Weybridge | |
| N3194 | VS300 Spitfire I <R> (BAPC 220) [GR-Z] | RAF Biggin Hill, on display | |
| N3200 | VS300 Spitfire IA (wreck) | Privately owned, Braintree | |
| N3289 | VS300 Spitfire I <R> (BAPC 65) [DW-K] | Kent Battle of Britain Museum, Hawkinge | |
| N3310 | VS361 Spitfire IX [A] <R> | Privately owned, Wellesbourne Mountford | |
| N3313 | VS300 Spitfire I <R> (MH314/BAPC 69) [KL-B] | Kent Battle of Britain Museum, Hawkinge | |
| N3317 | VS361 Spitfire IX <R> (BAPC 268) | Privately owned, St Mawgan | |
| N3378 | Boulton Paul P82 Defiant I | Boulton Paul Association, Wolverhampton | |
| N3788 | Miles M14A Magister I (V1075/G-AKPF) | Privately owned, Old Warden | |
| N4389 | Fairey Albacore (N4172) [4M] | FAA Museum, RNAS Yeovilton | |
| N4877 | Avro 652A Anson I (G-AMDA) [MK-V] | Imperial War Museum, Duxford | |
| N5177 | Sopwith 1? Strutter <R> | Privately owned, Wingates, Lancs | |
| N5182 | Sopwith Pup <R> (G-APUP/9213M) | RAF Museum, Hendon | |
| N5195 | Sopwith Pup (G-ABOX) | Museum of Army Flying, Middle Wallop | |
| N5459 | Sopwith Triplane <R> (BAPC 111) | FAA Museum, RNAS Yeovilton | |
| N5492 | Sopwith Triplane <R> (BAPC 111) | Repainted as N5459 | |
| N5579 | Gloster Sea Gladiator | FAA Museum, RNAS Yeovilton | |
| N5628 | Gloster Gladiator II | RAF Museum, Hendon | |
| N5719 | Gloster Gladiator II (G-CBHO) | Privately owned, Dursley, Glos | |
| N5903 | Gloster Gladiator II (N2276/G-GLAD) [H] | The Fighter Collection, Duxford | |
| N5912 | Sopwith Triplane (8385M) | RAF Museum, Hendon | |
| N6181 | Sopwith Pup (G-EBKY/N5180) | Repainted as 9917 by May 2005 | |
| N6290 | Sopwith Triplane <R> (G-BOCK) | The Shuttleworth Collection, Old Warden | |
| N6452 | Sopwith Pup <R> (G-BIAU) | FAA Museum, RNAS Yeovilton | |
| N6466 | DH82A Tiger Moth (G-ANKZ) | Privately owned, Winchester | |
| N6473 | DH82A Tiger Moth (G-AOBO) | Privately owned, Perranporth | |
| N6537 | DH82A Tiger Moth (G-AOHY) | AAC Historic Aircraft Flt, Middle Wallop | |
| N6720 | DH82A Tiger Moth (G-BYTN/ 7014M) [RUO-B] | Privately owned, Hatch | |
| N6797 | DH82A Tiger Moth (G-ANEH) | Privately owned, Swyncombe | |
| N6812 | Sopwith 2F.1 Camel | Imperial War Museum, Lambeth | |
| N6847 | DH82A Tiger Moth (G-APAL) | Privately owned, Leicester | |
| N6965 | DH82A Tiger Moth (G-AJTW) [FL-J] (wreck) | Privately owned, Tibenham | |
| N7033 | Noorduyn AT-16 Harvard IIB (FX442) | Kent Battle of Britain Museum, Hawkinge | |
| N9191 | DH82A Tiger Moth (G-ALND) | Privately owned, Pontypool | |
| N9192 | DH82A Tiger Moth (G-DHZF) [RCO-N] | Privately owned, Sywell | |
| N9389 | DH82A Tiger Moth (G-ANJA) | Privately owned, Seething | |
| N9899 | Supermarine Southampton I (fuselage) | RAF Museum, Hendon | |
| P1344 | HP52 Hampden I (9175M) [PL-K] | RAF Museum Restoration Centre, Cosford | |

| Notes | Serial | Type (other identity) [code] | Owner/operator, location or fate |
|---|---|---|---|
| | P1344 | HP52 Hampden I <rf> (parts Hereford L6012) | RAF Museum, Hendon |
| | P2617 | Hawker Hurricane I (8373M) [AF-A] | RAF Museum, Hendon |
| | P2725 | Hawker Hurricane I (wreck) | Imperial War Museum, Lambeth |
| | P2793 | Hawker Hurricane I <R> (BAPC 236) [SD-M] | Eden Camp Theme Park, Malton, North Yorkshire |
| | P2902 | Hawker Hurricane I (G-ROBT) | Privately owned, Billingshurst |
| | P2921 | Hawker Hurricane I <R> (BAPC 273) [GZ-L] | Kent Battle of Britain Museum, Hawkinge |
| | P2970 | Hawker Hurricane I <R> [US-X] | Battle of Britain Memorial, Capel le Ferne, Kent |
| | P3059 | Hawker Hurricane I <R> (BAPC 64) [SD-N] | Kent Battle of Britain Museum, Hawkinge |
| | P3175 | Hawker Hurricane I (wreck) | RAF Museum, Hendon |
| | P3179 | Hawker Hurricane I <ff> | Tangmere Military Aviation Museum |
| | P3208 | Hawker Hurricane I <R> (BAPC 63/L1592) [SD-T] | Kent Battle of Britain Museum, Hawkinge |
| | P3386 | Hawker Hurricane I <R> (BAPC 218) [FT-A] | RAF Bentley Priory, on display |
| | P3395 | Hawker Hurricane IV (KX829)[JX-B] | Millennium Discovery Centre, Birmingham |
| | P3554 | Hawker Hurricane I (composite) | The Air Defence Collection, Salisbury |
| | P3679 | Hawker Hurricane I <R> (BAPC 278) [GZ-K] | Kent Battle of Britain Museum, Hawkinge |
| | P3717 | Hawker Hurricane I (composite) (DR348) | Privately owned, Milden |
| | P3873 | Hawker Hurricane I <R> (BAPC 265) [YO-H] | Yorkshire Air Museum, Elvington |
| | P4139 | Fairey Swordfish II (HS618) [5H] | FAA Museum, RNAS Yeovilton |
| | P6382 | Miles M14A Hawk Trainer 3 (G-AJRS) [C] | The Shuttleworth Collection, Old Warden |
| | P7350 | VS329 Spitfire IIA (G-AWIJ) [XT-D] | RAF BBMF, Coningsby |
| | P7540 | VS329 Spitfire IIA [DU-W] | Dumfries & Galloway Avn Mus, Dumfries |
| | P7966 | VS329 Spitfire II <R> [D-B] | Manx Aviation & Military Museum, Ronaldsway |
| | P8140 | VS329 Spitfire II <R> (P9390/BAPC 71) [ZF-K] | Norfolk & Suffolk Avn Museum, Flixton |
| | P8448 | VS329 Spitfire II <R> (BAPC 225) [UM-D] | RAF Cranwell, on display |
| | P9374 | VS300 Spitfire IA (G-MKIA) | Privately owned, Braintree |
| | P9444 | VS300 Spitfire IA [RN-D] | Science Museum, South Kensington |
| | R1914 | Miles M14A Magister (G-AHUJ) | Privately owned, Strathallan |
| | R3821 | Bristol 149 Bolingbroke IVT (G-BPIV/Z5722) [UX-N] | The Aircraft Restoration Company, Duxford (damaged) |
| | R4115 | Hawker Hurricane I <R> (BAPC 267) [LE-X] | Imperial War Museum, Duxford |
| | R4118 | Hawker Hurricane I (G-HUPW) [UP-W] | Privately owned, Duxford |
| | R4922 | DH82A Tiger Moth II (G-APAO) | Privately owned, Duxford |
| | R4959 | DH82A Tiger Moth II (G-ARAZ) [59] | Privately owned, Temple Bruer |
| | R5136 | DH82A Tiger Moth II (G-APAP) | Privately owned, Henlow |
| | R5172 | DH82A Tiger Moth II (G-AOIS) [FIJ-E] | Privately owned, Sherburn-in-Elmet |
| | R5868 | Avro 683 Lancaster I (7325M) [PO-S] | RAF Museum, Hendon |
| | R6690 | VS300 Spitfire I <R> (BAPC 254) [PR-A] | Yorkshire Air Museum, Elvington |
| | R6915 | VS300 Spitfire I | Imperial War Museum, Lambeth |
| | R9125 | Westland Lysander III (8377M) [LX-L] | RAF Museum, Hendon |
| | R9371 | HP59 Halifax II <ff> | Privately owned, Charlton Kings |
| | S1287 | Fairey Flycatcher <R> (G-BEYB) | FAA Museum, RNAS Yeovilton |
| | S1579 | Hawker Nimrod I <R> (G-BBVO) [571] | Privately owned, Wreningham |
| | S1581 | Hawker Nimrod I (G-BWWK) [573] | The Fighter Collection, Duxford |
| | S1595 | Supermarine S6B | Science Museum, South Kensington |
| | T5298 | Bristol 156 Beaufighter I (4552M) <ff> | Midland Air Museum, Coventry |
| | T5424 | DH82A Tiger Moth II (G-AJOA) | Privately owned, Swindon |
| | T5672 | DH82A Tiger Moth II (G-ALRI) | Privately owned, Netheravon |
| | T5854 | DH82A Tiger Moth II (G-ANKK) | Privately owned, Baxterley |

| Serial | Type (other identity) [code] | Owner/operator, location or fate | Notes |
|--------|------------------------------|----------------------------------|-------|
| T5879 | DH82A Tiger Moth II (G-AXBW) [RUC-W] | Privately owned, Frensham | |
| T6296 | DH82A Tiger Moth II (8387M) | RAF Museum, Hendon | |
| T6313 | DH82A Tiger Moth II (G-AHVU) | Privately owned, Langham | |
| T6562 | DH82A Tiger Moth II (G-ANTE) | Privately owned, Sywell | |
| T6818 | DH82A Tiger Moth II (G-ANKT) [91] | The Shuttleworth Collection, Old Warden | |
| T6953 | DH82A Tiger Moth II (G-ANNI) | Privately owned, Goodwood | |
| T6991 | DH82A Tiger Moth II (HB-UPY/DE694) | Privately owned, Switzerland | |
| T7230 | DH82A Tiger Moth II (G-AFVE) | Privately owned, Booker | |
| T7281 | DH82A Tiger Moth II (G-ARTL) | Privately owned, Egton, nr Whitby | |
| T7404 | DH82A Tiger Moth II (G-ANMV) [04] | Sold as D-ECTM, 2005 | |
| T7793 | DH82A Tiger Moth II (G-ANKV) | Privately owned, Croydon, on display | |
| T7842 | DH82A Tiger Moth II (G-AMTF) | Sold as OO-TMW, December 2004 | |
| T7909 | DH82A Tiger Moth II (G-ANON) | Privately owned, Sherburn-in-Elmet | |
| T7997 | DH82A Tiger Moth II (NL750/G-AHUF) | Privately owned, Edburton | |
| T8191 | DH82A Tiger Moth II (G-BWMK) | Privately owned, | |
| T9707 | Miles M14A Magister I (G-AKKR/8378M/T9708) | Museum of Army Flying, Middle Wallop | |
| T9738 | Miles M14A Magister I (G-AKAT) | Privately owned, Breighton | |
| V1075 | Miles M14A Magister I (G-AKPF) | Repainted as N3788, 2005 | |
| V3388 | Airspeed AS10 Oxford I (G-AHTW) | Imperial War Museum, Duxford | |
| V6028 | Bristol 149 Bolingbroke IVT (G-MKIV) [GB-D] <rf> | The Aircraft Restoration Co, stored Duxford | |
| V6799 | Hawker Hurricane I <R> (BAPC 72/V7767) [SD-X] | Gloucestershire Avn Coll, stored Gloucester | |
| V7350 | Hawker Hurricane I (fuselage) | Brenzett Aeronautical Museum | |
| V7467 | Hawker Hurricane I <R> (BAPC 223) [LE-D] | RAF Coltishall, on display | |
| V7467 | Hawker Hurricane I <R> [LE-D] | Wonderland Pleasure Park, Farnsfield, Notts | |
| V7497 | Hawker Hurricane I (G-HRLI) | Hawker Restorations, Milden | |
| V9367 | Westland Lysander IIIA (G-AZWT) [MA-B] | The Shuttleworth Collection, Old Warden | |
| V9673 | Westland Lysander IIIA (V9300/G-LIZY) [MA-J] | Imperial War Museum, Duxford | |
| V9723 | Westland Lysander IIIA (2442/OO-SOT) [MA-D] | SABENA Old Timers, Brussels, Belgium | |
| V9312 | Westland Lysander IIIA (G-CCOM) | The Aircraft Restoration Co, Duxford | |
| W1048 | HP59 Halifax II (8465M) [TL-S] | RAF Museum, Hendon | |
| W2068 | Avro 652A Anson I (9261M/VH-ASM) [68] | RAF Museum, Hendon | |
| W2718 | VS Walrus I (G-RNLI) | Solent Sky, stored | |
| W4041 | Gloster E28/39 [G] | Science Museum, South Kensington | |
| W4050 | DH98 Mosquito | Mosquito Aircraft Museum, London Colney | |
| W5856 | Fairey Swordfish II (G-BMGC) [A2A] | RN Historic Flight, Yeovilton | |
| W9385 | DH87B Hornet Moth (G-ADND) [YG-L,3] | The Shuttleworth Collection, Old Warden | |
| X4276 | VS300 Spitfire I (G-CDGU) | Privately owned, Breighton | |
| X4590 | VS300 Spitfire I (8384M) [PR-F] | RAF Museum, Hendon | |
| X7688 | Bristol 156 Beaufighter I (3858M/G-DINT) | Privately owned, Hatch | |
| Z1206 | Vickers Wellington IV (fuselage) | Midland Warplane Museum, Baxterley | |
| Z2033 | Fairey Firefly I (G-ASTL) [275] | FAA Museum, RNAS Yeovilton | |
| Z2186 | Douglas Boston III | Privately owned, Hinckley, Leics | |
| Z2315 | Hawker Hurricane IIA [JU-E] | Imperial War Museum, Duxford | |
| Z2389 | Hawker Hurricane IIA | Brooklands Museum, Weybridge | |
| Z5140 | Hawker Hurricane XIIA (Z7381/G-HURI) [HA-C] | Historic Aircraft Collection, Duxford | |
| Z5207 | Hawker Hurricane IIB (G-BYDL) | Privately owned, Dursley, Glos | |
| Z5252 | Hawker Hurricane IIB (G-BWHA/Z5053) [GO-B] | Privately owned, Milden | |
| Z7015 | Hawker Sea Hurricane IB (G-BKTH) [7-L] | The Shuttleworth Collection, Old Warden | |
| Z7197 | Percival P30 Proctor III (G-AKZN/8380M) | RAF Museum Reserve Collection, Stafford | |

## Z7258 – EM720

| Notes | Serial | Type (other identity) [code] | Owner/operator, location or fate |
|-------|--------|------------------------------|----------------------------------|
| | Z7258 | DH89A Dragon Rapide (NR786/G-AHGD) | Privately owned, Membury (wreck) |
| | AB550 | VS349 Spitfire VB <R> (BAPC 230/AA908) [GE-P] | Eden Camp Theme Park, Malton, North Yorkshire |
| | AB910 | VS349 Spitfire VB (G-AISU) [IR-C] | RAF BBMF, Coningsby |
| | AD540 | VS349 Spitfire VB (wreck) | Kennet Aviation, North Weald |
| | AE436 | HP52 Hampden I [PL-J] (parts) | Lincolnshire Avn Heritage Centre, E Kirkby |
| | AL246 | Grumman Martlet I | FAA Museum, RNAS Yeovilton |
| | AP506 | Cierva C30A (G-ACWM) | The Helicopter Museum, Weston-super-Mare |
| | AP507 | Cierva C30A (G-ACWP) [KX-P] | Science Museum, South Kensington |
| | AR213 | VS300 Spitfire IA (K9853/G-AIST) [PR-D] | Privately owned, Booker |
| | AR501 | VS349 Spitfire LF VC (G-AWII/ AR4474) [NN-A] | The Shuttleworth Collection, Old Warden |
| | BB697 | DH82A Tiger Moth (G-ADGT) | Privately owned, Andrewsfield |
| | BB807 | DH82A Tiger Moth (G-ADWO) | Solent Sky, Southampton |
| | BE417 | Hawker Hurricane XIIB (G-HURR) [LK-A] | The Real Aeroplane Company, Breighton |
| | BE421 | Hawker Hurricane IIC <R> (BAPC 205) [XP-G] | RAF Museum, Hendon |
| | BL614 | VS349 Spitfire VB (4354M) [ZD-F] | RAF Museum, Hendon |
| | BL655 | VS349 Spitfire VB (wreck) | Lincolnshire Avn Heritage Centre, East Kirkby |
| | BL924 | VS349 Spitfire VB <R> (BAPC 242) [AZ-G] | Tangmere Military Aviation Museum |
| | BM361 | VS349 Spitfire VB <R> [XR-C] | RAF Lakenheath, on display |
| | BM593 | VS349 Spitfire VB <R> [JH-O] | Currently not known |
| | BM597 | VS349 Spitfire LF VB (5718M/G-MKVB) [U-2] | Historic Aircraft Collection, Duxford |
| | BN230 | Hawker Hurricane IIC (LF751/ 5466M) [FT-A] | RAF Manston, Memorial Pavilion |
| | BR600 | VS361 Spitfire IX <R> (BAPC 222) [SH-V] | RAF Uxbridge, on display |
| | BR600 | VS361 Spitfire IX <R> (fuselage) | Currently not known |
| | BW881 | Hawker Hurricane XIIA (G-KAMM) | Privately owned, Milden |
| | CB733 | SA122 Bulldog (G-BCUV/G-112) | Privately owned, Old Sarum |
| | DD931 | Bristol 152 Beaufort VIII (9131M) [L] | RAF Museum, Hendon |
| | DE208 | DH82A Tiger Moth II (G-AGYU) | Privately owned, Newtownards |
| | DE470 | DH82A Tiger Moth II (G-ANMY) [16] | Privately owned, RAF Cosford |
| | DE623 | DH82A Tiger Moth II (G-ANFI) | Privately owned, Withybush |
| | DE673 | DH82A Tiger Moth II (6948M/G-ADNZ) | Privately owned, Old Buckenham |
| | DE992 | DH82A Tiger Moth II (G-AXXV) | Privately owned, Upavon |
| | DE998 | DH82A Tiger Moth (comp G-APAO & G-APAP) [RCU-T] | Imperial War Museum, Duxford |
| | DF112 | DH82A Tiger Moth II (G-ANRM) | Privately owned, Clacton/Duxford |
| | DF128 | DH82A Tiger Moth II (G-AOJJ) [RCO-U] | Privately owned, White Waltham |
| | DF155 | DH82A Tiger Moth II (G-ANFV) | Privately owned, Shempston Farm, Lossiemouth |
| | DF198 | DH82A Tiger Moth II (G-BBRB) | Privately owned, Biggin Hill |
| | DG202 | Gloster F9/40 (5758M) [G] | RAF Museum, Cosford |
| | DG590 | Miles M2H Hawk Major (8379M/G-ADMW) | RAF Museum Reserve Collection, Stafford |
| | DP872 | Fairey Barracuda II (fuselage) | FAA Museum, RNAS Yeovilton |
| | DV372 | Avro 683 Lancaster I <ff> | Imperial War Museum, Lambeth |
| | EE416 | Gloster Meteor F3 <ff> | Martin Baker Aircraft, Chalgrove, fire section |
| | EE425 | Gloster Meteor F3 <ff> | Gloucestershire Avn Coll, stored Gloucester |
| | EE531 | Gloster Meteor F4 (7090M) | Midland Air Museum, Coventry |
| | EE549 | Gloster Meteor F4 (7008M) [A] | Tangmere Military Aviation Museum |
| | EF545 | VS349 Spitfire LF VC (G-CDGY) | Aero Vintage, Rye |
| | EJ693 | Hawker Tempest V (N7027E) [SA-J] | Privately owned, Booker |
| | EJ922 | Hawker Typhoon IB <ff> | Privately owned, Hawkinge |
| | EM720 | DH82A Tiger Moth II (G-AXAN) | Privately owned, Little Gransden |

| Serial | Type (other identity) [code] | Owner/operator, location or fate | Notes |
|--------|------------------------------|----------------------------------|-------|
| EN224 | VS366 Spitfire F XII (G-FXII) | Privately owned, Newport Pagnell | |
| EN343 | VS365 Spitfire PR XI <R> (BAPC 226) | RAF Benson, on display | |
| EN398 | VS361 Spitfire F IX <R> [JE-J] | Shropshire Wartime Aircraft Recovery Grp Mus, Sleap | |
| EN398 | VS361 Spitfire F IX <R> (BAPC 184) | Privately owned, North Weald | |
| EP120 | VS349 Spitfire LF VB (5377M/ 8070M/G-LFVB) [AE-A] | The Fighter Collection, Duxford | |
| EX976 | NA AT-6D Harvard III (FAP.1657) | FAA Museum, RNAS Yeovilton | |
| FB226 | Bonsall Mustang <R> (G-BDWM) [MT-A] | Privately owned, Gamston | |
| FE695 | Noorduyn AT-16 Harvard IIB (G-BTXI) [94] | The Fighter Collection, Duxford | |
| FE788 | CCF Harvard IV (MM54137/ G-CTKL) | Privately owned, Rochester | |
| FE905 | Noorduyn AT-16 Harvard IIB (LN-BNM) | RAF Museum, Hendon | |
| FJ992 | Boeing-Stearman PT-17 Kaydet (OO-JEH) [44] | Privately owned, Wevelgem, Belgium | |
| FL586 | Douglas C-47B Dakota (OO-SMA) [AI-N] (fuselage) | Privately owned, North Weald | |
| FR886 | Piper L-4J Cub (G-BDMS) | Privately owned, Old Sarum | |
| FR887 | Piper J-3C Cub 85 (G-BWEZ) | Privately owned, Cumbernauld | |
| FS628 | Fairchild Argus 2 (43-14601/G-AIZE) | RAF Museum, Cosford | |
| FS668 | Noorduyn AT-16 Harvard IIB (PH-TBR) | Privately owned, Gilze-Rijen, The Netherlands | |
| FS728 | Noorduyn AT-16 Harvard IIB (D-FRCP) | Privately owned, Gelnhausen, Germany | |
| FT118 | Noorduyn AT-16 Harvard IIB (G-BZHL) | Privately owned, Hemswell | |
| FT323 | NA AT-6D Harvard III (FAP 1513) | Air Engineering Services, Swansea | |
| FT391 | Noorduyn AT-16 Harvard IIB (G-AZBN) | Privately owned, Shoreham | |
| FX301 | NA AT-6D Harvard III (EX915/ G-JUDI) [FD-NQ] | Privately owned, Bryngwyn Bach, Clwyd | |
| FX322 | Noorduyn AT-16 Harvard IIB <ff> | Privately owned, Doncaster | |
| FX760 | Curtiss P-40N Kittyhawk IV (9150M) [GA-?] | RAF Museum, Hendon | |
| FZ626 | Douglas Dakota III (KN566/ G-AMPO) [YS-DH] | RAF Lyneham, on display | |
| HB275 | Beech C-45 Expeditor II (G-BKGM) | Privately owned, Exeter | |
| HB751 | Fairchild Argus III (G-BCBL) | Privately owned, Woolsery, Devon | |
| HG691 | DH89A Dragon Rapide (G-AIYR) | Privately owned, Clacton/Duxford | |
| HH268 | GAL48 Hotspur II (HH379/ BAPC 261) [H] | Museum of Army Flying, AAC Middle Wallop | |
| HJ711 | DH98 Mosquito NF II [VI-C] | Night-Fighter Preservation Tm, Elvington | |
| HM503 | Miles M12 Mohawk (G-AEKW) | RAF Museum Restoration Centre, Cosford | |
| HM580 | Cierva C-30A (G-ACUU) [KX-K] | Imperial War Museum, Duxford | |
| HS503 | Fairey Swordfish IV (BAPC 108) | RAF Museum Reserve Collection, Stafford | |
| JF343 | Pearson Spitfire 26 (G-CCZP) [JW-P] | Privately owned, Panshanger | |
| JG891 | VS349 Spitfire LF VC (A58-178/ G-LFVC) | Historic Flying Ltd, Duxford | |
| JP843 | Hawker Typhoon IB [Y] | Privately owned, Shrewsbury | |
| JR505 | Hawker Typhoon IB <ff> | Midland Air Museum, Coventry | |
| JV482 | Grumman Wildcat V | Ulster Aviation Society, Langford Lodge | |
| JV579 | Grumman FM-2 Wildcat (N4845V/ G-RUMW) [F] | The Fighter Collection, Duxford | |
| JV928 | Consolidated PBY-5A Catalina (N423RS) [Y] | Super Catalina Restoration, Lee-on-Solent | |
| KB889 | Avro 683 Lancaster B X (G-LANC) [NA-I] | Imperial War Museum, Duxford | |
| KB976 | Avro 683 Lancaster B X <ff> | Privately owned, Lee-on-Solent, Hants | |
| KB976 | Avro 683 Lancaster B X (G-BCOH) <rf> | Aeroventure, Doncaster | |
| KB994 | Avro 683 Lancaster B X (G-BVBP) <ff> | Privately owned, Greenham Common | |
| KD345 | Goodyear FG-1D Corsair (88297/ G-FGID) [130-A] | The Fighter Collection, Duxford | |

| Notes | Serial | Type (other identity) [code] | Owner/operator, location or fate |
|---|---|---|---|
| | KD431 | CV Corsair IV [E2-M] | FAA Museum, RNAS Yeovilton |
| | KE209 | Grumman Hellcat II | FAA Museum, RNAS Yeovilton |
| *KE418* | | Hawker Tempest <rf> | RAF Museum Restoration Centre, Cosford |
| | KF183 | Noorduyn AT-16 Harvard IIB [3] | DPA/AFD/QinetiQ, Boscombe Down |
| | KF435 | Noorduyn AT-16 Harvard IIB <ff> | Privately owned, Swindon |
| | KF488 | Noorduyn AT-16 Harvard IIB | Bournemouth Aviation Museum |
| | KF532 | Noorduyn AT-16 Harvard IIB <ff> | Newark Air Museum, Winthorpe |
| *KF584* | | CCF T-6J Texan (*FT239*/G-BIWX/ G-RAIX) [RAI-X] | Privately owned, Lee-on-Solent |
| *KF729* | | CCF T-6J Texan (G-BJST) | Privately owned, Thruxton |
| *KG374* | | Douglas Dakota IV (KN645/ 8355M) [YS] | *Repainted as KN645, 2005* |
| | KG651 | Douglas Dakota III (G-AMHJ) | Assault Glider Trust, Shawbury |
| *KJ351* | | Airspeed AS58 Horsa II (TL659/ BAPC 80) [23] | Museum of Army Flying, Middle Wallop |
| *KJ994* | | Douglas Dakota III (F-AZTE) | Dakota et Cie, La Ferté Alais, France |
| | KK116 | Douglas Dakota IV (G-AMPY) | Air Atlantique Classic Flight, Coventry |
| | KK151 | Douglas Dakota IV (G-AMRA) | *Restored as G-AMRA, November 2004* |
| | KK995 | Sikorsky Hoverfly I [E] | RAF Museum, Hendon |
| *KL216* | | Republic P-47D Thunderbolt (45-49295/9212M) [RS-L] | RAF Museum, Hendon |
| | KN353 | Douglas Dakota IV (G-AMYJ) | Yorkshire Air Museum, Elvington |
| | KN448 | Douglas Dakota IV <ff> | Science Museum, South Kensington |
| | KN645 | Douglas Dakota IV (*KG374*/8355M) | RAF Museum, Cosford |
| | KN751 | Consolidated Liberator C VI (IAF HE807) [F] | RAF Museum, Hendon |
| | KP208 | Douglas Dakota IV [YS] | Airborne Forces Museum, Aldershot |
| | KP220 | Douglas Dakota IV (G-ANAF) | *Restored as G-ANAF, November 2004* |
| | KZ191 | Hawker Hurricane IV (frame only) | Privately owned, East Garston, Bucks |
| *KZ321* | | Hawker Hurricane IV (G-HURY) [JV-N] | The Fighter Collection, Duxford |
| | LA198 | VS356 Spitfire F21 (7118M) [RAI-G] | Glasgow Museum of Transport |
| | LA226 | VS356 Spitfire F21 (7119M) | RAF Museum Reserve Collection, Stafford |
| | LA255 | VS356 Spitfire F21 (6490M) [JX-U] | RAF No 1 Sqn, Cottesmore (preserved) |
| | LB264 | Taylorcraft Plus D (G-AIXA) | RAF Museum, Hendon |
| | LB294 | Taylorcraft Plus D (G-AHWJ) | Museum of Army Flying, Whitchurch, Hants |
| | LB312 | Taylorcraft Plus D (*HH982*/ G-AHXE) | Privately owned, Netheravon |
| | LB367 | Taylorcraft Plus D (G-AHGZ) | Privately owned, Henstridge |
| | LB375 | Taylorcraft Plus D (G-AHGW) | Privately owned, Coventry |
| | LF363 | Hawker Hurricane IIC [US-C] | RAF BBMF, Coningsby |
| | LF738 | Hawker Hurricane IIC (5405M) [UH-A] | RAF Museum, Cosford |
| | LF789 | DH82 Queen Bee (K3584/ BAPC 186) [R2-K] | Mosquito Aircraft Museum, London Colney |
| | LF858 | DH82 Queen Bee (G-BLUZ) | Privately owned, Henlow |
| *LH291* | | Airspeed AS51 Horsa I <R> (BAPC 279) | Assault Glider Trust, RAF Shawbury |
| | LS326 | Fairey Swordfish II (G-AJVH) [L2] | RN Historic Flight, Yeovilton |
| *LV907* | | HP59 Halifax III (HR792) [NP-F] | Yorkshire Air Museum, Elvington |
| | LZ551 | DH100 Vampire | FAA Museum, RNAS Yeovilton |
| | LZ766 | Percival P34 Proctor III (G-ALCK) | Imperial War Museum, Duxford |
| | LZ842 | VS361 Spitfire F IX [EF-D] | Privately owned, Sandown |
| | MB293 | VS357 Seafire IIC (wreck) | Privately owned, Braintree |
| | MD338 | VS359 Spitfire LF VIII | Privately owned, Sandown |
| | MF628 | Vickers Wellington T10 (9210M) | RAF Museum, Hendon |
| | MH434 | VS361 Spitfire LF IXB (G-ASJV) [SZ-G] | The Old Flying Machine Company, Duxford |
| *MH486* | | VS361 Spitfire LF IX <R> (BAPC 206) [FF-A] | RAF Museum, Hendon |
| *MH415* | | VS361 Spitfire IX <R> (*MJ751*/ BAPC 209) [DU-V] | The Aircraft Restoration Co, Duxford |
| *MH777* | | VS361 Spitfire IX <R> (BAPC 221) [RF-N] | RAF Northolt, on display |
| | MJ147 | VS361 Spitfire LF IX | Privately owned, Kent |
| | MJ627 | VS509 Spitfire T9 (G-BMSB) [9G-P] | Privately owned, East Kirkby |
| *MJ832* | | VS361 Spitfire IX <R> (*L1096*/ BAPC 229) [DN-Y] | RAF Digby, on display |
| | MK356 | VS361 Spitfire LF IXC (5690M) [2I-V] | RAF BBMF, Coningsby |

| Serial | Type (other identity) [code] | Owner/operator, location or fate | Notes |
|--------|------------------------------|----------------------------------|-------|
| MK356 | VS361 Spitfire LF IXC <R> [2I-V] | Kent Battle of Britain Museum, Hawkinge | |
| MK356 | VS361 Spitfire LF IXC <R> | RAF Cosford, on display | |
| ML407 | VS509 Spitfire T9 (G-LFIX) [OU-V] | Privately owned, Duxford | |
| ML411 | VS361 Spitfire LF IXE (G-CBNU) | Privately owned, Ashford, Kent | |
| ML427 | VS361 Spitfire IX (6457M) [HK-A] | Millennium Discovery Centre, Birmingham | |
| ML796 | Short S25 Sunderland V | Imperial War Museum, Duxford | |
| ML824 | Short S25 Sunderland V [NS-Z] | RAF Museum, Hendon | |
| MN235 | Hawker Typhoon IB | RAF Museum, Hendon | |
| MP425 | Airspeed AS10 Oxford I (G-AITB) [G] | RAF Museum, Hendon | |
| MS902 | Miles M25 Martinet TT1 (TF-SHC) | Museum of Berkshire Aviation, Woodley | |
| MT197 | Auster IV (G-ANHS) | Privately owned, Spanhoe | |
| MT438 | Auster III (G-AREI) | Privately owned, Eggesford | |
| MT847 | VS379 Spitfire XIVE (6960M) [AX-H] | Gr Manchester Mus of Science & Industry | |
| MT928 | VS359 Spitfire HF VIIIC (G-BKMI/ MV154/AR654)[ZX-M] | Privately owned, East Garston, Bucks | |
| MV262 | VS379 Spitfire FR XIV (G-CCVV) | Privately owned, Booker | |
| MV268 | VS379 Spitfire FR XIVE (MV293/ G-SPIT) [JE-J] | The Fighter Collection, Duxford | |
| MW401 | Hawker Tempest II (IAF HA604/ G-PEST) | Privately owned, Hemswell, Lincs | |
| MW763 | Hawker Tempest II (IAF HA586/ G-TEMT) [HF-A] | Privately owned, Gamston | |
| NF370 | Fairey Swordfish III [NH-L] | Imperial War Museum, Duxford | |
| NF389 | Fairey Swordfish III [D] | RN Historic Flight, Yeovilton | |
| NJ633 | Auster 5D (G-AKXP) | Privately owned, English Bicknor | |
| NJ673 | Auster 5D (G-AOCR) | Privately owned, Bagby | |
| NJ695 | Auster 4 (G-AJXV) | Privately owned, Newark | |
| NJ703 | Auster 5 (G-AKPI) | Privately owned, Croft, Lincs | |
| NJ719 | Auster 5 (TW385/G-ANFU) | Newcastle Motor Museum | |
| NL750 | DH82A Tiger Moth II (T7997/ G-AOBH) | Privately owned, Thruxton | |
| NL985 | DH82A Tiger Moth I (7015M/ G-BWIK) | Privately owned, Sywell | |
| NM181 | DH82A Tiger Moth I (G-AZGZ) | Privately owned, Dunkeswell | |
| NP294 | Percival P31 Proctor IV [TB-M] | Lincolnshire Avn Heritage Centre, E Kirkby | |
| NV778 | Hawker Tempest TT5 (8386M) | RAF Museum, Hendon | |
| NX534 | Auster III (G-BUDL) | Privately owned, Netheravon | |
| NX611 | Avro 683 Lancaster B VII (8375M/ G-ASXX) [DX-C,LE-C] | Lincolnshire Avn Heritage Centre, E Kirkby | |
| PA474 | Avro 683 Lancaster B I [QR-M] | RAF BBMF, Coningsby | |
| PD685 | Slingsby T7 Cadet TX1 | Boulton Paul Association, Wolverhampton | |
| PF179 | HS Gnat T1 (XR541/8602M) | Global Aviation, stored Humberside | |
| PK624 | VS356 Spitfire F22 (8072M) [RAU-T] | The Fighter Collection, Duxford | |
| PK664 | VS356 Spitfire F22 (7759M) [V6-B] | Science Museum, South Kensington | |
| PK683 | VS356 Spitfire F24 (7150M) | Solent Sky, Southampton | |
| PK724 | VS356 Spitfire F24 (7288M) | RAF Museum, Hendon | |
| PL256 | VS361 Spitfire IX <R> [TM-L] | East Midlands Airport Aeropark | |
| PL965 | VS365 Spitfire PR XI (G-MKXI) [R] | Privately owned, North Weald | |
| PM631 | VS390 Spitfire PR XIX | RAF BBMF, Coningsby | |
| PM651 | VS390 Spitfire PR XIX (7758M) [X] | RAF Museum Reserve Collection, Stafford | |
| PN323 | HP Halifax VII <ff> | Imperial War Museum, Lambeth | |
| PP972 | VS358 Seafire LF IIIC (G-BUAR) | Privately owned, stored Greenham Common | |
| PR536 | Hawker Tempest II (IAF HA457) [OQ-H] | RAF Museum, Hendon | |
| PS853 | VS390 Spitfire PR XIX (G-RRGN) [C] | Rolls-Royce, Filton | |
| PS890 | VS390 Spitfire PR XIX (F-AZJS) | Privately owned, Dijon, France | |
| PS915 | VS390 Spitfire PR XIX (7548M/ 7711M) | RAF BBMF, Coningsby | |
| PT462 | VS509 Spitfire T9 (G-CTIX/ N462JC) [SW-A] | Privately owned, Caernarfon/Duxford | |
| PZ865 | Hawker Hurricane IIC (G-AMAU) [JX-E] | RAF BBMF, Coningsby | |
| RA848 | Slingsby T7 Cadet TX1 | The Aeroplane Collection, stored Wigan | |
| RA854 | Slingsby T7 Cadet TX1 | Yorkshire Air Museum, Elvington | |
| RA897 | Slingsby T7 Cadet TX1 | Newark Air Museum, Winthorpe | |
| RA905 | Slingsby T7 Cadet TX1 (BGA1143) | Trenchard Museum, RAF Halton | |

| Notes | Serial | Type (other identity) [code] | Owner/operator, location or fate |
|---|---|---|---|
| | RD220 | Bristol 156 Beaufighter TF X | Royal Scottish Mus'm of Flight, stored E Fortune |
| | RD253 | Bristol 156 Beaufighter TF X (7931M) | RAF Museum, Hendon |
| | RF342 | Avro 694 Lincoln B II (G-29-1/ G-APRJ) | *Sold to Australia, February 2005* |
| | RF398 | Avro 694 Lincoln B II (8376M) | RAF Museum, Cosford |
| | *RG333* | Miles M38 Messenger IIA (G-AIEK) | Privately owned, Felton, Bristol |
| | RH746 | Bristol 164 Brigand TF1 (fuselage) | Bristol Aero Collection, Kemble |
| | RL962 | DH89A Dominie II (G-AHED) | RAF Museum Reserve Collection, Stafford |
| | RM221 | Percival P31 Proctor IV (G-ANXR) | Privately owned, Biggin Hill |
| | RM689 | VS379 Spitfire F XIV (G-ALGT) (remains) | Rolls-Royce, Filton |
| | RM694 | VS379 Spitfire F XIV (6640M) | Privately owned, High Wycombe |
| | RM927 | VS379 Spitfire F XIV | Privately owned, High Wycombe |
| | RN201 | VS379 Spitfire FR XIV (SG-31/ SG-3/G-BSKP) | Historic Flying Ltd, Duxford |
| | *RN218* | Isaacs Spitfire <R> (G-BBJI) [N] | Privately owned, Builth Wells |
| | RR232 | VS361 Spitfire HF IXC (G-BRSF) | Privately owned, Sandown |
| | RT486 | Auster 5 (G-AJGJ) [PF-A] | Privately owned, Lee-on-Solent |
| | RT520 | Auster 5 (G-ALYB) | Aeroventure, Doncaster |
| | RT610 | Auster 5A-160 (G-AKWS) | Privately owned, Crowfield |
| | RW382 | VS361 Spitfire LF XVIE (7245M/ 8075M/N382RW) (wreck) | Privately owned, Sandown |
| | RW386 | VS361 Spitfire LF XVIE (6944M/ G-BXVI) [NG-D] | Historic Flying Ltd, Duxford |
| | RW388 | VS361 Spitfire LF XVIE (6946M) [U4-U] | Stoke-on-Trent City Museum, Hanley |
| | RW393 | VS361 Spitfire LF XVIE (7293M) [XT-A] | *Repainted as TB675, 2005* |
| | RX168 | VS358 Seafire L IIIC (IAC 157/ G-BWEM) | Privately owned, Exeter |
| | SL611 | VS361 Spitfire LF XVIE | Supermarine Aero Engineering, Stoke-on-Trent |
| | SL674 | VS361 Spitfire LF IX (8392M) [RAS-H] | RAF Museum Reserve Collection, Stafford |
| | SM520 | VS361 Spitfire LF IX (G-BXHZ/ G-ILDA) | Privately owned, Thruxton |
| | SM969 | VS394 Spitfire F XVIIIE (G-BRAF) | Privately owned, Great Yarmouth |
| | SM845 | VS394 Spitfire FR XVIII (G-BUOS) [GZ-J] | Silver Victory Collection, Duxford |
| | SX137 | VS384 Seafire F XVII | FAA Museum, RNAS Yeovilton |
| | SX336 | VS384 Seafire F XVII (G-KASX) | Kennet Aviation, North Weald |
| | TA122 | DH98 Mosquito FB VI [UP-G] | Mosquito Aircraft Museum, London Colney |
| | TA634 | DH98 Mosquito TT35 (G-AWJV) [8K-K] | Mosquito Aircraft Museum, London Colney |
| | TA639 | DH98 Mosquito TT35 (7806M) [AZ-E] | RAF Museum, Cosford |
| | TA719 | DH98 Mosquito TT35 (G-ASKC) | Imperial War Museum, Duxford |
| | TA805 | VS361 Spitfire HF IX (G-PMNF) [FX-M] | Privately owned, Duxford |
| | TB382 | VS361 Spitfire LF XVIE (X4277/MK673) | RAF BBMF, stored Coningsby |
| | *TB675* | VS361 Spitfire LF XVIE (RW393/ 7293M) [4D-V] | RAF Museum Reserve Collection, Stafford |
| | TB752 | VS361 Spitfire LF XVIE (8086M) [KH-Z] | RAF Manston, Memorial Pavilion |
| | TD248 | VS361 Spitfire LF XVIE (7246M/] G-OXVI [CR-S | Spitfire Limited, Duxford |
| | TD248 | VS361 Spitfire LF XVIE [8Q-T] (fuselage) | Norfolk & Suffolk Avn Mus'm, Flixton |
| | TD314 | VS361 Spitfire LF IX (N601DA) | Privately owned, Norwich |
| | TE184 | VS361 Spitfire LF XVIE (6850M/ G-MXVI) [D] | Privately owned, Duxford (French insignia) |
| | TE311 | VS361 Spitfire LF XVIE (MK178/7241M) | RAF BBMF, Coningsby (on rebuild) |
| | TE462 | VS361 Spitfire LF XVIE (7243M) | Royal Scottish Mus'm of Flight, E Fortune |
| | TE517 | VS361 Spitfire LF IXE (G-CCIX) [HL-K] | Privately owned, stored Booker |
| | TG263 | Saro SR A1 (G-12-1) | Solent Sky, Southampton |
| | TG511 | HP67 Hastings C1 (8554M) | RAF Museum, Cosford |

| Serial | Type (other identity) [code] | Owner/operator, location or fate | Notes |
|---|---|---|---|
| TG517 | HP67 Hastings T5 | Newark Air Museum, Winthorpe | |
| TG528 | HP67 Hastings C1A | Imperial War Museum, Duxford | |
| TJ118 | DH98 Mosquito TT35 <ff> | Mosquito Aircraft Museum, stored London Colney | |
| TJ138 | DH98 Mosquito B35 (7607M) [VO-L] | RAF Museum, Hendon | |
| TJ343 | Auster 5 (G-AJXC) | Privately owned, Hook | |
| TJ398 | Auster AOP6 (BAPC 70) | Aircraft Pres'n Soc of Scotland, E Fortune | |
| TJ534 | Auster 5 (G-AKSY) | Privately owned, Breighton | |
| TJ569 | Auster 5 (G-AKOW) | Museum of Army Flying, Middle Wallop | |
| TJ652 | Auster 5D (G-AMVD) | Privately owned, Hardwick, Norfolk | |
| TJ672 | Auster 5D (G-ANIJ) [TS-D] | Bournemouth Aviation Museum | |
| TJ704 | Beagle A61 Terrier 2 (VW993/ G-ASCD) [JA] | Yorkshire Air Museum, Elvington | |
| TK718 | GAL59 Hamilcar I | National Tank Museum, Bovington | |
| TK777 | GAL59 Hamilcar I (fuselage) | Museum of Army Flying, Middle Wallop | |
| TS291 | Slingsby T7 Cadet TX1 (BGA852) | Royal Scottish Mus'm of Flight, stored E Fortune | |
| TS798 | Avro 685 York C1 (G-AGNV) | RAF Museum, Cosford | |
| TV959 | DH98 Mosquito T III [AF-V] | The Fighter Collection, stored Duxford | |
| TV959 | DH98 Mosquito T III <R> | Currently not known | |
| TW439 | Auster 5 (G-ANRP) | The Real Aeroplane Company, Breighton | |
| TW467 | Auster 5 (G-ANIE) | Privately owned, Spanhoe | |
| TW511 | Auster 5 (G-APAF) | Privately owned, Henstridge | |
| TW536 | Auster AOP6 (7704M/G-BNGE) [TS-V] | Privately owned, Netheravon | |
| TW591 | Auster 6A (G-ARIH) [N] | Privately owned, Compton Abbas | |
| TW641 | Beagle A61 Terrier 2 (G-ATDN) | Privately owned, Biggin Hill | |
| TX213 | Avro 652A Anson C19 (G-AWRS) | North-East Aircraft Museum, Usworth | |
| TX214 | Avro 652A Anson C19 (7817M) | RAF Museum, Cosford | |
| TX226 | Avro 652A Anson C19 (7865M) | Air Atlantique Classic Flight, Coventry | |
| TX235 | Avro 652A Anson C19 | Air Atlantique Classic Flight, Coventry | |
| VF301 | DH100 Vampire F1 (7060M) [RAL-G] | Midland Air Museum, Coventry | |
| VF512 | Auster 6A (G-ARRX) [PF-M] | Privately owned, Popham | |
| VF516 | Beagle A61 Terrier 2 (G-ASMZ) [T] | Privately owned, Eggesford | |
| VF526 | Auster 6A (G-ARXU) [T] | Privately owned, Netheravon | |
| VF560 | Auster 6A (frame) | Aeroventure, Doncaster | |
| VF581 | Beagle A61 Terrier 1 (G-ARSL) | Privately owned, Eggesford | |
| VH127 | Fairey Firefly TT4 [200/R] | FAA Museum, RNAS Yeovilton | |
| VL348 | Avro 652A Anson C19 (G-AVVO) | Newark Air Museum, Winthorpe | |
| VL349 | Avro 652A Anson C19 (G-AWSA) [V7-Q] | Norfolk & Suffolk Avn Mus'm, Flixton | |
| VM325 | Avro 652A Anson C19 | Privately owned, stored Gloucester | |
| VM360 | Avro 652A Anson C19 (G-APHV) | Royal Scottish Mus'm of Flight, E Fortune | |
| VM684 | Slingsby Cadet T2 (BGA791) | NW Aviation Heritage Museum, Hooton Park | |
| VM687 | Slingsby T8 Tutor (BGA794) | Privately owned, Strubby | |
| VM791 | Slingsby Cadet TX3 (XA312/8876M) | RAF Manston History Museum | |
| VN485 | VS356 Spitfire F24 (7326M) | Imperial War Museum, Duxford | |
| VN799 | EE Canberra T4 (WJ874/G-CDSX) | Air Atlantique Classic Flight, Coventry | |
| VP293 | Avro 696 Shackleton T4 [A] <ff> | Newark Air Museum, Winthorpe | |
| VP519 | Avro 652A Anson C19 (G-AVVR) <ff> | Privately owned, Wolverhampton | |
| VP952 | DH104 Devon C2 (8820M) | RAF Museum, Cosford | |
| VP955 | DH104 Devon C2 (G-DVON) | Privately owned, Kemble | |
| VP957 | DH104 Devon C2 (8822M) <ff> | No 1137 Sqn ATC, Belfast | |
| VP967 | DH104 Devon C2 (G-KOOL) | Privately owned, Redhill | |
| VP975 | DH104 Devon C2 [M] | Science Museum, Wroughton | |
| VP981 | DH104 Devon C2 (G-DHDV) | Air Atlantique Classic Flight, Coventry | |
| VR137 | Westland Wyvern TF1 | FAA Museum, RNAS Yeovilton | |
| VR192 | Percival P40 Prentice T1 (G-APIT) | SWWAPS, Lasham | |
| VR249 | Percival P40 Prentice T1 (G-APIY) [FA-EL] | Newark Air Museum, Winthorpe | |
| VR259 | Percival P40 Prentice T1 (G-APJB) [M] | Air Atlantique Classic Flight, Coventry | |
| VR930 | Hawker Sea Fury FB11 (8382M) [110/O] | RN Historic Flight, Yeovilton | |
| VS356 | Percival P40 Prentice T1 (G-AOLU) | Privately owned, Montrose | |
| VS562 | Avro 652A Anson T21 (8012M) | Maes Artro Craft Village, Llanbedr | |
| VS610 | Percival P40 Prentice T1 (G-AOKL)[K-L] | The Shuttleworth Collection, Old Warden | |
| VS623 | Percival P40 Prentice T1 (G-AOKZ)[KQ-F] | Midland Air Museum, Coventry | |

| Notes | Serial | Type (other identity) [code] | Owner/operator, location or fate |
|---|---|---|---|
| | VT409 | Fairey Firefly AS5 <rf> | North-East Aircraft Museum, stored Usworth |
| | VT812 | DH100 Vampire F3 (7200M) [N] | RAF Museum, Hendon |
| | VT871 | DH100 Vampire FB6 (J-1173/ LZ551/G-DHXX) [G] | Source Classic Jet Flight, Bournemouth |
| | VT935 | Boulton Paul P111A (VT769) | Midland Air Museum, Coventry |
| | VT987 | Auster AOP6 (G-BKXP) | Privately owned, Thruxton |
| | VV106 | Supermarine 510 (7175M) | FAA Museum, stored RNAS Yeovilton |
| | VV217 | DH100 Vampire FB5 (7323M) | North-East Aircraft Museum, stored Usworth |
| | VV612 | DH112 Venom FB50 (J-1523/ WE402/G-VENI) | Source Classic Jet Flight, Bournemouth |
| | VV901 | Avro 652A Anson T21 | Yorkshire Air Museum, Elvington |
| | VW453 | Gloster Meteor T7 (8703M) [Z] | RAF Innsworth, on display |
| | VW957 | DH103 Hornet NF21 <rf> | Privately owned, Fyvie, Grampian Region |
| | VX113 | Auster AOP6 (G-ARNO) | Privately owned, Eggesford |
| | VX118 | Auster AOP6 (G-ASNB) | Privately owned, Shotteswell |
| | VX147 | Alon A2 Aircoupe (G-AVIL) | Privately owned, Kent |
| | VX185 | EE Canberra B(I)8 (7631M) <ff> | Royal Scottish Mus'm of Flight, E Fortune |
| | VX250 | DH103 Sea Hornet NF21 [48] <rf> | Mosquito Aircraft Museum, London Colney |
| | VX272 | Hawker P.1052 (7174M) | FAA Museum, stored RNAS Yeovilton |
| | VX275 | Slingsby T21B Sedbergh TX1 (8884M/BGA572) | RAF Museum Reserve Collection, Stafford |
| | VX573 | Vickers Valetta C2 (8389M) | RAF Museum, stored Cosford |
| | VX580 | Vickers Valetta C2 | Norfolk & Suffolk Avn Museum, Flixton |
| | VX595 | WS51 Dragonfly HR1 | FAA Museum, stored RNAS Yeovilton |
| | VX665 | Hawker Sea Fury FB11 <rf> | RN Historic Flight, at BAE Systems Brough |
| | VX926 | Auster T7 (G-ASKJ) | Privately owned, |
| | VX927 | Auster T7 (G-ASYG) | Privately owned, Hemswell |
| | VZ345 | Hawker Sea Fury T20S | RN Historic Flight, stored Yeovilton |
| | VZ477 | Gloster Meteor F8 (7741M) <ff> | Midland Air Museum, Coventry |
| | VZ608 | Gloster Meteor FR9 | Newark Air Museum, Winthorpe |
| | VZ634 | Gloster Meteor T7 (8657M) | Newark Air Museum, Winthorpe |
| | VZ638 | Gloster Meteor T7 (G-JETM) [HF] | Gatwick Aviation Museum, Charlwood, Surrey |
| | VZ728 | RS4 Desford Trainer (G-AGOS) | Snibston Discovery Park, stored Coalville |
| | VZ962 | WS51 Dragonfly HR1 [904] | The Helicopter Museum, Weston-super-Mare |
| | WA346 | DH100 Vampire FB5 | RAF Museum Restoration Centre, Cosford |
| | WA473 | VS Attacker F1 [102/J] | FAA Museum, RNAS Yeovilton |
| | WA576 | Bristol 171 Sycamore 3 (7900M /G-ALSS) | Dumfries & Galloway Avn Mus, Dumfries |
| | WA577 | Bristol 171 Sycamore 3 (7718M/ G-ALST) | North-East Aircraft Museum, Usworth |
| | WA591 | Gloster Meteor T7 (7917M/ G-BWMF) [W] | Meteor Flight, Yatesbury |
| | WA630 | Gloster Meteor T7 [69] <ff> | Robertsbridge Aviation Society, Newhaven |
| | WA634 | Gloster Meteor T7/8 | RAF Museum, Cosford |
| | WA638 | Gloster Meteor T7(mod) | Martin Baker Aircraft, Chalgrove |
| | WA662 | Gloster Meteor T7 | Aeroventure, Doncaster |
| | WA829 | Gloster Meteor F8 (WA984) [A] | Tangmere Military Aviation Museum |
| | WB188 | Hawker Hunter F3 (7154M) | Tangmere Military Aviation Museum |
| | WB188 | Hawker Hunter GA11 (WV256/ G-BZPB) | Hunter Flying Club, Exeter (duck egg green) |
| | WB188 | Hawker Hunter GA11 (XF300/ G-BZPC) | Hunter Flying Club, Exeter (red) |
| | WB440 | Fairey Firefly AS6 <ff> | Privately owned, Newton-le-Willows |
| | WB491 | Avro 706 Ashton 2 (TS897/ G-AJJW) <ff> | Newark Air Museum, Winthorpe |
| | WB556 | DHC1 Chipmunk T10 (fuselage) | RAF Halton |
| | WB560 | DHC1 Chipmunk T10 (comp WG403) | Aeroventure, Doncaster |
| | WB565 | DHC1 Chipmunk T10 (G-PVET) [X] | Privately owned, Kemble |
| | WB569 | DHC1 Chipmunk T10 (G-BYSJ) [R] | Privately owned, Duxford |
| | WB571 | DHC1 Chipmunk T10 (G-AOSF) [34] | Privately owned, Trier, Germany |
| | WB584 | DHC1 Chipmunk T10 (7706M) <ff> | Royal Scottish Mus'm of Flight, stored E Fortune |
| | WB585 | DHC1 Chipmunk T10 (G-AOSY) [M] | Privately owned, Seething |
| | WB588 | DHC1 Chipmunk T10 (G-AOTD) [D] | Privately owned, Old Sarum |
| | WB615 | DHC1 Chipmunk T10 (G-BXIA) [E] | Privately owned, Blackpool |
| | WB624 | DHC1 Chipmunk T10 <ff> | Newark Air Museum, Winthorpe |
| | WB626 | DHC1 Chipmunk T10 <ff> | No 1365 Sqn ATC, Aylesbury |

| Serial | Type (other identity) [code] | Owner/operator, location or fate | Notes |
|---|---|---|---|
| WB627 | DHC1 Chipmunk T10 (9248M) [N] | Dulwich College CCF | |
| WB652 | DHC1 Chipmunk T10 (G-CHPY) [V] | Privately owned, Portimao, Portugal | |
| WB654 | DHC1 Chipmunk T10 (G-BXGO) [U] | Privately owned, Booker | |
| WB657 | DHC1 Chipmunk T10 [908] | RN Historic Flight, Yeovilton | |
| WB670 | DHC1 Chipmunk T10 (comp WG303)(8361M) | Privately owned, Currie, Edinburgh | |
| WB671 | DHC1 Chipmunk T10 (G-BWTG) [910] | Privately owned, Epse, The Netherlands | |
| WB685 | DHC1 Chipmunk T10 (comp WP969/G-ATHC) [C] | North-East Aircraft Museum, Usworth | |
| WB685 | DHC1 Chipmunk T10 <rf> | North-East Aircraft Museum, stored Usworth | |
| WB697 | DHC1 Chipmunk T10 (G-BXCT) [95] | Privately owned, Wickenby | |
| WB702 | DHC1 Chipmunk T10 (G-AOFE) | Privately owned, Kindford | |
| WB703 | DHC1 Chipmunk T10 (G-ARMC) | Privately owned, White Waltham | |
| WB711 | DHC1 Chipmunk T10 (G-APPM) | Privately owned, Sywell | |
| WB726 | DHC1 Chipmunk T10 (G-AOSK) [E] | Privately owned, Audley End | |
| WB733 | DHC1 Chipmunk T10 (comp WG422) | Aeroventure, Doncaster | |
| WB758 | DHC1 Chipmunk T10 (7729M) [P] | *Scrapped* | |
| WB763 | DHC1 Chipmunk T10 (G-BBMR) [14] | Privately owned, Tollerton | |
| WB915 | DHC1 Chipmunk T10 (G-BXIA) [E] | Privately owned, Blackpool | |
| WB922 | Slingsby T21B Sedbergh TX1 (BGA4366) | Privately owned, Hullavington | |
| WB924 | Slingsby T21B Sedbergh TX1 (BGA3901) | Privately owned, Dunstable | |
| WB943 | Slingsby T21B Sedbergh TX1 (BGA2941) | Privately owned, Rufforth | |
| WB944 | Slingsby T21B Sedbergh TX1 (BGA3160) | Privately owned, Bicester | |
| WB971 | Slingsby T21B Sedbergh TX1 (BGA 3324) | Privately owned, Tibenham | |
| WB975 | Slingsby T21B Sedbergh TX1 (BGA 3288) | Privately owned, Drumshade, Fife | |
| WB981 | Slingsby T21B Sedbergh TX1 (BGA 3238) | Privately owned, Keevil | |
| WD286 | DHC1 Chipmunk T10 (G-BBND) | Privately owned, Little Gransden | |
| WD292 | DHC1 Chipmunk T10 (G-BCRX) | Privately owned, White Waltham | |
| WD293 | DHC1 Chipmunk T10 (7645M) <ff> | No 30F Sqn ATC, Cardiff | |
| WD305 | DHC1 Chipmunk T10 (G-ARGG) | Privately owned, Prestwick | |
| WD310 | DHC1 Chipmunk T10 (G-BWUN) [B] | Privately owned, Deanland | |
| WD325 | DHC1 Chipmunk T10 [N] | AAC Historic Aircraft Flight, Middle Wallop | |
| WD331 | DHC1 Chipmunk T10 (G-BXDH) [J] | Privately owned, Enstone | |
| WD347 | DHC1 Chipmunk T10 (G-BBRV) | Privately owned, Sheffield | |
| *WD355* | DHC1 Chipmunk T10 (WD335/ G-CBAJ) | Privately owned, Stamford | |
| WD363 | DHC1 Chipmunk T10 (G-BCIH) [5] | Privately owned, Audley End | |
| WD370 | DHC1 Chipmunk T10 <ff> | No 225 Sqn ATC, Brighton | |
| WD373 | DHC1 Chipmunk T10 (G-BXDI) [12] | Privately owned, Duxford | |
| WD377 | DHC1 Chipmunk T10 <ff> | RAF Millom Museum, Haverigg | |
| *WD379* | DHC1 Chipmunk T10 (WB696/ G-APLO) [K] | Privately owned, Jersey | |
| WD386 | DHC1 Chipmunk T10 (comp WD377) | Dumfries & Galloway Avn Mus, Prestwick | |
| WD390 | DHC1 Chipmunk T10 (G-BWNK) [68] | Privately owned, Breighton | |
| WD413 | Avro 652A Anson T21 (7881M/G-VROE) | Air Atlantique Classic Flight, Coventry | |
| *WD615* | Gloster Meteor TT20 (WD646/8189M) [R] | RAF Manston History Museum | |
| WD686 | Gloster Meteor NF11 | Muckleburgh Collection, Weybourne | |
| WD790 | Gloster Meteor NF11 (8743M)<ff> | North-East Aircraft Museum, Usworth | |
| WD889 | Fairey Firefly AS5 <ff> | North-East Aircraft Museum, Usworth | |
| WD931 | EE Canberra B2 <ff> | RAF Museum, stored Cosford | |
| WD935 | EE Canberra B2 (8440M) <ff> | Aeroventure, Doncaster | |
| WD954 | EE Canberra B2 <ff> | Privately owned, St Mawgan | |
| WE113 | EE Canberra B2 <ff> | Privately owned, Woodhurst, Cambridgeshire | |
| WE122 | EE Canberra TT18 [845] <ff> | Blyth Valley Aviation Collection, Walpole, Suffolk | |

| Notes | Serial | Type (other identity) [code] | Owner/operator, location or fate |
|---|---|---|---|
| | WE139 | EE Canberra PR3 (8369M) | RAF Museum, Hendon |
| | WE168 | EE Canberra PR3 (8049M) <ff> | Norfolk & Suffolk Avn Museum, Flixton |
| | WE173 | EE Canberra PR3 (8740M) <ff> | Robertsbridge Aviation Society, Mayfield |
| | WE188 | EE Canberra T4 | Solway Aviation Society, Carlisle |
| | WE192 | EE Canberra T4 <ff> | Blyth Valley Aviation Collection, Walpole, Suffolk |
| | *WE275* | DH112 Venom FB50 (J-1601/G-VIDI) | BAE Systems Hawarden, Fire Section |
| | WE569 | Auster T7 (G-ASAJ) | Privately owned, Bourn, Lincs |
| | WE591 | Auster T7 (G-ASAK) [Y] | *Sold as F-AZTJ, 24 March 2005* |
| | WE600 | Auster T7 Antarctic (7602M) | RAF Museum, Cosford |
| | *WE724* | Hawker Sea Fury FB11 (VX653/G-BUCM) [062] | The Fighter Collection, Duxford |
| | WE982 | Slingsby T30B Prefect TX1 (8781M) | RAF Museum, stored Cosford |
| | WE987 | Slingsby T30B Prefect TX1 (BGA2517) | Aeroventure, Doncaster |
| | WE990 | Slingsby T30B Prefect TX1 (BGA2583) | Privately owned, stored Beds |
| | WE992 | Slingsby T30B Prefect TX1 (BGA2692) | Privately owned, Keevil |
| | WF118 | Percival P57 Sea Prince T1 (G-DACA) | Gatwick Aviation Museum, Charlwood, Surrey |
| | WF122 | Percival P57 Sea Prince T1 [575/CU] | Aeroventure, Doncaster |
| | WF128 | Percival P57 Sea Prince T1 (8611M) | Norfolk & Suffolk Avn Museum, Flixton |
| | WF137 | Percival P57 Sea Prince C1 | SWWAPS, Lasham |
| | WF145 | Hawker Sea Hawk F1 <ff> | Privately owned, Ingatestone, Essex |
| | WF225 | Hawker Sea Hawk F1 [CU] | RNAS Culdrose, at main gate |
| | WF259 | Hawker Sea Hawk F2 [171/A] | Royal Scottish Mus'm of Flight, E Fortune |
| | WF369 | Vickers Varsity T1 [F] | Newark Air Museum, Winthorpe |
| | WF372 | Vickers Varsity T1 [A] | Brooklands Museum, Weybridge |
| | WF376 | Vickers Varsity T1 | Bristol Airport Fire Section |
| | WF408 | Vickers Varsity T1 (8395M) | Privately owned, East Grinstead |
| | WF410 | Vickers Varsity T1 [F] | *Scrapped at Lulsgate, May 2004* |
| | WF643 | Gloster Meteor F8 [P] | Norfolk & Suffolk Avn Museum, Flixton |
| | *WF714* | Gloster Meteor F8 (WK914) | North-West Aviation Heritage, Hooton Park, Cheshire |
| | WF784 | Gloster Meteor T7 (7895M) | Gloucestershire Avn Coll, stored Gloucester |
| | WF825 | Gloster Meteor T7 (8359M) [A] | Meteor Flight, Yatesbury |
| | WF911 | EE Canberra B2 [CO] <ff> | The Griffin Trust, Hooton Park, Cheshire |
| | WF922 | EE Canberra PR3 | Midland Air Museum, Coventry |
| | WG303 | DHC1 Chipmunk T10 (8208M) <ff> | *Currently not known* |
| | WG308 | DHC1 Chipmunk T10 (G-BYHL) [71] | Privately owned, RAF Cranwell |
| | WG316 | DHC1 Chipmunk T10 (G-BCAH) | Privately owned, Leicester |
| | WG321 | DHC1 Chipmunk T10 (G-DHCC) | Privately owned, Wevelgem, Belgium |
| | WG348 | DHC1 Chipmunk T10 (G-BBMV) | Privately owned, Sywell |
| | WG350 | DHC1 Chipmunk T10 (G-BPAL) | Privately owned, Cascais, Portugal |
| | WG362 | DHC1 Chipmunk T10 (8437M/8630M/*WX643*) <ff> | No 1094 Sqn ATC, Ely |
| | WG407 | DHC1 Chipmunk T10 (G-BWMX) [67] | Privately owned, Croydon, Cambs |
| | WG418 | DHC1 Chipmunk T10 (8209M/G-ATDY) <ff> | No 1940 Sqn ATC, Levenshulme, Gr Manchester |
| | WG419 | DHC1 Chipmunk T10 (8206M) <ff> | No 1053 Sqn ATC, Armthorpe |
| | WG422 | DHC1 Chipmunk T10 (8394M/G-BFAX) [16] | Privately owned, Eggesford |
| | WG432 | DHC1 Chipmunk T10 [L] | Museum of Army Flying, Middle Wallop |
| | WG458 | DHC1 Chipmunk T10 (N458BG) [2] | Privately owned, Breighton |
| | WG465 | DHC1 Chipmunk T10 (G-BCEY) | Privately owned, White Waltham |
| | WG469 | DHC1 Chipmunk T10 (G-BWJY) [72] | Privately owned, Sligo, Eire |
| | WG471 | DHC1 Chipmunk T10 (8210M) <ff> | Thameside Aviation Museum, East Tilbury |
| | WG472 | DHC1 Chipmunk T10 (G-AOTY) | Privately owned, Bryngwyn Bach, Clwyd |
| | WG477 | DHC1 Chipmunk T10 (8362M/G-ATDP) <ff> | No 281 Sqn ATC, Birkdale, Merseyside |
| | WG486 | DHC1 Chipmunk T10 [G] | RAF BBMF, Coningsby |
| | WG498 | Slingsby T21B Sedbergh TX1 (BGA3245) | Privately owned, Aston Down |
| | WG511 | Avro 696 Shackleton T4 (fuselage) | Flambards Village Theme Park, Helston |

| Serial | Type (other identity) [code] | Owner/operator, location or fate | Notes |
|---|---|---|---|
| WG719 | WS51 Dragonfly HR5 (G-BRMA) | The Helicopter Museum, Weston-super-Mare | |
| WG724 | WS51 Dragonfly HR5 [932] | North-East Aircraft Museum, Usworth | |
| WG751 | WS51 Dragonfly HR5 [710/GJ] | World Naval Base, Chatham | |
| WG760 | EE P1A (7755M) | RAF Museum, Cosford | |
| WG763 | EE P1A (7816M) | Gr Manchester Mus of Science & Industry | |
| WG768 | Short SB5 (8005M) | RAF Museum, Cosford | |
| WG774 | BAC 221 | Science Museum, at FAA Museum, RNAS Yeovilton | |
| WG777 | Fairey FD2 (7986M) | RAF Museum, Cosford | |
| WG789 | EE Canberra B2/6 <ff> | Norfolk & Suffolk Avn Museum, Flixton | |
| WH132 | Gloster Meteor T7 (7906M) [J] | No 276 Sqn ATC, Chelmsford | |
| WH166 | Gloster Meteor T7 (8052M) [A] | Privately owned, Birlingham, Worcs | |
| WH291 | Gloster Meteor F8 | SWWAPS, Lasham | |
| WH301 | Gloster Meteor F8 (7930M) [T] | RAF Museum, Hendon | |
| WH364 | Gloster Meteor F8 (8169M) | Gloucestershire Avn Coll, stored Gloucester | |
| WH453 | Gloster Meteor D16 [L] | Bentwaters Cold War Air Museum | |
| WH646 | EE Canberra T17A <ff> | Midland Air Museum, Coventry | |
| WH657 | EE Canberra B2 | Brenzett Aeronautical Museum | |
| WH665 | EE Canberra T17 (8763M) [J] | BAE Systems Filton, Fire Section | |
| WH725 | EE Canberra B2 | Imperial War Museum, Duxford | |
| WH734 | EE Canberra B2(mod) <ff> | Privately owned, Pershore | |
| WH739 | EE Canberra B2 <ff> | No 2475 Sqn ATC, Ammanford, Dyfed | |
| WH740 | EE Canberra T17 (8762M) [K] | East Midlands Airport Aeropark | |
| WH773 | EE Canberra PR7 (8696M) | Gatwick Aviation Museum, Charlwood, Surrey | |
| WH775 | EE Canberra PR7 (8128M/8868M) <ff> | Privately owned, Welshpool | |
| WH779 | EE Canberra PR7 <ff> | Boscombe Down Aviation Collection | |
| WH779 | EE Canberra PR7 [BP] <rf> | RAF, stored Shawbury | |
| WH791 | EE Canberra PR7 (8165M/8176M/8187M) | Newark Air Museum, Winthorpe | |
| WH840 | EE Canberra T4 (8350M) | Privately owned, Flixton | |
| WH846 | EE Canberra T4 | Yorkshire Air Museum, Elvington | |
| WH849 | EE Canberra T4 | Scrapped at Shawbury, October 2005 | |
| WH850 | EE Canberra T4 <ff> | Privately owned, Narborough | |
| WH863 | EE Canberra T17 (8693M) [CP] <ff> | Newark Air Museum, Winthorpe | |
| WH876 | EE Canberra B2(mod) <ff> | Boscombe Down Aviation Collection | |
| WH887 | EE Canberra TT18 [847] <ff> | Privately owned, Farnborough | |
| WH903 | EE Canberra B2 <ff> | Yorkshire Air Museum, Elvington | |
| WH904 | EE Canberra T19 | Newark Air Museum, Winthorpe | |
| WH953 | EE Canberra B6(mod) <ff> | Blyth Valley Aviation Collection, Walpole, Suffolk | |
| WH957 | EE Canberra E15 (8869M) <ff> | Lincolnshire Avn Heritage Centre, East Kirkby | |
| WH960 | EE Canberra B15 (8344M) <ff> | Rolls-Royce Heritage Trust, Derby | |
| WH964 | EE Canberra E15 (8870M) <ff> | Privately owned, Lewes | |
| WH984 | EE Canberra B15 (8101M) <ff> | Privately owned, Mold | |
| WH991 | WS51 Dragonfly HR3 | Yorkshire Helicopter Preservation Group, Elvington | |
| WJ231 | Hawker Sea Fury FB11 (WE726) [115/O] | FAA Museum, Yeovilton | |
| WJ306 | Slingsby T21B Sedbergh TX1 (BGA3240) [FGB] | Privately owned, Weston-on-the-Green | |
| WJ358 | Auster AOP6 (G-ARYD) | Museum of Army Flying, Middle Wallop | |
| WJ565 | EE Canberra T17 (8871M) <ff> | Aeroventure, Doncaster | |
| WJ567 | EE Canberra B2 <ff> | Privately owned, Houghton, Cambs | |
| WJ576 | EE Canberra T17 <ff> | Boulton Paul Association, Wolverhampton | |
| WJ581 | EE Canberra PR7 <ff> | Privately owned, Canterbury | |
| WJ633 | EE Canberra T17 [EF] <ff> | RAF Wyton | |
| WJ639 | EE Canberra TT18 [39] | North-East Aircraft Museum, Usworth | |
| WJ640 | EE Canberra B2 (8722M) <ff> | Privately owned, | |
| WJ676 | EE Canberra B2 (7796M) <ff> | North-West Aviation Heritage, Hooton Park, Cheshire | |
| WJ677 | EE Canberra B2 <ff> | Privately owned, Redruth | |
| WJ717 | EE Canberra TT18 (9052M) <ff> | RAF St Athan, Fire Section | |
| WJ721 | EE Canberra TT18 [21] <ff> | Privately owned, Oban | |
| WJ731 | EE Canberra B2T [BK] <ff> | Privately owned, Golders Green | |
| WJ821 | EE Canberra PR7 (8668M) | Army, Bassingbourn, on display | |
| WJ865 | EE Canberra T4 | Privately owned, Bromsgrove | |

| Notes | Serial | Type (other identity) [code] | Owner/operator, location or fate |
|---|---|---|---|
| | WJ880 | EE Canberra T4 (8491M) <ff> | Dumfries & Galloway Avn Mus, Dumfries |
| | WJ903 | Vickers Varsity T1 <ff> | Aeroventure, Doncaster |
| | WJ945 | Vickers Varsity T1 (G-BEDV) [21] | Imperial War Museum, Duxford |
| | WJ975 | EE Canberra T19 [S] | Bomber County Aviation Museum, Hemswell |
| | WJ992 | EE Canberra T4 | Bournemouth Int'l Airport, Fire Section |
| | | | |
| | WK102 | EE Canberra T17 (8780M) <ff> | Privately owned, Welshpool |
| | WK118 | EE Canberra TT18 <ff> | Privately owned, Chipperfield, Herts |
| | WK122 | EE Canberra TT18 <ff> | Privately owned, Chipperfield, Herts |
| | WK124 | EE Canberra TT18 (9093M) [CR] | MoD FSCTE, Manston |
| | WK126 | EE Canberra TT18 (N2138J) [843] | Gloucestershire Avn Coll, stored Gloucester |
| | WK127 | EE Canberra TT18 (8985M) <ff> | Privately owned, Peterborough |
| | WK128 | EE Canberra B2 <ff> | *Sold to New Zealand, February 2005* |
| | WK146 | EE Canberra B2 <ff> | Gatwick Aviation Museum, Charlwood, Surrey |
| | WK163 | EE Canberra B2/6 (G-BVWC) | Air Atlantique Classic Flight, Coventry |
| | WK198 | VS Swift F4 (7428M) (fuselage) | North-East Aircraft Museum, Usworth |
| | WK275 | VS Swift F4 | Privately owned, Upper Hill, nr Leominster |
| | WK277 | VS Swift FR5 (7719M) [N] | Newark Air Museum, Winthorpe |
| | WK281 | VS Swift FR5 (7712M) [S] | Tangmere Military Aviation Museum |
| | WK393 | DH112 Venom FB1 <ff> | Aeroventure, Doncaster |
| | *WK436* | DH112 Venom FB50 (J-1614/G-VENM) | Kennet Aviation, North Weald |
| | WK512 | DHC1 Chipmunk T10 (G-BXIM) [A] | Privately owned, Brize Norton |
| | WK514 | DHC1 Chipmunk T10 (G-BBMO) | Privately owned, Wellesbourne Mountford |
| | WK517 | DHC1 Chipmunk T10 (G-ULAS) | Privately owned, Denham |
| | WK518 | DHC1 Chipmunk T10 [K] | RAF BBMF, Coningsby |
| | WK522 | DHC1 Chipmunk T10 (G-BCOU) | Privately owned, Duxford |
| | WK549 | DHC1 Chipmunk T10 (G-BTWF) | Privately owned, Breighton |
| | WK570 | DHC1 Chipmunk T10 (8211M) <ff> | No 424 Sqn ATC, Solent Sky, Southampton |
| | WK576 | DHC1 Chipmunk T10 (8357M) <ff> | No 1206 Sqn ATC, Lichfield |
| | WK577 | DHC1 Chipmunk T10 (G-BCYM) | Privately owned, Kemble |
| | WK584 | DHC1 Chipmunk T10 (7556M) <ff> | No 2008 Sqn ATC, Bawtry |
| | WK585 | DHC1 Chipmunk T10 (9265M/G-BZGA) | Privately owned, Duxford |
| | WK586 | DHC1 Chipmunk T10 (G-BXGX) [V] | Privately owned, Slinfold |
| | WK590 | DHC1 Chipmunk T10 (G-BWVZ) [69] | Privately owned, Spanhoe |
| | WK608 | DHC1 Chipmunk T10 [906] | RN Historic Flight, Yeovilton |
| | WK609 | DHC1 Chipmunk T10 (G-BXDN) [93] | Privately owned, Booker |
| | WK611 | DHC1 Chipmunk T10 (G-ARWB) | Privately owned, Thruxton |
| | WK620 | DHC1 Chipmunk T10 [T] (fuselage) | Privately owned, Twyford, Bucks |
| | WK622 | DHC1 Chipmunk T10 (G-BCZH) | Privately owned, Horsford |
| | WK624 | DHC1 Chipmunk T10 (G-BWHI) | Privately owned, Woodvale |
| | WK626 | DHC1 Chipmunk T10 (8213M) <ff> | Aeroventure, stored Doncaster |
| | WK628 | DHC1 Chipmunk T10 (G-BBMW) | Privately owned, Goodwood |
| | WK630 | DHC1 Chipmunk T10 (G-BXDG) | Privately owned, Felthorpe |
| | WK633 | DHC1 Chipmunk T10 (G-BXEC) [A] | Privately owned, Redhill |
| | WK638 | DHC1 Chipmunk T10 (G-BWJZ) (fuselage) | Privately owned, Eccleshall, Staffs |
| | WK640 | DHC1 Chipmunk T10 (G-BWUV) [C] | Privately owned, Bagby |
| | WK642 | DHC1 Chipmunk T10 (G-BXDP) [94] | Privately owned, Kilrush, Eire |
| | WK654 | Gloster Meteor F8 (8092M) [B] | City of Norwich Aviation Museum |
| | WK800 | Gloster Meteor D16 [Z] | DPA/QinetiQ, Boscombe Down (wfu) |
| | *WK864* | Gloster Meteor F8 (WL168/7750M) [C] | Yorkshire Air Museum, Elvington |
| | WK914 | Gloster Meteor F8 (*WF714*) | Hooton Park Trust, Cheshire |
| | WK935 | Gloster Meteor Prone Pilot (7869M) | RAF Museum, Cosford |
| | WK991 | Gloster Meteor F8 (7825M) | Imperial War Museum, Duxford |
| | WL131 | Gloster Meteor F8 (7751M) <ff> | Aeroventure, Doncaster |
| | WL181 | Gloster Meteor F8 [X] | North-East Aircraft Museum, Usworth |
| | WL332 | Gloster Meteor T7 [888] | Privately owned, Long Marston |
| | WL345 | Gloster Meteor T7 | St Leonard's Motors, Hollington, E Sussex |
| | WL349 | Gloster Meteor T7 [Z] | Gloucestershire Airport, Staverton, on display |
| | WL360 | Gloster Meteor T7 (7920M) [G] | Meteor Flight, Yatesbury |
| | WL375 | Gloster Meteor T7(mod) | Dumfries & Galloway Avn Mus, Dumfries |
| | WL405 | Gloster Meteor T7 | Meteor Flight, Yatesbury |
| | WL419 | Gloster Meteor T7 | Martin Baker Aircraft, Chalgrove |
| | WL505 | DH100 Vampire FB9 (7705M/G-FBIX) | Vampire Preservation Society, Bournemouth |

| Serial | Type (other identity) [code] | Owner/operator, location or fate | Notes |
|--------|------------------------------|----------------------------------|-------|
| *WL505* | DH100 Vampire FB6 (J-1167/*VZ304*/G-MKVI) | Privately owned, Hibaldstow | |
| WL626 | Vickers Varsity T1 (G-BHDD) [P] | East Midlands Airport Aeropark | |
| WL627 | Vickers Varsity T1 (8488M) [D] <ff> | Privately owned, Preston, E Yorkshire | |
| WL679 | Vickers Varsity T1 (9155M) | RAF Museum, Cosford | |
| WL732 | BP P108 Sea Balliol T21 | RAF Museum, Cosford | |
| WL795 | Avro 696 Shackleton MR2C (8753M) [T] | RAF St Mawgan, on display | |
| WL798 | Avro 696 Shackleton MR2C (8114M) <ff> | Privately owned, Elgin | |
| *WL925* | Slingsby T31B Cadet TX3 (WV925) <ff> | *Currently not known* | |
| WM145 | AW Meteor NF11 <ff> | Privately owned, Gatenby, Lincs | |
| WM167 | AW Meteor NF11 (G-LOSM) | Air Atlantique Classic Flight, Coventry | |
| WM267 | Gloster Meteor NF11 <ff> | Blyth Valley Aviation Collection, Walpol Suffolk | |
| WM292 | AW Meteor TT20 [841] | FAA Museum, stored RNAS Yeovilton | |
| *WM311* | AW Meteor TT20 (WM224/8177M) | East Midlands Airport Aeropark | |
| WM366 | AW Meteor NF13 (4X-FNA) (comp VZ462) | SWWAPS, Lasham | |
| WM367 | AW Meteor NF13 <ff> | Jet Avn Preservation Grp, Long Marston | |
| WM571 | DH112 Sea Venom FAW21 [VL] | Solent Sky, stored | |
| WM729 | DH113 Vampire NF10 <ff> | Mosquito Aircraft Museum, London Colney | |
| WM913 | Hawker Sea Hawk FB5 (8162M) [456/J] | Newark Air Museum, Winthorpe | |
| WM961 | Hawker Sea Hawk FB5 [J] | Caernarfon Air World | |
| WM969 | Hawker Sea Hawk FB5 [10/Z] | Imperial War Museum, Duxford | |
| *WN105* | Hawker Sea Hawk FB3 (WF299/8164M) | Privately owned, Birlingham, Worcs | |
| WN108 | Hawker Sea Hawk FB5 [033] | Ulster Aviation Society, Langford Lodge | |
| WN149 | BP P108 Balliol T2 | Boulton Paul Association, Wolverhampton | |
| WN411 | Fairey Gannet AS1 (fuselage) | Privately owned, Sholing, Hants | |
| WN493 | WS51 Dragonfly HR5 | FAA Museum, RNAS Yeovilton | |
| WN499 | WS51 Dragonfly HR5 [Y] | Caernarfon Airfield Fire Section | |
| WN516 | BP P108 Balliol T2 <ff> | North-East Aircraft Museum, Usworth | |
| WN534 | BP P108 Balliol T2 <ff> | Boulton Paul Association, Wolverhampton | |
| WN890 | Hawker Hunter F2 <ff> | Boscombe Down Aviation Collection | |
| WN904 | Hawker Hunter F2 (7544M) [3] | RE 39 Regt, Waterbeach, on display | |
| WN907 | Hawker Hunter F2 (7416M) <ff> | Robertsbridge Aviation Society, Newhaven | |
| WN957 | Hawker Hunter F5 <ff> | No 2445 Sqn ATC, Llanbedr | |
| WP185 | Hawker Hunter F5 (7583M) | Privately owned, Great Dunmow, Essex | |
| WP190 | Hawker Hunter F5 (7582M/8473M/*WP180*) [K] | Tangmere Military Aviation Museum | |
| WP250 | DH113 Vampire NF10 <ff> | Privately owned, Tamworth | |
| WP255 | DH113 Vampire NF10 <ff> | Aeroventure, Doncaster | |
| WP270 | EoN Eton TX1 (8598M) | RAF Museum Reserve Collection, Stafford | |
| WP308 | Percival P57 Sea Prince T1 (G-GACA) [572/CU] | Gatwick Aviation Museum, Charlwood, Surrey | |
| WP313 | Percival P57 Sea Prince T1 [568/CU] | FAA Museum, stored RNAS Yeovilton | |
| WP314 | Percival P57 Sea Prince T1 (8634M) [573/CU] | Privately owned, Carlisle Airport | |
| WP321 | Percival P57 Sea Prince T1 (N7SY) | Bournemouth Aviation Museum | |
| WP515 | EE Canberra B2 <ff> | *Sold to Germany, January 2005* | |
| WP772 | DHC1 Chipmunk T10 [Q] (wreck) | RAF Manston History Museum | |
| WP784 | DHC1 Chipmunk T10 <ff> | Jet Avn Preservation Grp, Long Marston | |
| WP788 | DHC1 Chipmunk T10 (G-BCHL) | Privately owned, Sleap | |
| WP790 | DHC1 Chipmunk T10 (G-BBNC) [T] | Mosquito Aircraft Museum, London Colney | |
| WP795 | DHC1 Chipmunk T10 (G-BVZZ) [901] | Privately owned, Lee-on-Solent | |
| WP800 | DHC1 Chipmunk T10 (G-BCXN) [2] | Privately owned, Halton | |
| WP803 | DHC1 Chipmunk T10 (G-HAPY) [G] | Privately owned, Booker | |
| WP805 | DHC1 Chipmunk T10 (G-MAJR) [D] | Privately owned, Lee-on-Solent | |
| WP808 | DHC1 Chipmunk T10 (G-BDEU) | Privately owned, Hurstbourne Tarrant, Hants | |
| WP809 | DHC1 Chipmunk T10 (G-BVTX) [78] | Privately owned, Husbands Bosworth | |
| WP833 | DHC1 Chipmunk T10 (G-BZDU) [H] | Privately owned, Newcastle | |
| WP835 | DHC1 Chipmunk T10 (D-ERTY) | Privately owned, The Netherlands | |
| WP839 | DHC1 Chipmunk T10 (G-BZXE) [A] | Privately owned, Blackpool | |
| WP840 | DHC1 Chipmunk T10 (G-BXDM) [9] | Privately owned, Halton | |

| Notes | Serial | Type (other identity) [code] | Owner/operator, location or fate |
|---|---|---|---|
| | WP844 | DHC1 Chipmunk T10 (G-BWOX) [85] | Privately owned, Shobdon |
| | WP856 | DHC1 Chipmunk T10 (G-BVWP) [904] | Privately owned, Horsham |
| | WP857 | DHC1 Chipmunk T10 (G-BDRJ) [24] | Privately owned, Prestwick |
| | WP859 | DHC1 Chipmunk T10 (G-BXCP) [E] | Privately owned, Spanhoe |
| | WP860 | DHC1 Chipmunk T10 (G-BXDA) [6] | Privately owned, Perth |
| | WP863 | DHC1 Chipmunk T10 (8360M/G-ATJI) <ff> | No 1011 Sqn ATC, Boscombe Down |
| | WP869 | DHC1 Chipmunk T10 (8215M) <ff> | Privately owned, Rush Green |
| | WP870 | DHC1 Chipmunk T10 (G-BCOI) [12] | Privately owned, Rayne Hall Farm, Essex |
| | WP871 | DHC1 Chipmunk T10 [W] | Sold to South Africa |
| | WP896 | DHC1 Chipmunk T10 (G-BWVY) | Privately owned, White Waltham |
| | WP901 | DHC1 Chipmunk T10 (G-BWNT) [B] | Privately owned, East Midlands Airport |
| | WP903 | DHC1 Chipmunk T10 (G-BCGC) | Privately owned, Henlow |
| | WP912 | DHC1 Chipmunk T10 (8467M) | RAF Museum, Cosford |
| | WP921 | DHC1 Chipmunk T10 (G-ATJJ) <ff> | Privately owned, Brooklands |
| | WP925 | DHC1 Chipmunk T10 (G-BXHA) [C] | Privately owned, Seppe, The Netherlands |
| | WP927 | DHC1 Chipmunk T10 (8216M/G-ATJK) <ff> | Mosquito Aircraft Museum, London Colney |
| | WP928 | DHC1 Chipmunk T10 (G-BXGM) [D] | Privately owned, Shoreham |
| | WP929 | DHC1 Chipmunk T10 (G-BXCV) [F] | Privately owned, Duxford |
| | WP930 | DHC1 Chipmunk T10 (G-BXHF) [J] | Privately owned, Redhill |
| | WP962 | DHC1 Chipmunk T10 [C] | RAF Museum, Hendon |
| | WP964 | DHC1 Chipmunk T10 [Y] | Sold to South Africa |
| | WP971 | DHC1 Chipmunk T10 (G-ATHD) | Privately owned, Denham |
| | WP977 | DHC1 Chipmunk T10 (G-BHRD) <ff> | Privately owned, Yateley, Hants |
| | WP983 | DHC1 Chipmunk T10 (G-BXNN) [B] | Privately owned, Eggesford |
| | WP984 | DHC1 Chipmunk T10 (G-BWTO) [H] | Privately owned, Little Gransden |
| | WR360 | DH112 Venom FB50 (J-1626/G-DHSS) [K] | Source Classic Jet Flight, Bournemouth |
| | WR410 | DH112 Venom FB50 (J-1539/G-DHUU/WE410) | Source Classic Jet Flight, Bournemouth |
| | WR410 | DH112 Venom FB54 (J-1790/G-BLKA) [N] | Mosquito Aircraft Museum, London Colney |
| | WR421 | DH112 Venom FB50 (J-1611/G-DHTT) | Bournemouth Aviation Museum |
| | WR470 | DH112 Venom FB50 (J-1542/G-DHVM) | Air Atlantique Classic Flight, Coventry |
| | WR539 | DH112 Venom FB4 (8399M) <ff> | Mosquito Aircraft Museum, London Colney |
| | WR960 | Avro 696 Shackleton AEW2 (8772M) | Gr Manchester Mus of Science & Industry |
| | WR963 | Avro 696 Shackleton AEW2 | Air Atlantique Classic Flight, Coventry |
| | WR971 | Avro 696 Shackleton MR3 (8119M) [Q] | Fenland & W Norfolk Aviation Museum, Wisbech |
| | WR974 | Avro 696 Shackleton MR3 (8117M) [K] | Gatwick Aviation Museum, Charlwood, Surrey |
| | WR977 | Avro 696 Shackleton MR3 (8186M) [B] | Newark Air Museum, Winthorpe |
| | WR982 | Avro 696 Shackleton MR3 (8106M) [J] | Gatwick Aviation Museum, Charlwood, Surrey |
| | WR985 | Avro 696 Shackleton MR3 (8103M) [H] | Privately owned, Long Marston |
| | WS103 | Gloster Meteor T7 [709/VL] | FAA Museum, stored RNAS Yeovilton |
| | WS692 | Gloster Meteor NF12 (7605M) [C] | Newark Air Museum, Winthorpe |
| | WS726 | Gloster Meteor NF14 (7960M) [G] | No 1855 Sqn ATC, Royton, Gr Manchester |
| | WS739 | Gloster Meteor NF14 (7961M) | Newark Air Museum, Winthorpe |
| | WS760 | Gloster Meteor NF14 (7964M) | Meteor Flight, stored Yatesbury |
| | WS774 | Gloster Meteor NF14 (7959M) | Privately owned, Quedgeley, Glos |
| | WS776 | Gloster Meteor NF14 (7716M) [K] | Bournemouth Aviation Museum |
| | WS788 | Gloster Meteor NF14 (7967M) [Z] | Yorkshire Air Museum, Elvington |
| | WS792 | Gloster Meteor NF14 (7965M) [K] | Brighouse Bay Caravan Park, Borgue, D&G |
| | WS807 | Gloster Meteor NF14 (7973M) [N] | Gloucestershire Avn Coll, stored Gloucester |
| | WS832 | Gloster Meteor NF14 [W] | Solway Aviation Society, Carlisle |
| | WS838 | Gloster Meteor NF14 | Midland Air Museum, Coventry |
| | WS843 | Gloster Meteor NF14 (7937M) [Y] | RAF Museum Restoration Centre, Cosford |
| | WT121 | Douglas Skyraider AEW1 [415/CU] | FAA Museum, stored RNAS Yeovilton |
| | WT205 | EE Canberra B15 <ff> | RAF Manston History Museum |

| Serial | Type (other identity) [code] | Owner/operator, location or fate | Notes |
|--------|------------------------------|----------------------------------|-------|
| WT308 | EE Canberra B(I)6 | RN, Predannack Fire School | |
| WT309 | EE Canberra B(I)6 <ff> | Farnborough Air Sciences Trust, Farnborough | |
| WT319 | EE Canberra B(I)6 <ff> | Privately owned, Lavendon, Bucks | |
| WT333 | EE Canberra B6(mod) (G-BVXC) | Privately owned, Bruntingthorpe | |
| WT339 | EE Canberra B(I)8 (8198M) | RAF Barkston Heath Fire Section | |
| WT480 | EE Canberra T4 [AT] | *Scrapped at Shawbury, October 2005* | |
| WT482 | EE Canberra T4 <ff> | *Currently not known* | |
| WT483 | EE Canberra T4 [83] | Privately owned, Long Marston | |
| WT486 | EE Canberra T4 (8102M) <ff> | Privately owned, Newtownards | |
| WT507 | EE Canberra PR7 (8131M/8548M) [44] <ff> | No 384 Sqn ATC, Mansfield | |
| WT509 | EE Canberra PR7 [BR] | *Scrapped* | |
| WT519 | EE Canberra PR7 [CH] | RAF Wyton, Fire Section | |
| WT520 | EE Canberra PR7 (8094M/8184M) <ff> | No 967 Sqn ATC, Warton | |
| WT525 | EE Canberra T22 <ff> | Privately owned, South Woodham Ferrers | |
| WT532 | EE Canberra PR7 (8728M/8890M) <ff> | Bournemouth Aviation Museum | |
| WT534 | EE Canberra PR7 (8549M) [43] <ff> | Aeroventure, Doncaster | |
| WT536 | EE Canberra PR7 (8063M) <ff> | Privately owned, Shirrell Heath, Hants | |
| WT537 | EE Canberra PR7 | BAE Systems Samlesbury, on display | |
| WT555 | Hawker Hunter F1 (7499M) | Vanguard Haulage, Greenford, London | |
| WT569 | Hawker Hunter F1 (7491M) | No 2117 Sqn ATC, Kenfig Hill, Mid-Glamorgan | |
| WT612 | Hawker Hunter F1 (7496M) | RAF Henlow, on display | |
| WT619 | Hawker Hunter F1 (7525M) | Gr Manchester Mus of Science & Industry | |
| WT648 | Hawker Hunter F1 (7530M) <ff> | Boscombe Down Aviation Collection | |
| WT651 | Hawker Hunter F1 (7532M) | Newark Air Museum, Winthorpe | |
| WT660 | Hawker Hunter F1 (7421M) [C] | Highland Aviation Museum, Inverness | |
| WT680 | Hawker Hunter F1 (7533M) [J] | Privately owned, Holbeach, Lincs | |
| WT684 | Hawker Hunter F1 (7422M) <ff> | Privately owned, Lavendon, Bucks | |
| WT694 | Hawker Hunter F1 (7510M) | Caernarfon Air World | |
| WT711 | Hawker Hunter GA11 [833/DD] | Air Atlantique Classic Flight, Coventry | |
| *WT720* | Hawker Hunter F51 (RDAF E-408/8565M) [B] | RAF Sealand, on display | |
| WT722 | Hawker Hunter T8C (G-BWGN) [878/VL] | Hunter Flying Club, Exeter | |
| WT723 | Hawker Hunter PR11 (G-PRII) [866/VL,3] | Privately owned, Exeter | |
| WT744 | Hawker Hunter GA11 [868/VL] | South West Aviation Heritage, Eaglescott | |
| WT799 | Hawker Hunter T8C [879] | Hunter Flying Club, Exeter | |
| WT804 | Hawker Hunter GA11 [831/DD] | FETC, Moreton-in-Marsh, Glos | |
| WT806 | Hawker Hunter GA11 | Northbrook College, Shoreham Airport | |
| WT859 | Supermarine 544 <ff> | Boscombe Down Aviation Collection | |
| WT867 | Slingsby T31B Cadet TX3 | Privately owned, Eaglescott | |
| WT871 | Slingsby T31B Cadet TX3 (BGA3149) | *Sold to The Netherlands* | |
| WT877 | Slingsby T31B Cadet TX3 | Boulton Paul Association, Wolverhampton | |
| WT899 | Slingsby T31B Cadet TX3 | Privately owned, stored Swindon | |
| WT900 | Slingsby T31B Cadet TX3 (BGA33372) | Privately owned, Lee-on-Solent | |
| WT905 | Slingsby T31B Cadet TX3 | Privately owned, Keevil | |
| WT908 | Slingsby T31B Cadet TX3 (BGA3487) | Privately owned, Dunstable | |
| WT910 | Slingsby T31B Cadet TX3 (BGA3953) | Privately owned, Llantisilio | |
| WT914 | Slingsby T31B Cadet TX3 (BGA3194) (fuselage) | Privately owned, Tibenham | |
| WT933 | Bristol 171 Sycamore 3 (G-ALSW/7709M) | Newark Air Museum, Winthorpe | |
| WV106 | Douglas Skyraider AEW1 [427/C] | FAA Museum, stored Yeovilton | |
| WV198 | Sikorsky S55 Whirlwind HAR21 (G-BJWY) [K] | Solway Aviation Society, Carlisle | |
| WV276 | Hawker Hunter F4 (7847M) [D] | *Sold to Germany, September 2005* | |
| WV318 | Hawker Hunter T7B (9236M/G-FFOX) | Delta Jets, Kemble | |
| WV322 | Hawker Hunter T8C (G-BZSE/9096M) [Y] | Privately owned, Kemble | |
| WV332 | Hawker Hunter F4 (7673M) <ff> | Tangmere Military Aircraft Museum | |
| WV372 | Hawker Hunter T7 (G-BXFI) [R] | Privately owned, Kemble | |

| Notes | Serial | Type (other identity) [code] | Owner/operator, location or fate |
|---|---|---|---|
| | WV381 | Hawker Hunter GA11 [732/VL] (fuselage) | UKAEA, Culham, Oxon |
| | WV382 | Hawker Hunter GA11 [830/VL] | Jet Avn Preservation Grp, Long Marston |
| | WV383 | Hawker Hunter T7 | Farnborough Air Sciences Trust, Farnborough |
| | WV396 | Hawker Hunter T8C (9249M) [91] | RAF Valley, at main gate |
| | WV483 | Percival P56 Provost T1 (7693M) [N-E] | *Currently not known* |
| | WV486 | Percival P56 Provost T1 (7694M) [N-D] | Privately owned, Thatcham, Berks |
| | WV493 | Percival P56 Provost T1 (G-BDYG/7696M) [29] | Royal Scottish Mus'm of Flight, stored E Fortune |
| | WV499 | Percival P56 Provost T1 (G-BZRF/7698M) [P-G] | Privately owned, Booker |
| | WV562 | Percival P56 Provost T1 (7606M) [P-C] | RAF Museum, Cosford |
| | WV605 | Percival P56 Provost T1 [T-B] | Norfolk & Suffolk Avn Museum, Flixton |
| | WV606 | Percival P56 Provost T1 (7622M)[P-B] | Newark Air Museum, Winthorpe |
| | WV679 | Percival P56 Provost T1 (7615M) [O-J] | Wellesbourne Wartime Museum |
| | WV705 | Percival P66 Pembroke C1 <ff> | Privately owned, Awbridge, Hants |
| | WV740 | Percival P66 Pembroke C1 (G-BNPH) | Privately owned, Bournemouth |
| | WV746 | Percival P66 Pembroke C1 (8938M) | RAF Museum, Cosford |
| | WV781 | Bristol 171 Sycamore HR12 (G-ALTD/7839M) | Caernarfon Air World |
| | WV783 | Bristol 171 Sycamore HR12 (G-ALSP/7841M) | RAF Museum, Hendon |
| | WV787 | EE Canberra B2/8 (8799M) | Newark Air Museum, Winthorpe |
| | WV795 | Hawker Sea Hawk FGA6 (8151M) | Farnborough Air Sciences Trust, Farnborough |
| | WV797 | Hawker Sea Hawk FGA6 (8155M) [491/J] | Midland Air Museum, Coventry |
| | WV798 | Hawker Sea Hawk FGA6 [026/CU] | SWWAPS, Lasham |
| | WV838 | Hawker Sea Hawk FGA4 <ff> | Privately owned, Liverpool |
| | WV856 | Hawker Sea Hawk FGA6 [163] | FAA Museum, RNAS Yeovilton |
| | WV903 | Hawker Sea Hawk FGA4 (8153M) [128/C] | RN Historic Flight, stored Yeovilton |
| | WV908 | Hawker Sea Hawk FGA6 (8154M) [188/A] | RN Historic Flight, Yeovilton |
| | WV910 | Hawker Sea Hawk FGA6 <ff> | Boscombe Down Aviation Collection |
| | WV911 | Hawker Sea Hawk FGA4 [115/C] | RN Historic Flight, stored Yeovilton |
| | WW138 | DH112 Sea Venom FAW22 [227/Z] | FAA Museum, stored RNAS Yeovilton |
| | WW145 | DH112 Sea Venom FAW22 [680/LM] | Royal Scottish Mus'm of Flight, E Fortune |
| | WW217 | DH112 Sea Venom FAW22 [351] | Newark Air Museum, Winthorpe |
| | WW388 | Percival P56 Provost T1 (7616M) [O-F] | Shropshire Wartime Aircraft Recovery Grp, Sleap |
| | *WW421* | Percival P56 Provost T1 (WW450/G-BZRE/7689M) [P-B] | Privately owned, Bournemouth |
| | WW442 | Percival P56 Provost T1 (7618M) [N] | Gatwick Aviation Museum, Charlwood, Surrey |
| | WW444 | Percival P56 Provost T1 [D] | Privately owned, Brownhills, Staffs |
| | WW447 | Percival P56 Provost T1 | Privately owned, Grazeley, Berks |
| | WW453 | Percival P56 Provost T1 (G-TMKI) [W-S] | Privately owned, Clevedon |
| | WW654 | Hawker Hunter GA11 [834/DD] | Privately owned, Ford, W Sussex |
| | WX788 | DH112 Venom NF3 | Aeroventure, Doncaster |
| | WX853 | DH112 Venom NF3 (7443M) | Mosquito Aircraft Museum, London Colney |
| | WX905 | DH112 Venom NF3 (7458M) | Newark Air Museum, Winthorpe |
| | WZ425 | DH115 Vampire T11 | Privately owned, Birlingham, Worcs |
| | WZ450 | DH115 Vampire T11 <ff> | Lashenden Air Warfare Museum, Headcorn |
| | WZ507 | DH115 Vampire T11 (G-VTII) [74] | Vampire Preservation Society, Bournemouth |
| | WZ515 | DH115 Vampire T11 [60] | Solway Aviation Society, Carlisle |
| | WZ518 | DH115 Vampire T11 | North-East Aircraft Museum, Usworth |
| | WZ549 | DH115 Vampire T11 (8118M) [F] | Ulster Aviation Society, Langford Lodge |
| | WZ553 | DH115 Vampire T11 (G-DHYY) [40] | Air Atlantique Classic Flight, Coventry |

| Serial | Type (other identity) [code] | Owner/operator, location or fate | Notes |
|--------|------------------------------|----------------------------------|-------|
| WZ557 | DH115 Vampire T11 | Privately owned, Chop Gate, N Yorks | |
| WZ572 | DH115 Vampire T11 (8124M) [65] <ff> | Privately owned, Sholing, Hants | |
| WZ581 | DH115 Vampire T11 <ff> | The Vampire Collection, Hemel Hempstead | |
| WZ584 | DH115 Vampire T11 (G-BZRC) [K] | Privately owned, Booker | |
| WZ589 | DH115 Vampire T11 [19] | Privately owned, Rochester | |
| WZ589 | DH115 Vampire T55 (U-1230/G-DHZZ) | Source Classic Jet Flight, Bournemouth | |
| WZ590 | DH115 Vampire T11 [19] | Imperial War Museum, Duxford | |
| WZ662 | Auster AOP9 (G-BKVK) | Privately owned, Eggesford | |
| WZ706 | Auster AOP9 (7851M/G-BURR) | Privately owned, Middle Wallop | |
| WZ711 | Auster AOP9/Beagle E3 (G-AVHT) | Privately owned, Spanhoe | |
| WZ721 | Auster AOP9 | Museum of Army Flying, Middle Wallop | |
| WZ724 | Auster AOP9 (7432M) | AAC Middle Wallop, at main gate | |
| WZ729 | Auster AOP9 (G-BXON) | Privately owned, Newark-on-Trent | |
| WZ736 | Avro 707A (7868M) | Gr Manchester Mus of Science & Industry | |
| WZ744 | Avro 707C (7932M) | RAF Museum, Cosford | |
| WZ753 | Slingsby T38 Grasshopper TX1 | Solent Sky, Southampton | |
| WZ755 | Slingsby T38 Grasshopper TX1 (BGA3481) | Boulton Paul Association, Wolverhampton | |
| WZ757 | Slingsby T38 Grasshopper TX1 (comp XK820) | Privately owned, Kirton-in-Lindsey, Lincs | |
| WZ767 | Slingsby T38 Grasshopper TX1 | North-East Aircraft Museum, stored Usworth | |
| WZ772 | Slingsby T38 Grasshopper TX1 | Museum of Army Flying, stored Middle Wallop | |
| WZ773 | Slingsby T38 Grasshopper TX1 | Edinburgh Academy | |
| WZ779 | Slingsby T38 Grasshopper TX1 | *Currently not known* | |
| WZ784 | Slingsby T38 Grasshopper TX1 | Solway Aviation Society, Carlisle | |
| WZ791 | Slingsby T38 Grasshopper TX1 (8944M) | RAF Museum, Hendon | |
| WZ792 | Slingsby T38 Grasshopper TX1 | Privately owned, Sproughton | |
| WZ793 | Slingsby T38 Grasshopper TX1 | Privately owned, Keevil | |
| WZ798 | Slingsby T38 Grasshopper TX1 | Bournemouth Aviation Museum | |
| WZ816 | Slingsby T38 Grasshopper TX1 (BGA3979) | Privately owned, Redhill | |
| WZ819 | Slingsby T38 Grasshopper TX1 (BGA3498) | Privately owned, Halton | |
| WZ820 | Slingsby T38 Grasshopper TX1 | Sywell Aviation Museum | |
| WZ822 | Slingsby T38 Grasshopper TX1 | Aeroventure, stored Doncaster | |
| WZ824 | Slingsby T38 Grasshopper TX1 | Privately owned, stored Strathaven, Strathclyde | |
| WZ826 | Vickers Valiant B(K)1 (XD826/7872M) <ff> | Privately owned, Rayleigh, Essex | |
| WZ827 | Slingsby T38 Grasshopper TX1 | *Broken up at Keevil* | |
| WZ828 | Slingsby T38 Grasshopper TX1 (BGA4421) | Privately owned, Bicester | |
| WZ831 | Slingsby T38 Grasshopper TX1 | Privately owned, stored Nympsfield, Glos | |
| WZ846 | DHC1 Chipmunk T10 (G-BCSC/8439M) | No 2427 Sqn ATC, Biggin Hill | |
| WZ847 | DHC1 Chipmunk T10 (G-CPMK) [F] | Privately owned, Sleap | |
| WZ872 | DHC1 Chipmunk T10 (G-BZGB) [E] | Privately owned, Newcastle | |
| WZ876 | DHC1 Chipmunk T10 (G-BBWN) <ff> | Privately owned, Yateley, Hants | |
| WZ879 | DHC1 Chipmunk T10 (G-BWUT) [X] | Privately owned, Duxford | |
| WZ882 | DHC1 Chipmunk T10 (G-BXGP) [K] | Privately owned, Eaglescott | |
| XA109 | DH115 Sea Vampire T22 | Royal Scottish Mus'm of Flight, E Fortune | |
| XA127 | DH115 Sea Vampire T22 <ff> | FAA Museum, RNAS Yeovilton | |
| XA129 | DH115 Sea Vampire T22 | FAA Museum, stored RNAS Yeovilton | |
| XA225 | Slingsby T38 Grasshopper TX1 | Privately owned, Upavon | |
| XA226 | Slingsby T38 Grasshopper TX1 | Norfolk & Suffolk Avn Museum, Flixton | |
| XA228 | Slingsby T38 Grasshopper TX1 | Royal Scottish Mus'm of Flight, stored E Fortune | |
| XA230 | Slingsby T38 Grasshopper TX1 (BGA4098) | Privately owned, Henlow | |
| XA231 | Slingsby T38 Grasshopper TX1 (8888M) | RAF Manston History Museum | |
| XA240 | Slingsby T38 Grasshopper TX1 (BGA4556) | Privately owned, Keevil | |
| XA241 | Slingsby T38 Grasshopper TX1 | Shuttleworth Collection, Old Warden | |

| Notes | Serial | Type (other identity) [code] | Owner/operator, location or fate |
|---|---|---|---|
| | XA243 | Slingsby T38 Grasshopper TX1 (8886M) | Privately owned, Gransden Lodge, Cambs |
| | XA244 | Slingsby T38 Grasshopper TX1 | Privately owned, Keevil |
| | XA282 | Slingsby T31B Cadet TX3 | Caernarfon Air World |
| | XA289 | Slingsby T31B Cadet TX3 | Privately owned, Eaglescott |
| | XA290 | Slingsby T31B Cadet TX3 | Privately owned, stored Rufforth |
| | XA293 | Slingsby T31B Cadet TX3 <ff> | Privately owned, Breighton |
| | XA295 | Slingsby T31B Cadet TX3 (BGA3336) | Privately owned, Aston Down |
| | XA302 | Slingsby T31B Cadet TX3 (BGA3786) | Privately owned, Syerston |
| | XA310 | Slingsby T31B Cadet TX3 (BGA4963) | Privately owned, Keevil |
| | XA459 | Fairey Gannet ECM6 [E] | Privately owned, Lambourn, Berks |
| | XA460 | Fairey Gannet ECM6 [768/BY] | Aeroventure, Doncaster |
| | XA466 | Fairey Gannet COD4 [777/LM] | FAA Museum, stored Yeovilton |
| | XA508 | Fairey Gannet T2 [627/GN] | FAA Museum, at Midland Air Museum, Coventry |
| | XA564 | Gloster Javelin FAW1 (7464M) | RAF Museum, Cosford |
| | XA634 | Gloster Javelin FAW4 (7641M) | RAF Leeming, on display |
| | XA699 | Gloster Javelin FAW5 (7809M) | Midland Air Museum, Coventry |
| | XA847 | EE P1B (8371M) | Privately owned, Stowmarket, Suffolk |
| | XA862 | WS55 Whirlwind HAR1 (G-AMJT) <ff> | Yorkshire Helicopter Preservation Group, Elvington |
| | XA864 | WS55 Whirlwind HAR1 | FAA Museum, stored Yeovilton |
| | XA870 | WS55 Whirlwind HAR1 [911] | Aeroventure, Doncaster |
| | XA880 | DH104 Devon C2 (G-BVXR) | Privately owned, Kemble |
| | XA893 | Avro 698 Vulcan B1 (8591M) <ff> | RAF Museum, Cosford |
| | XA903 | Avro 698 Vulcan B1 <ff> | Privately owned, Wellesbourne Mountford |
| | XA917 | HP80 Victor B1 (7827M) <ff> | Privately owned, Cupar, Fife |
| | XB259 | Blackburn B101 Beverley C1 (G-AOAI) | Fort Paull Armoury |
| | XB261 | Blackburn B101 Beverley C1 <ff> | Newark Air Museum, Winthorpe |
| | XB446 | Grumman TBM-3 Avenger ECM6B | FAA Museum, Yeovilton |
| | XB480 | Hiller HT1 [537] | FAA Museum, stored Yeovilton |
| | XB812 | Canadair CL-13 Sabre F4 (9227M) [U] | RAF Museum, Cosford |
| | XD145 | Saro SR53 | RAF Museum, Cosford |
| | XD163 | WS55 Whirlwind HAR10 (8645M) [X] | The Helicopter Museum, Weston-super-Mare |
| | XD165 | WS55 Whirlwind HAR10 (8673M) [B] | Yorkshire Helicopter Pres Grp, stored Doncaster |
| | XD215 | VS Scimitar F1 <ff> | Privately owned, Cheltenham |
| | XD235 | VS Scimitar F1 <ff> | Privately owned, Ingatestone, Essex |
| | XD317 | VS Scimitar F1 [112/R] | FAA Museum, RNAS Yeovilton |
| | XD332 | VS Scimitar F1 [194/C] | Solent Sky, stored |
| | XD377 | DH115 Vampire T11 (8203M) <ff> | Aeroventure, stored Doncaster |
| | XD382 | DH115 Vampire T11 (8033M) | East Midlands Airport Aeropark |
| | XD425 | DH115 Vampire T11 <ff> | RAF Millom Museum, Haverigg |
| | XD434 | DH115 Vampire T11 [25] | Fenland & W Norfolk Aviation Museum, Wisbech |
| | XD445 | DH115 Vampire T11 | Bomber County Aviation Museum, Hemswell |
| | XD447 | DH115 Vampire T11 [50] | Jet Avn Preservation Grp, Long Marston |
| | XD452 | DH115 Vampire T11 (7990M) [66] <ff> | Privately owned, Chester |
| | XD459 | DH115 Vampire T11 [63] <ff> | Aeroventure, stored Doncaster |
| | XD506 | DH115 Vampire T11 (7983M) | Gloucestershire Avn Coll, stored Gloucester |
| | XD515 | DH115 Vampire T11 (7998M/XM515) | Privately owned, Rugeley, Staffs |
| | XD525 | DH115 Vampire T11 (7882M) <ff> | Campbell College, Belfast |
| | XD534 | DH115 Vampire T11 [41] | East Midlands Airport Aeropark |
| | XD542 | DH115 Vampire T11 (7604M) [N] | Montrose Air Station Museum |
| | XD547 | DH115 Vampire T11 [Z] (composite) | Dumfries & Galloway Avn Mus, Dumfries |
| | XD593 | DH115 Vampire T11 [50] | Newark Air Museum, Winthorpe |
| | XD595 | DH115 Vampire T11 <ff> | Privately owned, Glentham, Lincs |
| | XD596 | DH115 Vampire T11 (7939M) | Solent Sky, Southampton |
| | XD599 | DH115 Vampire T11 [A] <ff> | Sywell Aviation Museum |

| Serial | Type (other identity) [code] | Owner/operator, location or fate | Notes |
|---|---|---|---|
| XD602 | DH115 Vampire T11 (7737M) (composite) | Privately owned, South Shields | |
| XD616 | DH115 Vampire T11 [56] | Mosquito Aircraft Museum, stored Gloucester | |
| XD622 | DH115 Vampire T11 (8160M) | No 2214 Sqn ATC, Usworth | |
| XD624 | DH115 Vampire T11 [O] | Manchester Airport, on display | |
| XD626 | DH115 Vampire T11 [Q] | Midland Air Museum, Coventry | |
| XD674 | Hunting Jet Provost T1 (7570M) [T] | RAF Museum, stored Cosford | |
| XD693 | Hunting Jet Provost T1 (XM129/G-AOBU) [Z-Q] | Kennet Aviation, North Weald | |
| XD816 | Vickers Valiant B(K)1 <ff> | Brooklands Museum, Weybridge | |
| XD818 | Vickers Valiant B(K)1 (7894M) | RAF Museum, Cosford | |
| XD857 | Vickers Valiant B(K)1 <ff> | Norfolk & Suffolk Aviation Museum, Flixton | |
| XD875 | Vickers Valiant B(K)1 <ff> | Highland Aviation Museum, Inverness | |
| XE317 | Bristol 171 Sycamore HR14 (G-AMWO) [S-N] | Aeroventure, stored Doncaster | |
| XE339 | Hawker Sea Hawk FGA6 (8156M) [149/E] | RN Historic Flight, stored Yeovilton | |
| XE340 | Hawker Sea Hawk FGA6 [131/Z] | FAA Museum, at Montrose Air Station Museum | |
| XE368 | Hawker Sea Hawk FGA6 [200/J] | Phoenix Aviation, Bruntingthorpe | |
| XE489 | Hawker Sea Hawk FGA6 (G-JETH) | Gatwick Aviation Museum, Charlwood, Surrey | |
| XE521 | Fairey Rotodyne Y (parts) | The Helicopter Museum, Weston-super-Mare | |
| XE584 | Hawker Hunter FGA9 <ff> | NW Aviation Heritage Group, Hooton Park | |
| XE597 | Hawker Hunter FGA9 (8874M) <ff> | Privately owned, Bromsgrove | |
| XE601 | Hawker Hunter FGA9 (G-ETPS) | Skyblue Aviation Ltd, Exeter | |
| XE606 | Hawker Hunter F6A (XJ673/8841M) | RAF Cottesmore, preserved | |
| XE624 | Hawker Hunter FGA9 (8875M) [G] | Privately owned, Sileby, Leics | |
| XE627 | Hawker Hunter F6A [T] | Imperial War Museum, Duxford | |
| XE643 | Hawker Hunter FGA9 (8586M) <ff> | RAF M&RU, Aldergrove | |
| XE650 | Hawker Hunter FGA9 (G-9-449) <ff> | Farnborough Air Sciences Trust, Farnborough | |
| XE664 | Hawker Hunter F4 <ff> | Gloucestershire Avn Coll, stored Gloucester | |
| XE665 | Hawker Hunter T8C (G-BWGM) [876/VL] | Hunter Flying Club, Exeter | |
| XE668 | Hawker Hunter GA11 [832/DD] | RN, Predannack Fire School | |
| XE670 | Hawker Hunter F4 (7762M/8585M) <ff> | RAF Museum, Cosford | |
| XE683 | Hawker Hunter F51 (RDAF E-409) [G] | City of Norwich Aviation Museum | |
| XE685 | Hawker Hunter GA11 (G-GAII) [861/VL] | Privately owned, Exeter | |
| XE689 | Hawker Hunter GA11 (G-BWGK) [864/VL] | Hunter Flying Club, Exeter | |
| XE786 | Slingsby T31B Cadet TX3 (BGA4033) | Privately owned, Arbroath | |
| XE793 | Slingsby T31B Cadet TX3 (8666M) | Privately owned, Tamworth | |
| XE796 | Slingsby T31B Cadet TX3 | Privately owned, stored North Weald | |
| XE799 | Slingsby T31B Cadet TX3 (8943M) [R] | Boulton Paul Association, Wolverhampton | |
| XE802 | Slingsby T31B Cadet TX3 | Privately owned, stored Cupar, Fife | |
| XE849 | DH115 Vampire T11 (7928M) [V3] | Privately owned, Corby | |
| XE852 | DH115 Vampire T11 [H] | No 2247 Sqn ATC, Hawarden | |
| XE855 | DH115 Vampire T11 | Midland Air Museum, Coventry | |
| XE856 | DH115 Vampire T11 (G-DUSK) | Privately owned, Bournemouth | |
| XE864 | DH115 Vampire T11(comp XD435) <ff> | Privately owned, Ingatstone, Essex | |
| XE872 | DH115 Vampire T11 [62] | Midland Air Museum, Coventry | |
| XE874 | DH115 Vampire T11 (8582M) | Montrose Air Station Museum | |
| XE897 | DH115 Vampire T11 (XD403) | Privately owned, Errol, Tayside | |
| XE897 | DH115 Vampire T55 (U-1214/G-DHVV) | Source Classic Jet Flight, Bournemouth | |
| XE920 | DH115 Vampire T11 (8196M/G-VMPR) [A] | The Jet Fighter Experience, Swansea | |
| XE921 | DH115 Vampire T11 [64] <ff> | Privately owned, Yarmouth, IoW | |
| XE935 | DH115 Vampire T11 | Aeroventure, Doncaster | |
| XE946 | DH115 Vampire T11 (7473M) <ff> | RAF Cranwell Aviation Heritage Centre | |
| XE956 | DH115 Vampire T11 (G-OBLN) | De Havilland Aviation, stored Rochester | |
| XE979 | DH115 Vampire T11 [54] | Privately owned, Birlingham, Worcs | |

| Notes | Serial | Type (other identity) [code] | Owner/operator, location or fate |
|---|---|---|---|
| | XE982 | DH115 Vampire T11 (7564M) [01] | Privately owned, Weston, Eire |
| | XE985 | DH115 Vampire T11 (*WZ476*) | Privately owned, Exeter |
| | XE993 | DH115 Vampire T11 (8161M) | Privately owned, Cosford |
| | XE998 | DH115 Vampire T11 (*U-1215*) | Solent Sky, Southampton |
| | XF113 | VS Swift F7 [19] <ff> | Boscombe Down Aviation Collection |
| | XF114 | VS Swift F7 (G-SWIF) | Southampton Hall of Aviation, stored |
| | XF303 | Hawker Hunter F58A (J-4105/G-BWOU) [105,A] | The Old Flying Machine Company, Scampton |
| | *XF314* | Hawker Hunter F51 (RDAF E-412) [N] | Brooklands Museum, Weybridge |
| | XF321 | Hawker Hunter T7 <ff> | The Cockpit Collection, RAF Coltishall |
| | XF321 | Hawker Hunter T7 <rf> | Phoenix Aviation, Bruntingthorpe |
| | *XF324* | Hawker Hunter F51 (RDAF E-427) [D] | *Currently not known* |
| | XF358 | Hawker Hunter T8C [870/VL] <rf> | Privately owned, Exeter |
| | XF375 | Hawker Hunter F6A (8736M/G-BUEZ) [05] | Privately owned, Spanhoe |
| | XF382 | Hawker Hunter F6A [15] | Midland Air Museum, Coventry |
| | XF383 | Hawker Hunter F6 (8706M) <ff> | Privately owned, Kidlington |
| | *XF383* | Hawker Hunter F51 (RDAF E-409) [G] | City of Norwich Aviation Museum |
| | *XF418* | Hawker Hunter F51 (RDAF E-430) | Gatwick Aviation Museum, Charlwood, Surrey |
| | *XF506* | Hawker Hunter F4 (WT746/7770M) [A] | Dumfries & Galloway Avn Mus, Dumfries |
| | XF509 | Hawker Hunter F6 (8708M) | Humbrol Paints, Marfleet, E Yorkshire |
| | XF515 | Hawker Hunter F6A (8830M/G-KAXF) [R] | Kennet Aviation, North Weald |
| | XF522 | Hawker Hunter F6 <ff> | No 2532 Sqn ATC, Milton Keynes |
| | XF526 | Hawker Hunter F6 (8679M) [78/E] | Privately owned, Birlingham, Worcs |
| | XF527 | Hawker Hunter F6 (8680M) | RAF Halton, on display |
| | XF545 | Percival P56 Provost T1 (7957M) [O-K] | Privately owned, Thatcham |
| | XF597 | Percival P56 Provost T1 (G-BKFW) [AH] | Privately owned, Thatcham |
| | XF603 | Percival P56 Provost T1 (G-KAPW) | Kennet Aviation, North Weald |
| | XF690 | Percival P56 Provost T1 (8041M/G-MOOS) | Kennet Aviation, North Weald |
| | XF708 | Avro 716 Shackleton MR3 [203/C] | Imperial War Museum, Duxford |
| | XF785 | Bristol 173 (7648M/G-ALBN) | Bristol Aero Collection, Kemble |
| | XF836 | Percival P56 Provost T1 (8043M/G-AWRY) [JG] | Privately owned, Thatcham |
| | XF844 | Percival P56 Provost T1 [70] | Phoenix Aviation, Bruntingthorpe |
| | XF877 | Percival P56 Provost T1 (G-AWVF) [JX] | Privately owned, Brimpton, Berks |
| | XF926 | Bristol 188 (8368M) | RAF Museum, Cosford |
| | XF994 | Hawker Hunter T8C [873/VL] | Boscombe Down Aviation Collection |
| | XF995 | Hawker Hunter T8B (G-BZSF/9237M) [K] | Delta Jets, Kemble |
| | XG154 | Hawker Hunter FGA9 (8863M) [54] | RAF Museum, Hendon |
| | XG160 | Hawker Hunter F6A (8831M/G-BWAF) [U] | Bournemouth Aviation Museum |
| | XG164 | Hawker Hunter F6 (8681M) | Privately owned, Wellington, Somerset |
| | *XG168* | Hawker Hunter F6A (XG172/8832M) [A] | City of Norwich Aviation Museum |
| | *XG190* | Hawker Hunter F51 (RDAF E-425) [C] | Midland Air Museum, Coventry |
| | *XG193* | Hawker Hunter FGA9 (XG297) (comp with WT741) | Bomber County Aviation Museum, Hemswell |
| | XG195 | Hawker Hunter FGA9 <ff> | Privately owned, Lewes |
| | XG196 | Hawker Hunter F6A (8702M) [31] | Army, Mytchett, Surrey, on display |
| | XG209 | Hawker Hunter F6 (8709M) <ff> | *Currently not known* |
| | XG210 | Hawker Hunter F6 | Privately owned, Beck Row, Suffolk |
| | XG225 | Hawker Hunter F6A (8713M) [S] | DCAE Cosford, at main gate |
| | XG226 | Hawker Hunter F6A (8800M) [28] <ff> | RAF Manston History Museum |
| | XG252 | Hawker Hunter FGA9 (8840M) [U] | Privately owned, Bosbury, Hereford |
| | XG254 | Hawker Hunter FGA9 (8881M) | Norfolk & Suffolk Avn Museum, Flixton |
| | XG274 | Hawker Hunter F6 (8710M) [71] | Privately owned, Newmarket |
| | XG290 | Hawker Hunter F6 (8711M) <ff> | Boscombe Down Aviation Collection |
| | XG297 | Hawker Hunter FGA9 <ff> | Aeroventure, Doncaster |
| | XG325 | EE Lightning F1 <ff> | No 1476 Sqn ATC, Southend |

WHSmith Retail Ltd

73-75 New George Street
Plymouth
City PL1 1RP
Tel: 01752 669973

Visit our website at www.whsmith.co.uk

MILITARY AIRCRAFT MARKING                 9.99

Total                                     9.99

Cash                                     10.00
Cash Change                               0.01

1 Item(s) sold
0 Item(s) returned
JANET served you today

Thank you for shopping at WHSmith
Please retain your receipt
as proof of purchase

18/08/2006 15:51:29 05654 001 1645 15218

0565401214r152180806

| Serial | Type (other identity) [code] | Owner/operator, location or fate | Notes |
|---|---|---|---|
| XG329 | EE Lightning F1 (8050M) | Privately owned, Flixton | |
| XG331 | EE Lightning F1 <ff> | Gloucestershire Avn Coll, stored Gloucester | |
| XG337 | EE Lightning F1 (8056M) [M] | RAF Museum, Cosford | |
| XG452 | Bristol 192 Belvedere HC1 (7997M/G-BRMB) | The Helicopter Museum, Weston-super-Mare | |
| XG454 | Bristol 192 Belvedere HC1 (8366M) | Gr Manchester Mus of Science & Industry | |
| XG462 | Bristol 192 Belvedere HC1 <ff> | The Helicopter Museum, stored Weston-super-Mare | |
| XG474 | Bristol 192 Belvedere HC1 (8367M) [O] | RAF Museum, Hendon | |
| XG502 | Bristol 171 Sycamore HR14 | Museum of Army Flying, Middle Wallop | |
| XG518 | Bristol 171 Sycamore HR14 (8009M) [S-E] | Norfolk & Suffolk Avn Museum, Flixton | |
| XG523 | Bristol 171 Sycamore HR14 <ff> [K] | Norfolk & Suffolk Avn Museum, Flixton | |
| XG544 | Bristol 171 Sycamore HR14 | *Currently not known* | |
| XG547 | Bristol 171 Sycamore HR14 (G-HAPR) [S-T] | The Helicopter Museum, Weston-super-Mare | |
| XG574 | WS55 Whirlwind HAR3 [752/PO] | FAA Museum, stored RNAS Yeovilton | |
| XG588 | WS55 Whirlwind HAR3 (G-BAMH/VR-BEP) | East Midlands Airport Aeropark | |
| XG592 | WS55 Whirlwind HAS7 | *Task Force* Adventure Park, Cowbridge, S Glam | |
| XG594 | WS55 Whirlwind HAS7 [517/PO] | FAA Museum, stored Yeovilton | |
| XG596 | WS55 Whirlwind HAS7 [66] | The Helicopter Museum, Weston-super-Mare | |
| XG613 | DH112 Sea Venom FAW21 | Imperial War Museum, Duxford | |
| XG629 | DH112 Sea Venom FAW22 | Privately owned, Stone, Staffs | |
| XG680 | DH112 Sea Venom FAW22 [438] | North-East Aircraft Museum, Usworth | |
| XG691 | DH112 Sea Venom FAW22 [93/J] | *To Malta, September 2005* | |
| XG692 | DH112 Sea Venom FAW22 [668/LM] | Privately owned, Stone, Staffs | |
| XG730 | DH112 Sea Venom FAW22 [499/A] | Mosquito Aircraft Museum, London Colney | |
| XG736 | DH112 Sea Venom FAW22 | Privately owned, East Midlands | |
| XG737 | DH112 Sea Venom FAW22 [220/Z] | Jet Avn Preservation Grp, stored Long Marston | |
| XG743 | DH115 Sea Vampire T22 [597/LM] | Imperial War Museum, Duxford | |
| *XG775* | DH115 Vampire T55 (U-1219/G-DHWW) [VL] | Source Classic Jet Flight, Bournemouth | |
| XG797 | Fairey Gannet ECM6 [277] | Imperial War Museum, Duxford | |
| XG831 | Fairey Gannet ECM6 [396] | Flambards Village Theme Park, Helston | |
| XG882 | Fairey Gannet T5 (8754M) [771/LM] | Privately owned, Errol, Tayside | |
| XG883 | Fairey Gannet T5 [773/BY] | FAA Museum, at Museum of Berkshire Aviation, Woodley | |
| XG900 | Short SC1 | Science Museum, South Kensington | |
| XG905 | Short SC1 | Ulster Folk & Transpt Mus, Holywood, Co Down | |
| XH131 | EE Canberra PR9 | RAF No 39(1 PRU) Sqn, Marham | |
| XH134 | EE Canberra PR9 | RAF No 39(1 PRU) Sqn, Marham | |
| XH135 | EE Canberra PR9 | RAF No 39(1 PRU) Sqn, Marham | |
| XH136 | EE Canberra PR9 (8782M) [W] <ff> | Phoenix Aviation, Bruntingthorpe | |
| XH165 | EE Canberra PR9 <ff> | Blyth Valley Aviation Collection, Walpole | |
| XH168 | EE Canberra PR9 | RAF Marham Fire Section | |
| XH169 | EE Canberra PR9 | RAF Marham (wfu) | |
| XH170 | EE Canberra PR9 (8739M) | RAF Wyton, on display | |
| XH171 | EE Canberra PR9 (8746M) [U] | RAF Museum, Cosford | |
| XH174 | EE Canberra PR9 <ff> | RAF, stored Shawbury | |
| XH175 | EE Canberra PR9 <ff> | Privately owned, Stock, Essex | |
| XH177 | EE Canberra PR9 <ff> | Newark Air Museum, Winthorpe | |
| XH278 | DH115 Vampire T11 (8595M/7866M) [42] | Yorkshire Air Museum, Elvington | |
| XH312 | DH115 Vampire T11 [18] | Privately owned, Dodleston, Cheshire | |
| XH313 | DH115 Vampire T11 (G-BZRD) [E] | Privately owned, Surrey | |
| XH318 | DH115 Vampire T11 (7761M) [64] | Privately owned, Sholing, Hants | |
| XH328 | DH115 Vampire T11 <ff> | Mosquito Aircraft Museum, London Colney | |
| XH330 | DH115 Vampire T11 [73] | Privately owned, Camberley, Surrey | |
| XH537 | Avro 698 Vulcan B2MRR (8749M) <ff> | Bournemouth Aviation Museum | |
| XH558 | Avro 698 Vulcan B2 (G-VLCN) | Vulcan To The Sky Trust, Bruntingthorpe | |
| XH560 | Avro 698 Vulcan K2 <ff> | Privately owned, Foulness | |
| XH563 | Avro 698 Vulcan B2MRR <ff> | Privately owned, Bruntingthorpe | |
| XH568 | EE Canberra B6(mod) (G-BVIC) | Classic Aviation Projects, Bruntingthorpe | |

| Notes | Serial | Type (other identity) [code] | Owner/operator, location or fate |
|---|---|---|---|
| | XH584 | EE Canberra T4 (G-27-374) <ff> | Aeroventure, Doncaster |
| | XH592 | HP80 Victor K1A (8429M) <ff> | Phoenix Aviation, Bruntingthorpe |
| | XH648 | HP80 Victor K1A | Imperial War Museum, Duxford |
| | XH669 | HP80 Victor K2 (9092M) <ff> | Privately owned, Foulness |
| | XH670 | HP80 Victor SR2 <ff> | Privately owned, Foulness |
| | XH672 | HP80 Victor K2 (9242M) | RAF Museum, Cosford |
| | XH673 | HP80 Victor K2 (8911M) | RAF Marham, on display |
| | XH767 | Gloster Javelin FAW9 (7955M) [L] | Yorkshire Air Museum, Elvington |
| | XH783 | Gloster Javelin FAW7 (7798M) <ff> | Privately owned, Catford |
| | XH837 | Gloster Javelin FAW7 (8032M) <ff> | Caernarfon Air World |
| | XH892 | Gloster Javelin FAW9R (7982M) [J] | Norfolk & Suffolk Avn Museum, Flixton |
| | XH897 | Gloster Javelin FAW9 | Imperial War Museum, Duxford |
| | XH903 | Gloster Javelin FAW9 (7938M) | Gloucestershire Avn Coll, stored Gloucester |
| | XH992 | Gloster Javelin FAW8 (7829M) [P] | Newark Air Museum, Winthorpe |
| | XJ314 | RR Thrust Measuring Rig | Science Museum, South Kensington |
| | XJ380 | Bristol 171 Sycamore HR14 (8628M) | Montrose Air Station Museum |
| | XJ389 | Fairey Jet Gyrodyne (XD759/G-AJJP) | Museum of Berkshire Aviation, Woodley |
| | XJ398 | WS55 Whirlwind HAR10 (XD768/G-BDBZ) | Aeroventure, Doncaster |
| | XJ409 | WS55 Whirlwind HAR10 (XD779) | Maes Artro Craft Village, Llanbedr |
| | XJ435 | WS55 Whirlwind HAR10 (XD804/8671M) [V] | RAF Manston History Museum, spares use |
| | XJ476 | DH110 Sea Vixen FAW1 <ff> | No 424 Sqn ATC, Solent Sky, Southampton |
| | XJ481 | DH110 Sea Vixen FAW1 [VL] | FAA Museum, stored RNAS Yeovilton |
| | XJ482 | DH110 Sea Vixen FAW1 [713/VL] | Norfolk & Suffolk Avn Museum, Flixton |
| | XJ488 | DH110 Sea Vixen FAW1 <ff> | Robertsbridge Aviation Society, Mayfield |
| | XJ494 | DH110 Sea Vixen FAW2 | Privately owned, Bruntingthorpe |
| | XJ560 | DH110 Sea Vixen FAW2 (8142M) [242] | Newark Air Museum, Winthorpe |
| | XJ565 | DH110 Sea Vixen FAW2 [127/E] | Mosquito Aircraft Museum, London Colney |
| | XJ571 | DH110 Sea Vixen FAW2 (8140M) [242/R] | Solent Sky, Southampton |
| | XJ575 | DH110 Sea Vixen FAW2 <ff> [SAH-13] | Wellesbourne Wartime Museum |
| | XJ579 | DH110 Sea Vixen FAW2 <ff> | Midland Air Museum, Coventry |
| | XJ580 | DH110 Sea Vixen FAW2 [131/E] | Tangmere Military Aviation Museum |
| | XJ615 | Hawker Hunter T8C(mod) (XF357/G-BWGL) | Privately owned, Cranwell |
| | XJ639 | Hawker Hunter F6A (8687M) [H] | Hunter Flying Club, Exeter |
| | XJ714 | Hawker Hunter FR10 (comp XG226) | Jet Avn Preservation Grp, Long Marston |
| | XJ723 | WS55 Whirlwind HAR10 | Montrose Air Station Museum |
| | XJ726 | WS55 Whirlwind HAR10 [F] | Caernarfon Air World |
| | XJ727 | WS55 Whirlwind HAR10 (8661M) [L] | RAF Manston History Museum |
| | XJ758 | WS55 Whirlwind HAR10 (8464M) <ff> | Privately owned, Welshpool |
| | XJ771 | DH115 Vampire T55 (U-1215/G-HELV) | Air Atlantique Classic Flight, Coventry |
| | XJ772 | DH115 Vampire T11 [H] | Mosquito Aircraft Museum, London Colney |
| | XJ823 | Avro 698 Vulcan B2A | Solway Aviation Society, Carlisle |
| | XJ824 | Avro 698 Vulcan B2A | Imperial War Museum, Duxford |
| | XJ917 | Bristol 171 Sycamore HR14 [H-S] | Bristol Sycamore Group, stored Kemble |
| | XJ918 | Bristol 171 Sycamore HR14 (8190M) | RAF Museum, Cosford |
| | XK416 | Auster AOP9 (7855M/G-AYUA) | Privately owned, Widmerpool |
| | XK417 | Auster AOP9 (G-AVXY) | Privately owned, Widmerpool |
| | XK418 | Auster AOP9 (7976M) | SWWAPS, Lasham |
| | XK421 | Auster AOP9 (8365M) (frame) | Privately owned, Eggesford |
| | XK488 | Blackburn NA39 Buccaneer S2 | FAA Museum, stored RNAS Yeovilton |
| | XK526 | Blackburn NA39 Buccaneer S2 (8648M) | RAF Honington, at main gate |
| | XK527 | Blackburn NA39 Buccaneer S2D (8818M) <ff> | Privately owned, North Wales |
| | XK532 | Blackburn NA39 Buccaneer S1 (8867M) [632/LM] | Highland Aviation Museum, Inverness |
| | XK533 | Blackburn NA39 Buccaneer S1 <ff> | Royal Scottish Mus'm of Flight, stored E Fortune |
| | XK590 | DH115 Vampire T11 [V] | Wellesbourne Wartime Museum |
| | XK623 | DH115 Vampire T11 (G-VAMP) [56] | Caernarfon Air World |
| | XK624 | DH115 Vampire T11 [32] | Norfolk & Suffolk Avn Museum, Flixton |

| Serial | Type (other identity) [code] | Owner/operator, location or fate | Notes |
|--------|------------------------------|----------------------------------|-------|
| XK625 | DH115 Vampire T11 [14] | Brenzett Aeronautical Museum | |
| XK627 | DH115 Vampire T11 | Privately owned, Lavendon, Bucks | |
| XK637 | DH115 Vampire T11 [56] | RAF Millom Museum, Haverigg | |
| XK655 | DH106 Comet C2(RC) (G-AMXA) <ff> | *Currently not known* | |
| XK695 | DH106 Comet C2(RC) (G-AMXH/9164M) <ff> | Mosquito Aircraft Museum, London Colney | |
| XK699 | DH106 Comet C2 (7971M) | RAF Lyneham on display | |
| XK724 | Folland Gnat F1 (7715M) | RAF Museum, Cosford | |
| XK740 | Folland Gnat F1 (8396M) | Solent Sky, Southampton | |
| XK776 | ML Utility 1 | Museum of Army Flying, Middle Wallop | |
| XK788 | Slingsby T38 Grasshopper TX1 | Privately owned, Sproughton | |
| XK789 | Slingsby T38 Grasshopper TX1 | Midland Air Museum, stored Coventry | |
| XK790 | Slingsby T38 Grasshopper TX1 | Privately owned, stored Husbands Bosworth | |
| XK819 | Slingsby T38 Grasshopper TX1 | Privately owned, Selby | |
| XK822 | Slingsby T38 Grasshopper TX1 | Boulton Paul Association, Wolverhampton | |
| XK895 | DH104 Sea Devon C20 (G-SDEV) [19/CU] | Air Atlantique Classic Flight, Coventry | |
| XK896 | DH104 Sea Devon C20 (G-RNAS) (fuselage) | National Diving Centre, Chepstow, Mon | |
| XK907 | WS55 Whirlwind HAS7 [U] | Midland Air Museum, Coventry | |
| XK911 | WS55 Whirlwind HAS7 [519/PO] | Privately owned, Chipping Sodbury | |
| XK936 | WS55 Whirlwind HAS7 [62] | Imperial War Museum, Duxford | |
| XK940 | WS55 Whirlwind HAS7 (G-AYXT) [911] | The Helicopter Museum, Weston-super-Mare | |
| XK970 | WS55 Whirlwind HAR10 (8789M) | Army, Bramley, Hants | |
| XL149 | Blackburn B101 Beverley C1 (7988M) <ff> | Aeroventure, Doncaster | |
| XL160 | HP80 Victor K2 (8910M) <ff> | Norfolk & Suffolk Avn Museum, Flixton | |
| XL164 | HP80 Victor K2 (9215M) <ff> | Gatwick Aviation Museum, Charlwood, Surrey | |
| XL190 | HP80 Victor K2 (9216M) <ff> | RAF Manston History Museum | |
| XL231 | HP80 Victor K2 | Yorkshire Air Museum, Elvington | |
| XL318 | Avro 698 Vulcan B2 (8733M) | RAF Museum, Hendon | |
| XL319 | Avro 698 Vulcan B2 | North-East Aircraft Museum, Usworth | |
| XL360 | Avro 698 Vulcan B2A | Midland Air Museum, Coventry | |
| XL388 | Avro 698 Vulcan B2 <ff> | Aeroventure, Doncaster | |
| XL391 | Avro 698 Vulcan B2 | Privately owned, Blackpool | |
| XL426 | Avro 698 Vulcan B2 (G-VJET) | Vulcan Restoration Trust, Southend | |
| XL445 | Avro 698 Vulcan K2 (8811M) <ff> | Norfolk & Suffolk Avn Museum, Flixton | |
| XL449 | Fairey Gannet AEW3 <ff> | Privately owned, Camberley, Surrey | |
| XL472 | Fairey Gannet AEW3 [044/R] | Gatwick Aviation Museum, Charlwood, Surrey | |
| XL497 | Fairey Gannet AEW3 [041/R] | RN, Prestwick | |
| XL500 | Fairey Gannet AEW3 (G-KAEW) [CU] | Kennet Aviation, North Weald | |
| XL502 | Fairey Gannet AEW3 (8610M/G-BMYP) | Yorkshire Air Museum, Elvington | |
| XL503 | Fairey Gannet AEW3 [070/E] | FAA Museum, RNAS Yeovilton | |
| XL563 | Hawker Hunter T7 (9218M) | Privately owned, Bosbury, Hereford | |
| XL564 | Hawker Hunter T7 (fuselage) | Boscombe Down Aviation Collection | |
| XL565 | Hawker Hunter T7 (parts of WT745) | Privately owned, Bruntingthorpe | |
| XL568 | Hawker Hunter T7A (9224M) [C] | RAF Museum, Cosford | |
| XL569 | Hawker Hunter T7 (8833M) | East Midlands Airport Aeropark | |
| *XL571* | Hawker Hunter T7 (XL572/8834M/G-HNTR) [V] | Yorkshire Air Museum, Elvington | |
| XL573 | Hawker Hunter T7 (G-BVGH) | Privately owned, Humberside | |
| XL577 | Hawker Hunter T7 (G-BXKF/8676M) | Delta Jets, Kemble | |
| XL578 | Hawker Hunter T7 (fuselage) [77] | Privately owned, Kemble | |
| XL580 | Hawker Hunter T8M [723] | FAA Museum, RNAS Yeovilton | |
| XL586 | Hawker Hunter T7 <rf> | Delta Jets, Kemble | |
| XL587 | Hawker Hunter T7 (8807M/G-HPUX) [Z] | Hawker Hunter Aviation, stored Scampton | |
| XL591 | Hawker Hunter T7 | Gatwick Aviation Museum, Charlwood, Surrey | |
| XL592 | Hawker Hunter T7 (8836M) [Y] | Hunter Flying Club, Exeter | |
| XL601 | Hawker Hunter T7 (G-BZSR) [874/VL] | Classic Fighters, Brustem, Belgium | |
| XL602 | Hawker Hunter T8M (G-BWFT) | Hunter Flying Club, Exeter | |
| XL609 | Hawker Hunter T7 <ff> | Boscombe Down Aviation Collection | |
| XL612 | Hawker Hunter T7 [2] | Privately owned, Exeter | |
| XL618 | Hawker Hunter T7 (8892M) [05] | Caernarfon Air World | |

| Notes | Serial | Type (other identity) [code] | Owner/operator, location or fate |
|---|---|---|---|
| | XL621 | Hawker Hunter T7 (G-BNCX) | Privately owned, Dunsfold |
| | XL623 | Hawker Hunter T7 (8770M) | The Planets Leisure Centre, Woking |
| | XL629 | EE Lightning T4 | DPA/QinetiQ Boscombe Down, at main gate |
| | XL703 | SAL Pioneer CC1 (8034M) | RAF Museum, Cosford |
| | XL714 | DH82A Tiger Moth II (T6099/G-AOGR) | Privately owned, Boughton, Lincs |
| | XL716 | DH82A Tiger Moth II (T7363/G-AOIL) | Privately owned, Compton Abbas |
| | XL735 | Saro Skeeter AOP12 | *Currently not known* |
| | XL738 | Saro Skeeter AOP12 (7860M) | Privately owned, Leeds |
| | XL739 | Saro Skeeter AOP12 | AAC Wattisham, on display |
| | XL762 | Saro Skeeter AOP12 (8017M) | Royal Scottish Mus'm of Flight, E Fortune |
| | XL763 | Saro Skeeter AOP12 | Privately owned, Leeds |
| | XL764 | Saro Skeeter AOP12 (7940M) [J] | Newark Air Museum, Winthorpe |
| | XL765 | Saro Skeeter AOP12 | Privately owned, Melksham, Wilts |
| | XL770 | Saro Skeeter AOP12 (8046M) | Solent Sky, Southampton |
| | XL809 | Saro Skeeter AOP12 (G-BLIX) | Privately owned, Wilden, Beds |
| | XL811 | Saro Skeeter AOP12 | The Helicopter Museum, Weston-super-Mare |
| | XL812 | Saro Skeeter AOP12 (G-SARO) | AAC Historic Aircraft Flt, stored Middle Wallop |
| | XL813 | Saro Skeeter AOP12 | Museum of Army Flying, Middle Wallop |
| | XL814 | Saro Skeeter AOP12 | AAC Historic Aircraft Flight, Middle Wallop |
| | XL824 | Bristol 171 Sycamore HR14 (8021M) | Gr Manchester Mus of Science & Industry |
| | XL829 | Bristol 171 Sycamore HR14 | Bristol Industrial Museum |
| | XL840 | WS55 Whirlwind HAS7 | Privately owned, Bawtry |
| | XL853 | WS55 Whirlwind HAS7 [PO] | FAA Museum, stored RNAS Yeovilton |
| | XL875 | WS55 Whirlwind HAR9 | Perth Technical College |
| | XL929 | Percival P66 Pembroke C1 (G-BNPU) | Air Atlantique Classic Flight, stored Coventry |
| | XL954 | Percival P66 Pembroke C1 (9042M/N4234C/G-BXES) | Air Atlantique Classic Flight, Coventry |
| | XL993 | SAL Twin Pioneer CC1 (8388M) | RAF Museum, Cosford |
| | XM135 | BAC Lightning F1 [B] | Imperial War Museum, Duxford |
| | XM144 | BAC Lightning F1 (8417M) <ff> | Privately owned, Pershore |
| | XM169 | BAC Lightning F1A (8422M) <ff> | Highland Aviation Museum, Inverness |
| | XM172 | BAC Lightning F1A (8427M) | Privately owned, Booker |
| | XM173 | BAC Lightning F1A (8414M) [A] | RAF Bentley Priory, at main gate |
| | XM191 | BAC Lightning F1A (7854M/8590M) <ff> | RAF M&RU, Bottesford |
| | XM192 | BAC Lightning F1A (8413M) [K] | TCVC, Tattershall Thorpe, Lincs |
| | XM223 | DH104 Devon C2 (G-BWWC) [J] | Air Atlantique Classic Flight, Coventry |
| | XM279 | EE Canberra B(I)8 <ff> | Privately owned, Flixton |
| | XM300 | WS58 Wessex HAS1 | Welsh Industrial & Maritime Mus'm, stored Cardiff |
| | XM328 | WS58 Wessex HAS3 [653/PO] | The Helicopter Museum, Weston-super-Mare |
| | XM330 | WS58 Wessex HAS1 | The Helicopter Museum, Weston-super-Mare |
| | XM349 | Hunting Jet Provost T3A (9046M) [T] | Global Aviation, Humberside |
| | XM350 | Hunting Jet Provost T3A (9036M) [89] | Aeroventure, Doncaster |
| | XM351 | Hunting Jet Provost T3 (8078M) [Y] | RAF Museum, Cosford |
| | XM355 | Hunting Jet Provost T3 (8229M) [D] | Privately owned, Bruntingthorpe |
| | XM358 | Hunting Jet Provost T3A (8987M) [53] | Privately owned, Newbridge, Powys |
| | XM362 | Hunting Jet Provost T3 (8230M) | RAF No 1 SoTT, Cosford |
| | XM365 | Hunting Jet Provost T3A (G-BXBH) [37] | Privately owned, Norwich |
| | XM369 | Hunting Jet Provost T3 (8084M) [C] | Privately owned, Rossendale, Lancs |
| | XM370 | Hunting Jet Provost T3A (G-BVSP) [10] | Privately owned, Long Marston |
| | XM383 | Hunting Jet Provost T3A [90] | Newark Air Museum, Winthorpe |
| | XM402 | Hunting Jet Provost T3 (8055AM) [J] | Fenland & W Norfolk Aviation Museum, Wisbech |
| | XM404 | Hunting Jet Provost T3 (8055BM) | FETC, Moreton-in-Marsh, Glos |
| | XM409 | Hunting Jet Provost T3 (8082M) <ff> | Air Scouts, Guernsey Airport |
| | XM410 | Hunting Jet Provost T3 (8054AM) [B] | DEODS, Chattenden, Kent |
| | XM411 | Hunting Jet Provost T3 (8434M) <ff> | Aeroventure, Doncaster |
| | XM412 | Hunting Jet Provost T3A (9011M) [41] | Privately owned, Kinross, Scotland |

| Serial | Type (other identity) [code] | Owner/operator, location or fate | Notes |
|---|---|---|---|
| XM414 | Hunting Jet Provost T3A (8996M) | Ulster Aviation Society, Langford Lodge | |
| XM417 | Hunting Jet Provost T3 (8054BM) [D] <ff> | Privately owned, Cannock | |
| XM419 | Hunting Jet Provost T3A (8990M) [102] | DARA Training School, RAF St Athan | |
| XM425 | Hunting Jet Provost T3A (8995M) [88] | Privately owned, Longton, Staffs | |
| XM463 | Hunting Jet Provost T3A [38] (fuselage) | RAF Museum, Hendon | |
| XM468 | Hunting Jet Provost T3 (8081M) | Fenland & W Norfolk Aviation Museum, stored Wisbech | |
| XM473 | Hunting Jet Provost T3A (8974M/G-TINY) | Bedford College, instructional use | |
| XM474 | Hunting Jet Provost T3 (8121M) <ff> | No 2517 Sqn ATC, Levenshulme | |
| XM478 | Hunting Jet Provost T3A (8983M/G-BXDL) | Privately owned, Swansea | |
| XM479 | Hunting Jet Provost T3A (G-BVEZ) [54] | Privately owned, Newcastle | |
| XM480 | Hunting Jet Provost T3 (8080M) | 4x4 Car Centre, Chesterfield | |
| XM496 | Bristol 253 Britannia C1 (EL-WXA) | Britannia Preservation Society, Kemble | |
| XM529 | Saro Skeeter AOP12 (7979M/G-BDNS) | Privately owned, Handforth | |
| XM553 | Saro Skeeter AOP12 (G-AWSV) | Privately owned, Middle Wallop | |
| XM555 | Saro Skeeter AOP12 (8027M) | RAF Museum, Cosford | |
| XM561 | Saro Skeeter AOP12 (7980M) | Aeroventure, Doncaster | |
| XM564 | Saro Skeeter AOP12 | National Tank Museum, Bovington | |
| XM569 | Avro 698 Vulcan B2 <ff> | Gloucestershire Avn Coll, stored Gloucester | |
| XM575 | Avro 698 Vulcan B2A (G-BLMC) | East Midlands Airport Aeropark | |
| XM594 | Avro 698 Vulcan B2 | Newark Air Museum, Winthorpe | |
| XM597 | Avro 698 Vulcan B2 | Royal Scottish Mus'm of Flight, E Fortune | |
| XM598 | Avro 698 Vulcan B2 (8778M) | RAF Museum, Cosford | |
| XM602 | Avro 698 Vulcan B2 (8771M) <ff> | Vulcan To The Sky Trust, Bruntingthorpe | |
| XM603 | Avro 698 Vulcan B2 | Avro Aircraft Heritage Society, Woodford | |
| XM607 | Avro 698 Vulcan B2 (8779M) | RAF Waddington, on display | |
| XM612 | Avro 698 Vulcan B2 | City of Norwich Aviation Museum | |
| XM652 | Avro 698 Vulcan B2 <ff> | Privately owned, Welshpool | |
| XM655 | Avro 698 Vulcan B2 (G-VULC) | Privately owned, Wellesbourne Mountford | |
| XM660 | WS55 Whirlwind HAS7 | RAF Millom Museum, Haverigg | |
| XM685 | WS55 Whirlwind HAS7 (G-AYZJ) [513/PO] | Newark Air Museum, Winthorpe | |
| XM692 | HS Gnat T1 <ff> | Thameside Aviation Museum, East Tilbury | |
| XM693 | HS Gnat T1 (7891M) | BAE Systems Hamble, on display | |
| XM697 | HS Gnat T1 (G-NAAT) | Privately owned, Exeter | |
| XM708 | HS Gnat T1 (8573M) | Privately owned, Lytham St Annes | |
| XM715 | HP80 Victor K2 | Cold War Jets Collection, Bruntingthorpe | |
| XM717 | HP80 Victor K2 <ff> | RAF Museum, Hendon | |
| *XM819* | Lancashire EP9 Prospector (G-APXW) | Museum of Army Flying, Middle Wallop | |
| XM833 | WS58 Wessex HAS3 | SWWAPS, Lasham | |
| XM870 | WS58 Wessex HAS3 [PO] | RN, Predannack Fire School | |
| XN126 | WS55 Whirlwind HAR10 (8655M) [S] | Pinewood Studios, Elstree | |
| XN157 | Slingsby T21B Sedbergh TX1 (BGA3255) | Privately owned, stored Long Mynd | |
| XN185 | Slingsby T21B Sedbergh TX1 (8942M/BGA4077) | RAF Museum Reserve Collection, Stafford | |
| XN187 | Slingsby T21B Sedbergh TX1 (BGA3903) | Privately owned, Seighford | |
| XN198 | Slingsby T31B Cadet TX3 | Privately owned, | |
| XN238 | Slingsby T31B Cadet TX3 <ff> | Aeroventure, Doncaster | |
| XN239 | Slingsby T31B Cadet TX3 (8889M) [G] | Imperial War Museum, Duxford | |
| XN246 | Slingsby T31B Cadet TX3 | Solent Sky, Southampton | |
| XN258 | WS55 Whirlwind HAR9 [589/CU] | North-East Aircraft Museum, Usworth | |
| XN263 | WS55 Whirlwind HAS7 | *Scrapped at Bosham, December 2004* | |
| *XN297* | WS55 Whirlwind HAR9 (XN311) [12] | Privately owned, Hull | |
| XN298 | WS55 Whirlwind HAR9 [810/LS] | International Fire Training Centre, Chorley | |
| XN299 | WS55 Whirlwind HAS7 [758] | Tangmere Military Aviation Museum | |
| XN304 | WS55 Whirlwind HAS7 [64] | Norfolk & Suffolk Avn Museum, Flixton | |
| XN332 | Saro P531 (G-APNV) [759] | FAA Museum, stored RNAS Yeovilton | |
| XN334 | Saro P531 | FAA Museum, stored RNAS Yeovilton | |

| Notes | Serial | Type (other identity) [code] | Owner/operator, location or fate |
|---|---|---|---|
| | XN341 | Saro Skeeter AOP12 (8022M) | Stondon Transport Mus & Garden Centre, Beds |
| | XN344 | Saro Skeeter AOP12 (8018M) | Science Museum, South Kensington |
| | XN351 | Saro Skeeter AOP12 (G-BKSC) | Privately owned, Ipswich |
| | XN380 | WS55 Whirlwind HAS7 | RAF Manston History Museum |
| | XN385 | WS55 Whirlwind HAS7 | *Currently not known* |
| | XN386 | WS55 Whirlwind HAR9 [435/ED] | Aeroventure, Doncaster |
| | XN412 | Auster AOP9 | Auster 9 Group, Melton Mowbray |
| | XN435 | Auster AOP9 (G-BGBU) | *Currently not known* |
| | XN437 | Auster AOP9 (G-AXWA) | Privately owned, North Weald |
| | XN441 | Auster AOP9 (G-BGKT) | Privately owned, Eggesford |
| | XN458 | Hunting Jet Provost T3 (8234M/*XN594*) | Privately owned, Northallerton |
| | XN459 | Hunting Jet Provost T3A (G-BWOT) | Transair(UK) Ltd, North Weald |
| | XN462 | Hunting Jet Provost T3A [17] | FAA Museum, stored RNAS Yeovilton |
| | XN466 | Hunting Jet Provost T3A [29] <ff> | No 1005 Sqn ATC, Radcliffe, Gtr Manchester |
| *XN493* | | Hunting Jet Provost T3 (XN137) <ff> | Privately owned, Camberley |
| | XN494 | Hunting Jet Provost T3A (9012M) [43] | Crawley Technical College |
| | XN497 | Hunting Jet Provost T3A [52] | *Scrapped* |
| | XN500 | Hunting Jet Provost T3A [48] | Farnborough Air Sciences Trust, Farnborough |
| | XN501 | Hunting Jet Provost T3A (8958M) [G] | *Sold to the USA* |
| | XN503 | Hunting Jet Provost T3 <ff> | Boscombe Down Aviation Collection |
| | XN508 | Hunting Jet Provost T3A <ff> | RAF/DARA, St Athan |
| | XN510 | Hunting Jet Provost T3A (G-BXBI) [40] | Privately owned, Sproughton |
| | XN511 | Hunting Jet Provost T3 [64] <ff> | Aeroventure, Doncaster |
| | XN549 | Hunting Jet Provost T3 (8235M) [32,P] | RAF Shawbury Fire Section |
| | XN550 | Hunting Jet Provost T3 <ff> | *Scrapped at Stone, November 2004* |
| | XN551 | Hunting Jet Provost T3A (8984M) | DARA Training School, RAF St Athan |
| | XN554 | Hunting Jet Provost T3 (8436M) [K] | Privately owned, Sproughton |
| | XN573 | Hunting Jet Provost T3 [E] <ff> | Newark Air Museum, Winthorpe |
| | XN579 | Hunting Jet Provost T3A (9137M) [14] | Privately owned, Sproughton |
| | XN582 | Hunting Jet Provost T3A (8957M) [95,H] | *Currently not known* |
| | XN584 | Hunting Jet Provost T3A (9014M) [E] | Phoenix Aviation, Bruntingthorpe |
| | XN586 | Hunting Jet Provost T3A (9039M) [91,S] | Brooklands Technical College |
| | XN589 | Hunting Jet Provost T3A (9143M) [46] | RAF Linton-on-Ouse, on display |
| *XN594* | | Hunting Jet Provost T3 (8234M/XN458) | *Restored as XN458, 2005* |
| | XN597 | Hunting Jet Provost T3 (7984M) <ff> | RAF Millom Museum, Haverigg |
| | XN607 | Hunting Jet Provost T3 <ff> | Highland Aviation Museum, Inverness |
| *XN623* | | Hunting Jet Provost T3 (XN632/8352M) | Privately owned, Birlingham, Worcs |
| | XN629 | Hunting Jet Provost T3A (G-BVEG/G-KNOT) [49] | Privately owned, North Weald |
| | XN634 | Hunting Jet Provost T3A <ff> | Privately owned, Preston, Lancs |
| | XN634 | Hunting Jet Provost T3A [53] <rf> | BAE Systems Warton Fire Section |
| | XN636 | Hunting Jet Provost T3A (9045M) [15] | *Currently not known* |
| | XN637 | Hunting Jet Provost T3 (G-BKOU) [03] | Privately owned, North Weald |
| | XN647 | DH110 Sea Vixen FAW2 <ff> | Privately owned, Bicester |
| | XN650 | DH110 Sea Vixen FAW2 <ff> | Privately owned, Newton Abbot |
| | XN651 | DH110 Sea Vixen FAW2 <ff> | Privately owned, stored Lavendon, Bucks |
| | XN685 | DH110 Sea Vixen FAW2 (8173M) [03/VL] | Midland Air Museum, Coventry |
| | XN696 | DH110 Sea Vixen FAW2 <ff> | *Currently not known* |
| | XN714 | Hunting H126 | RAF Museum, Cosford |
| | XN726 | EE Lightning F2A (8545M) <ff> | Boscombe Down Aviation Collection |
| | XN728 | EE Lightning F2A (8546M) [V] | Privately owned, Balderton, Notts |
| | XN774 | EE Lightning F2A (8551M) <ff> | Privately owned, Boston |
| | XN776 | EE Lightning F2A (8535M) [C] | Royal Scottish Mus'm of Flight, E Fortune |
| | XN795 | EE Lightning F2A <ff> | Privately owned, Foulness |
| | XN817 | AW660 Argosy C1 | QinetiQ West Freugh Fire Section |

| Serial | Type (other identity) [code] | Owner/operator, location or fate | Notes |
|--------|------------------------------|----------------------------------|-------|
| XN819 | AW660 Argosy C1 (8205M) <ff> | Newark Air Museum, Winthorpe | |
| XN923 | HS Buccaneer S1 [13] | Gatwick Aviation Museum, Charlwood, Surrey | |
| XN928 | HS Buccaneer S1 (8179M) <ff> | Privately owned, Gravesend | |
| XN957 | HS Buccaneer S1 [630/LM] | FAA Museum, RNAS Yeovilton | |
| XN964 | HS Buccaneer S1 [613/LM] | Newark Air Museum, Winthorpe | |
| XN967 | HS Buccaneer S1 [103] <ff> | The Cockpit Collection, RAF Coltishall | |
| *XN972* | HS Buccaneer S1 (8183M/XN962) <ff> | RAF Museum, Hendon | |
| XN974 | HS Buccaneer S2A | Yorkshire Air Museum, Elvington | |
| XN981 | HS Buccaneer S2B (fuselage) | *Scrapped at Erroll* | |
| XN983 | HS Buccaneer S2B <ff> | Fenland & W Norfolk Aviation Museum, Wisbech | |
| XP110 | WS58 Wessex HAS3 [55/FL] | RN AESS, *HMS Sultan*, Gosport, BDRT | |
| XP137 | WS58 Wessex HAS3 [711/DD] | RN, Predannack Fire School | |
| XP142 | WS58 Wessex HAS3 | FAA Museum, stored Yeovilton | |
| XP150 | WS58 Wessex HAS3 [LS] | FETC, Moreton-in-Marsh, Glos | |
| XP165 | WS Scout AH1 | The Helicopter Museum, Weston-super-Mare | |
| XP190 | WS Scout AH1 | Aeroventure, Doncaster | |
| XP191 | WS Scout AH1 | Privately owned, Dunkeswell | |
| XP226 | Fairey Gannet AEW3 [073/E] | Newark Air Museum, Winthorpe | |
| XP241 | Auster AOP9 | Privately owned, Eggesford | |
| XP242 | Auster AOP9 (G-BUCI) | AAC Historic Aircraft Flight, Middle Wallop | |
| XP244 | Auster AOP9 (7864M/*M7922*) | Privately owned, Stretton on Dunsmore | |
| *XP248* | Auster AOP9 (7863M/WZ679) | Privately owned, Sandy, Beds | |
| XP254 | Auster AOP11 (G-ASCC) | Privately owned, Widmerpool | |
| XP279 | Auster AOP9 (G-BWKK) | Privately owned, Popham | |
| XP280 | Auster AOP9 | Snibston Discovery Park, Coalville | |
| XP281 | Auster AOP9 | Imperial War Museum, Duxford | |
| XP283 | Auster AOP9 (7859M) (frame) | *Currently not known* | |
| XP286 | Auster AOP9 | Privately owned, Eggesford | |
| XP299 | WS55 Whirlwind HAR10 (8726M) | RAF Museum, Hendon | |
| XP330 | WS55 Whirlwind HAR10 | CAA Fire School, Durham/Tees Valley | |
| XP344 | WS55 Whirlwind HAR10 (8764M) [H723] | RAF North Luffenham Training Area | |
| XP345 | WS55 Whirlwind HAR10 (8792M) [UN] | Yorkshire Helicopter Preservation Group, Doncaster | |
| XP346 | WS55 Whirlwind HAR10 (8793M) | Privately owned, Long Marston | |
| XP350 | WS55 Whirlwind HAR10 | *Currently not known* | |
| XP351 | WS55 Whirlwind HAR10 (8672M) [Z] | Gatwick Aviation Museum, Charlwood, Surrey | |
| XP355 | WS55 Whirlwind HAR10 (8463M/G-BEBC) | City of Norwich Aviation Museum | |
| XP360 | WS55 Whirlwind HAR10 [V] | Privately owned, Bicton, nr Leominster | |
| XP398 | WS55 Whirlwind HAR10 (8794M) | Gatwick Aviation Museum, Charlwood, Surrey | |
| XP399 | WS55 Whirlwind HAR10 | *Currently not known* | |
| XP404 | WS55 Whirlwind HAR10 (8682M) | The Helicopter Museum, Weston-super-Mare | |
| XP411 | AW660 Argosy C1 (8442M) [C] | RAF Museum, Cosford | |
| XP454 | Slingsby T38 Grasshopper TX1 | Privately owned, Sywell | |
| XP463 | Slingsby T38 Grasshopper TX1 (BGA4372) | Privately owned, Lasham | |
| XP488 | Slingsby T38 Grasshopper TX1 | Fenland & W Norfolk Aviation Museum, stored Wisbech | |
| XP490 | Slingsby T38 Grasshopper TX1 (BGA4552) | Privately owned, stored Watton | |
| XP492 | Slingsby T38 Grasshopper TX1 (BGA3480) | Privately owned, Gallows Hill, Dorset | |
| XP493 | Slingsby T38 Grasshopper TX1 | Privately owned, stored Aston Down | |
| XP494 | Slingsby T38 Grasshopper TX1 | Privately owned, Rattlesden, Suffolk | |
| XP502 | HS Gnat T1 (8576M) | Privately owned, Kemble | |
| XP505 | HS Gnat T1 | Science Museum, Wroughton | |
| XP516 | HS Gnat T1 (8580M) [16] | Farnborough Air Sciences Trust, Farnborough | |
| XP540 | HS Gnat T1 (8608M) [62] | Privately owned, North Weald | |
| XP542 | HS Gnat T1 (8575M) | Solent Sky, Southampton | |
| XP556 | Hunting Jet Provost T4 (9027M) [B] | RAF Cranwell Aviation Heritage Centre | |
| XP557 | Hunting Jet Provost T4 (8494M) [72] | Dumfries & Galloway Avn Mus, Dumfries | |
| XP558 | Hunting Jet Provost T4 (8627M) <ff> | Privately owned, Eckington, Derbyshire | |

| Notes | Serial | Type (other identity) [code] | Owner/operator, location or fate |
|-------|--------|------------------------------|----------------------------------|
| | XP558 | Hunting Jet Provost T4 (8627M)[20] <rf> | Privately owned, Sproughton |
| | XP563 | Hunting Jet Provost T4 (9028M) [C] | Privately owned, Sproughton |
| | XP568 | Hunting Jet Provost T4 | Jet Avn Preservation Grp, Long Marston |
| | XP573 | Hunting Jet Provost T4 (8236M) [19] | Jersey Airport Fire Section |
| | XP585 | Hunting Jet Provost T4 (8407M) [24] | NE Wales Institute, Wrexham |
| | XP627 | Hunting Jet Provost T4 | North-East Aircraft Museum, Usworth |
| | XP629 | Hunting Jet Provost T4 (9026M) [P] | Privately owned, Sproughton |
| | XP640 | Hunting Jet Provost T4 (8501M) [27] | Yorkshire Air Museum, Elvington |
| | XP642 | Hunting Jet Provost T4 <ff> | Privately owned, Lavendon, Bucks |
| | XP672 | Hunting Jet Provost T4 (8458M/G-RAFI) [03] | Privately owned, Sproughton |
| | XP680 | Hunting Jet Provost T4 (8460M) | FETC, Moreton-in-Marsh, Glos |
| | XP686 | Hunting Jet Provost T4 (8401M/8502M) [G] | Privately owned, Sproughton |
| | XP688 | Hunting Jet Provost T4 (9031M) | *Sunk at The Delph Diving Centre, Lancs, August 2005* |
| | XP701 | BAC Lightning F3 (8924M) <ff> | Robertsbridge Aviation Society, Mayfield |
| | XP703 | BAC Lightning F3 <ff> | The Cockpit Collection, RAF Coltishall |
| | XP706 | BAC Lightning F3 (8925M) | Aeroventure, Doncaster |
| | XP743 | BAC Lightning F3 <ff> | No 351 Sqn ATC, Burton-upon-Trent |
| | XP745 | BAC Lightning F3 (8453M) <ff> | Greenford Haulage, West London |
| | XP772 | DHC2 Beaver AL1 (G-BUCJ) | AAC Historic Aircraft Flight, stored Duxford |
| | XP775 | DHC2 Beaver AL1 | *Currently not known* |
| | XP820 | DHC2 Beaver AL1 | AAC Historic Aircraft Flight, Middle Wallop |
| | XP821 | DHC2 Beaver AL1 [MCO] | Museum of Army Flying, Middle Wallop |
| | XP822 | DHC2 Beaver AL1 | Museum of Army Flying, Middle Wallop |
| | XP831 | Hawker P.1127 (8406M) | Science Museum, South Kensington |
| | XP841 | Handley-Page HP115 | FAA Museum, RNAS Yeovilton |
| | XP847 | WS Scout AH1 | Museum of Army Flying, Middle Wallop |
| | XP848 | WS Scout AH1 | AAC Arborfield, on display |
| | XP853 | WS Scout AH1 | Privately owned, Sutton, Surrey |
| | XP854 | WS Scout AH1 (7898M/TAD043) | Privately owned, Sproughton |
| | XP855 | WS Scout AH1 | Army SEAE, Arborfield |
| | XP856 | WS Scout AH1 | Privately owned, Dunkeswell |
| | XP883 | WS Scout AH1 | Privately owned, Bruntingthorpe |
| | XP884 | WS Scout AH1 | AAC Middle Wallop, instructional use |
| | XP885 | WS Scout AH1 | AAC Wattisham, instructional use |
| | XP886 | WS Scout AH1 | Yeovil College |
| | XP888 | WS Scout AH1 | Privately owned, Sproughton |
| | XP890 | WS Scout AH1 [G] (fuselage) | Privately owned, Ipswich |
| | XP893 | WS Scout AH1 | AAC Middle Wallop, BDRT |
| | XP899 | WS Scout AH1 [D] | Army SEAE, Arborfield |
| | XP900 | WS Scout AH1 | AAC Wattisham, instructional use |
| | XP902 | WS Scout AH1 <ff> | Aeroventure, Doncaster |
| | XP905 | WS Scout AH1 | Privately owned, Sproughton |
| | XP907 | WS Scout AH1 (G-SROE) | Privately owned, Wattisham |
| | XP910 | WS Scout AH1 | Museum of Army Flying, Middle Wallop |
| | XP919 | DH110 Sea Vixen FAW2 (8163M) [706/VL] | Blyth Valley Aviation Collection, Walpole |
| | XP925 | DH110 Sea Vixen FAW2 [752] <ff> | No 1268 Sqn ATC, Haslemere, Surrey |
| | XP980 | Hawker P.1127 | FAA Museum, RNAS Yeovilton |
| | XP984 | Hawker P.1127 | Brooklands Museum, Weybridge |
| | XR220 | BAC TSR2 (7933M) | RAF Museum, Cosford |
| | XR222 | BAC TSR2 | Imperial War Museum, Duxford |
| | XR232 | Sud Alouette AH2 (F-WEIP) | Museum of Army Flying, Middle Wallop |
| | XR239 | Auster AOP9 | Privately owned, Stretton on Dunsmore |
| | XR240 | Auster AOP9 (G-BDFH) | Privately owned, Eggesford |
| | XR241 | Auster AOP9 (G-AXRR) | Privately owned, Eggesford |
| | XR244 | Auster AOP9 | AAC Historic Aircraft Flight, Middle Wallop |
| | XR246 | Auster AOP9 (7862M/G-AZBU) | Privately owned, North Coates |
| | XR267 | Auster AOP9 (G-BJXR) | Privately owned, Widmerpool |
| | XR271 | Auster AOP9 | Royal Artillery Experience, Woolwich |
| | XR371 | SC5 Belfast C1 | RAF Museum, Cosford |
| | XR379 | Sud Alouette AH2 | AAC Historic Aircraft Flight, Middle Wallop |
| | XR453 | WS55 Whirlwind HAR10 (8873M) [A] | RAF Odiham, on gate |
| | XR458 | WS55 Whirlwind HAR10 (8662M) [H] | Privately owned, Chipping Sodbury |
| | XR485 | WS55 Whirlwind HAR10 [Q] | Norfolk & Suffolk Avn Museum, Flixton |
| | XR486 | WS55 Whirlwind HCC12 (8727M/G-RWWW) | The Helicopter Museum, Weston-super-Mare |
| | XR498 | WS58 Wessex HC2 (9342M) [X] | RAF No 1 SoTT, Cosford |

| Serial | Type (other identity) [code] | Owner/operator, location or fate | Notes |
|--------|------------------------------|----------------------------------|-------|
| XR501 | WS58 Wessex HC2 | Army, Keogh Barracks, Aldershot, instructional use | |
| XR502 | WS58 Wessex HC2 (G-CCUP) [Z] | Privately owned, Redhill | |
| XR503 | WS58 Wessex HC2 | MoD FSCTE, Manston | |
| XR506 | WS58 Wessex HC2 (9343M) [V] | RAF No 1 SoTT, Cosford | |
| XR507 | WS58 Wessex HC2 | Privately owned, Hixon, Staffs | |
| XR508 | WS58 Wessex HC2 [B] | RN AESS, *HMS Sultan*, Gosport | |
| XR516 | WS58 Wessex HC2 [V] | RAF Shawbury, for display | |
| XR517 | WS58 Wessex HC2 [N] | Ulster Aviation Society, Langford Lodge | |
| XR518 | WS58 Wessex HC2 [J] | RN AESS, *HMS Sultan*, Gosport | |
| XR523 | WS58 Wessex HC2 [M] | RN *HMS Raleigh*, Torpoint, instructional use | |
| XR525 | WS58 Wessex HC2 [G] | RAF Museum, Cosford | |
| XR526 | WS58 Wessex HC2 (8147M) | The Helicopter Museum, Weston-super-Mare | |
| XR528 | WS58 Wessex HC2 | SFDO, RNAS Culdrose | |
| XR529 | WS58 Wessex HC2 (9268M) [E] | RAF Aldergrove, on display | |
| XR534 | HS Gnat T1 (8578M) [65] | Newark Air Museum, Winthorpe | |
| XR537 | HS Gnat T1 (8642M/G-NATY) | Privately owned, Bournemouth | |
| XR538 | HS Gnat T1 (8621M/G-RORI) [01] | Privately owned, North Weald | |
| XR571 | HS Gnat T1 (8493M) | RAF *Red Arrows*, Scampton, on display | |
| XR574 | HS Gnat T1 (8631M) [72] | RAF No 1 SoTT, Cosford | |
| XR595 | WS Scout AH1 (G-BWHU) [M] | Privately owned, Staddon Heights, Devon | |
| XR597 | WS Scout AH1 (fuselage) | Privately owned, Sproughton | |
| XR601 | WS Scout AH1 | Army SEAE, Arborfield | |
| XR627 | WS Scout AH1 [X] | Privately owned, Townhill, Fife | |
| XR628 | WS Scout AH1 | Privately owned, Ipswich | |
| XR629 | WS Scout AH1 (fuselage) | Privately owned, Ipswich | |
| XR635 | WS Scout AH1 | Coventry University, instructional use | |
| XR650 | Hunting Jet Provost T4 (8459M) [28] | Boscombe Down Aviation Collection | |
| XR654 | Hunting Jet Provost T4 <ff> | Privately owned, Chester | |
| XR658 | Hunting Jet Provost T4 (8192M) | Deeside College, Connah's Quay, Clwyd | |
| XR662 | Hunting Jet Provost T4 (8410M) [25] | Boulton Paul Association, Wolverhampton | |
| XR672 | Hunting Jet Provost T4 (8495M) [50] | RAF Halton, Fire Section | |
| XR673 | Hunting Jet Provost T4 (G-BXLO/9032M) [L] | Privately owned, Sandtoft | |
| XR681 | Hunting Jet Provost T4 (8588M) <ff> | Robertsbridge Aviation Society, Mayfield | |
| XR700 | Hunting Jet Provost T4 (8589M) <ff> | RAF Aldergrove | |
| XR713 | BAC Lightning F3 (8935M) [C] | RAF Leuchars, on display | |
| XR718 | BAC Lightning F6 (8932M) [DA] | Privately owned, Over Dinsdale, N Yorks | |
| XR724 | BAC Lightning F6 (G-BTSY) | The Lightning Association, Binbrook | |
| XR725 | BAC Lightning F6 | Privately owned, Binbrook | |
| XR726 | BAC Lightning F6 <ff> | Privately owned, Harrogate | |
| XR728 | BAC Lightning F6 [JS] | Lightning Preservation Grp, Bruntingthorpe | |
| XR747 | BAC Lightning F6 <ff> | Privately owned, Cubert, Cornwall | |
| XR749 | BAC Lightning F3 (8934M) [DA] | Highland Aviation Museum, Inverness | |
| XR751 | BAC Lightning F3 | Privately owned, Tremar, Cornwall | |
| XR753 | BAC Lightning F6 (8969M) [XI] | RAF Coningsby, on display | |
| *XR753* | BAC Lightning F53 (ZF578) | Tangmere Military Aviation Museum | |
| XR754 | BAC Lightning F6 (8972M) <ff> | Aeroventure, Doncaster | |
| XR755 | BAC Lightning F6 | Privately owned, Callington, Cornwall | |
| XR757 | BAC Lightning F6 <ff> | Privately owned, Grainthorpe, Lincs | |
| XR759 | BAC Lightning F6 <ff> | Privately owned, Haxey, Lincs | |
| XR770 | BAC Lightning F6 [AA] | Privately owned, Grainthorpe, Lincs | |
| XR771 | BAC Lightning F6 [BM] | Midland Air Museum, Coventry | |
| XR806 | BAC VC10 C1K <ff> | RAF Brize Norton, BDRT | |
| XR807 | BAC VC10 C1K | RAF/DARA, St Athan | |
| XR808 | BAC VC10 C1K | RAF No 101 Sqn, Brize Norton | |
| XR810 | BAC VC10 C1K | RAF/DARA St Athan | |
| *XR944* | Wallis WA116 (G-ATTB) | Norfolk & Suffolk Avn Museum, Flixton | |
| XR954 | HS Gnat T1 (8570M) [30] | Privately owned, Bournemouth | |
| XR977 | HS Gnat T1 (8640M) [3] | RAF Museum, Cosford | |
| *XR991* | HS Gnat T1 (8624M/XS102/G-MOUR) | Delta Jets, Kemble | |
| *XR993* | HS Gnat T1 (8620M/XP534/G-BVPP) | Kennet Aviation, North Weald | |
| XS100 | HS Gnat T1 (8561M) <ff> | Privately owned, London SW3 | |
| XS104 | HS Gnat T1 (8604M/G-FRCE) | Privately owned, North Weald | |
| *XS111* | HS Gnat T1 (8618M/XP504/G-TIMM) | Kennet Aviation, North Weald | |
| XS122 | WS58 Wessex HAS3 [655/PO] | RN AESS, *HMS Sultan*, Gosport | |

| Notes | Serial | Type (other identity) [code] | Owner/operator, location or fate |
|-------|--------|------------------------------|----------------------------------|
| | XS149 | WS58 Wessex HAS3 (661/GL] | The Helicopter Museum, Weston-super-Mare |
| | *XS165* | Hiller UH12E (G-ASAZ) [37] | Privately owned, Sherburn-in-Elmet |
| | XS176 | Hunting Jet Provost T4 (8514M) <ff> | Highland Aviation Museum, Inverness |
| | XS177 | Hunting Jet Provost T4 (9044M) [N] | RAF No 1 SoTT, Cosford |
| | XS179 | Hunting Jet Provost T4 (8237M) [20] | Gr Manchester Mus of Science & Industry |
| | XS180 | Hunting Jet Provost T4 (8238M) [21] | RAF St Athan, Fire Section |
| | XS181 | Hunting Jet Provost T4 (9033M) <ff> | Privately owned, Bruntingthorpe |
| | XS183 | Hunting Jet Provost T4 <ff> | Privately owned, Plymouth |
| | XS186 | Hunting Jet Provost T4 (8408M) [M] | Metheringham Airfield Visitors Centre |
| | XS209 | Hunting Jet Provost T4 (8409M) | Privately owned, Bruntingthorpe |
| | XS215 | Hunting Jet Provost T4 (8507M) [17] | RAF Halton |
| | XS216 | Hunting Jet Provost T4 <ff> | No 2357 Sqn ATC, Goole |
| | XS217 | Hunting Jet Provost T4 (9029M) | Privately owned, Bruntingthorpe |
| | XS218 | Hunting Jet Provost T4 (8508M) <ff> | No 447 Sqn ATC, Henley-on-Thames, Berks |
| | XS231 | BAC Jet Provost T5 (G-ATAJ) | Privately owned, Barnstaple |
| | XS235 | DH106 Comet 4C (G-CPDA) | Cold War Jets Collection, Bruntingthorpe |
| | XS416 | BAC Lightning T5 | Privately owned, Grainthorpe, Lincs |
| | XS417 | BAC Lightning T5 [DZ] | Newark Air Museum, Winthorpe |
| | XS420 | BAC Lightning T5 | Farnborough Air Sciences Trust, Farnborough |
| | XS421 | BAC Lightning T5 <ff> | Privately owned, Foulness |
| | XS456 | BAC Lightning T5 [DX] | Privately owned, Wainfleet |
| | XS457 | BAC Lightning T5 <ff> | Privately owned, Grainthorpe, Lincs |
| | XS458 | BAC Lightning T5 [T] | T5 Projects, Cranfield |
| | XS459 | BAC Lightning T5 [AW] | Fenland & W Norfolk Aviation Museum, Wisbech |
| | XS463 | WS Wasp HAS1 (comp XT431) | Crawley College, West Sussex |
| | XS481 | WS58 Wessex HU5 | Aeroventure, Doncaster |
| | XS482 | WS58 Wessex HU5 | RAF Manston History Museum |
| | XS486 | WS58 Wessex HU5 (9272M) [524/CU,F] | The Helicopter Museum, Weston-super-Mare |
| | XS488 | WS58 Wessex HU5 (9056M) [XK] | RN AESS, *HMS Sultan*, Gosport |
| | XS489 | WS58 Wessex HU5 [R] | Privately owned, Redhill |
| | XS493 | WS58 Wessex HU5 | RN/DARA, stored Fleetlands |
| | XS496 | WS58 Wessex HU5 [625/PO] | RN AESS, *HMS Sultan*, Gosport |
| | XS498 | WS58 Wessex HC5C (comp XS677) [WK] | Privately owned, Hixon, Staffs |
| | XS507 | WS58 Wessex HU5 | RN AESS, *HMS Sultan*, Gosport |
| | XS508 | WS58 Wessex HU5 | FAA Museum, stored RNAS Yeovilton |
| | XS510 | WS58 Wessex HU5 [626/PO] | No 1414 Sqn ATC, Crowborough, Sussex |
| | XS511 | WS58 Wessex HU5 [M] | Tangmere Military Aircraft Museum |
| | XS513 | WS58 Wessex HU5 [419/CU] | RNAS Yeovilton Fire Section |
| | XS514 | WS58 Wessex HU5 [L] | RN AESS, *HMS Sultan*, Gosport |
| | XS515 | WS58 Wessex HU5 [N] | Army, Keogh Barracks, Aldershot, instructional use |
| | XS516 | WS58 Wessex HU5 [Q] | RN, Predannack Fire School |
| | XS520 | WS58 Wessex HU5 [F] | RN AESS, *HMS Sultan*, Gosport |
| | XS522 | WS58 Wessex HU5 [ZL] | RN, Predannack Fire School |
| | XS527 | WS Wasp HAS1 | FAA Museum, RNAS Yeovilton |
| | XS529 | WS Wasp HAS1 | RN, Predannack Fire School |
| | XS539 | WS Wasp HAS1 [435] | DARA Fleetlands Apprentice School |
| | XS567 | WS Wasp HAS1 [434/E] | Imperial War Museum, Duxford |
| | XS568 | WS Wasp HAS1 [441] | RN AESS, *HMS Sultan*, Gosport |
| | XS569 | WS Wasp HAS1 | DARA Fleetlands Apprentice School |
| | XS570 | WS Wasp HAS1 [445/P] | Warship Preservation Trust, Birkenhead |
| | XS576 | DH110 Sea Vixen FAW2 [125/E] | Imperial War Museum, Duxford |
| | XS587 | DH110 Sea Vixen FAW(TT)2 (8828M/G-VIXN) | Gatwick Aviation Museum, Charlwood, Surrey |
| | XS590 | DH110 Sea Vixen FAW2 [131/E] | FAA Museum, RNAS Yeovilton |
| | XS596 | HS Andover C1(PR) | DPA/AFD/*Open Skies*, Boscombe Down |
| | XS598 | HS Andover C1 (fuselage) | FETC, Moreton-in-Marsh, Glos |
| | XS606 | HS Andover C1 | DPA/ETPS, Boscombe Down |
| | XS639 | HS Andover E3A (9241M) | RAF Museum, Cosford |
| | XS641 | HS Andover C1(PR) (9198M) [Z] | Privately owned, Sandbach, Cheshire |
| | XS643 | HS Andover E3A (9278M) <ff> | Privately owned, Stock, Essex |
| | XS646 | HS Andover C1(mod) | DPA/AFD/QinetiQ, Boscombe Down |
| | XS652 | Slingsby T45 Swallow TX1 (BGA1107) | Privately owned, Rufforth |
| | XS674 | WS58 Wessex HC2 [R] | Privately owned, Hixon, Staffs |
| | XS695 | HS Kestrel FGA1 | RAF Museum Restoration Centre, Cosford |
| | XS709 | HS125 Dominie T1 [M] | RAF No 3 FTS/55(R) Sqn, Cranwell |

| Serial | Type (other identity) [code] | Owner/operator, location or fate | Notes |
|--------|------------------------------|----------------------------------|-------|
| XS710 | HS125 Dominie T1 (9259M) [O] | RAF No 1 SoTT, Cosford | |
| XS711 | HS125 Dominie T1 [L] | RAF No 3 FTS/55(R) Sqn, Cranwell | |
| XS712 | HS125 Dominie T1 [A] | RAF No 3 FTS/55(R) Sqn, Cranwell | |
| XS713 | HS125 Dominie T1 [C] | RAF No 3 FTS/55(R) Sqn, Cranwell | |
| XS714 | HS125 Dominie T1 (9246M) [P] | MoD FSCTE, Manston | |
| XS726 | HS125 Dominie T1 (9273M) [T] | RAF No 1 SoTT, Cosford | |
| XS727 | HS125 Dominie T1 [D] | RAF No 3 FTS/55(R) Sqn, Cranwell | |
| XS728 | HS125 Dominie T1 [E] | RAF No 3 FTS/55(R) Sqn, Cranwell | |
| XS729 | HS125 Dominie T1 (9275M) [G] | RAF No 1 SoTT, Cosford | |
| XS730 | HS125 Dominie T1 [H] | RAF No 3 FTS/55(R) Sqn, Cranwell | |
| XS731 | HS125 Dominie T1 [J] | RAF No 3 FTS/55(R) Sqn, Cranwell | |
| XS733 | HS125 Dominie T1 (9276M) [Q] | RAF No 1 SoTT, Cosford | |
| XS734 | HS125 Dominie T1 (9260M) [N] | RAF No 1 SoTT, Cosford | |
| XS735 | HS125 Dominie T1 (9264M) [R] | DARA Training School, RAF St Athan | |
| XS736 | HS125 Dominie T1 [S] | RAF No 3 FTS/55(R) Sqn, Cranwell | |
| XS737 | HS125 Dominie T1 [K] | RAF No 1 SoTT, Cosford | |
| XS738 | HS125 Dominie T1 (9274M) [U] | RAF No 1 SoTT, Cosford | |
| XS739 | HS125 Dominie T1 [F] | RAF No 3 FTS/55(R) Sqn, Cranwell | |
| XS743 | Beagle B206Z Basset CC1 | DPA/ETPS, Boscombe Down | |
| XS765 | Beagle B206Z Basset CC1 (G-BSET) | DPA, QinetiQ, Boscombe Down (spares use) | |
| XS770 | Beagle B206Z Basset CC1 (G-HRHI) | Privately owned, Cranfield | |
| XS790 | HS748 Andover CC2 <ff> | Boscombe Down Aviation Collection | |
| XS791 | HS748 Andover CC2 (fuselage) | Privately owned, Stock, Essex | |
| XS862 | WS58 Wessex HAS3 | Privately owned, Hixon, Staffs | |
| XS863 | WS58 Wessex HAS1 [304] | Imperial War Museum, Duxford | |
| XS876 | WS58 Wessex HAS1 [523/PO] | East Midlands Airport Aeropark | |
| XS885 | WS58 Wessex HAS1 [512/DD] | SFDO, RNAS Culdrose | |
| XS886 | WS58 Wessex HAS1 [527/CU] | Sea Scouts, Evesham, Worcs | |
| XS887 | WS58 Wessex HAS1 [403/FI] | Flambards Village Theme Park, Helston | |
| XS888 | WS58 Wessex HAS1 [521] | Guernsey Airport Fire Section | |
| XS897 | BAC Lightning F6 | Aeroventure, Doncaster | |
| XS898 | BAC Lightning F6 <ff> | Privately owned, Lavendon, Bucks | |
| XS899 | BAC Lightning F6 <ff> | The Cockpit Collection, RAF Coltishall | |
| XS903 | BAC Lightning F6 [BA] | Yorkshire Air Museum, Elvington | |
| XS904 | BAC Lightning F6 [BQ] | Lightning Preservation Grp, Bruntingthorpe | |
| XS919 | BAC Lightning F6 | Wonderland Pleasure Park, Farnsfield, Notts | |
| XS922 | BAC Lightning F6 (8973M) <ff> | The Air Defence Collection, Salisbury | |
| XS923 | BAC Lightning F6 <ff> | Privately owned, Welshpool | |
| XS925 | BAC Lightning F6 (8961M) [BA] | RAF Museum, Hendon | |
| XS928 | BAC Lightning F6 [D] | BAE Systems Warton, on display | |
| XS932 | BAC Lightning F6 <ff> | Farnborough Air Sciences Trust, Farnborough | |
| XS933 | BAC Lightning F6 <ff> | Privately owned, Farnham | |
| XS936 | BAC Lightning F6 | Castle Motors, Liskeard, Cornwall | |
| XT108 | Agusta-Bell 47G-3 Sioux AH1 [U] | Museum of Army Flying, Middle Wallop | |
| *XT123* | WS Sioux AH1 (XT827) [D] | AAC Middle Wallop, at main gate | |
| XT131 | Agusta-Bell 47G-3 Sioux AH1 [B] | AAC Historic Aircraft Flight, Middle Wallop | |
| XT133 | Agusta-Bell 47G-3 Sioux AH1 (7923M) | Royal Engineers' Museum, stored Chattenden | |
| XT140 | Agusta-Bell 47G-3 Sioux AH1 | Perth Technical College | |
| XT141 | Agusta-Bell 47G-3 Sioux AH1 | Privately owned, Pontypridd | |
| XT150 | Agusta-Bell 47G-3 Sioux AH1 (7883M) [R] | AAC Netheravon, at main gate | |
| XT151 | WS Sioux AH1 [W] | Museum of Army Flying, stored Middle Wallop | |
| XT175 | WS Sioux AH1 (TAD175) | Privately owned, Cambs | |
| XT176 | WS Sioux AH1 [U] | FAA Museum, stored RNAS Yeovilton | |
| XT190 | WS Sioux AH1 | The Helicopter Museum, Weston-super-Mare | |
| XT200 | WS Sioux AH1 [F] | Newark Air Museum, Winthorpe | |
| XT223 | WS Sioux AH1 (G-XTUN) | Privately owned, Sherburn-in-Elmet | |
| XT236 | WS Sioux AH1 (frame only) | North-East Aircraft Museum, stored Usworth | |
| XT242 | WS Sioux AH1 (composite) [12] | Aeroventure, Doncaster | |
| XT257 | WS58 Wessex HAS3 (8719M) | Bournemouth Aviation Museum | |
| XT277 | HS Buccaneer S2A (8853M) <ff> | Privately owned, Welshpool | |
| XT280 | HS Buccaneer S2A <ff> | Dumfries & Galloway Avn Mus, Dumfries | |
| XT284 | HS Buccaneer S2A (8855M) <ff> | Privately owned, Felixstowe | |

| Notes | Serial | Type (other identity) [code] | Owner/operator, location or fate |
|---|---|---|---|
| | XT288 | HS Buccaneer S2B (9134M) | Royal Scottish Museum of Flight, stored E Fortune |
| | XT420 | WS Wasp HAS1 (G-CBUI) [606] | Privately owned, Thruxton |
| | XT427 | WS Wasp HAS1 [606] | FAA Museum, stored RNAS Yeovilton |
| | XT434 | WS Wasp HAS1 [455] | DARA Fleetlands Apprentice School |
| | XT435 | WS Wasp HAS1 (NZ3907/G-RIMM) [430] | Privately owned, Cranfield |
| | XT437 | WS Wasp HAS1 [423] | Boscombe Down Aviation Collection |
| | XT439 | WS Wasp HAS1 [605] | Privately owned, Hemel Hempstead |
| | XT443 | WS Wasp HAS1 [422/AU] | The Helicopter Museum, Weston-super-Mare |
| | XT453 | WS58 Wessex HU5 [A/B] | RN AESS, HMS Sultan, Gosport |
| | XT455 | WS58 Wessex HU5 [U] | RN AESS, HMS Sultan, Gosport |
| | XT456 | WS58 Wessex HU5 (8941M) [XZ] | RAF Aldergrove, BDRT |
| | XT458 | WS58 Wessex HU5 [622] | RN AESS, HMS Sultan, Gosport |
| | XT463 | WS58 Wessex HC5C (comp XR508) [Clubs] | Privately owned, Hixon, Staffs |
| | XT466 | WS58 Wessex HU5 (8921M) [XV] | RN AESS, HMS Sultan, Gosport |
| | XT467 | WS58 Wessex HU5 (8922M) [BF] | Privately owned, Sproughton |
| | XT468 | WS58 Wessex HU5 (comp XT460) [628] | RN, Predannack Fire School |
| | XT469 | WS58 Wessex HU5 (8920M) | RAF No 16 MU, Stafford, ground instruction |
| | XT472 | WS58 Wessex HU5 [XC] | The Helicopter Museum, Weston-super-Mare |
| | XT480 | WS58 Wessex HU5 [468/RG] | East Midlands Airport Aeropark |
| | XT482 | WS58 Wessex HU5 [ZM/VL] | FAA Museum, RNAS Yeovilton |
| | XT484 | WS58 Wessex HU5 [H] | RN AESS, HMS Sultan, Gosport |
| | XT485 | WS58 Wessex HU5 | RN AESS, HMS Sultan, Gosport |
| | XT550 | WS Sioux AH1 [D] | AAC, stored Middle Wallop |
| | XT575 | Vickers Viscount 837 <ff> | Brooklands Museum, Weybridge |
| | XT596 | McD F-4K Phantom FG1 | FAA Museum, RNAS Yeovilton |
| | XT597 | McD F-4K Phantom FG1 | Boscombe Down Aviation Collection |
| | XT601 | WS58 Wessex HC2 (9277M) (composite) | RAF Odiham, BDRT |
| | XT604 | WS58 Wessex HC2 | East Midlands Airport Aeropark |
| | XT607 | WS58 Wessex HC2 [P] | RN AESS, HMS Sultan, Gosport |
| | XT617 | WS Scout AH1 | AAC Wattisham, on display |
| | XT621 | WS Scout AH1 | R. Military College of Science, Shrivenham |
| | XT623 | WS Scout AH1 | Army SEAE, Arborfield |
| | XT626 | WS Scout AH1 [Q] | AAC Historic Aircraft Flt, Middle Wallop |
| | XT630 | WS Scout AH1 (G-BXRL) [X] | Privately owned, Bruntingthorpe |
| | XT631 | WS Scout AH1 [D] | Privately owned, Ipswich |
| | XT632 | WS Scout AH1 (G-BZBD) | Privately owned, North Weald (spares use) |
| | XT633 | WS Scout AH1 | Army SEAE, Arborfield |
| | XT634 | WS Scout AH1 (G-BYRX) [T] | Privately owned, Tollerton |
| | XT638 | WS Scout AH1 [N] | AAC Middle Wallop, at gate |
| | XT640 | WS Scout AH1 | Privately owned, Sproughton |
| | XT643 | WS Scout AH1 [Z] | Army, Thorpe Camp, East Wretham |
| | XT645 | WS Scout AH1 (fuselage) | Privately owned, Ipswich |
| | XT671 | WS58 Wessex HC2 (G-BYRC) [D] | Privately owned, Redhill |
| | XT672 | WS58 Wessex HC2 [WE] | RAF Shawbury, on display |
| | XT677 | WS58 Wessex HC2 (8016M) | Privately owned, Stock, Essex |
| | XT681 | WS58 Wessex HC2 (9279M) [U] | RAF Benson, BDRT |
| | XT761 | WS58 Wessex HU5 | RN AESS, HMS Sultan, Gosport |
| | XT762 | WS58 Wessex HU5 | RN, Predannack Fire School |
| | XT765 | WS58 Wessex HU5 [J] | RNAS Yeovilton, on display |
| | XT769 | WS58 Wessex HU5 [823] | FAA Museum, RNAS Yeovilton |
| | XT770 | WS58 Wessex HU5 (9055M) [P] | Privately owned, Shawell, Leics |
| | XT771 | WS58 Wessex HU5 [620/PO] | RN AESS, HMS Sultan, Gosport |
| | XT772 | WS58 Wessex HU5 (8805M) | SARTU RAF Valley, ground instruction |
| | XT773 | WS58 Wessex HU5 (9123M) [822/CU] | RAF Shawbury Fire Section |
| | XT778 | WS Wasp HAS1 [430] | FAA Museum, stored Yeovilton |
| | XT780 | WS Wasp HAS1 [636] | DARA Fleetlands Apprentice School |
| | XT781 | WS Wasp HAS1 (NZ3908/G-KAWW) [426] | Sold to South Africa, December 2005 |
| | XT787 | WS Wasp HAS1 (NZ3905/G-KAXT) | Kennet Aviation, North Weald |
| | XT788 | WS Wasp HAS1 (G-BMIR) [316] (painted as XT78?) | Privately owned, Dunkeswell |
| | XT793 | WS Wasp HAS1 (G-BZPP) [456] | Privately owned, Otley |
| | XT852 | McD YF-4M Phantom FGR2 | QinetiQ West Freugh Fire Section |
| | XT863 | McD F-4K Phantom FG1 <ff> | Privately owned, Cowes, IOW |

| Serial | Type (other identity) [code] | Owner/operator, location or fate | Notes |
|--------|------------------------------|----------------------------------|-------|
| XT864 | McD F-4K Phantom FG1 (8998M/*XT684*) [BJ] | RAF Leuchars on display | |
| XT891 | McD F-4M Phantom FGR2 (9136M) [Z] | RAF Coningsby, at main gate | |
| XT903 | McD F-4M Phantom FGR2 <ff> | RAF Museum Restoration Centre, Cosford | |
| XT905 | McD F-4M Phantom FGR2 [P] | RAF North Luffenham Training Area | |
| XT907 | McD F-4M Phantom FGR2 (9151M) [W] | DEODS, Chattenden, Kent | |
| XT914 | McD F-4M Phantom FGR2 (9269M) [Z] | RAF Brampton, Cambs, on display | |
| XV101 | BAC VC10 C1K | RAF/DARA, St Athan | |
| XV102 | BAC VC10 C1K | RAF No 101 Sqn, Brize Norton | |
| XV104 | BAC VC10 C1K | RAF No 101 Sqn, Brize Norton | |
| XV105 | BAC VC10 C1K | RAF No 101 Sqn, Brize Norton | |
| XV106 | BAC VC10 C1K | RAF No 101 Sqn, Brize Norton | |
| XV107 | BAC VC10 C1K | RAF No 101 Sqn, Brize Norton | |
| XV108 | BAC VC10 C1K | RAF No 101 Sqn, Brize Norton | |
| XV109 | BAC VC10 C1K | RAF/DARA, St Athan | |
| XV118 | WS Scout AH1 (9141M) | Privately owned, North Weald | |
| XV122 | WS Scout AH1 [D] | R. Military College of Science, Shrivenham | |
| XV123 | WS Scout AH1 | RAF Shawbury, on display | |
| XV124 | WS Scout AH1 [W] | Army SEAE, Arborfield | |
| XV127 | WS Scout AH1 | Museum of Army Flying, Middle Wallop | |
| XV130 | WS Scout AH1 (G-BWJW) [R] | Privately owned, Bournemouth | |
| XV131 | WS Scout AH1 [Y] | AAC 70 Aircraft Workshops, Middle Wallop, BDRT | |
| XV134 | WS Scout AH1 (G-BWLX) [P] | Privately owned, Oaksey Park | |
| XV136 | WS Scout AH1 [X] | AAC Netheravon, on display | |
| XV137 | WS Scout AH1 (G-CRUM) | Privately owned, Chiseldon, Wilts | |
| *XV137* | WS Scout AH1 (XV139) | AAC, Wattisham | |
| XV138 | WS Scout AH1 | Privately owned, East Dereham, Norfolk | |
| XV140 | WS Scout AH1 (G-KAXL) [K] | Kennet Aviation, North Weald | |
| XV141 | WS Scout AH1 | REME Museum, Arborfield | |
| XV148 | HS Nimrod MR1(mod) <ff> | Privately owned, Malmesbury | |
| XV161 | HS Buccaneer S2B (9117M) <ff> | Privately owned, North Wales | |
| XV165 | HS Buccaneer S2B <ff> | Farnborough Air Sciences Trust, Farnborough | |
| XV168 | HS Buccaneer S2B | BAE Systems Brough, on display | |
| XV177 | Lockheed C-130K Hercules C3 | RAF Lyneham Transport Wing | |
| XV179 | Lockheed C-130K Hercules C1 | *Crashed 30 January 2005, Iraq* | |
| XV184 | Lockheed C-130K Hercules C3 | RAF Lyneham Transport Wing | |
| XV188 | Lockheed C-130K Hercules C3 | RAF Lyneham Transport Wing | |
| XV196 | Lockheed C-130K Hercules C1 | RAF Lyneham Transport Wing | |
| XV197 | Lockheed C-130K Hercules C3 | RAF Lyneham Transport Wing | |
| XV199 | Lockheed C-130K Hercules C3 | RAF Lyneham Transport Wing | |
| XV200 | Lockheed C-130K Hercules C1 | RAF Lyneham Transport Wing | |
| XV201 | Lockheed C-130K Hercules C1K (fuselage) | Marshalls, Cambridge | |
| XV202 | Lockheed C-130K Hercules C3 | RAF Lyneham Transport Wing | |
| XV205 | Lockheed C-130K Hercules C1 | RAF Lyneham Transport Wing | |
| XV206 | Lockheed C-130K Hercules C1 | RAF Lyneham Transport Wing | |
| XV208 | Lockheed C-130K Hercules W2 | DPA/Marshalls, Cambridge | |
| XV209 | Lockheed C-130K Hercules C3 | RAF Lyneham Transport Wing | |
| XV212 | Lockheed C-130K Hercules C3 | RAF Lyneham Transport Wing | |
| XV214 | Lockheed C-130K Hercules C3 | RAF Lyneham Transport Wing | |
| XV217 | Lockheed C-130K Hercules C3 | RAF Lyneham Transport Wing | |
| XV220 | Lockheed C-130K Hercules C3 | RAF Lyneham Transport Wing | |
| XV221 | Lockheed C-130K Hercules C3 | RAF Lyneham Transport Wing | |
| XV226 | HS Nimrod MR2 | RAF Kinloss MR Wing | |
| XV227 | HS Nimrod MR2 | BAE Systems, Woodford | |
| XV228 | HS Nimrod MR2 | BAE Systems, Woodford | |
| XV229 | HS Nimrod MR2 | RAF Kinloss MR Wing | |
| XV230 | HS Nimrod MR2 | RAF Kinloss MR Wing | |
| XV231 | HS Nimrod MR2 | RAF Kinloss MR Wing | |
| XV232 | HS Nimrod MR2 | RAF Kinloss MR Wing | |
| XV235 | HS Nimrod MR2 | RAF Kinloss MR Wing | |
| XV236 | HS Nimrod MR2 | RAF Kinloss MR Wing | |
| *XV238* | HS Nimrod <R> (parts of G-ALYW) | RAF M&RU, Bottesford | |
| XV240 | HS Nimrod MR2 | RAF Kinloss MR Wing | |
| XV241 | HS Nimrod MR2 | RAF Kinloss MR Wing | |
| XV243 | HS Nimrod MR2 | RAF Kinloss MR Wing | |
| XV244 | HS Nimrod MR2 | RAF Kinloss MR Wing | |

| Notes | Serial | Type (other identity) [code] | Owner/operator, location or fate |
|---|---|---|---|
| | XV245 | HS Nimrod MR2 | BAE Systems, Woodford |
| | XV246 | HS Nimrod MR2 | RAF Kinloss MR Wing |
| | XV248 | HS Nimrod MR2 | RAF Kinloss MR Wing |
| | XV249 | HS Nimrod R1 | RAF No 51 Sqn, Waddington |
| | XV250 | HS Nimrod MR2 | RAF Kinloss MR Wing |
| | XV252 | HS Nimrod MR2 | RAF Kinloss MR Wing |
| | XV253 | HS Nimrod MR2 (9118M) | DPA/BAE Systems, Woodford |
| | XV254 | HS Nimrod MR2 | RAF Kinloss MR Wing |
| | XV255 | HS Nimrod MR2 | RAF Kinloss MR Wing |
| | XV259 | BAe Nimrod AEW3 <ff> | Privately owned, Carlisle |
| | XV260 | HS Nimrod MR2 | RAF Kinloss MR Wing |
| | XV263 | BAe Nimrod AEW3P (8967M) <ff> | BAE Systems, Brough |
| | XV263 | BAe Nimrod AEW3P (8967M) <rf> | DPA/BAE Systems, Woodford |
| | XV268 | DHC2 Beaver AL1 (G-BVER) | Privately owned, Cumbernauld |
| | XV277 | HS P.1127(RAF) | Royal Scottish Mus'm of Flight, E Fortune |
| | XV279 | HS P.1127(RAF) (8566M) | RAF Harrier Maintenance School, Wittering |
| | XV280 | HS P.1127(RAF) <ff> | RNAS Yeovilton Fire Section |
| | XV290 | Lockheed C-130K Hercules C3 | RAF Lyneham Transport Wing |
| | XV294 | Lockheed C-130K Hercules C3 | RAF Lyneham Transport Wing |
| | XV295 | Lockheed C-130K Hercules C1 | RAF Lyneham Transport Wing |
| | XV299 | Lockheed C-130K Hercules C3 | RAF Lyneham Transport Wing |
| | XV301 | Lockheed C-130K Hercules C3 | RAF Lyneham Transport Wing |
| | XV302 | Lockheed C-130K Hercules C3 | Marshalls, Cambridge, fatigue test airframe |
| | XV303 | Lockheed C-130K Hercules C3 | RAF Lyneham Transport Wing |
| | XV304 | Lockheed C-130K Hercules C3 | RAF Lyneham Transport Wing |
| | XV305 | Lockheed C-130K Hercules C3 | RAF Lyneham Transport Wing |
| | XV307 | Lockheed C-130K Hercules C3 | RAF Lyneham Transport Wing |
| | XV328 | BAC Lightning T5 <ff> | Phoenix Aviation, Bruntingthorpe |
| | XV333 | HS Buccaneer S2B [234/H] | FAA Museum, RNAS Yeovilton |
| | XV337 | HS Buccaneer S2C (8852M) <ff> | Privately owned, Diseworth, Leics |
| | XV344 | HS Buccaneer S2C | QinetiQ Farnborough, on display |
| | XV350 | HS Buccaneer S2B | East Midlands Airport Aeropark |
| | XV352 | HS Buccaneer S2B <ff> | RAF Manston History Museum |
| | XV353 | HS Buccaneer S2B (9144M) <ff> | *Currently not known* |
| | XV359 | HS Buccaneer S2B [035/R] | Privately owned, Topsham, Devon |
| | XV361 | HS Buccaneer S2B | Ulster Aviation Society, Langford Lodge |
| | XV370 | Sikorsky SH-3D [260] | RN AESS, *HMS Sultan*, Gosport |
| | XV371 | WS61 Sea King HAS1(DB) [261] | SFDO, RNAS Culdrose |
| | XV372 | WS61 Sea King HAS1 | RAF HMF, St Mawgan |
| | XV401 | McD F-4M Phantom FGR2 [I] | Boscombe Down Aviation Collection |
| | XV402 | McD F-4M Phantom FGR2 <ff> | Robertsbridge Aviation Society, Mayfield |
| | XV406 | McD F-4M Phantom FGR2 (9098M) [CK] | Solway Aviation Society, Carlisle |
| | XV408 | McD F-4M Phantom FGR2 (9165M) [Z] | Tangmere Military Aviation Museum |
| | XV411 | McD F-4M Phantom FGR2 (9103M) [L] | MoD FSCTE, Manston |
| | XV415 | McD F-4M Phantom FGR2 (9163M) [E] | RAF Boulmer, on display |
| | XV420 | McD F-4M Phantom FGR2 (9247M) [BT] | *Scrapped at Neatishead, July 2005* |
| | XV424 | McD F-4M Phantom FGR2 (9152M) [I] | RAF Museum, Hendon |
| | XV426 | McD F-4M Phantom FGR2 <ff> | The Cockpit Collection, RAF Coltishall |
| | XV426 | McD F-4M Phantom FGR2 [P] <rf> | RAF Coningsby, BDRT |
| | XV435 | McD F-4M Phantom FGR2 [R] | *Scrapped at Llanbedr, December 2004* |
| | XV460 | McD F-4M Phantom FGR2 <ff> | No 2214 Sqn ATC, Usworth |
| | XV474 | McD F-4M Phantom FGR2 [T] | The Old Flying Machine Company, Duxford |
| | XV490 | McD F-4M Phantom FGR2 <ff> | Privately owned, Nantwich |
| | XV497 | McD F-4M Phantom FGR2 [D] | RAF No 23 Sqn Waddington, (preserved) |
| | *XV498* | McD F-4M Phantom FGR2 (XV500/9113M) [U] | RAF St Athan, on display |
| | XV499 | McD F-4M Phantom FGR2 | RAF Leeming, WLT |
| | XV581 | McD F-4K Phantom FG1 (9070M) <ff> | No 2481 Sqn ATC, Bridge of Don |
| | XV582 | McD F-4K Phantom FG1 (9066M) [M] | RAF Leuchars, on display |
| | XV586 | McD F-4K Phantom FG1 (9067M) [AJ] | RAF Leuchars, on display |
| | XV591 | McD F-4K Phantom FG1 <ff> | RAF Museum, Cosford |

| Serial | Type (other identity) [code] | Owner/operator, location or fate | Notes |
|---|---|---|---|
| XV625 | WS Wasp HAS1 [471] | RN, stored *HMS Sultan*, Gosport | |
| XV631 | WS Wasp HAS1 (fuselage) | QinetiQ Acoustics Dept, Farnborough | |
| XV642 | WS61 Sea King HAS2A [259] | RN AESS, *HMS Sultan*, Gosport | |
| XV643 | WS61 Sea King HAS6 [262] | ATTF, RAF St Athan | |
| XV647 | WS61 Sea King HU5 [28] | RN No 771 Sqn, Culdrose | |
| XV648 | WS61 Sea King HU5 [818/CU] | RN No 771 Sqn, Culdrose | |
| XV649 | WS61 Sea King AEW7 [180/CU] | RN No 849 Sqn, HQ Flt, Culdrose | |
| XV651 | WS61 Sea King HU5 [824/CU] | RN No 771 Sqn, Culdrose | |
| XV653 | WS61 Sea King HAS6 (9326M) [63/CU] | RAF No 1 SoTT, Cosford | |
| XV654 | WS61 Sea King HAS6 [705] (wreck) | SFDO, RNAS Culdrose | |
| XV655 | WS61 Sea King HAS6 [270/N] | RN, stored *HMS Sultan*, Gosport | |
| XV656 | WS61 Sea King AEW7 [185/N] | RN No 849 Sqn, B Flt, Culdrose | |
| XV657 | WS61 Sea King HAS5 (ZA135) [32/DD] | SFDO, RNAS Culdrose | |
| XV659 | WS61 Sea King HAS6 (9324M) [62/CU] | RAF No 1 SoTT, Cosford | |
| XV660 | WS61 Sea King HAS6 [69] | RN, stored *HMS Sultan*, Gosport | |
| XV661 | WS61 Sea King HU5 [26] | RN No 771 Sqn, Culdrose | |
| XV663 | WS61 Sea King HAS6 | RN, stored *HMS Sultan*, Gosport | |
| XV664 | WS61 Sea King AEW7 [187/R] | RN No 849 Sqn, A Flt, Culdrose | |
| XV665 | WS61 Sea King HAS6 [507/CU] | RN, stored *HMS Sultan*, Gosport | |
| XV666 | WS61 Sea King HU5 [22] | RN No 771 Sqn, Culdrose | |
| XV670 | WS61 Sea King HU5 [588] | RN/Westland Helicopters, Yeovil | |
| XV671 | WS61 Sea King AEW7 [183/N] | RN No 849 Sqn, B Flt, Culdrose | |
| XV672 | WS61 Sea King AEW7 [187] | RN No 849 Sqn, A Flt, Culdrose | |
| XV673 | WS61 Sea King HU5 [827/CU] | RN No 771 Sqn, Culdrose | |
| XV674 | WS61 Sea King HAS6 [015/L] | *Sold to Australia, November 2005* | |
| XV675 | WS61 Sea King HAS6 [701/PW] | RN, stored *HMS Sultan*, Gosport | |
| XV676 | WS61 Sea King HC6 [ZE] | RN/DARA, Fleetlands (under conversion) | |
| XV677 | WS61 Sea King HAS6 [269] | RN, stored *HMS Sultan*, Gosport | |
| XV696 | WS61 Sea King HAS6 [267/N] | RN, stored *HMS Sultan*, Gosport | |
| XV697 | WS61 Sea King AEW7 [181/CU] | RN No 849 Sqn, HQ Flt, Culdrose | |
| XV699 | WS61 Sea King HU5 [823/CU] | RN No 771 Sqn, Culdrose | |
| XV700 | WS61 Sea King HC6 [ZC] | RN No 846 Sqn, Yeovilton | |
| XV701 | WS61 Sea King HAS6 [268/N] | RAF No 1 SoTT, Cosford | |
| XV703 | WS61 Sea King HC6 [ZD] | RN No 846 Sqn, Yeovilton | |
| XV705 | WS61 Sea King HAR5 [29] | RN No 771 Sqn, Culdrose | |
| XV706 | WS61 Sea King HAS6 [017/L] | RN ETS, Culdrose | |
| XV707 | WS61 Sea King AEW7 [184] | RN No 849 Sqn, B Flt, Culdrose | |
| XV708 | WS61 Sea King HAS6 [501/CU] | RN, stored *HMS Sultan*, Gosport | |
| XV709 | WS61 Sea King HAS6 (9303M) [263] | RAF St Mawgan, instructional use | |
| XV710 | WS61 Sea King HAS6 (9325M) [64/CU] | *Sold to Australia, November 2005* | |
| XV711 | WS61 Sea King HAS6 [515/CT] | RN, stored *HMS Sultan*, Gosport | |
| XV712 | WS61 Sea King HAS6 [269] | RN | |
| XV713 | WS61 Sea King HAS6 [018] | RN, stored *HMS Sultan*, Gosport | |
| XV714 | WS61 Sea King AEW7 [188/R] | RN No 849 Sqn, A Flt, Culdrose | |
| XV720 | WS58 Wessex HC2 | RN, stored *HMS Sultan*, Gosport | |
| XV722 | WS58 Wessex HC2 [WH] | Privately owned, Hixon, Staffs | |
| XV724 | WS58 Wessex HC2 | RN AESS, *HMS Sultan*, Gosport | |
| XV725 | WS58 Wessex HC2 [C] | RAF No 1 SoTT, Cosford | |
| XV726 | WS58 Wessex HC2 [J] | Privately owned, Hixon, Staffs | |
| XV728 | WS58 Wessex HC2 [A] | Newark Air Museum, Winthorpe | |
| XV731 | WS58 Wessex HC2 [Y] | Privately owned, stored Redhill | |
| XV732 | WS58 Wessex HCC4 | RAF Museum, Hendon | |
| XV733 | WS58 Wessex HCC4 | The Helicopter Museum, Weston-super-Mare | |
| XV741 | HS Harrier GR3 [41] | SFDO, RNAS Culdrose | |
| XV744 | HS Harrier GR3 (9167M) [3K] | R. Military College of Science, Shrivenham | |
| XV748 | HS Harrier GR3 [3D] | Yorkshire Air Museum, Elvington | |
| XV751 | HS Harrier GR3 | Gatwick Aviation Museum, Charlwood | |
| XV752 | HS Harrier GR3 (9075M) [B,HF] | Bletchley Park Museum, Bucks | |
| XV753 | HS Harrier GR3 (9078M) [53] | SFDO, RNAS Culdrose | |
| XV755 | HS Harrier GR3 [M] | RNAS Yeovilton Fire Section | |
| XV759 | HS Harrier GR3 [O] <ff> | Privately owned, Hitchin, Herts | |
| XV760 | HS Harrier GR3 <ff> | Privately owned, Sussex | |
| XV779 | HS Harrier GR3 (8931M) | RAF Wittering on display | |
| XV783 | HS Harrier GR3 [83] | SFDO, RNAS Culdrose | |
| XV784 | HS Harrier GR3 (8909M) <ff> | Boscombe Down Aviation Collection | |
| XV786 | HS Harrier GR3 <ff> | RNAS Culdrose | |
| XV786 | HS Harrier GR3 [S] <rf> | RN, Predannack Fire School | |

| Notes | Serial | Type (other identity) [code] | Owner/operator, location or fate |
|---|---|---|---|
| | XV798 | HS Harrier GR1 (mod) | Bristol Aero Collection, stored Kemble |
| | XV804 | HS Harrier GR3 (9280M) [O] | RAF North Luffenham Training Area |
| | XV808 | HS Harrier GR3 (9076M) [08] | SFDO, RNAS Culdrose |
| | XV810 | HS Harrier GR3 (9038M) [K] | Privately owned, Bruntingthorpe |
| | XV814 | DH106 Comet 4 (G-APDF) <ff> | Privately owned, Chipping Campden |
| | XV863 | HS Buccaneer S2B | RAF Lossiemouth |
| | | (9115M/9139M/9145M) [S] | |
| | XV864 | HS Buccaneer S2B (9234M) | MoD FSCTE, Manston |
| | XV865 | HS Buccaneer S2B (9226M) | Imperial War Museum, Duxford |
| | XV867 | HS Buccaneer S2B <ff> | Highland Aviation Museum, Inverness |
| | XW175 | HS Harrier T4(VAAC) | DPA/AFD/QinetiQ, Boscombe Down |
| | XW198 | WS Puma HC1 | RAF No 230 Sqn, Aldergrove |
| | XW199 | WS Puma HC1 | RAF No 33 Sqn, Benson |
| | XW200 | WS Puma HC1 (wreck) | RAF, stored Shawbury |
| | XW201 | WS Puma HC1 | RAF Benson (spares use) |
| | XW202 | WS Puma HC1 | RAF, stored Shawbury |
| | XW204 | WS Puma HC1 | RAF No 1563 Flt, Basrah, Iraq |
| | XW206 | WS Puma HC1 | RAF Benson (spares use) |
| | XW207 | WS Puma HC1 | RAF No 33 Sqn, Benson |
| | XW208 | WS Puma HC1 | RAF No 1563 Flt, Basrah, Iraq |
| | XW209 | WS Puma HC1 | RAF No 230 Sqn, Aldergrove |
| | XW210 | WS Puma HC1 (comp XW215) | RAF No 230 Sqn, Aldergrove |
| | XW211 | WS Puma HC1 | RAF No 33 Sqn, Benson |
| | XW212 | WS Puma HC1 | RAF No 230 Sqn, Aldergrove |
| | XW213 | WS Puma HC1 | RAF No 1563 Flt, Basrah, Iraq |
| | XW214 | WS Puma HC1 | RAF No 33 Sqn, Benson |
| | XW216 | WS Puma HC1 | RAF No 33 Sqn, Benson |
| | XW217 | WS Puma HC1 | RAF No 230 Sqn, Aldergrove |
| | XW218 | WS Puma HC1 | RAF No 33 Sqn, Benson |
| | XW219 | WS Puma HC1 | RAF No 1563 Flt, Basrah, Iraq |
| | XW220 | WS Puma HC1 | RAF No 1563 Flt, Basrah, Iraq |
| | XW222 | WS Puma HC1 | RAF No 33 Sqn, Benson |
| | XW223 | WS Puma HC1 | RAF No 33 Sqn, Benson |
| | XW224 | WS Puma HC1 | RAF No 230 Sqn, Aldergrove |
| | XW226 | WS Puma HC1 | RAF No 230 Sqn, Aldergrove |
| | XW227 | WS Puma HC1 | DPA/Westland Helicopters, Yeovil (on repair) |
| | XW229 | WS Puma HC1 | RAF No 230 Sqn, Aldergrove |
| | XW231 | WS Puma HC1 | RAF No 230 Sqn, Aldergrove |
| | XW232 | WS Puma HC1 | RAF No 230 Sqn, Aldergrove |
| | XW235 | WS Puma HC1 | RAF No 230 Sqn, Aldergrove |
| | XW236 | WS Puma HC1 | RAF No 33 Sqn, Benson |
| | XW237 | WS Puma HC1 | RAF No 33 Sqn, Benson |
| | XW241 | Sud SA330E Puma | QinetiQ Avionics & Sensors Dept, Farnborough |
| | XW264 | HS Harrier T2 <ff> | Gloucestershire Avn Coll, stored Gloucester |
| | XW265 | HS Harrier T4A (9258M) <ff> | No 2345 Sqn ATC, RAF Leuchars |
| | XW265 | HS Harrier T4A (9258M) <rf> | DARA, St Athan |
| | XW267 | HS Harrier T4 (9263M) [SA] | Territorial Army, Toton, Notts |
| | XW269 | HS Harrier T4 | Boscombe Down Aviation Collection |
| | XW270 | HS Harrier T4 (fuselage) | Coventry University, instructional use |
| | XW271 | HS Harrier T4 [71] | SFDO, RNAS Culdrose |
| | XW272 | HS Harrier T4 (8783M) (fuselage) (comp XV281) | Marsh Lane Technical School, Preston |
| | XW276 | Aérospatiale SA341 Gazelle (F-ZWRI) | Newark Air Museum, Winthorpe |
| | XW281 | WS Scout AH1 (G-BYNZ) [T] | Privately owned, Wembury, Devon |
| | XW283 | WS Scout AH1 [U] | RM, stored Yeovilton |
| | XW289 | BAC Jet Provost T5A (G-BVXT/G-JPVA) [73] | Kennet Aviation, North Weald |
| | XW290 | BAC Jet Provost T5A (9199M) [41,MA] | RAF No 1 SoTT, Cosford |
| | XW292 | BAC Jet Provost T5A (9128M) [32] | RAF No 1 SoTT, Cosford |
| | XW293 | BAC Jet Provost T5 (G-BWCS) [Z] | Privately owned, Bournemouth |
| | XW294 | BAC Jet Provost T5A (9129M) [45] | RAF No 1 SoTT, Cosford |
| | XW299 | BAC Jet Provost T5A (9146M) [60,MB] | RAF No 1 SoTT, Cosford |
| | XW301 | BAC Jet Provost T5A (9147M) [63,MC] | RAF No 1 SoTT, Cosford |
| | XW303 | BAC Jet Provost T5A (9119M) [127] | RAF No 1 SoTT, Cosford |
| | XW304 | BAC Jet Provost T5 (9172M) [MD] | RAF No 1 SoTT, Cosford |

| Serial | Type (other identity) [code] | Owner/operator, location or fate | Notes |
|--------|------------------------------|----------------------------------|-------|
| XW309 | BAC Jet Provost T5 (9179M) [V,ME] | RAF No 1 SoTT, Cosford | |
| XW311 | BAC Jet Provost T5 (9180M) [W,MF] | RAF No 1 SoTT, Cosford | |
| XW312 | BAC Jet Provost T5A (9109M) [64] | RAF No 1 SoTT, Cosford | |
| XW315 | BAC Jet Provost T5A <ff> | Privately owned, Wolverhampton | |
| XW318 | BAC Jet Provost T5A (9190M) [78,MG] | RAF No 1 SoTT, Cosford | |
| XW320 | BAC Jet Provost T5A (9015M) [71] | RAF No 1 SoTT, Cosford | |
| XW321 | BAC Jet Provost T5A (9154M) [62,MH] | RAF No 1 SoTT, Cosford | |
| XW323 | BAC Jet Provost T5A (9166M) [86] | RAF Museum, Hendon | |
| XW324 | BAC Jet Provost T5 (G-BWSG) [K] | Privately owned, North Weald | |
| XW325 | BAC Jet Provost T5B (G-BWGF) [E] | Privately owned, Blackpool | |
| XW327 | BAC Jet Provost T5A (9130M) [62] | RAF No 1 SoTT, Cosford | |
| XW328 | BAC Jet Provost T5A (9177M) [75,MI] | RAF No 1 SoTT, Cosford | |
| XW330 | BAC Jet Provost T5A (9195M) [82,MJ] | RAF No 1 SoTT, Cosford | |
| XW333 | BAC Jet Provost T5A (G-BVTC) | Global Aviation, Humberside | |
| XW335 | BAC Jet Provost T5A (9061M) [74] | RAF No 1 SoTT, Cosford | |
| XW351 | BAC Jet Provost T5A (9062M) [31] | RAF No 1 SoTT, Cosford | |
| XW353 | BAC Jet Provost T5A (9090M) [3] | RAF Cranwell, on display | |
| *XW354* | BAC Jet Provost T5A (XW355/G-JPTV) | Privately owned, Sandtoft | |
| XW358 | BAC Jet Provost T5A (9181M) [59,MK] | RAF No 1 SoTT, Cosford | |
| XW360 | BAC Jet Provost T5A (9153M) [61,ML] | RAF No 1 SoTT, Cosford | |
| XW361 | BAC Jet Provost T5A (9192M) [81,MM] | RAF No 1 SoTT, Cosford | |
| XW363 | BAC Jet Provost T5A [36] | BAE Systems North West Heritage Group, Warton | |
| XW364 | BAC Jet Provost T5A (9188M) [35,MN] | RAF No 1 SoTT, Cosford | |
| XW365 | BAC Jet Provost T5A (9018M) [73] | RAF No 1 SoTT, Cosford | |
| XW366 | BAC Jet Provost T5A (9097M) [75] | RAF No 1 SoTT, Cosford | |
| XW367 | BAC Jet Provost T5A (9193M) [64,MO] | RAF No 1 SoTT, Cosford | |
| XW370 | BAC Jet Provost T5A (9196M) [72,MP] | RAF No 1 SoTT, Cosford | |
| XW375 | BAC Jet Provost T5A (9149M) [52] | RAF No 1 SoTT, Cosford | |
| XW404 | BAC Jet Provost T5A (9049M) | DARA Training School, RAF St Athan | |
| XW405 | BAC Jet Provost T5A (9187M) [J,MQ] | RAF No 1 SoTT, Cosford | |
| XW409 | BAC Jet Provost T5A (9047M) | DARA Training School, RAF St Athan | |
| XW410 | BAC Jet Provost T5A (9125M) [80,MR] | RAF No 1 SoTT, Cosford | |
| XW413 | BAC Jet Provost T5A (9126M) [69] | RAF No 1 SoTT, Cosford | |
| XW416 | BAC Jet Provost T5A (9191M) [84,MS] | RAF No 1 SoTT, Cosford | |
| XW418 | BAC Jet Provost T5A (9173M) [MT] | RAF No 1 SoTT, Cosford | |
| XW419 | BAC Jet Provost T5A (9120M) [125] | RAF No 1 SoTT, Cosford | |
| XW420 | BAC Jet Provost T5A (9194M) [83,MU] | RAF No 1 SoTT, Cosford | |
| XW421 | BAC Jet Provost T5A (9111M) [60] | RAF No 1 SoTT, Cosford | |
| XW422 | BAC Jet Provost T5A (G-BWEB) [3] | Privately owned, Kemble | |
| XW423 | BAC Jet Provost T5A (G-BWUW) [14] | Deeside College, Connah's Quay, Clwyd | |
| XW425 | BAC Jet Provost T5A (9200M) [H,MV] | RAF No 1 SoTT, Cosford | |
| XW427 | BAC Jet Provost T5A (9124M) [67] | RAF No 1 SoTT, Cosford | |
| XW430 | BAC Jet Provost T5A (9176M) [77,MW] | RAF No 1 SoTT, Cosford | |
| XW432 | BAC Jet Provost T5A (9127M) [76,MX] | RAF No 1 SoTT, Cosford | |
| XW433 | BAC Jet Provost T5A (G-JPRO) | Global Aviation, Humberside | |
| XW434 | BAC Jet Provost T5A (9091M) [78,MY] | RAF No 1 SoTT, Cosford | |
| XW436 | BAC Jet Provost T5A (9148M) [68] | RAF No 1 SoTT, Cosford | |
| XW530 | HS Buccaneer S2B | Buccaneer Service Station, Elgin | |
| XW541 | HS Buccaneer S2B (8858M) <ff> | Privately owned, Mold | |
| XW544 | HS Buccaneer S2B (8857M) [Y] | Privately owned, Bruntingthorpe | |

| Notes | Serial | Type (other identity) [code] | Owner/operator, location or fate |
|---|---|---|---|
| | XW547 | HS Buccaneer S2B (9095M/9169M) [R] | RAF Museum, Hendon |
| | XW550 | HS Buccaneer S2B <ff> | Privately owned, West Horndon, Essex |
| | XW560 | SEPECAT Jaguar S <ff> | Boscombe Down Aviation Collection |
| | XW563 | SEPECAT Jaguar S (XX822/8563M) | RAF Coltishall, on display |
| | XW566 | SEPECAT Jaguar B | Farnborough Air Sciences Trust, Farnborough |
| | XW616 | WS Scout AH1 | AAC Dishforth, instructional use |
| | XW630 | HS Harrier GR3 | RNAS Yeovilton, Fire Section |
| | XW635 | Beagle D5/180 (G-AWSW) | Privately owned, Spanhoe |
| | XW664 | HS Nimrod R1 | RAF No 51 Sqn, Waddington |
| | XW665 | HS Nimrod R1 | RAF No 51 Sqn, Waddington |
| | XW666 | HS Nimrod R1 <ff> | Aeroventure, Doncaster |
| | XW750 | HS748 Series 107 | DPA/AFD/QinetiQ, Boscombe Down |
| | XW763 | HS Harrier GR3 (9002M/9041M) <ff> | Privately owned, Wigston, Leics |
| | XW768 | HS Harrier GR3 (9072M) [N] | RAF No 1 SoTT, Cosford |
| | XW784 | Mitchell-Procter Kittiwake I (G-BBRN) [VL] | Privately owned, RNAS Yeovilton |
| | XW795 | WS Scout AH1 | Blessingbourne Museum, Fivemiletown, Co Tyrone, NI |
| | XW796 | WS Scout AH1 | Privately owned, Sproughton |
| | XW838 | WS Lynx (TAD 009) | Army SEAE, Arborfield |
| | XW839 | WS Lynx | The Helicopter Museum, Weston-super-Mare |
| | XW844 | WS Gazelle AH1 | DARA Fleetlands Apprentice School |
| | XW846 | WS Gazelle AH1 | AAC No 665 Sqn/5 Regt, Aldergrove |
| | XW847 | WS Gazelle AH1 [H] | AAC No 665 Sqn/5 Regt, Aldergrove |
| | XW848 | WS Gazelle AH1 [D] | AAC No 671 Sqn/2 Regt, Middle Wallop |
| | XW849 | WS Gazelle AH1 [G] | RM, stored Shawbury |
| | XW851 | WS Gazelle AH1 | RM, stored Shawbury |
| | XW852 | WS Gazelle HCC4 (9331M) | RAF No 1 SoTT, Cosford |
| | XW854 | WS Gazelle HT2 (G-CBSD) [46/CU] | Privately owned, Earls Colne |
| | XW855 | WS Gazelle HCC4 | RAF Museum, Hendon |
| | XW856 | WS Gazelle HT2 (G-GAZL) [49/CU] | Privately owned, Addison Mains |
| | XW858 | WS Gazelle HT3 (G-DMSS) [C] | Privately owned, Murton, York |
| | XW860 | WS Gazelle HT2 (TAD021) | Army SEAE, Arborfield |
| | XW861 | WS Gazelle HT2 (G-BZFJ) [52/CU] | Privately owned, Goodwood |
| | XW862 | WS Gazelle HT3 (G-CBKC) [D] | Privately owned, Stapleford Tawney |
| | XW863 | WS Gazelle HT2 (TAD022) [42/CU] | Army SEAE, Arborfield |
| | XW864 | WS Gazelle HT2 [54/CU] | FAA Museum, stored RNAS Yeovilton |
| | XW865 | WS Gazelle AH1 [5C] | AAC No 29 Flt, BATUS, Suffield, Canada |
| | XW866 | WS Gazelle HT3 (G-BXTH) [E] | Flightline Ltd, Southend |
| | XW870 | WS Gazelle HT3 [F] | MoD FSCTE, Manston |
| | XW871 | WS Gazelle HT2 (G-CBSC) [44/CU] | Privately owned, Goodwood |
| | XW888 | WS Gazelle AH1 (TAD017) | Army SEAE, Arborfield |
| | XW889 | WS Gazelle AH1 (TAD018) | Army SEAE, Arborfield |
| | XW890 | WS Gazelle HT2 | RNAS Yeovilton, on display |
| | XW892 | WS Gazelle AH1 (9292M) [C] | Privately owned, Sproughton |
| | XW893 | WS Gazelle AH1 <ff> | Privately owned, East Garston, Bucks |
| | XW895 | WS Gazelle HT2 (G-BXZD) [51/CU] | Privately owned, Babcary, Somerset |
| | XW897 | WS Gazelle AH1 | AAC, stored Shawbury |
| | XW898 | WS Gazelle HT3 (G-CBXT) [G] | Privately owned, Redhill |
| | XW899 | WS Gazelle AH1 [Z] | AAC No 658 Sqn/7 Regt, Netheravon |
| | XW900 | WS Gazelle AH1 (TAD900) | Army SEAE, Arborfield |
| | XW902 | WS Gazelle HT3 [H] | DPA/QinetiQ, Boscombe Down, spares use |
| | XW904 | WS Gazelle AH1 [H] | AAC, stored Shawbury |
| | XW906 | WS Gazelle HT3 [J] | QinetiQ Boscombe Down, Apprentice School |
| | XW908 | WS Gazelle AH1 [A] | AAC No 666(V) Sqn/7 Regt, Netheravon |
| | XW909 | WS Gazelle AH1 | AAC, stored Shawbury |
| | XW912 | WS Gazelle AH1 (TAD019) | Army SEAE, Arborfield |
| | XW913 | WS Gazelle AH1 | AAC, stored Shawbury |
| | XW917 | HS Harrier GR3 (8975M) | RAF Cottesmore, at main gate |
| | XW919 | HS Harrier GR3 [W] | R. Military College of Science, Shrivenham |
| | XW922 | HS Harrier GR3 (8885M) | MoD FSCTE, Manston |
| | XW923 | HS Harrier GR3 (8724M) <ff> | RAF Wittering, Fire Section |
| | XW924 | HS Harrier GR3 (9073M) [G] | RAF Cottesmore, preserved |
| | XW934 | HS Harrier T4 [Y] | DPA, QinetiQ Farnborough (wfu) |
| | XX105 | BAC 1-11/201AC (G-ASJD) | Boscombe Down Aviation Collection |
| | XX108 | SEPECAT Jaguar GR3 | Imperial War Museum, Duxford |

| Serial | Type (other identity) [code] | Owner/operator, location or fate | Notes |
|---|---|---|---|
| XX109 | SEPECAT Jaguar GR1 (8918M) [US] | City of Norwich Aviation Museum | |
| XX110 | SEPECAT Jaguar GR1 (8955M) [EP] | RAF No 1 SoTT, Cosford | |
| *XX110* | SEPECAT Jaguar GR1 <R> (BAPC 169) | RAF No 1 SoTT, Cosford | |
| XX112 | SEPECAT Jaguar GR3A [EA] | RAF No 6 Sqn, Coltishall | |
| XX115 | SEPECAT Jaguar GR1 (8821M) (fuselage) | RAF No 1 SoTT, Cosford | |
| XX116 | SEPECAT Jaguar GR3A [EO] | MoD FSCTE, Manston, Kent | |
| XX117 | SEPECAT Jaguar GR3A [ES] | RAF No 1 SoTT, Cosford | |
| XX119 | SEPECAT Jaguar GR3A (8898M) [EB] | RAF No 6 Sqn, Coltishall | |
| XX121 | SEPECAT Jaguar GR1 [EQ] | Privately owned, Charlwood, Surrey | |
| XX139 | SEPECAT Jaguar T4 [PT] | Privately owned, Sproughton | |
| XX140 | SEPECAT Jaguar T2 (9008M) [D,JJ] | Privately owned, Charlwood, Surrey | |
| XX141 | SEPECAT Jaguar T2A (9297M) [T] | AMIF, RAFC Cranwell | |
| XX144 | SEPECAT Jaguar T2A [U] | Privately owned, Sproughton | |
| XX145 | SEPECAT Jaguar T2A | DPA/ETPS, Boscombe Down | |
| XX146 | SEPECAT Jaguar T4 [GT] | Privately owned, Sproughton | |
| XX150 | SEPECAT Jaguar T4 [FY] | RAF No 41 Sqn, Coltishall | |
| XX153 | WS Lynx AH1 | Museum of Army Flying, Middle Wallop | |
| XX154 | HS Hawk T1 | DPA/ETPS, Boscombe Down | |
| XX156 | HS Hawk T1 | RAF No 4 FTS/*208(R) Sqn*, Valley | |
| XX157 | HS Hawk T1A | RAF No 4 FTS/*208(R) Sqn*, Valley | |
| XX158 | HS Hawk T1A | RAF No 4 FTS/*19(R) Sqn*, Valley | |
| XX159 | HS Hawk T1A | RAF No 4 FTS/*208(R) Sqn*, Valley | |
| XX160 | HS Hawk T1 | RN, stored Shawbury | |
| XX161 | HS Hawk T1W | RN FRADU, Culdrose | |
| XX162 | HS Hawk T1 | RAF Aviation Medicine Flt, Boscombe Down | |
| XX165 | HS Hawk T1 | RN FRADU, Culdrose | |
| XX167 | HS Hawk T1W | RAF No 4 FTS/*208(R) Sqn*, Valley | |
| XX168 | HS Hawk T1 | RN FRADU, Culdrose | |
| XX169 | HS Hawk T1 | RAF No 4 FTS/*208(R) Sqn*, Valley | |
| XX170 | HS Hawk T1 | RN FRADU, Culdrose | |
| XX171 | HS Hawk T1 | RN FRADU, Culdrose | |
| XX172 | HS Hawk T1 | RN FRADU, Culdrose | |
| XX173 | HS Hawk T1 | RN, stored Shawbury | |
| XX174 | HS Hawk T1 | RAF No 4 FTS/*208(R) Sqn*, Valley | |
| XX175 | HS Hawk T1 | RN FRADU, Culdrose | |
| XX176 | HS Hawk T1W | RAF No 4 FTS/*19(R) Sqn*, Valley | |
| XX177 | HS Hawk T1 | RAF, stored Shawbury | |
| XX178 | HS Hawk T1W | RAF No 4 FTS/*208(R) Sqn*, Valley | |
| XX179 | HS Hawk T1W | RAF *Red Arrows*, Scampton | |
| XX181 | HS Hawk T1W | RN FRADU, Culdrose | |
| XX184 | HS Hawk T1 | RN FRADU, Culdrose | |
| XX185 | HS Hawk T1 | RAF No 4 FTS/*208(R) Sqn*, Valley | |
| XX187 | HS Hawk T1A | RAF No 4 FTS/*208(R) Sqn*, Valley | |
| XX188 | HS Hawk T1A [CF] | RAF No 100 Sqn, Leeming | |
| XX189 | HS Hawk T1A | RAF No 4 FTS/*208(R) Sqn*, Valley | |
| XX190 | HS Hawk T1A [CN] | RAF No 100 Sqn, Leeming | |
| XX191 | HS Hawk T1A [CC] | RAF No 100 Sqn/JFACTSU, Leeming | |
| XX194 | HS Hawk T1A [CL] | RAF No 100 Sqn, Leeming | |
| XX195 | HS Hawk T1W | RAF No 4 FTS/*19(R) Sqn*, Valley | |
| XX196 | HS Hawk T1A | RAF No 4 FTS/*19(R) Sqn*, Valley | |
| XX198 | HS Hawk T1A | RAF No 100 Sqn, Leeming | |
| XX199 | HS Hawk T1A | DPA/BAE Systems, Warton | |
| XX200 | HS Hawk T1A [CG] | RAF No 100 Sqn, Leeming | |
| XX201 | HS Hawk T1A | RAF No 4 FTS/*208(R) Sqn*, Valley | |
| XX202 | HS Hawk T1A | RAF No 4 FTS/*19(R) Sqn*, Valley | |
| XX203 | HS Hawk T1A | RAF No 4 FTS/*19(R) Sqn*, Valley | |
| XX204 | HS Hawk T1A | RAF No 4 FTS/*19(R) Sqn*, Valley | |
| XX205 | HS Hawk T1A | RAF No 4 FTS/*208(R) Sqn*, Valley | |
| XX217 | HS Hawk T1A | RAF No 4 FTS/*208(R) Sqn*, Valley | |
| XX218 | HS Hawk T1A | RAF No 4 FTS/*208(R) Sqn*, Valley | |
| XX219 | HS Hawk T1A | RAF, stored Shawbury | |
| XX220 | HS Hawk T1A | RAF No 4 FTS/*208(R) Sqn*, Valley | |
| XX221 | HS Hawk T1A | RAF No 4 FTS/*19(R) Sqn*, Valley | |
| XX222 | HS Hawk T1A [CI] | RAF No 100 Sqn, Leeming | |
| XX223 | HS Hawk T1 <ff> | Privately owned, Charlwood, Surrey | |
| XX224 | HS Hawk T1W | RN FRADU, Culdrose | |
| XX225 | HS Hawk T1 [CS] | RN FRADU, Culdrose | |

| Notes | Serial | Type (other identity) [code] | Owner/operator, location or fate |
|---|---|---|---|
| | XX226 | HS Hawk T1 | RN FRADU, Culdrose |
| | *XX227* | HS Hawk T1 <R> (*XX226*/BAPC 152) | RAF M&RU, Bottesford |
| | XX227 | HS Hawk T1A | RAF/DARA, St Athan |
| | XX228 | HS Hawk T1A | RAF No 4 FTS/*208(R) Sqn*, Valley |
| | XX230 | HS Hawk T1A [CH] | RAF No 100 Sqn, Leeming |
| | XX231 | HS Hawk T1W | RAF No 4 FTS/*208(R) Sqn*, Valley |
| | XX232 | HS Hawk T1 | RAF No 4 FTS/*208(R) Sqn*, Valley |
| | XX233 | HS Hawk T1 | RAF *Red Arrows*, Scampton |
| | XX234 | HS Hawk T1 | RN FRADU, Culdrose |
| | XX235 | HS Hawk T1W | RN FRADU, Culdrose |
| | XX236 | HS Hawk T1W | RAF No 4 FTS/*19(R) Sqn*, Valley |
| | XX237 | HS Hawk T1 | RAF *Red Arrows*, Scampton |
| | XX238 | HS Hawk T1 | RAF No 4 FTS/*208(R) Sqn*, Valley |
| | XX239 | HS Hawk T1W | RAF No 4 FTS/*19(R) Sqn*, Valley |
| | XX240 | HS Hawk T1 | RAF/DARA, St Athan |
| | XX242 | HS Hawk T1 | RN FRADU, Culdrose |
| | XX244 | HS Hawk T1 | RAF No 4 FTS/*208(R) Sqn*, Valley |
| | XX245 | HS Hawk T1 | RAF No 4 FTS/*208(R) Sqn*, Valley |
| | XX246 | HS Hawk T1A | RAF No 4 FTS/*19(R) Sqn*, Valley |
| | XX246 | HS Hawk T1A <rf> | RAF CTTS, St Athan |
| | XX247 | HS Hawk T1A [CM] | RAF No 100 Sqn, Leeming |
| | XX248 | HS Hawk T1A [CJ] | RAF No 100 Sqn, Leeming |
| | XX250 | HS Hawk T1 | RAF No 4 FTS/*19(R) Sqn*, Valley |
| | XX253 | HS Hawk T1A | RAF *Red Arrows*, Scampton |
| | XX254 | HS Hawk T1A <ff> | RAF/DARA, St Athan |
| | XX254 | HS Hawk T1A | DPA/BAE Systems, stored Scampton |
| | *XX254* | HS Hawk T1A <R> | Privately owned, Marlow, Bucks |
| | XX255 | HS Hawk T1A | RAF No 4 FTS/*208(R) Sqn*, Valley |
| | XX256 | HS Hawk T1A | RAF No 4 FTS/*19(R) Sqn*, Valley |
| | XX257 | HS Hawk T1A (fuselage) | Privately owned, Charlwood, Surrey |
| | XX258 | HS Hawk T1A | RAF No 4 FTS/*19(R) Sqn*, Valley |
| | XX260 | HS Hawk T1A | RAF *Red Arrows*, Scampton |
| | XX261 | HS Hawk T1A | RAF No 4 FTS/*208(R) Sqn*, Valley |
| | XX263 | HS Hawk T1A | RAF No 4 FTS/*208(R) Sqn*, Valley |
| | *XX263* | HS Hawk T1 <R> (*XX253*/BAPC 171) | RAF M&RU, Bottesford |
| | XX264 | HS Hawk T1A | RAF *Red Arrows*, Scampton |
| | XX265 | HS Hawk T1A [CK] | RAF No 100 Sqn/JFACTSU, Leeming |
| | XX266 | HS Hawk T1A | RAF *Red Arrows*, Scampton |
| | XX278 | HS Hawk T1A [CD] | RAF No 100 Sqn, Leeming |
| | XX280 | HS Hawk T1A | RAF No 4 FTS/*19(R) Sqn*, Valley |
| | XX281 | HS Hawk T1A | RAF No 4 FTS/*19(R) Sqn*, Valley |
| | XX283 | HS Hawk T1W | RAF No 4 FTS/*19(R) Sqn*, Valley |
| | XX284 | HS Hawk T1A [CA] | RAF No 100 Sqn, Leeming |
| | XX285 | HS Hawk T1A [CB] | RAF No 100 Sqn, Leeming |
| | XX286 | HS Hawk T1A | RAF No 4 FTS/*19(R) Sqn*, Valley |
| | XX287 | HS Hawk T1A | RAF No 4 FTS/*19(R) Sqn*, Valley |
| | XX289 | HS Hawk T1A [CO] | RAF No 100 Sqn, Leeming |
| | XX290 | HS Hawk T1W [CG] | RAF No 100 Sqn, Leeming |
| | XX292 | HS Hawk T1 | RAF *Red Arrows*, Scampton |
| | XX294 | HS Hawk T1 | RAF *Red Arrows*, Scampton |
| | XX295 | HS Hawk T1W | RAF No 4 FTS/*208(R) Sqn*, Valley |
| | XX296 | HS Hawk T1 | RAF, stored Shawbury |
| | XX299 | HS Hawk T1W [CH] | RAF No 4 FTS/*208(R) Sqn*, Valley |
| | XX301 | HS Hawk T1A | RAF No 4 FTS/*208(R) Sqn*, Valley |
| | XX303 | HS Hawk T1A | RAF No 4 FTS/*208(R) Sqn*, Valley |
| | XX304 | HS Hawk T1A <rf> | Cardiff International Airport Fire Section |
| | XX306 | HS Hawk T1A | RAF *Red Arrows*, Scampton |
| | XX307 | HS Hawk T1 | RAF/DARA, St Athan |
| | XX308 | HS Hawk T1 | RAF *Red Arrows*, Scampton |
| | XX309 | HS Hawk T1 | RAF No 4 FTS/*208(R) Sqn*, Valley |
| | XX310 | HS Hawk T1W | RAF No 4 FTS/*208(R) Sqn*, Valley |
| | XX311 | HS Hawk T1 | RAF No 4 FTS/*19(R) Sqn*, Valley |
| | XX312 | HS Hawk T1W | RAF No 4 FTS/*208(R) Sqn*, Valley |
| | XX313 | HS Hawk T1W [CE] | RAF No 4 FTS/*208(R) Sqn*, Valley |
| | XX314 | HS Hawk T1W [CN] | RAF No 4 FTS/*208(R) Sqn*, Valley |
| | XX315 | HS Hawk T1A | RAF No 4 FTS/*19(R) Sqn*, Valley |
| | XX316 | HS Hawk T1A | RAF No 4 FTS/*19(R) Sqn*, Valley |
| | XX317 | HS Hawk T1A | RAF No 4 FTS/19(R) Sqn, Valley |
| | XX318 | HS Hawk T1A | RAF No 4 FTS/*19(R) Sqn*, Valley |
| | XX319 | HS Hawk T1A | RN FRADU, Culdrose |
| | XX320 | HS Hawk T1A | RAF, stored Shawbury |
| | XX321 | HS Hawk T1A [CE] | RAF No 100 Sqn, Leeming |

| Serial | Type (other identity) [code] | Owner/operator, location or fate | Notes |
|--------|------------------------------|----------------------------------|-------|
| XX322 | HS Hawk T1A | RAF, stored Shawbury | |
| XX323 | HS Hawk T1A | RAF, stored Shawbury | |
| XX324 | HS Hawk T1A | RAF/DARA, St Athan | |
| XX325 | HS Hawk T1A [CT] | RN FRADU, Culdrose | |
| XX326 | HS Hawk T1A <ff> | RAF/DARA, St Athan | |
| XX326 | HS Hawk T1A | DPA/BAE Systems, Brough (on rebuild) | |
| XX327 | HS Hawk T1 | RAF Aviation Medicine Flt, Boscombe Down | |
| XX329 | HS Hawk T1A | RAF No 4 FTS/*19(R) Sqn*, Valley | |
| XX330 | HS Hawk T1A | RAF No 4 FTS/*208(R) Sqn*, Valley | |
| XX331 | HS Hawk T1A [CP] | RAF No 100 Sqn, Leeming | |
| XX332 | HS Hawk T1A | RAF No 4 FTS/*19(R) Sqn*, Valley | |
| XX335 | HS Hawk T1A [CR] | RAF No 100 Sqn, Leeming | |
| XX337 | HS Hawk T1A | RAF No 4 FTS/*208(R) Sqn*, Valley | |
| XX338 | HS Hawk T1 | RAF No 4 FTS/*19(R) Sqn*, Valley | |
| XX339 | HS Hawk T1A | RAF No 4 FTS/*19(R) Sqn*, Valley | |
| XX341 | HS Hawk T1 ASTRA [1] | DPA/ETPS, Boscombe Down | |
| XX342 | HS Hawk T1 [2] | DPA/ETPS, Boscombe Down | |
| XX343 | HS Hawk T1 [3] (wreck) | Boscombe Down Aviation Collection | |
| XX344 | HS Hawk T1 (8847M) (fuselage) | QinetiQ Farnborough Fire Section | |
| XX345 | HS Hawk T1A | RAF No 4 FTS/*19(R) Sqn*, Valley | |
| XX346 | HS Hawk T1A | RAF No 4 FTS/*19(R) Sqn*, Valley | |
| XX348 | HS Hawk T1A | RAF No 4 FTS/*19(R) Sqn*, Valley | |
| XX349 | HS Hawk T1W [CO] | RAF No 4 FTS/*208(R) Sqn*, Valley | |
| XX350 | HS Hawk T1A | RAF No 4 FTS/*19(R) Sqn*, Valley | |
| XX351 | HS Hawk T1A [CQ] | RAF No 100 Sqn, Leeming | |
| XX370 | WS Gazelle AH1 (G-CDNL) | Privately owned, Dorchester | |
| XX371 | WS Gazelle AH1 | AAC No 12 Flt, Brüggen | |
| XX372 | WS Gazelle AH1 | AAC No 654 Sqn/4 Regt, Wattisham | |
| XX375 | WS Gazelle AH1 | AAC, stored Shawbury | |
| XX378 | WS Gazelle AH1 [Q] | AAC No 671 Sqn/2 Regt, Middle Wallop | |
| XX379 | WS Gazelle AH1 | AAC, stored Shawbury | |
| XX380 | WS Gazelle AH1 [A] | RM, stored Shawbury | |
| XX381 | WS Gazelle AH1 [C] | RM, stored Shawbury | |
| XX382 | WS Gazelle HT3 (G-BZYB) [M] | Privately owned, Tadcaster | |
| XX383 | WS Gazelle AH1 [D] | AAC No 666(V) Sqn/7 Regt, Netheravon | |
| XX384 | WS Gazelle AH1 | AAC, stored Shawbury | |
| XX385 | WS Gazelle AH1 | RAF, stored Shawbury | |
| XX386 | WS Gazelle AH1 | AAC No 12 Flt, Brüggen | |
| XX387 | WS Gazelle AH1 (TAD 014) | Army SEAE, Arborfield | |
| XX388 | WS Gazelle AH1 <ff> | Privately owned, East Garston, Bucks | |
| XX389 | WS Gazelle AH1 | AAC, stored Shawbury | |
| XX392 | WS Gazelle AH1 | AAC, stored Shawbury | |
| XX393 | WS Gazelle AH1 (fuselage) | Privately owned, East Garston, Bucks | |
| XX394 | WS Gazelle AH1 [X] | AAC, stored Shawbury | |
| XX396 | WS Gazelle HT3 (8718M) [N] | ATF, RAFC Cranwell | |
| XX398 | WS Gazelle AH1 | AAC No 3 Regt, Wattisham | |
| XX399 | WS Gazelle AH1 [V] | AAC No 671 Sqn/2 Regt, Middle Wallop | |
| XX403 | WS Gazelle AH1 [U] | AAC No 671 Sqn/2 Regt, Middle Wallop | |
| XX405 | WS Gazelle AH1 | AAC No 665 Sqn/5 Regt, Aldergrove | |
| XX406 | WS Gazelle HT3 (G-CBSH) [P] | Privately owned, Redhill | |
| XX409 | WS Gazelle AH1 | AAC, stored Shawbury | |
| XX411 | WS Gazelle AH1 | Aeroventure, Doncaster | |
| XX411 | WS Gazelle AH1 <rf> | FAA Museum, RNAS Yeovilton | |
| XX412 | WS Gazelle AH1 [B] | RM, stored Shawbury | |
| XX413 | WS Gazelle AH1 <ff> | Privately owned, East Garston, Bucks | |
| XX414 | WS Gazelle AH1 [V] | AAC, stored *HMS Sultan*, Gosport | |
| XX416 | WS Gazelle AH1 | AAC, stored Shawbury | |
| XX417 | WS Gazelle AH1 | AAC, stored Shawbury | |
| XX418 | WS Gazelle AH1 | Privately owned, East Garston, Bucks | |
| XX419 | WS Gazelle AH1 | AAC No 654 Sqn/4 Regt, Wattisham | |
| XX431 | WS Gazelle HT2 (9300M) [43/CU] | RAF Shawbury, for display | |
| XX432 | WS Gazelle AH1 (G-CDNO) | Privately owned, Hurstbourne Tarrant, Hants | |
| XX433 | WS Gazelle AH1 <ff> | Privately owned, East Garston, Bucks | |
| XX435 | WS Gazelle AH1 [V] | AAC No 658 Sqn/7 Regt, Netheravon | |
| XX436 | WS Gazelle HT2 (G-CBSE) [39/CU] | *Sold as G-ZLLE, May 2005* | |
| XX437 | WS Gazelle AH1 | AAC, stored Shawbury | |
| XX438 | WS Gazelle AH1 | AAC No 653 Sqn/3 Regt, Wattisham | |
| XX439 | WS Gazelle AH1 | AAC, stored Shawbury | |
| XX440 | WS Gazelle AH1 (G-BCHN) | DARA Fleetlands Apprentice School | |
| XX442 | WS Gazelle AH1 [E] | AAC No 666(V) Sqn/7 Regt, Netheravon | |

| Notes | Serial | Type (other identity) [code] | Owner/operator, location or fate |
|---|---|---|---|
| | XX443 | WS Gazelle AH1 [Y] | AAC Stockwell Hall, Middle Wallop, instructional use |
| | XX444 | WS Gazelle AH1 | AAC Wattisham, instructional use |
| | XX445 | WS Gazelle AH1 [T] | AAC No 658 Sqn/7 Regt, Netheravon |
| | XX447 | WS Gazelle AH1 [D1] | AAC No 671 Sqn/2 Regt, Middle Wallop |
| | XX448 | WS Gazelle AH1 [S] | AAC No 671 Sqn/2 Regt, Middle Wallop |
| | XX449 | WS Gazelle AH1 | AAC No 654 Sqn/4 Regt, Wattisham |
| | XX450 | WS Gazelle AH1 [D] | Privately owned, East Garston, Bucks |
| | XX453 | WS Gazelle AH1 | AAC No 4 Regt, Wattisham |
| | XX454 | WS Gazelle AH1 (TAD 023) (fuselage) | Army SEAE, Arborfield |
| | XX455 | WS Gazelle AH1 | AAC, stored Shawbury |
| | XX456 | WS Gazelle AH1 | AAC No 3(V) Flt/7 Regt, Leuchars |
| | XX457 | WS Gazelle AH1 <ff> | Jet Avn Preservation Grp, Long Marston |
| | XX460 | WS Gazelle AH1 | AAC, stored Shawbury |
| | XX462 | WS Gazelle AH1 [W] | AAC No 658 Sqn/7 Regt, Netheravon |
| | XX467 | HS Hunter T66B/T7 (XL605/G-TVII) [86] | Privately owned, Exeter |
| | XX475 | HP137 Jetstream T2 (N1036S) | Northbrook College, Shoreham, instructional use |
| | XX476 | HP137 Jetstream T2 (N1037S) [561/CU] | RN No 750 Sqn, Culdrose |
| | XX477 | HP137 Jetstream T1 (G-AXXS/8462M) <ff> | Privately owned, Askern, Doncaster |
| | XX478 | HP137 Jetstream T2 (G-AXXT) [564/CU] | RN No 750 Sqn, Culdrose |
| | XX479 | HP137 Jetstream T2 (G-AXUR) | RN, Predannack Fire School |
| | XX481 | HP137 Jetstream T2 (G-AXUP) [560/CU] | RN No 750 Sqn, Culdrose |
| | XX482 | SA Jetstream T1 [J] | Privately owned, Hixon, Staffs |
| | XX483 | SA Jetstream T2 [562] <ff> | Dumfries & Galloway Avn Mus, Dumfries |
| | XX484 | SA Jetstream T2 [566/CU] | RN No 750 Sqn, Culdrose |
| | XX486 | SA Jetstream T2 [567/CU] | RN No 750 Sqn, Culdrose |
| | XX487 | SA Jetstream T2 [568/CU] | RN No 750 Sqn, Culdrose |
| | XX488 | SA Jetstream T2 [562/CU] | RN No 750 Sqn, Culdrose |
| | XX491 | SA Jetstream T1 [K] | Northbrook College, Shoreham, instructional use |
| | XX492 | SA Jetstream T1 [A] | Newark Air Museum, Winthorpe |
| | XX494 | SA Jetstream T1 [B] | Privately owned, Sproughton |
| | XX495 | SA Jetstream T1 [C] | Privately owned, Sproughton |
| | XX496 | SA Jetstream T1 [D] | RAF Museum, Cosford |
| | XX497 | SA Jetstream T1 [E] | Scrapped at Hixon, Staffs by August 2005 |
| | XX499 | SA Jetstream T1 [G] | RAF, stored Shawbury |
| | XX500 | SA Jetstream T1 [H] | Privately owned, Sproughton |
| | XX510 | WS Lynx HAS2 [69/DD] | SFDO, RNAS Culdrose |
| | XX513 | SA Bulldog T1 (G-CCMI) [10] | Privately owned, Meppershall |
| | XX515 | SA Bulldog T1 (G-CBBC) [4] | Privately owned, Blackbushe |
| | XX518 | SA Bulldog T1 (G-UDOG) [S] | Privately owned, North Weald |
| | XX520 | SA Bulldog T1 (9288M) [A] | No 172 Sqn ATC, Haywards Heath |
| | XX521 | SA Bulldog T1 (G-CBEH) [H] | Privately owned, East Dereham, Norfolk |
| | XX522 | SA Bulldog T1 (G-DAWG) [06] | Privately owned, Barton |
| | XX524 | SA Bulldog T1 (G-DDOG) [04] | Privately owned, North Weald |
| | XX525 | SA Bulldog T1 (G-CBJJ) [8] | Privately owned, Norwich |
| | XX528 | SA Bulldog T1 (G-BZON) [D] | Privately owned, Carlisle |
| *XX530* | SA Bulldog T1 (XX637/9197M) [F] | No 2175 Sqn ATC, Hillington |
| | XX534 | SA Bulldog T1 (G-EDAV) [B] | Privately owned, Tollerton |
| | XX537 | SA Bulldog T1 (G-CBCB) [C] | Privately owned, North Weald |
| | XX538 | SA Bulldog T1 (G-TDOG) [O] | Privately owned, Shobdon |
| | XX539 | SA Bulldog T1 [L] | Privately owned, Shobdon |
| | XX543 | SA Bulldog T1 (G-CBAB) [F] | Privately owned, Duxford |
| | XX546 | SA Bulldog T1 (G-WINI) [03] | Privately owned, Blackbushe |
| | XX549 | SA Bulldog T1 (G-CBID) [6] | Privately owned, White Waltham |
| | XX550 | SA Bulldog T1 (G-CBBL) [Z] | Privately owned, Fenland |
| | XX551 | SA Bulldog T1 (G-BZDP) [E] | Privately owned, RAF Lyneham |
| | XX554 | SA Bulldog T1 (G-BZMD) [09] | Privately owned, Wellesbourne Mountford |
| | XX557 | SA Bulldog T1 | Privately owned, Paull, Yorks |
| | XX561 | SA Bulldog T1 (G-BZEP) [7] | Privately owned, Biggin Hill |
| | XX611 | SA Bulldog T1 (G-CBDK) [7] | Privately owned, Coventry |
| | XX612 | SA Bulldog T1 (G-BZXC) [A,03] | Privately owned, Wellesbourne Mountford |
| | XX614 | SA Bulldog T1 (G-GGRR) [V] | Privately owned, White Waltham |
| | XX619 | SA Bulldog T1 (G-CBBW) [T] | Privately owned, Coventry |
| | XX621 | SA Bulldog T1 (G-CBEF) [H] | Privately owned, Tollerton |
| | XX622 | SA Bulldog T1 (G-CBGX) [B] | Privately owned, Findon, Sussex |

| Serial | Type (other identity) [code] | Owner/operator, location or fate | Notes |
|---|---|---|---|
| XX623 | SA Bulldog T1 [M] | Privately owned, Hurstbourne Tarrant, Hants | |
| XX624 | SA Bulldog T1 (G-KDOG) [E] | Privately owned, North Weald | |
| XX625 | SA Bulldog T1 (G-CBBR) [01,N] | Privately owned, Norwich | |
| XX626 | SA Bulldog T1 (9290M) [W,02] | DARA Training School, RAF St Athan | |
| XX628 | SA Bulldog T1 (G-CBFU) [9] | Privately owned, Faversham | |
| XX629 | SA Bulldog T1 (G-BZXZ) [V] | Privately owned, Sleap | |
| XX630 | SA Bulldog T1 (G-SIJW) [5] | Privately owned, Shenington | |
| XX631 | SA Bulldog T1 (G-BZXS) [W] | Privately owned, Sligo, Eire | |
| XX633 | SA Bulldog T1 [X] | Privately owned, Mansfield | |
| XX634 | SA Bulldog T1 [T] | Newark Air Museum, Notts | |
| XX635 | SA Bulldog T1 (8767M) | DARA Training School, RAF St Athan | |
| XX636 | SA Bulldog T1 (G-CBFP) [Y] | Privately owned, Cranfield | |
| XX638 | SA Bulldog T1 (G-DOGG) | Privately owned, Hurstbourne Tarrant, Hants | |
| XX653 | SA Bulldog T1 [E] | DPA/QinetiQ, stored Boscombe Down | |
| XX654 | SA Bulldog T1 [3] | RAF Museum, Cosford | |
| XX656 | SA Bulldog T1 [C] | Privately owned, Wellesbourne Mountford | |
| XX658 | SA Bulldog T1 (G-BZPS) [07] | Privately owned, Wellesbourne Mountford | |
| XX659 | SA Bulldog T1 [E] | Privately owned, Hixon, Staffs | |
| XX664 | SA Bulldog T1 (G-CBCT) [04] | Privately owned, Sleap | |
| XX665 | SA Bulldog T1 (9289M) | No 2409 Sqn ATC, Halton | |
| XX667 | SA Bulldog T1 (G-BZFN) [16] | Privately owned, Staverton | |
| XX668 | SA Bulldog T1 (G-CBAN) [1] | Privately owned, Colerne | |
| XX669 | SA Bulldog T1 (8997M) [B] | *Scrapped at Halton, October 2005* | |
| XX671 | SA Bulldog T1 [D] | Privately owned, Wellesbourne Mountford | |
| XX672 | SA Bulldog T1 [E] | Barry Technical College, Cardiff Airport | |
| XX686 | SA Bulldog T1 (9291M) [5] | DARA Training School, RAF St Athan | |
| XX687 | SA Bulldog T1 [F] | Barry Technical College, Cardiff Airport | |
| XX690 | SA Bulldog T1 [A] | James Watt College, Greenock | |
| XX692 | SA Bulldog T1 (G-BZMH) [A] | Privately owned, Wellesbourne Mountford | |
| XX694 | SA Bulldog T1 (G-CBBS) [E] | Privately owned, Durham/Tees Valley | |
| XX695 | SA Bulldog T1 (G-CBBT) [3] | Privately owned, Durham/Tees Valley | |
| XX698 | SA Bulldog T1 (G-BZME) [9] | Privately owned, Breighton | |
| XX699 | SA Bulldog T1 (G-CBCV) [F] | Privately owned, Wickenby | |
| XX700 | SA Bulldog T1 (G-CBEK) [17] | Privately owned, Blackbushe | |
| XX702 | SA Bulldog T1 (G-CBCR) [∂] | Privately owned, Fenland | |
| XX705 | SA Bulldog T1 [5] | QinetiQ Boscombe Down, Apprentice School | |
| XX707 | SA Bulldog T1 (G-CBDS) [4] | Privately owned, Sleap | |
| XX711 | SA Bulldog T1 (G-CBBU) [X] | Privately owned, Egginton | |
| XX713 | SA Bulldog T1 (G-CBJK) [2] | Privately owned, Norwich | |
| XX720 | SEPECAT Jaguar GR3A [FL] | RAF St Athan (wfu) | |
| XX722 | SEPECAT Jaguar GR1 (fuselage) | ATTF, RAF St Athan | |
| XX723 | SEPECAT Jaguar GR3A [FF] | RAF No 41 Sqn, Coltishall | |
| XX724 | SEPECAT Jaguar GR3A [EC] | RAF No 6 Sqn, Coltishall | |
| XX725 | SEPECAT Jaguar GR3A [FE] | RAF No 41 Sqn, Coltishall | |
| XX726 | SEPECAT Jaguar GR1 (8947M) [EB] | RAF No 1 SoTT, Cosford | |
| XX727 | SEPECAT Jaguar GR1 (8951M) [ER] | RAF No 1 SoTT, Cosford | |
| XX729 | SEPECAT Jaguar GR3A [EL] | RAF No 6 Sqn, Coltishall | |
| XX730 | SEPECAT Jaguar GR1 (8952M) [EC] | RAF No 1 SoTT, Cosford | |
| XX733 | SEPECAT Jaguar GR1B [EB] (wreck) | Privately owned, Faygate | |
| XX734 | SEPECAT Jaguar GR1 (8816M) | Gatwick Aviation Museum, Charlwood | |
| XX736 | SEPECAT Jaguar GR1 (9110M) <ff> | BAE Systems Brough | |
| XX737 | SEPECAT Jaguar GR3A [EE] | RAF No 6 Sqn, Coltishall | |
| XX738 | SEPECAT Jaguar GR3A [ED] | RAF No 6 Sqn, Coltishall | |
| XX739 | SEPECAT Jaguar GR1 (8902M) [I] | RAF No 1 SoTT, Cosford | |
| XX741 | SEPECAT Jaguar GR1A [04] | Privately owned, Sproughton | |
| XX743 | SEPECAT Jaguar GR1 (8949M) [EG] | RAF No 1 SoTT, Cosford | |
| XX744 | SEPECAT Jaguar GR1 | Privately owned, Sproughton | |
| XX745 | SEPECAT Jaguar GR1A [GV] | DPA/QinetiQ, Boscombe Down | |
| XX746 | SEPECAT Jaguar GR1 (8895M/9251M) [S] | RAF No 1 SoTT, Cosford | |
| XX747 | SEPECAT Jaguar GR1 (8903M) | ATF, RAFC Cranwell | |
| XX748 | SEPECAT Jaguar GR3A [GK] | DPA/AFD/QinetiQ, Boscombe Down | |
| XX751 | SEPECAT Jaguar GR1 (8937M) [10] | RAF No 1 SoTT, Cosford | |

| Notes | Serial | Type (other identity) [code] | Owner/operator, location or fate |
|---|---|---|---|
| | XX752 | SEPECAT Jaguar GR3A [EK] | RAF No 6 Sqn, Coltishall |
| | XX753 | SEPECAT Jaguar GR1 (9087M) <ff> | RAF M&RU, Bottesford |
| | XX756 | SEPECAT Jaguar GR1 (8899M) [AM] | RAF No 1 SoTT, Cosford |
| | XX757 | SEPECAT Jaguar GR1 (8948M) [CU] | RAF No 1 SoTT, Cosford |
| | XX761 | SEPECAT Jaguar GR1 (8600M) <ff> | Boscombe Down Aviation Collection |
| | XX763 | SEPECAT Jaguar GR1 (9009M) | DARA Training School, RAF St Athan |
| | XX764 | SEPECAT Jaguar GR1 (9010M) | DARA Training School, RAF St Athan |
| | XX765 | SEPECAT Jaguar ACT | RAF Museum, Cosford |
| | XX766 | SEPECAT Jaguar GR3A [EF] | RAF/DARA, St Athan |
| | XX767 | SEPECAT Jaguar GR3A [FK] | RAF No 41 Sqn, Coltishall |
| | XX818 | SEPECAT Jaguar GR1 (8945M) [DE] | RAF No 1 SoTT, Cosford |
| | XX819 | SEPECAT Jaguar GR1 (8923M) [CE] | RAF No 1 SoTT, Cosford |
| | XX821 | SEPECAT Jaguar GR1 (8896M) [P] | AMIF, RAFC Cranwell |
| | XX824 | SEPECAT Jaguar GR1 (9019M) [AD] | RAF No 1 SoTT, Cosford |
| | XX825 | SEPECAT Jaguar GR1 (9020M) [BN] | RAF No 1 SoTT, Cosford |
| | XX826 | SEPECAT Jaguar GR1 (9021M) [34,JH] | RAF No 1 SoTT, Cosford |
| | XX829 | SEPECAT Jaguar T2A [GZ] | Privately owned, Sproughton |
| | XX830 | SEPECAT Jaguar T2 <ff> | The Cockpit Collection, RAF Coltishall |
| | XX832 | SEPECAT Jaguar T2A [EZ] | Privately owned, Sproughton |
| | XX833 | SEPECAT Jaguar T2B | DPA/AFD/QinetiQ, Boscombe Down |
| | XX835 | SEPECAT Jaguar T4 [EX] | RAF No 6 Sqn, Coltishall |
| | XX836 | SEPECAT Jaguar T2A [X] | Privately owned, Sproughton |
| | XX837 | SEPECAT Jaguar T2 (8978M) [I] | RAF No 1 SoTT, Cosford |
| | XX838 | SEPECAT Jaguar T4 [FZ] | RAF St Athan (wfu) |
| | XX840 | SEPECAT Jaguar T4 [PS] | RAF/DARA, St Athan |
| | XX841 | SEPECAT Jaguar T4 [EW] | RAF No 6 Sqn, Coltishall |
| | XX842 | SEPECAT Jaguar T2A [FX] | RAF No 41 Sqn, Coltishall |
| | XX845 | SEPECAT Jaguar T4 [EV] | RAF St Athan (wfu) |
| | XX846 | SEPECAT Jaguar T4 [PV] | *Scrapped at Coltishall, August 2005* |
| | XX847 | SEPECAT Jaguar T4 [EZ] | RAF No 6 Sqn, Coltishall |
| | XX885 | HS Buccaneer S2B (9225M/G-HHAA) | Hawker Hunter Aviation, Scampton |
| | XX888 | HS Buccaneer S2B <ff> | Privately owned, Barnstaple |
| | XX889 | HS Buccaneer S2B [T] | Gloucestershire Avn Coll, stored Gloucester |
| | XX892 | HS Buccaneer S2B <ff> | Privately owned, Perthshire |
| | XX893 | HS Buccaneer S2B <ff> | Privately owned, Portmoak, Tayside |
| | XX894 | HS Buccaneer S2B [020/R] | Buccaneer Supporters Club, Bruntingthorpe |
| | XX895 | HS Buccaneer S2B <ff> | *Currently not known* |
| | XX897 | HS Buccaneer S2B(mod) | Bournemouth Aviation Museum |
| | XX899 | HS Buccaneer S2B <ff> | Midland Air Museum, Coventry |
| | XX900 | HS Buccaneer S2B | Cold War Jets Collection, Bruntingthorpe |
| | XX901 | HS Buccaneer S2B | Yorkshire Air Museum, Elvington |
| | XX907 | WS Lynx AH1 | Westland Helicopters, Yeovil, Fire Section |
| | XX910 | WS Lynx HAS2 | The Helicopter Museum, Weston-super-Mare |
| | XX914 | BAC VC10/1103 (8777M) <rf> | RAF Defence Movements School, Brize Norton |
| | XX919 | BAC 1-11/402AP (PI-C1121) <ff> | Boscombe Down Aviation Collection |
| | XX946 | Panavia Tornado (P02) (8883M) | RAF Museum, Cosford |
| | XX947 | Panavia Tornado (P03) (8797M) | Shoreham Airport, on display |
| | XX955 | SEPECAT Jaguar GR1A [GK] | *Sold to Germany, September 2005* |
| | XX956 | SEPECAT Jaguar GR1 (8950M) [BE] | RAF No 1 SoTT, Cosford |
| | XX958 | SEPECAT Jaguar GR1 (9022M) [BK,JG] | RAF No 1 SoTT, Cosford |
| | XX959 | SEPECAT Jaguar GR1 (8953M) [CJ] | RAF No 1 SoTT, Cosford |
| | XX962 | SEPECAT Jaguar GR1B (9257M) [E] | RAF No 1 SoTT, Cosford |
| | XX965 | SEPECAT Jaguar GR1A (9254M) [C] | AMIF, RAFC Cranwell |

| Serial | Type (other identity) [code] | Owner/operator, location or fate | Notes |
|--------|------------------------------|----------------------------------|-------|
| XX966 | SEPECAT Jaguar GR1 (8904M) [EL,JJ] | RAF No 1 SoTT, Cosford | |
| XX967 | SEPECAT Jaguar GR1 (9006M) [AC,JD] | RAF No 1 SoTT, Cosford | |
| XX968 | SEPECAT Jaguar GR1 (9007M) [AJ,JE] | RAF No 1 SoTT, Cosford | |
| XX969 | SEPECAT Jaguar GR1 (8897M) [01] | RAF No 1 SoTT, Cosford | |
| XX970 | SEPECAT Jaguar GR3A [EH] | RAF No 6 Sqn, Coltishall | |
| XX974 | SEPECAT Jaguar GR3 [FE] | Privately owned, Sproughton | |
| XX975 | SEPECAT Jaguar GR1 (8905M) [07] | RAF No 1 SoTT, Cosford | |
| XX976 | SEPECAT Jaguar GR1 (8906M) [BD] | RAF No 1 SoTT, Cosford | |
| XX977 | SEPECAT Jaguar GR1 (9132M) [DL,05] | ATTF, RAF St Athan | |
| XX979 | SEPECAT Jaguar GR1A (9306M) <rf> | RAF Coltishall, instructional use | |
| XZ101 | SEPECAT Jaguar GR1A (9282M) [D] | DPA/QinetiQ Boscombe Down, GI use | |
| XZ103 | SEPECAT Jaguar GR3A [FP] | RAF No 41 Sqn, Coltishall | |
| XZ104 | SEPECAT Jaguar GR3A [FM] | RAF No 1 SoTT, Cosford | |
| XZ106 | SEPECAT Jaguar GR3A [FW] | RAF St Athan (wfu) | |
| XZ107 | SEPECAT Jaguar GR3A [FH] | RAF No 41 Sqn, Coltishall | |
| XZ109 | SEPECAT Jaguar GR3A [EN] | RAF No 6 Sqn, Coltishall | |
| XZ112 | SEPECAT Jaguar GR3A [GW] | RAF No 41 Sqn, Coltishall | |
| XZ113 | SEPECAT Jaguar GR3 | RAF AWC/FJWOEU, Coningsby | |
| XZ114 | SEPECAT Jaguar GR3 [EO] | RAF No 6 Sqn, Coltishall | |
| XZ115 | SEPECAT Jaguar GR3 [ER] | RAF No 6 Sqn, Coltishall | |
| XZ117 | SEPECAT Jaguar GR3 [FB] | RAF No 41 Sqn, Coltishall | |
| XZ118 | SEPECAT Jaguar GR3 [FR] | RAF/DARA, St Athan | |
| XZ119 | SEPECAT Jaguar GR1A (9266M) [F] | AMIF, RAFC Cranwell | |
| XZ129 | HS Harrier GR3 [ETS] | *Sold to New Zealand, January 2005* | |
| XZ130 | HS Harrier GR3 (9079M) [A,HE] | No 1034 Sqn ATC, Tolworth, Surrey | |
| XZ131 | HS Harrier GR3 (9174M) <ff> | No 2156 Sqn ATC, Brierley Hill, W Midlands | |
| XZ132 | HS Harrier GR3 (9168M) [C] | ATF, RAFC Cranwell | |
| XZ133 | HS Harrier GR3 [10] | Imperial War Museum, Duxford | |
| XZ135 | HS Harrier GR3 (8848M) <ff> | RAF M&RU, Bottesford | |
| XZ138 | HS Harrier GR3 (9040M) <ff> | RAFC Cranwell, Trenchard Hall | |
| XZ145 | HS Harrier T4 [45] | SFDO, RNAS Culdrose | |
| XZ146 | HS Harrier T4 (9281M) [S] | RAF Wittering, on display | |
| XZ170 | WS Lynx AH9 | DPA/Westland Helicopters, Yeovil | |
| XZ171 | WS Lynx AH7 | AAC No 659 Sqn/4 Regt, Wattisham | |
| XZ172 | WS Lynx AH7 | AAC No 653 Sqn/3 Regt, Wattisham | |
| XZ173 | WS Lynx AH7 | AAC No 669 Sqn/4 Regt, Wattisham | |
| XZ174 | WS Lynx AH7 <ff> | RAF Defence Movements School, Brize Norton | |
| XZ175 | WS Lynx AH7 | *Reduced to spares, Yeovil* | |
| XZ176 | WS Lynx AH7 | AAC No 655 Sqn/5 Regt, Aldergrove | |
| XZ177 | WS Lynx AH7 | AAC No 655 Sqn/5 Regt, Aldergrove | |
| XZ178 | WS Lynx AH7 | AAC No 655 Sqn/5 Regt, Aldergrove | |
| XZ179 | WS Lynx AH7 | AAC No 655 Sqn/5 Regt, Aldergrove | |
| XZ180 | WS Lynx AH7 [R] | RM No 847 Sqn, Yeovilton | |
| XZ181 | WS Lynx AH1 | AAC/DARA, stored Fleetlands | |
| XZ182 | WS Lynx AH7 | RM No 847 Sqn, Yeovilton | |
| XZ183 | WS Lynx AH7 | AAC/DARA, stored Fleetlands | |
| XZ184 | WS Lynx AH7 [Z] | AAC No 655 Sqn/5 Regt, Aldergrove | |
| XZ185 | WS Lynx AH7 | AAC No 653 Sqn/3 Regt, Wattisham | |
| XZ187 | WS Lynx AH7 | Army SEAE, Arborfield | |
| XZ188 | WS Lynx AH7 | Army SEAE, Arborfield | |
| XZ190 | WS Lynx AH7 | AAC/DARA, stored Fleetlands | |
| XZ191 | WS Lynx AH7 [A] | AAC No 671 Sqn/2 Regt, Middle Wallop | |
| XZ192 | WS Lynx AH7 | DPA/Westland Helicopters, Yeovil (on rebuild) | |
| XZ193 | WS Lynx AH7 [I] | AAC No 671 Sqn/2 Regt, Middle Wallop | |
| XZ194 | WS Lynx AH7 | AAC No 4 Regt, Wattisham | |
| XZ195 | WS Lynx AH7 | AAC No 652 Sqn/1 Regt, Gütersloh | |
| XZ196 | WS Lynx AH7 | AAC No 653 Sqn/3 Regt, Wattisham | |
| XZ197 | WS Lynx AH7 <ff> | AAC/DARA, stored Fleetlands | |
| XZ198 | WS Lynx AH7 | AAC/DARA, stored Fleetlands | |
| XZ203 | WS Lynx AH7 [L] | AAC No 671 Sqn/2 Regt, Middle Wallop | |
| XZ205 | WS Lynx AH7 | AAC No 669 Sqn/4 Regt, Wattisham | |
| XZ206 | WS Lynx AH7 | AAC No 653 Sqn/3 Regt, Wattisham | |
| XZ207 | WS Lynx AH7 | Army SEAE, Arborfield | |

| Notes | Serial | Type (other identity) [code] | Owner/operator, location or fate |
|---|---|---|---|
| | XZ208 | WS Lynx AH7 | AAC No 672 Sqn/9 Regt, Dishforth |
| | XZ209 | WS Lynx AH7 | AAC No 655 Sqn/5 Regt, Aldergrove |
| | XZ210 | WS Lynx AH7 | AAC No 672 Sqn/9 Regt, Dishforth |
| | XZ211 | WS Lynx AH7 | AAC No 655 Sqn/5 Regt, Aldergrove |
| | XZ212 | WS Lynx AH7 | AAC No 672 Sqn/9 Regt, Dishforth |
| | XZ213 | WS Lynx AH1 (TAD 213) | DARA Fleetlands Apprentice School |
| | XZ214 | WS Lynx AH7 | AAC No 657 Sqn, Odiham |
| | XZ215 | WS Lynx AH7 | AAC No 653 Sqn/3 Regt, Wattisham |
| | XZ216 | WS Lynx AH7 | AAC No 653 Sqn/3 Regt, Wattisham |
| | XZ217 | WS Lynx AH7 | AAC No 672 Sqn/9 Regt, Dishforth |
| | XZ218 | WS Lynx AH7 | Privately owned, Sproughton |
| | XZ219 | WS Lynx AH7 | AAC No 669 Sqn/4 Regt, Wattisham |
| | XZ220 | WS Lynx AH7 | AAC No 653 Sqn/3 Regt, Wattisham |
| | XZ221 | WS Lynx AH7 | AAC No 659 Sqn/4 Regt, Wattisham |
| | XZ222 | WS Lynx AH7 | AAC No 657 Sqn, Odiham |
| | XZ228 | WS Lynx HAS3S | RN No 815 Sqn, Yeovilton |
| | XZ229 | WS Lynx HAS3S [411/EB] | RN No 815 Sqn, *Edinburgh* Flt, Yeovilton |
| | XZ230 | WS Lynx HAS3S [302] | RN/DARA, stored Fleetlands |
| | XZ232 | WS Lynx HAS3S [305] | RN No 815 Sqn, HQ Flt, Yeovilton |
| | XZ233 | WS Lynx HAS3 [644] | RN No 702 Sqn, Yeovilton |
| | XZ234 | WS Lynx HAS3S [635] | RN No 702 Sqn, Yeovilton |
| | XZ235 | WS Lynx HAS3S [633] | RN No 702 Sqn, Yeovilton |
| | XZ236 | WS Lynx HMA8 | DPA/AFD/QinetiQ, Boscombe Down |
| | XZ237 | WS Lynx HAS3S [303] | RN No 815 Sqn, HQ Flt, Yeovilton |
| | XZ238 | WS Lynx HAS3S(ICE) [434/EE] | RN No 815 Sqn, *Endurance* Flt, Yeovilton |
| | XZ239 | WS Lynx HAS3S [425/KT] | RN No 815 Sqn, *Kent* Flt, Yeovilton |
| | XZ243 | WS Lynx HAS3 <ff> | *Scrapped* |
| | XZ245 | WS Lynx HAS3S [332/LP] | RN No 815 Sqn, *Liverpool* Flt, Yeovilton |
| | XZ246 | WS Lynx HAS3S(ICE) [435/EE] | RN No 815 Sqn, *Endurance* Flt, Yeovilton |
| | XZ248 | WS Lynx HAS3S [638] | RN/DARA, Fleetlands |
| | XZ250 | WS Lynx HAS3S [304] | RN No 815 Sqn, HQ Flt, Yeovilton |
| | XZ252 | WS Lynx HAS3S | RN MASU, Fleetlands |
| | XZ254 | WS Lynx HAS3S [303] | RN AMG, Yeovilton |
| | XZ255 | WS Lynx HMA8 [318] | RN No 815 Sqn OEU, Yeovilton |
| | XZ257 | WS Lynx HAS3S [301] | RN No 815 Sqn, HQ Flt, Yeovilton |
| | XZ287 | BAe Nimrod AEW3 (9140M) (fuselage) | RAF TSW, Stafford |
| | XZ290 | WS Gazelle AH1 | Army No 70 Aircraft Workshops, Middle Wallop |
| | XZ291 | WS Gazelle AH1 | AAC No 12 Flt, Brüggen |
| | XZ292 | WS Gazelle AH1 | AAC No 654 Sqn/4 Regt, Wattisham |
| | XZ294 | WS Gazelle AH1 [X] | AAC No 658 Sqn/7 Regt, Netheravon |
| | XZ295 | WS Gazelle AH1 | AAC No 12 Flt, Brüggen |
| | XZ296 | WS Gazelle AH1 | RAF No 7 Sqn, Odiham |
| | XZ298 | WS Gazelle AH1 | AAC, stored Shawbury |
| | XZ299 | WS Gazelle AH1 | Privately owned, Breighton |
| | XZ300 | WS Gazelle AH1 [L] (wreck) | Army, Bramley, Hants |
| | XZ301 | WS Gazelle AH1 [U] | AAC, stored Shawbury |
| | XZ303 | WS Gazelle AH1 | AAC No 6(V) Flt/7 Regt, Shawbury |
| | XZ304 | WS Gazelle AH1 | AAC No 6(V) Flt/7 Regt, Shawbury |
| | XZ305 | WS Gazelle AH1 (TAD020) | AAC Middle Wallop, instructional use |
| | XZ307 | WS Gazelle AH1 | DARA Fleetlands Apprentice School |
| | XZ308 | WS Gazelle AH1 | AAC No 654 Sqn/4 Regt, Wattisham |
| | XZ309 | WS Gazelle AH1 | Privately owned, Hixon, Staffs |
| | XZ311 | WS Gazelle AH1 | AAC No 6(V) Flt/7 Regt, Shawbury |
| | XZ312 | WS Gazelle AH1 | AAC, stored Shawbury |
| | XZ313 | WS Gazelle AH1 | AAC, stored Shawbury |
| | XZ314 | WS Gazelle AH1 | AAC No 8 Flt, Credenhill |
| | XZ315 | WS Gazelle AH1 | Privately owned, Sproughton |
| | XZ316 | WS Gazelle AH1 [B] | AAC No 666(V) Sqn/7 Regt, Netheravon |
| | XZ318 | WS Gazelle AH1 (fuselage) | AAC, stored Shawbury |
| | XZ320 | WS Gazelle AH1 | AAC No 665 Sqn/5 Regt, Aldergrove |
| | XZ321 | WS Gazelle AH1 (G-CDNS) | Privately owned, Hurstbourne Tarrant, Hants |
| | XZ322 | WS Gazelle AH1 (9283M) [N] | ATTF, RAF St Athan |
| | XZ323 | WS Gazelle AH1 [H] | AAC No 666(V) Sqn/7 Regt, Netheravon |
| | XZ324 | WS Gazelle AH1 | AAC No 3(V) Flt/7 Regt, Leuchars |
| | XZ325 | WS Gazelle AH1 [T] | Army SEAE, Arborfield |
| | XZ326 | WS Gazelle AH1 | AAC No 665 Sqn/5 Regt, Aldergrove |
| | XZ327 | WS Gazelle AH1 | AAC No 3(V) Flt/7 Regt, Leuchars |
| | XZ328 | WS Gazelle AH1 [C] | AAC No 666(V) Sqn/7 Regt, Netheravon |
| | XZ329 | WS Gazelle AH1 (G-BZYD) [J] | Privately owned, East Garston, Bucks |
| | XZ330 | WS Gazelle AH1 [Y] | AAC Wattisham, instructional use |

| Serial | Type (other identity) [code] | Owner/operator, location or fate | Notes |
|--------|------------------------------|----------------------------------|-------|
| XZ331 | WS Gazelle AH1 | AAC No 654 Sqn/4 Regt, Wattisham | |
| XZ332 | WS Gazelle AH1 [O] | Army SEAE, Arborfield | |
| XZ333 | WS Gazelle AH1 [A] | Army SEAE, Arborfield | |
| XZ334 | WS Gazelle AH1 | AAC, Middle Wallop | |
| XZ335 | WS Gazelle AH1 | AAC No 6(V) Flt/7 Regt, Shawbury | |
| XZ337 | WS Gazelle AH1 | AAC, stored RAF Shawbury | |
| XZ338 | WS Gazelle AH1 [Y] | AAC No 671 Sqn/2 Regt, Middle Wallop | |
| XZ340 | WS Gazelle AH1 [5B] | AAC No 29 Flt, BATUS, Suffield, Canada | |
| XZ341 | WS Gazelle AH1 | AAC No 665 Sqn/5 Regt, Aldergrove | |
| XZ342 | WS Gazelle AH1 | AAC No 8 Flt, Credenhill | |
| XZ343 | WS Gazelle AH1 | AAC/DARA, Fleetlands | |
| XZ344 | WS Gazelle AH1 [Y] | AAC No 658 Sqn/7 Regt, Netheravon | |
| XZ345 | WS Gazelle AH1 | AAC No 6(V) Flt/7 Regt, Shawbury | |
| XZ346 | WS Gazelle AH1 | AAC, stored Shawbury | |
| XZ347 | WS Gazelle AH1 | AAC, stored Shawbury | |
| XZ348 | WS Gazelle AH1 (wreck) | AAC/DARA, stored Fleetlands | |
| XZ349 | WS Gazelle AH1 | AAC No 3(V) Flt/7 Regt, Leuchars | |
| XZ355 | SEPECAT Jaguar GR3A [FJ] | RAF No 41 Sqn, Coltishall | |
| XZ356 | SEPECAT Jaguar GR3A [FU] | RAF No 41 Sqn, Coltishall | |
| XZ357 | SEPECAT Jaguar GR3A | RAF St Athan (wfu) | |
| XZ358 | SEPECAT Jaguar GR1A (9262M) [L] | AMIF, RAFC Cranwell | |
| XZ360 | SEPECAT Jaguar GR3 [FN] | RAF No 41 Sqn, Coltishall | |
| XZ361 | SEPECAT Jaguar GR3 [FT] | Privately owned, Sproughton | |
| *XZ363* | SEPECAT Jaguar GR1A <R> (*XX824*/BAPC 151) [A] | RAF M&RU, Bottesford | |
| XZ364 | SEPECAT Jaguar GR3A [FS] | RAF St Athan (wfu) | |
| XZ366 | SEPECAT Jaguar GR3A [FC] | RAF No 41 Sqn, Coltishall | |
| XZ367 | SEPECAT Jaguar GR3 [GP] | RAF Coltishall, instructional use | |
| XZ368 | SEPECAT Jaguar GR1 [8900M] [E] | RAF No 1 SoTT, Cosford | |
| XZ369 | SEPECAT Jaguar GR3A [EU] | RAF St Athan (wfu) | |
| XZ370 | SEPECAT Jaguar GR1 (9004M) [JB] | RAF No 1 SoTT, Cosford | |
| XZ371 | SEPECAT Jaguar GR1 (8907M) [AP] | RAF No 1 SoTT, Cosford | |
| XZ372 | SEPECAT Jaguar GR3 [FV] | RAF St Athan (wfu) | |
| XZ374 | SEPECAT Jaguar GR1 (9005M) [JC] | RAF No 1 SoTT, Cosford | |
| XZ375 | SEPECAT Jaguar GR1A (9255M) <ff> | The Cockpit Collection, RAF Coltishall | |
| XZ377 | SEPECAT Jaguar GR3A [EP] | RAF No 6 Sqn, Coltishall | |
| XZ378 | SEPECAT Jaguar GR1A [EP] | RAF | |
| XZ382 | SEPECAT Jaguar GR1 (8908M) [AE] | Cold War Jets Collection, Bruntingthorpe | |
| XZ383 | SEPECAT Jaguar GR1 (8901M) [AF] | RAF No 1 SoTT, Cosford | |
| XZ384 | SEPECAT Jaguar GR1 (8954M) [BC] | RAF No 1 SoTT, Cosford | |
| XZ385 | SEPECAT Jaguar GR3A [FT] | RAF/DARA, St Athan | |
| XZ389 | SEPECAT Jaguar GR1 (8946M) [BL] | RAF No 1 SoTT, Cosford | |
| XZ390 | SEPECAT Jaguar GR1 (9003M) [35,JA] | RAF No 1 SoTT, Cosford | |
| XZ391 | SEPECAT Jaguar GR3A [ET] | RAF No 6 Sqn, Coltishall | |
| XZ392 | SEPECAT Jaguar GR3A [EM] | RAF No 6 Sqn, Coltishall | |
| XZ394 | SEPECAT Jaguar GR3 [FG] | RAF No 41 Sqn, Coltishall | |
| XZ396 | SEPECAT Jaguar GR3A [EQ] | RAF/DARA, St Athan | |
| XZ398 | SEPECAT Jaguar GR3A [FA] | RAF No 41 Sqn, Coltishall | |
| XZ399 | SEPECAT Jaguar GR3A [EJ] | RAF No 6 Sqn, Coltishall | |
| XZ400 | SEPECAT Jaguar GR3A [FQ] | RAF St Athan (wfu) | |
| XZ431 | HS Buccaneer S2B (9233M) <ff> | Privately owned, Shawbury | |
| XZ439 | BAe Sea Harrier FA2 | Sold to USA, October 2005 | |
| XZ440 | BAe Sea Harrier FA2 [002] | RN No 801 Sqn, Yeovilton | |
| XZ455 | BAe Sea Harrier FA2 [001] (wreck) | Privately owned, Sproughton | |
| XZ457 | BAe Sea Harrier FA2 | Boscombe Down Aviation Collection | |
| XZ459 | BAe Sea Harrier FA2 | Privately owned, Charlwood | |
| XZ492 | BAe Sea Harrier FA2 (wreck) | Privately owned, Faygate | |
| XZ493 | BAe Sea Harrier FRS1 (comp XV760) [001/N] | FAA Museum, RNAS Yeovilton | |
| XZ493 | BAe Sea Harrier FRS1 <ff> | RN Yeovilton, Fire Section | |
| XZ494 | BAe Sea Harrier FA2 | Privately owned, Sproughton | |
| XZ497 | BAe Sea Harrier FA2 [126] | Privately owned, Charlwood | |
| XZ499 | BAe Sea Harrier FA2 [003] | FAA Museum, stored Yeovilton | |
| XZ559 | Slingsby T61F Venture T2 (G-BUEK) | Privately owned, Tibenham | |
| XZ570 | WS61 Sea King HAS5(mod) | RN, stored HMS Sultan, Gosport | |
| XZ571 | WS61 Sea King HAS6 [016/L] | Sold to Australia, November 2005 | |
| XZ574 | WS61 Sea King HAS6 [33/CU] | RN/DARA, stored Fleetlands | |
| XZ575 | WS61 Sea King HU5 | DPA/AFD/QinetiQ, Boscombe Down | |
| XZ576 | WS61 Sea King HAS6 | RN, stored HMS Sultan, Gosport | |

| Notes | Serial | Type (other identity) [code] | Owner/operator, location or fate |
|---|---|---|---|
| | XZ578 | WS61 Sea King HU5 [708/PW] | RN No 771 Sqn, Prestwick |
| | XZ579 | WS61 Sea King HAS6 [707/PW] | RN, stored HMS Sultan, Gosport |
| | XZ580 | WS61 Sea King HC6 [ZB] | RN No 846 Sqn, Yeovilton |
| | XZ581 | WS61 Sea King HAS6 [69/CU] | RN, stored HMS Sultan, Gosport |
| | XZ585 | WS61 Sea King HAR3 [A] | RAF No 203(R) Sqn, St Mawgan |
| | XZ586 | WS61 Sea King HAR3 [B] | RAF 202 Sqn, E Flt, Leconfield |
| | XZ587 | WS61 Sea King HAR3 [C] | RAF No 202 Sqn, D Flt, Lossiemouth |
| | XZ588 | WS61 Sea King HAR3 [D] | RAF HMF, St Mawgan |
| | XZ589 | WS61 Sea King HAR3 [E] | RAF HMF, St Mawgan |
| | XZ590 | WS61 Sea King HAR3 [F] | DPA/Westland Helicopters, Yeovil |
| | XZ591 | WS61 Sea King HAR3 [G] | RAF HMF, St Mawgan |
| | XZ592 | WS61 Sea King HAR3 | RAF No 78 Sqn, Mount Pleasant, FI |
| | XZ593 | WS61 Sea King HAR3 [I] | RAF No 203(R) Sqn, St Mawgan |
| | XZ594 | WS61 Sea King HAR3 [J] | RAF No 78 Sqn, Mount Pleasant, FI |
| | XZ595 | WS61 Sea King HAR3 | RAF No 202 Sqn, A Flt, Boulmer |
| | XZ596 | WS61 Sea King HAR3 [L] | RAF No 203(R) Sqn, St Mawgan |
| | XZ597 | WS61 Sea King HAR3 [M] | RAF No 202 Sqn, A Flt, Boulmer |
| | XZ598 | WS61 Sea King HAR3 | RAF HMF, St Mawgan |
| | XZ599 | WS61 Sea King HAR3 [P] | RAF No 202 Sqn, D Flt, Lossiemouth |
| | XZ605 | WS Lynx AH7 [Y] | AAC No 669 Sqn/4 Regt, Wattisham |
| | XZ606 | WS Lynx AH7 | AAC No 667 Sqn, Middle Wallop |
| | XZ607 | WS Lynx AH7 | AAC No 659 Sqn/4 Regt, Wattisham |
| | XZ608 | WS Lynx AH7 | AAC No 657 Sqn, Odiham |
| | XZ609 | WS Lynx AH7 | AAC No 655 Sqn/5 Regt, Aldergrove |
| | XZ611 | WS Lynx AH7 [X] | AAC No 671 Sqn/2 Regt, Middle Wallop |
| | XZ612 | WS Lynx AH7 [N] | RM No 847 Sqn, Yeovilton |
| | XZ613 | WS Lynx AH7 [F] | AAC/DARA, stored Fleetlands |
| | XZ614 | WS Lynx AH7 [X] | RM No 847 Sqn, Yeovilton |
| | XZ615 | WS Lynx AH7 | RM No 847 Sqn, Yeovilton |
| | XZ616 | WS Lynx AH7 | AAC No 657 Sqn, Odiham |
| | XZ617 | WS Lynx AH7 | AAC No 669 Sqn/4 Regt, Wattisham |
| | XZ630 | Panavia Tornado GR1 (8976M) | RAF Halton, on display |
| | XZ631 | Panavia Tornado GR1 | Yorkshire Air Museum, Elvington |
| | XZ641 | WS Lynx AH7 | AAC No 655 Sqn/5 Regt, Aldergrove |
| | XZ642 | WS Lynx AH7 | AAC No 669 Sqn/4 Regt, Wattisham |
| | XZ643 | WS Lynx AH7 | AAC No 657 Sqn, Odiham |
| | XZ645 | WS Lynx AH7 | AAC No 4 Regt, Wattisham |
| | XZ646 | WS Lynx AH7 | Crashed 21 February 2005, Modrinje, Bosnia |
| | XZ646 | WS Lynx AH7 (really XZ649) | QinetiQ Structures Dept, Farnborough |
| | XZ647 | WS Lynx AH7 [Z] | AAC No 671 Sqn/2 Regt, Middle Wallop |
| | XZ648 | WS Lynx AH7 | AAC No 653 Sqn/3 Regt, Wattisham |
| | XZ651 | WS Lynx AH7 | AAC No 657 Sqn, Odiham |
| | XZ652 | WS Lynx AH7 [T] | AAC No 671 Sqn/2 Regt, Middle Wallop |
| | XZ653 | WS Lynx AH7 | AAC No 659 Sqn/4 Regt, Wattisham |
| | XZ654 | WS Lynx AH7 | AAC/DARA, Fleetlands |
| | XZ655 | WS Lynx AH7 [A] | AAC No 671 Sqn/2 Regt, Middle Wallop |
| | XZ661 | WS Lynx AH1 | AAC No 653 Sqn/3 Regt, Wattisham |
| | XZ663 | WS Lynx AH7 [I] | AAC No 671 Sqn/2 Regt, Middle Wallop |
| | XZ666 | WS Lynx AH7 | Army SEAE, Arborfield |
| | XZ669 | WS Lynx AH7 | AAC No 671 Sqn/2 Regt, Middle Wallop |
| | XZ670 | WS Lynx AH7 | AAC No 672 Sqn/9 Regt, Dishforth |
| | XZ671 | WS Lynx AH7 <ff> | Westland Helicopters, Yeovil, instructional use |
| | XZ672 | WS Lynx AH7 | AAC, Wattisham |
| | XZ673 | WS Lynx AH7 | AAC No 669 Sqn/4 Regt, Wattisham |
| | XZ674 | WS Lynx AH7 | AAC No 669 Sqn/4 Regt, Wattisham |
| | XZ675 | WS Lynx AH7 [E] | AAC No 653 Sqn/3 Regt, Wattisham |
| | XZ676 | WS Lynx AH7 [N] | AAC No 671 Sqn/2 Regt, Middle Wallop |
| | XZ677 | WS Lynx AH7 | AAC No 655 Sqn/5 Regt, Aldergrove |
| | XZ678 | WS Lynx AH7 | AAC No 669 Sqn/4 Regt, Wattisham |
| | XZ679 | WS Lynx AH7 | AAC No 672 Sqn/9 Regt, Dishforth |
| | XZ680 | WS Lynx AH7 [E] | AAC No 671 Sqn/2 Regt, Middle Wallop |
| | XZ689 | WS Lynx HMA8 | RN AMG, Yeovilton |
| | XZ690 | WS Lynx HMA8 [404/IR] | RN AMG, Yeovilton |
| | XZ691 | WS Lynx HMA8 [410/GC] | RN No 815 Sqn, Gloucester Flt, Yeovilton |
| | XZ692 | WS Lynx HMA8 [363] | RN No 815 Sqn Marlborough Flt, Yeovilton |
| | XZ693 | WS Lynx HAS3S [639] | RN No 702 Sqn, Yeovilton |
| | XZ694 | WS Lynx HAS3S [334] | RN No 815 Sqn, Southampton Flt, Yeovilton |
| | XZ695 | WS Lynx HMA8 [417] | Crashed 3 March 2005, Indian Ocean |
| | XZ696 | WS Lynx HAS3S [335/CF] | RN/DARA, Fleetlands |
| | XZ697 | WS Lynx HMA8 | RN No 815 Sqn, Portland Flt, Yeovilton |

| Serial | Type (other identity) [code] | Owner/operator, location or fate | Notes |
|---|---|---|---|
| XZ698 | WS Lynx HMA8 [348] | RN No 815 Sqn, *Chatham* Flt, Yeovilton | |
| XZ699 | WS Lynx HAS3 [303] | *Reduced to spares, Yeovilton* | |
| XZ719 | WS Lynx HMA8 [360/MC] | RN No 815 Sqn, *Manchester* Flt, Yeovilton | |
| XZ720 | WS Lynx HAS3S [407] | RN No 815 Sqn, *York* Flt, Yeovilton | |
| XZ721 | WS Lynx HMA8 [302] | RN No 815 Sqn, HQ Flt, Yeovilton | |
| XZ722 | WS Lynx HMA8 | RN No 702 Sqn, Yeovilton | |
| XZ723 | WS Lynx HMA8 [671] | RN No 702 Sqn, Yeovilton | |
| XZ725 | WS Lynx HMA8 [412] | RN No 815 Sqn, *Cornwall* Flt, Yeovilton | |
| XZ726 | WS Lynx HMA8 [319] | RN No 815 Sqn OEU, Yeovilton | |
| XZ727 | WS Lynx HAS3S [308] | RN No 815 Sqn, HQ Flt, Yeovilton | |
| XZ728 | WS Lynx HMA8 [MM] | RNAS Yeovilton, for display | |
| XZ729 | WS Lynx HMA8 [417] | RN No 815 Sqn, *Nottingham* Flt, Yeovilton | |
| XZ730 | WS Lynx HAS3S [632] | RN No 702 Sqn, Yeovilton | |
| XZ731 | WS Lynx HMA8 [307] | RN/DARA, stored Fleetlands | |
| XZ732 | WS Lynx HMA8 [348/CM] | RN No 702 Sqn, Yeovilton | |
| XZ733 | WS Lynx HAS3S | RN AMG, Yeovilton | |
| XZ735 | WS Lynx HAS3S [350/CL] | RN No 815 Sqn, *Cumberland* Flt, Yeovilton | |
| XZ736 | WS Lynx HMA8 [365] | RN AMG, Yeovilton | |
| XZ920 | WS61 Sea King HU5 [707/PW] | RN No 771 Sqn, Prestwick | |
| XZ921 | WS61 Sea King HAS6 [269/N] | RN, stored *HMS Sultan*, Gosport | |
| XZ922 | WS61 Sea King HC6 [ZA] | RN No 846 Sqn, Yeovilton | |
| XZ930 | WS Gazelle HT3 [Q] | RN AESS, *HMS Sultan*, Gosport | |
| XZ933 | WS Gazelle HT3 [T] | DPA/QinetiQ, Boscombe Down, spares use | |
| XZ934 | WS Gazelle HT3 (G-CBSI) [U] | Privately owned, Redhill | |
| XZ935 | WS Gazelle HCC4 | RAF No 1 SoTT, Cosford | |
| XZ936 | WS Gazelle HT2 [6] | DPA/ETPS, Boscombe Down | |
| XZ937 | WS Gazelle HT2 (G-CBKA) [Y] | Privately owned, Stapleford Tawney | |
| XZ938 | WS Gazelle HT2 [45/CU] | *Currently not known* | |
| XZ939 | WS Gazelle HT2 [9] | DPA/ETPS, Boscombe Down | |
| XZ940 | WS Gazelle HT2 (G-CBBV) [O] | Privately owned, Redhill | |
| XZ941 | WS Gazelle HT2 [B] | ATTF, RAF St Athan | |
| XZ942 | WS Gazelle HT2 [42/CU] | AAC, Middle Wallop, instructional use | |
| XZ964 | BAe Harrier GR3 [D] | Royal Engineers Museum, Chatham | |
| XZ966 | BAe Harrier GR3 (9221M) [G] | MoD FSCTE, Manston | |
| XZ968 | BAe Harrier GR3 (9222M) [3G] | Muckleborough Collection, Weybourne | |
| XZ969 | BAe Harrier GR3 [69] | RN, Predannack Fire School | |
| XZ971 | BAe Harrier GR3 (9219M) [G] | HQ DS&DC, Donnington, Shropshire, on display | |
| XZ987 | BAe Harrier GR3 (9185M) [C] | RAF Stafford, at main gate | |
| XZ990 | BAe Harrier GR3 <ff> | No 1220 Sqn ATC, March, Cambs | |
| XZ990 | BAe Harrier GR3 <rf> | RAF Wittering, derelict | |
| XZ991 | BAe Harrier GR3 (9162M) [3A] | ATTF, RAF St Athan | |
| XZ993 | BAe Harrier GR3 (9240M) (fuselage) | DARA, RAF St Athan, fire training | |
| XZ994 | BAe Harrier GR3 (9170M) [U] | RAF Defence Movements School, Brize Norton | |
| XZ995 | BAe Harrier GR3 (G-CBGK/9220M) [3G] | *Sold to the USA, March 2005* | |
| XZ996 | BAe Harrier GR3 [96] | SFDO, RNAS Culdrose | |
| XZ997 | BAe Harrier GR3 (9122M) [V] | RAF Museum, Hendon | |
| ZA101 | BAe Hawk 100 (G-HAWK) | DPA/BAE Systems, Warton | |
| ZA105 | WS61 Sea King HAR3 [Q] | RAF HMF, St Mawgan | |
| ZA110 | BAe Jetstream T2 (F-BTMI) [563/CU] | RN No 750 Sqn, Culdrose | |
| ZA111 | BAe Jetstream T2 (9Q-CTC) [565/CU] | RN No 750 Sqn, Culdrose | |
| ZA126 | WS61 Sea King HC6 [504/CU] | RN AMG, Yeovilton (conversion) | |
| ZA127 | WS61 Sea King HAS6 [509/CU] | RN, stored *HMS Sultan*, Gosport | |
| ZA128 | WS61 Sea King HAS6 [010] | RN, stored *HMS Sultan*, Gosport | |
| ZA129 | WS61 Sea King HAS6 [502/CU] | Westland Helicopters, Yeovil (spares recovery) | |
| ZA130 | WS61 Sea King HU5 [709/PW] | RN No 771 Sqn, Culdrose | |
| ZA131 | WS61 Sea King HAS6 [271/N] | RN, stored *HMS Sultan*, Gosport | |
| ZA133 | WS61 Sea King HAS6 [831/CU] | RN No 771 Sqn, Culdrose | |
| ZA134 | WS61 Sea King HU5 [825] | RN No 771 Sqn, Culdrose | |
| ZA135 | WS61 Sea King HAS6 [832] | RN No 771 Sqn, Culdrose | |
| ZA136 | WS61 Sea King HAS6 [018/L] | RN, AESS, *HMS Sultan*, Gosport (wreck) | |
| ZA137 | WS61 Sea King HU5 [820/CU] | RN/DARA, Fleetlands | |
| ZA147 | BAe VC10 K3 (5H-MMT) [F] | RAF No 101 Sqn, Brize Norton | |
| ZA148 | BAe VC10 K3 (5Y-ADA) [G] | RAF No 101 Sqn, Brize Norton | |
| ZA149 | BAe VC10 K3 (5X-UVJ) [H] | RAF No 101 Sqn, Brize Norton | |
| ZA150 | BAe VC10 K3 (5H-MOG) | RAF No 101 Sqn, Brize Norton | |

| Notes | Serial | Type (other identity) [code] | Owner/operator, location or fate |
|---|---|---|---|
| | ZA166 | WS61 Sea King HU5 [828/CU] | RN, stored AMG, Culdrose |
| | ZA167 | WS61 Sea King HU5 [822/CU] | RN No 771 Sqn, Culdrose |
| | ZA168 | WS61 Sea King HAS6 [830/CU] | RN No 771 Sqn, Culdrose |
| | ZA169 | WS61 Sea King HAS6 [515/CW] | RN, stored *HMS Sultan*, Gosport |
| | ZA170 | WS61 Sea King HAS5 | RN, stored *HMS Sultan*, Gosport |
| | ZA175 | BAe Sea Harrier FA2 | Norfolk & Suffolk Avn Museum, Flixton |
| | ZA176 | BAe Sea Harrier FA2 | Newark Air Museum, Winthorpe |
| | ZA195 | BAe Sea Harrier FA2 | Privately owned, Farnborough |
| | ZA250 | BAe Harrier T52 (G-VTOL) | Brooklands Museum, Weybridge |
| | ZA254 | Panavia Tornado F2 (9253M) (fuselage) | RAF Marham, instructional use |
| | ZA267 | Panavia Tornado F2 (9284M) | RAF Marham, instructional use |
| | ZA291 | WS61 Sea King HC4 | RN No 846 Sqn, Yeovilton |
| | ZA292 | WS61 Sea King HC4 [ZR] | DPA/Westland Helicopters, Yeovil |
| | ZA293 | WS61 Sea King HC4 [WO] | RN No 848 Sqn, Yeovilton |
| | ZA295 | WS61 Sea King HC4 [VU] | RN No 846 Sqn, Yeovilton |
| | ZA296 | WS61 Sea King HC4 [B] | RN No 845 Sqn, Yeovilton |
| | ZA297 | WS61 Sea King HC4 [C] | RN No 845 Sqn, Yeovilton |
| | ZA298 | WS61 Sea King HC4 [P] | RN No 845 Sqn, Yeovilton |
| | ZA299 | WS61 Sea King HC4 [D] | RN No 845 Sqn, Yeovilton |
| | ZA310 | WS61 Sea King HC4 [WY] | RN No 848 Sqn, Yeovilton |
| | ZA312 | WS61 Sea King HC4 [WS] | RN No 848 Sqn, Yeovilton |
| | ZA313 | WS61 Sea King HC4 [M] | RN No 845 Sqn, Yeovilton |
| | ZA314 | WS61 Sea King HC4 [WR] | RN No 848 Sqn, Yeovilton |
| | ZA319 | Panavia Tornado GR1 | Army, Bicester, on display |
| | ZA320 | Panavia Tornado GR1 (9314M) [TAW] | RAF No 1 SoTT, Cosford |
| | ZA322 | Panavia Tornado GR1 (9334M) [TAC] | RAF Marham, Fire Section |
| | ZA323 | Panavia Tornado GR1 [TAZ] | RAF No 1 SoTT, Cosford |
| | ZA324 | Panavia Tornado GR1 [TAY] | RAF Lossiemouth, BDRT |
| | ZA325 | Panavia Tornado GR1 [TAX] | ATTF, RAF St Athan |
| | ZA326 | Panavia Tornado GR1P | DPA/AFD/QinetiQ, Boscombe Down |
| | ZA327 | Panavia Tornado GR1 | BAE Systems, Warton (spares use) |
| | ZA328 | Panavia Tornado GR1 | BAE Systems, Warton (spares use) |
| | ZA353 | Panavia Tornado GR1 [B-53] | DPA, Boscombe Down (wfu) |
| | ZA354 | Panavia Tornado GR1 | Yorkshire Air Museum, Elvington |
| | ZA355 | Panavia Tornado GR1 [TAA] | RAF Lossiemouth, WLT |
| | ZA356 | Panavia Tornado GR1 <ff> | RAF Marham, instructional use |
| | ZA357 | Panavia Tornado GR1 [TTV] | RAF No 1 SoTT, Cosford |
| | ZA359 | Panavia Tornado GR1 | BAE Systems Warton, Overseas Customer Training Centre |
| | ZA360 | Panavia Tornado GR1 <ff> | RAF Marham, instructional use |
| | ZA361 | Panavia Tornado GR1 [TD] | RAF Marham, Fire Section |
| | ZA362 | Panavia Tornado GR1 [AJ-F] | Highland Aviation Museum, Inverness |
| | ZA365 | Panavia Tornado GR4 [AJ-Y] | RAF No 617 Sqn, Lossiemouth |
| | ZA367 | Panavia Tornado GR4 [FW] | RAF No 12 Sqn, Lossiemouth |
| | ZA369 | Panavia Tornado GR4A [FP] | RAF No 12 Sqn, Lossiemouth |
| | ZA370 | Panavia Tornado GR4A [DB] | RAF No 31 Sqn, Marham |
| | ZA371 | Panavia Tornado GR4A [C] | RAF No 14 Sqn, Lossiemouth |
| | ZA372 | Panavia Tornado GR4A [E] | RAF No 2 Sqn, Marham |
| | ZA373 | Panavia Tornado GR4A [H] | RAF No 2 Sqn, Marham |
| | ZA375 | Panavia Tornado GR1 (9335M) [AJ-W] | RAF Marham, Fire Section |
| | ZA393 | Panavia Tornado GR4 | RAF No 14 Sqn, Lossiemouth |
| | ZA395 | Panavia Tornado GR4A [FE] | RAF No 12 Sqn, Lossiemouth |
| | ZA398 | Panavia Tornado GR4A [S] | RAF No 617 Sqn, Lossiemouth |
| | ZA399 | Panavia Tornado GR1 [AJ-C] | ATTF, RAF St Athan |
| | ZA400 | Panavia Tornado GR4A [T] | RAF No 2 Sqn, Marham |
| | ZA401 | Panavia Tornado GR4A [XIII] | RAF No 13 Sqn, Marham |
| | ZA402 | Panavia Tornado GR4A | DPA/BAE Systems, Warton |
| | ZA404 | Panavia Tornado GR4A [BT] | RAF No 14 Sqn, Lossiemouth |
| | ZA405 | Panavia Tornado GR4A [Y] | RAF No 2 Sqn, Marham |
| | ZA406 | Panavia Tornado GR4 [FU] | RAF No 12 Sqn, Lossiemouth |
| | ZA407 | Panavia Tornado GR1 (9336M) [AJ-N] | RAF Marham, on display |
| | ZA409 | Panavia Tornado GR1 [VII] | RAF Lossiemouth (wfu) |
| | ZA410 | Panavia Tornado GR4 [TS] | RAF No 15(R) Sqn, Lossiemouth |
| | ZA411 | Panavia Tornado GR1 [TT] | RAF/DARA, stored St Athan |
| | ZA412 | Panavia Tornado GR4 [TT] | RAF No 15(R) Sqn, Lossiemouth |
| | ZA446 | Panavia Tornado GR4 [AF] | RAF No 9 Sqn, Marham |
| | ZA447 | Panavia Tornado GR4 [DE] | RAF No 31 Sqn, Marham |
| | ZA449 | Panavia Tornado GR4 [AJ-N] | RAF No 617 Sqn, Lossiemouth |

| Serial | Type (other identity) [code] | Owner/operator, location or fate | Notes |
|--------|------------------------------|----------------------------------|-------|
| ZA450 | Panavia Tornado GR1 (9317M) [TH] | RAF No 1 SoTT, Cosford | |
| ZA452 | Panavia Tornado GR4 | RAF No 31 Sqn, Marham | |
| ZA453 | Panavia Tornado GR4 [FH] | RAF No 12 Sqn, Lossiemouth | |
| ZA456 | Panavia Tornado GR4 [FI] | RAF No 12 Sqn, Lossiemouth | |
| ZA457 | Panavia Tornado GR1 [AJ-J] | RAF Museum, Hendon | |
| ZA458 | Panavia Tornado GR4 [DG] | RAF No 617 Sqn, Lossiemouth | |
| ZA459 | Panavia Tornado GR4 [F] | RAF No 15(R) Sqn, Lossiemouth | |
| ZA461 | Panavia Tornado GR4 [AC] | RAF No 9 Sqn, Marham | |
| ZA462 | Panavia Tornado GR4 [TL] | RAF No 15(R) Sqn, Lossiemouth | |
| ZA463 | Panavia Tornado GR4 [TL] | RAF Lossiemouth, WLT | |
| ZA465 | Panavia Tornado GR1 [FF] | Imperial War Museum, Duxford | |
| ZA469 | Panavia Tornado GR4 [TM] | RAF No 15(R) Sqn, Lossiemouth | |
| ZA470 | Panavia Tornado GR4 [BQ] | RAF/DARA, St Athan | |
| ZA472 | Panavia Tornado GR4 [AE] | RAF/DARA, St Athan | |
| ZA473 | Panavia Tornado GR4 | RAF No 617 Sqn, Lossiemouth | |
| ZA474 | Panavia Tornado GR1 | RAF Lossiemouth (wfu) | |
| ZA475 | Panavia Tornado GR1 | RAF Lossiemouth, on display | |
| ZA492 | Panavia Tornado GR4 [BO] | RAF No 14 Sqn, Lossiemouth | |
| ZA541 | Panavia Tornado GR4 [III] | RAF No 2 Sqn, Marham | |
| ZA542 | Panavia Tornado GR4 [DM] | RAF No 31 Sqn, Marham | |
| ZA543 | Panavia Tornado GR4 [FF] | RAF No 12 Sqn, Lossiemouth | |
| ZA544 | Panavia Tornado GR4 [FZ] | RAF/DARA, St Athan | |
| ZA546 | Panavia Tornado GR4 [AG] | RAF No 14 Sqn, Lossiemouth | |
| ZA547 | Panavia Tornado GR4 [FO] | RAF No 12 Sqn, Lossiemouth | |
| ZA548 | Panavia Tornado GR4 [AZ] | RAF No 9 Sqn, Marham | |
| ZA549 | Panavia Tornado GR4 [AJ-Z] | RAF No 617 Sqn, Lossiemouth | |
| ZA550 | Panavia Tornado GR4 [DD] | RAF No 31 Sqn, Marham | |
| ZA551 | Panavia Tornado GR4 [AX] | RAF No 15(R) Sqn, Lossiemouth | |
| ZA552 | Panavia Tornado GR4 [TX] | RAF No 9 Sqn, Marham | |
| ZA553 | Panavia Tornado GR4 [DI] | RAF No 31 Sqn, Marham | |
| ZA554 | Panavia Tornado GR4 [BF] | RAF No 9 Sqn, Marham | |
| ZA556 | Panavia Tornado GR4 [AJ-C] | RAF No 617 Sqn, Lossiemouth | |
| *ZA556* | Panavia Tornado GR1 <R> (*ZA368*/BAPC 155) [Z] | RAF M&RU, Bottesford | |
| ZA557 | Panavia Tornado GR4 [TJ] | RAF No 15(R) Sqn, Lossiemouth | |
| ZA559 | Panavia Tornado GR4 [AD] | RAF/DARA, St Athan | |
| ZA560 | Panavia Tornado GR4 [BC] | RAF No 14 Sqn, Lossiemouth | |
| ZA562 | Panavia Tornado GR4 [TO] | RAF No 31 Sqn, Marham | |
| ZA563 | Panavia Tornado GR4 [AG] | RAF/DARA, St Athan | |
| ZA564 | Panavia Tornado GR4 [DK] | RAF No 31 Sqn, Marham | |
| ZA585 | Panavia Tornado GR4 [AH] | RAF No 14 Sqn, Lossiemouth | |
| ZA587 | Panavia Tornado GR4 [AJ-M] | RAF No 617 Sqn, Lossiemouth | |
| ZA588 | Panavia Tornado GR4 [BB] | RAF No 14 Sqn, Lossiemouth | |
| ZA589 | Panavia Tornado GR4 [DN] | RAF No 31 Sqn, Marham | |
| ZA591 | Panavia Tornado GR4 [DJ] | RAF No 31 Sqn, Marham | |
| ZA592 | Panavia Tornado GR4 [Z] | RAF No 13 Sqn, Marham | |
| ZA594 | Panavia Tornado GR4 [DX] | RAF No 31 Sqn, Marham | |
| ZA595 | Panavia Tornado GR4 [FZ] | RAF No 12 Sqn, Lossiemouth | |
| ZA596 | Panavia Tornado GR4 [BL] | RAF/DARA, St Athan | |
| ZA597 | Panavia Tornado GR4 [AJ-O] | RAF No 617 Sqn, Lossiemouth | |
| ZA598 | Panavia Tornado GR4 [TW] | RAF No 15(R) Sqn, Lossiemouth | |
| ZA600 | Panavia Tornado GR4 [AJ-L] | RAF No 13 Sqn, Marham | |
| ZA601 | Panavia Tornado GR4 [O] | RAF No 2 Sqn, Marham | |
| ZA602 | Panavia Tornado GR4 [XIII] | RAF/DARA, St Athan | |
| ZA604 | Panavia Tornado GR4 [TY] | RAF No 15(R) Sqn, Lossiemouth | |
| ZA606 | Panavia Tornado GR4 [BD] | RAF No 14 Sqn, Lossiemouth | |
| ZA607 | Panavia Tornado GR4 [AB] | RAF No 9 Sqn, Marham | |
| ZA608 | Panavia Tornado GR4 | RAF/DARA, St Athan | |
| ZA609 | Panavia Tornado GR4 | RAF AWC/FJWOEU, Coningsby | |
| ZA611 | Panavia Tornado GR4 | RAF AWC/FJWOEU, Coningsby | |
| ZA612 | Panavia Tornado GR4 [IV] | RAF No 2 Sqn, Marham | |
| ZA613 | Panavia Tornado GR4 [AN] | RAF No 9 Sqn, Marham | |
| ZA614 | Panavia Tornado GR4 [DO] | RAF No 31 Sqn, Marham | |
| ZA634 | Slingsby T61F Venture T2 (G-BUHA) [C] | Privately owned, Saltby | |
| ZA652 | Slingsby T61F Venture T2 (G-BUDC) | Privately owned, Enstone | |
| ZA670 | B-V Chinook HC2 (N37010) | RAF No 27 Sqn, Odiham | |
| ZA671 | B-V Chinook HC2 (N37011) | RAF No 7 Sqn, Odiham | |
| ZA673 | B-V Chinook HC2 (N37016) [A] | RAF No 27 Sqn, Odiham | |
| ZA674 | B-V Chinook HC2 (N37019) | RAF No 27 Sqn, Odiham | |
| ZA675 | B-V Chinook HC2 (N37020) | RAF No 7 Sqn, Odiham | |
| ZA676 | B-V Chinook HC1 (N37021/9230M) [FG] (wreck) | AAC, Wattisham | |

| Notes | Serial | Type (other identity) [code] | Owner/operator, location or fate |
|---|---|---|---|
| | ZA677 | B-V Chinook HC2 (N37022) | RAF No 27 Sqn, Odiham |
| | ZA678 | B-V Chinook HC1 (N37023/9229M) [EZ] (wreck) | RAF Odiham, BDRT |
| | ZA679 | B-V Chinook HC2 (N37025) | RAF No 7 Sqn, Odiham |
| | ZA680 | B-V Chinook HC2 (N37026) | RAF No 18 Sqn, Odiham |
| | ZA681 | B-V Chinook HC2 (N37027) | RAF No 7 Sqn, Odiham |
| | ZA682 | B-V Chinook HC2 (N37029) | RAF No 18 Sqn, Odiham |
| | ZA683 | B-V Chinook HC2 (N37030) | RAF No 18 Sqn, Odiham |
| | ZA684 | B-V Chinook HC2 (N37031) | RAF/DARA, Fleetlands |
| | ZA704 | B-V Chinook HC2 (N37033) | RAF No 7 Sqn, Odiham |
| | ZA705 | B-V Chinook HC2 (N37035) | RAF No 18 Sqn, Odiham |
| | ZA707 | B-V Chinook HC2 (N37040) | RAF No 18 Sqn, Odiham |
| | ZA708 | B-V Chinook HC2 (N37042) | RAF No 78 Sqn, Mount Pleasant, Fl |
| | ZA709 | B-V Chinook HC2 (N37043) | RAF No 7 Sqn, Odiham |
| | ZA710 | B-V Chinook HC2 (N37044) | RAF/DARA, Fleetlands |
| | ZA711 | B-V Chinook HC2 (N37046) | RAF No 7 Sqn, Odiham |
| | ZA712 | B-V Chinook HC2 (N37047) [E] | RAF No 27 Sqn, Odiham |
| | ZA713 | B-V Chinook HC2 (N37048) | RAF/DARA, Fleetlands |
| | ZA714 | B-V Chinook HC2 (N37051) | RAF/DARA, Fleetlands |
| | ZA717 | B-V Chinook HC1 (N37056/9238M) (wreck) | Trenchard Hall, RAF Cranwell, instructional use |
| | ZA718 | B-V Chinook HC2 (N37058) [BN] | RAF/DARA, Fleetlands |
| | ZA720 | B-V Chinook HC2 (N37060) | RAF No 27 Sqn, Odiham |
| | ZA726 | WS Gazelle AH1 [F] | AAC No 671 Sqn/2 Regt, Middle Wallop |
| | ZA728 | WS Gazelle AH1 [E] | RM, stored Shawbury |
| | ZA729 | WS Gazelle AH1 | AAC Wattisham, BDRT |
| | ZA731 | WS Gazelle AH1 | AAC No 29 Flt, BATUS, Suffield, Canada |
| | ZA733 | WS Gazelle AH1 | DARA Fleetlands Apprentice School |
| | ZA734 | WS Gazelle AH1 | Privately owned, Hixon, Staffs |
| | ZA735 | WS Gazelle AH1 | Army SEAE, Arborfield |
| | ZA736 | WS Gazelle AH1 | AAC No 29 Flt, BATUS, Suffield, Canada |
| | ZA737 | WS Gazelle AH1 | Museum of Army Flying, Middle Wallop |
| | ZA766 | WS Gazelle AH1 | DPA/Westland Helicopters, Yeovil |
| | ZA768 | WS Gazelle AH1 [F] (wreck) | AAC/DARA, stored Fleetlands |
| | ZA769 | WS Gazelle AH1 [K] | Army SEAE, Arborfield |
| | ZA771 | WS Gazelle AH1 | AAC No 654 Sqn/4 Regt, Wattisham |
| | ZA772 | WS Gazelle AH1 | AAC, Middle Wallop |
| | ZA773 | WS Gazelle AH1 [F] | AAC, stored Shawbury |
| | ZA774 | WS Gazelle AH1 | AAC, stored Shawbury |
| | ZA775 | WS Gazelle AH1 | AAC, stored Shawbury |
| | ZA776 | WS Gazelle AH1 [F] | RM, stored Shawbury |
| | ZA804 | WS Gazelle HT3 [I] | DPA/QinetiQ Boscombe Down, spares use |
| | ZA934 | WS Puma HC1 [BZ] | RAF No 33 Sqn, Benson |
| | ZA935 | WS Puma HC1 | RAF No 33 Sqn, Benson |
| | ZA936 | WS Puma HC1 | RAF No 33 Sqn, Benson |
| | ZA937 | WS Puma HC1 | RAF No 33 Sqn, Benson |
| | ZA938 | WS Puma HC1 | RAF No 1563 Flt, Basrah, Iraq |
| | ZA939 | WS Puma HC1 | RAF No 230 Sqn, Aldergrove |
| | ZA940 | WS Puma HC1 | RAF No 230 Sqn, Aldergrove |
| | ZA947 | Douglas Dakota C3 [AI] | RAF BBMF, Coningsby |
| | ZB500 | WS Lynx 800 (G-LYNX/ZA500) | The Helicopter Museum, Weston-super-Mare |
| | ZB506 | WS61 Sea King Mk 4X | DPA/AFD/QinetiQ, Boscombe Down |
| | ZB507 | WS61 Sea King HC4 [WN] | RN No 848 Sqn, Yeovilton |
| | ZB601 | BAe Harrier T4 (fuselage) | RNAS Yeovilton, Fire Section |
| | ZB603 | BAe Harrier T8 [724] | RN SHOPS, Yeovilton |
| | ZB604 | BAe Harrier T8 [722] | RN, stored Shawbury |
| | ZB615 | SEPECAT Jaguar T2A | QinetiQ, stored Boscombe Down |
| | ZB625 | WS Gazelle HT3 [N] | DPA/AFD/QinetiQ, Boscombe Down |
| | ZB646 | WS Gazelle HT2 (G-CBGZ) [59/CU] | Privately owned, Knebworth |
| | ZB665 | WS Gazelle AH1 | AAC No 665 Sqn/5 Regt, Aldergrove |
| | ZB666 | WS Gazelle AH1 <ff> | Privately owned, Sproughton |
| | ZB667 | WS Gazelle AH1 | AAC No 665 Sqn/5 Regt, Aldergrove |
| | ZB668 | WS Gazelle AH1 (TAD 015) | Army SEAE, Arborfield |
| | ZB669 | WS Gazelle AH1 | AAC No 665 Sqn/5 Regt, Aldergrove |
| | ZB670 | WS Gazelle AH1 | AAC/DARA, stored Fleetlands |
| | ZB671 | WS Gazelle AH1 [2] | AAC No 29 Flt, BATUS, Suffield, Canada |
| | ZB672 | WS Gazelle AH1 | Army Training Regiment, Winchester |
| | ZB673 | WS Gazelle AH1 | AAC No 671 Sqn/2 Regt, Middle Wallop |
| | ZB674 | WS Gazelle AH1 | AAC, stored Shawbury |
| | ZB677 | WS Gazelle AH1 | AAC No 29 Flt, BATUS, Suffield, Canada |
| | ZB678 | WS Gazelle AH1 | DPA/Westland Helicopters, Yeovil |

| Serial | Type (other identity) [code] | Owner/operator, location or fate | Notes |
|--------|------------------------------|----------------------------------|-------|
| ZB679 | WS Gazelle AH1 | DPA/Westland Helicopters, Yeovil | |
| ZB682 | WS Gazelle AH1 | AAC/DARA, stored Fleetlands | |
| ZB683 | WS Gazelle AH1 | AAC No 665 Sqn/5 Regt, Aldergrove | |
| ZB684 | WS Gazelle AH1 | RAF Defence Movements School, Brize Norton | |
| ZB685 | WS Gazelle AH1 | Privately owned, Sproughton | |
| ZB686 | WS Gazelle AH1 <ff> | AAC Middle Wallop, instructional use | |
| ZB688 | WS Gazelle AH1 [H] | AAC No 671 Sqn/2 Regt, Middle Wallop | |
| ZB689 | WS Gazelle AH1 | AAC No 665 Sqn/5 Regt, Aldergrove | |
| ZB690 | WS Gazelle AH1 | AAC, stored Shawbury | |
| ZB691 | WS Gazelle AH1 | AAC, stored Shawbury | |
| ZB692 | WS Gazelle AH1 | AAC, stored Shawbury | |
| ZB693 | WS Gazelle AH1 | AAC No 665 Sqn/5 Regt, Aldergrove | |
| ZD230 | BAC Super VC10 K4 (G-ASGA) [K] | RAF St Athan (wfu) | |
| ZD234 | BAC Super VC10 K4 (G-ASGF/8700M) | RAF Brize Norton, tanker simulator | |
| ZD240 | BAC Super VC10 K4 (G-ASGL) [M] | RAF St Athan (wfu) | |
| ZD241 | BAC Super VC10 K4 (G-ASGM) [N] | RAF No 101 Sqn, Brize Norton | |
| ZD242 | BAC Super VC10 K4 (G-ASGP) [P] | RAF/DARA, St Athan | |
| ZD249 | WS Lynx HAS3S [637] | RN/DARA, Fleetlands | |
| ZD250 | WS Lynx HAS3S [630] | RN No 702 Sqn, Yeovilton | |
| ZD251 | WS Lynx HAS3S [637] | RN No 702 Sqn, Yeovilton | |
| ZD252 | WS Lynx HMA8 [671] | RN/DARA, stored Fleetlands | |
| ZD254 | WS Lynx HAS3S [638] | RN No 702 Sqn, Yeovilton | |
| ZD255 | WS Lynx HAS3S [422] | RN No 815 Sqn, *Sutherland* Flt, Yeovilton | |
| ZD257 | WS Lynx HMA8 [672] | RN No 815 Sqn OEU, Yeovilton | |
| ZD258 | WS Lynx HMA8 (*XZ258*) [404/IR] | RN No 815 Sqn, *Iron Duke* Flt, Yeovilton | |
| ZD259 | WS Lynx HMA8 [444/MR] | RN/DARA, Fleetlands | |
| ZD260 | WS Lynx HMA8 | RN AMG, Yeovilton | |
| ZD261 | WS Lynx HMA8 [437/GT] | RN No 815 Sqn, *Grafton* Flt, Yeovilton | |
| ZD262 | WS Lynx HMA8 | RN AMG, Yeovilton | |
| ZD263 | WS Lynx HAS3S [305] | RN/DARA, Fleetlands | |
| ZD264 | WS Lynx HAS3S [634] | RN No 702 Sqn, Yeovilton | |
| ZD265 | WS Lynx HMA8 [306] | RN No 815 Sqn, HQ Flt, Yeovilton | |
| ZD266 | WS Lynx HMA8 | RN/DARA, stored Fleetlands | |
| ZD267 | WS Lynx HMA8 | RN/DARA, stored Fleetlands | |
| ZD268 | WS Lynx HMA8 [317] | RN No 815 Sqn OEU, Yeovilton | |
| ZD272 | WS Lynx AH7 [H] | AAC No 671 Sqn/2 Regt, Middle Wallop | |
| ZD273 | WS Lynx AH7 | AAC No 653 Sqn/3 Regt, Wattisham | |
| ZD274 | WS Lynx AH7 | AAC/DARA, Fleetlands | |
| ZD276 | WS Lynx AH7 | AAC No 655 Sqn/5 Regt, Aldergrove | |
| ZD277 | WS Lynx AH7 | AAC No 653 Sqn/3 Regt, Wattisham | |
| ZD278 | WS Lynx AH7 [A] | AAC No 655 Sqn/5 Regt, Aldergrove | |
| ZD279 | WS Lynx AH7 | AAC No 672 Sqn/9 Regt, Dishforth | |
| ZD280 | WS Lynx AH7 | AAC No 655 Sqn/5 Regt, Aldergrove | |
| ZD281 | WS Lynx AH7 [K] | AAC No 671 Sqn/2 Regt, Middle Wallop | |
| ZD282 | WS Lynx AH7 [L] | RM No 847 Sqn, Yeovilton | |
| ZD283 | WS Lynx AH7 | AAC No 653 Sqn/3 Regt, Wattisham | |
| ZD284 | WS Lynx AH7 | AAC No 655 Sqn/5 Regt, Aldergrove | |
| ZD285 | WS Lynx AH7 | DPA/AFD/QinetiQ, Boscombe Down | |
| ZD318 | BAe Harrier GR7A | DPA/BAE Systems, Warton | |
| ZD319 | BAe Harrier GR7 | DPA/BAE Systems, Warton | |
| ZD320 | BAe Harrier GR9 | DPA/BAE Systems, Warton | |
| ZD321 | BAe Harrier GR7 [02] | RAF No 3 Sqn, Cottesmore | |
| ZD322 | BAe Harrier GR7 [03] | RAF HOCU/No 20(R) Sqn, Wittering | |
| ZD323 | BAe Harrier GR7 [04] | RAF HOCU/No 20(R) Sqn, Wittering | |
| ZD327 | BAe Harrier GR7A [08A] | RAF No 1 Sqn, Cottesmore | |
| ZD328 | BAe Harrier GR7 [09] | RAF No 1 Sqn, Cottesmore | |
| ZD329 | BAe Harrier GR7 [10] | RAF HOCU/No 20(R) Sqn, Wittering | |
| ZD330 | BAe Harrier GR7 [11] | RAF HOCU/No 20(R) Sqn, Wittering | |
| ZD346 | BAe Harrier GR7A [13A] | RAF No 1 Sqn, Cottesmore | |
| ZD347 | BAe Harrier GR7A [14A] | RAF No 1 Sqn, Cottesmore | |
| ZD348 | BAe Harrier GR7A [15A] | RAF No 1 Sqn, Cottesmore | |
| ZD350 | BAe Harrier GR5 (9189M) <ff> | Privately owned, Sproughton | |
| ZD351 | BAe Harrier GR7 [18] | RAF HOCU/No 20(R) Sqn, Wittering | |
| ZD352 | BAe Harrier GR7 [19] | DPA/AFD/QinetiQ, Boscombe Down | |
| ZD353 | BAe Harrier GR5 (fuselage) | BAE Systems, Brough | |
| ZD354 | BAe Harrier GR7 [21] | RAF HOCU/No 20(R) Sqn, Wittering | |
| ZD375 | BAe Harrier GR7 [23] | RAF HOCU/No 20(R) Sqn, Wittering | |
| ZD376 | BAe Harrier GR7A [24A] | RAF No 4 Sqn, Cottesmore | |
| ZD378 | BAe Harrier GR7A [26A] | RAF, Cottesmore | |
| ZD379 | BAe Harrier GR7 [27] | RAF No 1 Sqn, Cottesmore | |
| ZD380 | BAe Harrier GR7 [28] | RAF HOCU/No 20(R) Sqn, Wittering | |

| Notes | Serial | Type (other identity) [code] | Owner/operator, location or fate |
|---|---|---|---|
| | ZD401 | BAe Harrier GR7 [30] | RAF No 3 Sqn, Cottesmore |
| | ZD402 | BAe Harrier GR7 [31] | RAF No 3 Sqn, Cottesmore |
| | ZD403 | BAe Harrier GR7A [32A] | RAF No 4 Sqn, Cottesmore |
| | ZD404 | BAe Harrier GR7A [33A] | RAF No 1 Sqn, Cottesmore |
| | ZD405 | BAe Harrier GR7A [34A] | RAF No 1 Sqn, Cottesmore |
| | ZD406 | BAe Harrier GR7 [35] | RAF HOCU/No 20(R) Sqn, Wittering |
| | ZD407 | BAe Harrier GR7 [36] | RAF HOCU/No 20(R) Sqn, Wittering |
| | ZD408 | BAe Harrier GR7A [37A] | RAF No 4 Sqn, Cottesmore |
| | ZD409 | BAe Harrier GR7 [38] | RAF No 1 Sqn, Cottesmore |
| | ZD410 | BAe Harrier GR7 [39] | RAF No 3 Sqn, Cottesmore |
| | ZD411 | BAe Harrier GR7A [40A] | RAF No 3 Sqn, Cottesmore |
| | ZD412 | BAe Harrier GR5 (fuselage) | RAF/DARA, St Athan, instructional use |
| | ZD431 | BAe Harrier GR7A [43A] | RAF No 3 Sqn, Cottesmore |
| | ZD433 | BAe Harrier GR7A [45A] | RAF No 1 Sqn, Cottesmore |
| | ZD435 | BAe Harrier GR7 [47] | RAF No 1 Sqn, Cottesmore |
| | ZD436 | BAe Harrier GR7A [48A] | RAF HOCU/No 20(R) Sqn, Wittering |
| | ZD437 | BAe Harrier GR7A [49A] | RAF No 1 Sqn, Cottesmore |
| | ZD438 | BAe Harrier GR7 [50] | RAF HOCU/No 20(R) Sqn, Wittering |
| | ZD461 | BAe Harrier GR7A [51A] | RAF No 3 Sqn, Cottesmore |
| | ZD462 | BAe Harrier GR7 (9302M) [52] | ATTF, RAF St Athan |
| | ZD463 | BAe Harrier GR7 [53] | RAF No 3 Sqn, Cottesmore |
| | ZD465 | BAe Harrier GR7A [55A] | RAF No 1 Sqn, Cottesmore |
| | ZD466 | BAe Harrier GR7 [56] | RAF No 3 Sqn, Cottesmore |
| | ZD467 | BAe Harrier GR7 [57] | RAF No 4 Sqn, Cottesmore |
| | ZD468 | BAe Harrier GR7 [58] | RAF No 3 Sqn, Cottesmore |
| | ZD469 | BAe Harrier GR7A [59A] | RAF (on repair), Cottesmore |
| | ZD470 | BAe Harrier GR7 [60] | RAF HOCU/No 20(R) Sqn, Wittering |
| | ZD476 | WS61 Sea King HC4 [WU] | RN No 848 Sqn, Yeovilton |
| | ZD477 | WS61 Sea King HC4 [H] | RN No 845 Sqn, Yeovilton |
| | ZD478 | WS61 Sea King HC4 [J] | RN/DARA, Fleetlands (on repair) |
| | ZD479 | WS61 Sea King HC4 [WQ] | RN No 848 Sqn, Yeovilton |
| | ZD480 | WS61 Sea King HC4 [E] | RN No 845 Sqn, Yeovilton |
| | ZD559 | WS Lynx AH5X | DPA/AFD/QinetiQ, Boscombe Down |
| | ZD560 | WS Lynx AH7 | DPA/ETPS, Boscombe Down |
| | ZD565 | WS Lynx HMA8 [307] | RN No 815 Sqn, HQ Flt, Yeovilton |
| | ZD566 | WS Lynx HMA8 [444/MR] | RN No 815 Sqn, *Montrose* Flt, Yeovilton |
| | ZD574 | B-V Chinook HC2 (N37077) | RAF No 18 Sqn, Odiham |
| | ZD575 | B-V Chinook HC2 (N37078) | RAF/DARA, Fleetlands |
| | ZD578 | BAe Sea Harrier FA2 [000,122] | RNAS Yeovilton, at main gate |
| | ZD579 | BAe Sea Harrier FA2 [012/L] | RN No 801 Sqn, Yeovilton |
| | ZD580 | BAe Sea Harrier FA2 | Privately owned, Sproughton |
| | ZD581 | BAe Sea Harrier FA2 [124] | RN, Predannack Fire School |
| | ZD582 | BAe Sea Harrier FA2 | Privately owned, Colsterworth, Leics |
| | ZD607 | BAe Sea Harrier FA2 | RN AESS, *HMS Sultan*, Gosport |
| | ZD608 | BAe Sea Harrier FA2 [731] | Privately owned, Charlwood |
| | ZD610 | BAe Sea Harrier FA2 [006/N] | Privately owned, Dunsfold |
| | ZD611 | BAe Sea Harrier FA2 | RNAS Culdrose Fire Section |
| | ZD612 | BAe Sea Harrier FA2 | Privately owned, Topsham, Devon |
| | ZD613 | BAe Sea Harrier FA2 [127/R] | Privately owned, Leeds |
| | ZD614 | BAe Sea Harrier FA2 [122/R] | Privately owned, Sproughton |
| | ZD615 | BAe Sea Harrier FA2 | Privately owned, Charlwood |
| | ZD620 | BAe 125 CC3 | RAF No 32(The Royal) Sqn, Northolt |
| | ZD621 | BAe 125 CC3 | RAF No 32(The Royal) Sqn, Northolt |
| | ZD625 | WS61 Sea King HC4 [P] | RN No 848 Sqn, Yeovilton |
| | ZD626 | WS61 Sea King HC4 [ZZ] | RN No 848 Sqn, Yeovilton |
| | ZD627 | WS61 Sea King HC4 [VR] | RN No 846 Sqn, Yeovilton |
| | ZD630 | WS61 Sea King HAS6 [012/L] | RN, stored *HMS Sultan*, Gosport |
| | ZD631 | WS61 Sea King HAS6 [66] (fuselage) | RN, Predannack Fire School |
| | ZD633 | WS61 Sea King HAS6 [014/L] | RN, stored *HMS Sultan*, Gosport |
| | ZD634 | WS61 Sea King HAS6 [503] | RN, stored *HMS Sultan*, Gosport |
| | ZD636 | WS61 Sea King AEW7 [182/CU] | RN No 849 Sqn, HQ Flt, Culdrose |
| | ZD637 | WS61 Sea King HAS6 [700/PW] | RN, stored *HMS Sultan*, Gosport |
| | ZD667 | BAe Harrier GR3 (9201M) [67] | SFDO, RNAS Culdrose |
| | ZD668 | BAe Harrier GR3 (G-CBCU) [3E] | *Sold to the USA, March 2005* |
| | ZD670 | BAe Harrier GR3 [3A] | Privately owned, South Molton, Devon |
| | ZD703 | BAe 125 CC3 | RAF No 32(The Royal) Sqn, Northolt |
| | ZD704 | BAe 125 CC3 | RAF No 32(The Royal) Sqn, Northolt |
| | ZD707 | Panavia Tornado GR4 [TB] | RAF No 15(R) Sqn, Lossiemouth |
| | ZD708 | Panavia Tornado GR4 | DPA/BAE Systems, Warton |
| | ZD709 | Panavia Tornado GR4 [FA] | RAF No 12 Sqn, Lossiemouth |
| | ZD710 | Panavia Tornado GR1 <ff> | Privately owned, Barnstaple |
| | ZD711 | Panavia Tornado GR4 [TZ] | RAF No 15(R) Sqn, Lossiemouth |

| Serial | Type (other identity) [code] | Owner/operator, location or fate | Notes |
|--------|------------------------------|----------------------------------|-------|
| ZD712 | Panavia Tornado GR4 [TR] | RAF/DARA, St Athan | |
| ZD713 | Panavia Tornado GR4 [F] | DPA/AFD/QinetiQ, Boscombe Down | |
| ZD714 | Panavia Tornado GR4 [AJ-W] | RAF No 617 Sqn, Lossiemouth | |
| ZD715 | Panavia Tornado GR4 | RAF No 15(R) Sqn, Lossiemouth | |
| ZD716 | Panavia Tornado GR4 [AJ] | RAF No 9 Sqn, Marham | |
| ZD719 | Panavia Tornado GR4 [BS] | RAF No 14 Sqn, Lossiemouth | |
| ZD720 | Panavia Tornado GR4 [TA] | RAF No 15(R) Sqn, Lossiemouth | |
| ZD739 | Panavia Tornado GR4 | RAF AWC/FJWOEU, Coningsby | |
| ZD740 | Panavia Tornado GR4 [BG] | RAF No 14 Sqn, Lossiemouth | |
| ZD741 | Panavia Tornado GR4 [BZ] | RAF/DARA, St Athan | |
| ZD742 | Panavia Tornado GR4 [FY] | RAF/DARA, St Athan | |
| ZD743 | Panavia Tornado GR4 [TQ] | RAF No 15(R) Sqn, Lossiemouth | |
| ZD744 | Panavia Tornado GR4 [TK] | RAF No 15(R) Sqn, Lossiemouth | |
| ZD745 | Panavia Tornado GR4 | RAF/DARA, St Athan | |
| ZD746 | Panavia Tornado GR4 [TH] | RAF No 15(R) Sqn, Lossiemouth | |
| ZD747 | Panavia Tornado GR4 [AL] | RAF No 9 Sqn, Marham | |
| ZD748 | Panavia Tornado GR4 [FC] | RAF No 12 Sqn, Lossiemouth | |
| ZD749 | Panavia Tornado GR4 [AP] | RAF No 13 Sqn, Marham | |
| ZD788 | Panavia Tornado GR4 [BE] | RAF No 14 Sqn, Lossiemouth | |
| ZD789 | Panavia Tornado GR1 <ff> | Scrapped at Shawbury, 2002 | |
| ZD790 | Panavia Tornado GR4 [FM] | RAF No 12 Sqn, Lossiemouth | |
| ZD792 | Panavia Tornado GR4 [AJ-G] | RAF/DARA, St Athan | |
| ZD793 | Panavia Tornado GR4 [TE] | RAF No 12 Sqn, Lossiemouth | |
| ZD810 | Panavia Tornado GR4 [TD] | RAF No 15(R) Sqn, Lossiemouth | |
| ZD811 | Panavia Tornado GR4 | RAF No 13 Sqn, Marham | |
| ZD812 | Panavia Tornado GR4 [TU] | RAF No 15(R) Sqn, Lossiemouth | |
| ZD842 | Panavia Tornado GR4 [TV] | RAF No 15(R) Sqn, Lossiemouth | |
| ZD843 | Panavia Tornado GR4 [TG] | RAF No 15(R) Sqn, Lossiemouth | |
| ZD844 | Panavia Tornado GR4 [AJ-A] | RAF No 617 Sqn, Lossiemouth | |
| ZD847 | Panavia Tornado GR4 [AA] | RAF No 9 Sqn, Marham | |
| ZD848 | Panavia Tornado GR4 [V] | RAF No 13 Sqn, Marham | |
| ZD849 | Panavia Tornado GR4 [FG] | RAF/DARA, St Athan | |
| ZD850 | Panavia Tornado GR4 [AK] | RAF No 9 Sqn, Marham | |
| ZD851 | Panavia Tornado GR4 [S] | RAF No 2 Sqn, Marham | |
| ZD890 | Panavia Tornado GR4 [A] | RAF No 2 Sqn, Marham | |
| ZD892 | Panavia Tornado GR4 [TG] | RAF, stored St Athan | |
| ZD895 | Panavia Tornado GR4 [TI] | RAF No 15(R) Sqn, Lossiemouth | |
| ZD899 | Panavia Tornado F2 | DPA, Boscombe Down, spares use | |
| ZD902 | Panavia Tornado F2A(TIARA) | DPA/AFD/QinetiQ, Boscombe Down | |
| ZD906 | Panavia Tornado F2 (comp ZE294) <ff> | RAF Leuchars, BDRT | |
| ZD932 | Panavia Tornado F2 (comp ZE255) (fuselage) | ATTF, RAF St Athan | |
| ZD933 | Panavia Tornado F2 (comp ZE729) (fuselage) | RAF St Athan Fire Section | |
| ZD934 | Panavia Tornado F2 (comp ZE786) <ff> | RAF Leeming, GI use | |
| ZD936 | Panavia Tornado F2 (comp ZE251) <ff> | Boscombe Down Aviation Collection | |
| ZD938 | Panavia Tornado F2 (comp ZE295) <ff> | RAF, stored Shawbury | |
| ZD939 | Panavia Tornado F2 (comp ZE292) <ff> | DCAE Cosford, instructional use | |
| ZD948 | Lockheed TriStar KC1 (G-BFCA) | RAF No 216 Sqn, Brize Norton | |
| ZD949 | Lockheed TriStar K1 (G-BFCB) | RAF No 216 Sqn, Brize Norton | |
| ZD950 | Lockheed TriStar KC1 (G-BFCC) | RAF No 216 Sqn, Brize Norton | |
| ZD951 | Lockheed TriStar K1 (G-BFCD) | RAF No 216 Sqn, Brize Norton | |
| ZD952 | Lockheed TriStar KC1 (G-BFCE) | RAF No 216 Sqn, Brize Norton | |
| ZD953 | Lockheed TriStar KC1 (G-BFCF) | RAF No 216 Sqn, Brize Norton | |
| ZD980 | B-V Chinook HC2 (N37082) | RAF No 27 Sqn, Odiham | |
| ZD981 | B-V Chinook HC2 (N37083) | RAF/DARA, Fleetlands | |
| ZD982 | B-V Chinook HC2 (N37085) | RAF No 18 Sqn, Odiham | |
| ZD983 | B-V Chinook HC2 (N37086) | RAF No 27 Sqn, Odiham | |
| ZD984 | B-V Chinook HC2 (N37088) | RAF No 18 Sqn, Odiham | |
| ZD990 | BAe Harrier T8 [721] | RN SHOPS, Yeovilton | |
| ZD991 | BAe Harrier T8 (9228M) [722/VL] | Privately owned, Sproughton | |
| ZD993 | BAe Harrier T8 [723/VL] | RN No 801 Sqn, Yeovilton | |
| ZD996 | Panavia Tornado GR4A [I] | DPA/AFD/QinetiQ, Boscombe Down | |
| ZE116 | Panavia Tornado GR4A [X] | RAF No 13 Sqn, Marham | |
| ZE154 | Panavia Tornado F3 (comp ZD901) [LT] | RAF F3 OCU/No 56(R) Sqn, Leuchars | |
| ZE155 | Panavia Tornado F3 | DPA/BAE Systems, Warton | |

| Notes | Serial | Type (other identity) [code] | Owner/operator, location or fate |
|---|---|---|---|
| | ZE156 | Panavia Tornado F3 [WA] | RAF F3 OCU/No 56(R) Sqn, Leuchars |
| | ZE157 | Panavia Tornado F3 [TY] | RAF F3 OCU/No 56(R) Sqn, Leuchars |
| | ZE158 | Panavia Tornado F3 [HG] | RAF No 111 Sqn, Leuchars |
| | ZE159 | Panavia Tornado F3 [UV] | RAF St Athan (wfu) |
| | ZE160 | Panavia Tornado F3 [TX] | RAF Leuchars (wfu) |
| | ZE161 | Panavia Tornado F3 [GB] | RAF No 43 Sqn, Leuchars |
| | ZE162 | Panavia Tornado F3 [UR] | RAF/DARA, St Athan |
| | ZE163 | Panavia Tornado F3 (comp ZG753) [TW] | RAF F3 OCU/No 56(R) Sqn, Leuchars |
| | ZE164 | Panavia Tornado F3 [GD] | RAF St Athan (wfu) |
| | ZE165 | Panavia Tornado F3 [GE] | RAF St Athan (wfu) |
| | ZE168 | Panavia Tornado F3 [DN] | RAF No 25 Sqn, Leeming |
| | ZE199 | Panavia Tornado F3 [TV] | RAF Leeming (wfu) |
| | ZE200 | Panavia Tornado F3 [DB] | RAF No 111 Sqn, Leuchars |
| | ZE201 | Panavia Tornado F3 [UL] | RAF No 25 Sqn, Leeming |
| | ZE202 | Panavia Tornado F3 (MM55056) | RAF/DARA, St Athan |
| | ZE203 | Panavia Tornado F3 [DE] | RAF No 43 Sqn, Leuchars |
| | ZE204 | Panavia Tornado F3 [UJ] | RAF No 25 Sqn, Leeming |
| | ZE205 | Panavia Tornado F3 (MM55061) | Scrapped, January 2005 |
| | ZE206 | Panavia Tornado F3 [UI] | DPA/BAE Systems, Warton |
| | ZE207 | Panavia Tornado F3 [GC] | RAF Leeming (wfu) |
| | ZE208 | Panavia Tornado F3 (MM55060) | RAF/DARA, St Athan |
| | ZE209 | Panavia Tornado F3 [AX] | RAF/EADS, Munich, Germany |
| | ZE250 | Panavia Tornado F3 [TR] | RAF F3 OCU/No 56(R) Sqn, Leuchars |
| | ZE251 | Panavia Tornado F3 (comp ZD936) [UF] | RAF St Athan (wfu) |
| | ZE253 | Panavia Tornado F3 [AC] | RAF/EADS, Munich, Germany |
| | ZE254 | Panavia Tornado F3 (comp ZD941) [UD] | RAF No 25 Sqn, Leeming |
| | ZE255 | Panavia Tornado F3 (comp ZD932) | RAF No 25 Sqn, Leeming |
| | ZE256 | Panavia Tornado F3 [TP] | RAF Leuchars, instructional use |
| | ZE257 | Panavia Tornado F3 [GI] | RAF No 43 Sqn, Leuchars |
| | ZE258 | Panavia Tornado F3 (comp ZD905) [F] | RAF/DARA, St Athan |
| | ZE287 | Panavia Tornado F3 [TO] | RAF/DARA, St Athan (wfu) |
| | ZE288 | Panavia Tornado F3 (comp ZD940) [HA] | RAF No 111 Sqn, Leuchars |
| | ZE289 | Panavia Tornado F3 [VX] | RAF No 111 Sqn, Leuchars |
| | ZE290 | Panavia Tornado F3 [AG] | RAF/DARA, stored St Athan |
| | ZE291 | Panavia Tornado F3 [D] | RAF/DARA, St Athan |
| | ZE292 | Panavia Tornado F3 (comp ZD939) [YY] | RAF No 25 Sqn, Leeming |
| | ZE293 | Panavia Tornado F3 [GZ] | RAF Leeming (wfu) |
| | ZE294 | Panavia Tornado F3 (comp ZD906) [DD] | RAF Leeming (wfu) |
| | ZE295 | Panavia Tornado F3 (comp ZD938) | RAF AWC/FJWOEU, Coningsby |
| | ZE338 | Panavia Tornado F3 [GJ] | RAF No 43 Sqn, Leuchars |
| | ZE339 | Panavia Tornado F3 <ff> | RAF/DARA, stored St Athan |
| | ZE340 | Panavia Tornado F3 (ZE758/9298M) [GO] | RAF No 1 SoTT, Cosford |
| | ZE341 | Panavia Tornado F3 [GO] | RAF No 43 Sqn, Leuchars |
| | ZE342 | Panavia Tornado F3 | RAF No 25 Sqn, Leeming |
| | ZE343 | Panavia Tornado F3 (comp ZD900) [DZ] | RAF No 111 Sqn, Leuchars |
| | ZE350 | McD F-4J(UK) Phantom (9080M) <ff> | Privately owned, Ingatestone, Essex |
| | ZE352 | McD F-4J(UK) Phantom (9086M) <ff> | Privately owned, Preston, Lancs |
| | ZE360 | McD F-4J(UK) Phantom (9059M) [O] | MoD FSCTE, Manston |
| | ZE368 | WS61 Sea King HAR3 [R] | RAF No 202 Sqn, E Flt, Leconfield |
| | ZE369 | WS61 Sea King HAR3 [S] | RAF No 22 Sqn, C Flt, Valley |
| | ZE370 | WS61 Sea King HAR3 [T] | RAF No 22 Sqn, C Flt, Valley |
| | ZE375 | WS Lynx AH9 | AAC No 661 Sqn/1 Regt, Gütersloh |
| | ZE376 | WS Lynx AH9 | AAC No 661 Sqn/1 Regt, Gütersloh |
| | ZE378 | WS Lynx AH7 | AAC/DARA, Fleetlands |
| | ZE379 | WS Lynx AH7 | AAC/DARA, stored Fleetlands |
| | ZE380 | WS Lynx AH9 | AAC, Middle Wallop (on repair) |
| | ZE381 | WS Lynx AH7 [X] | DPA/Westland Helicopters, Yeovil |
| | ZE382 | WS Lynx AH9 | Crashed 9 September 2004, Námest, Czech Republic |
| | ZE395 | BAe 125 CC3 | RAF No 32(The Royal) Sqn, Northolt |
| | ZE396 | BAe 125 CC3 | RAF No 32(The Royal) Sqn, Northolt |

| Serial | Type (other identity) [code] | Owner/operator, location or fate | Notes |
|---|---|---|---|
| ZE410 | Agusta A109A (AE-334) | AAC No 8 Flt, Credenhill | |
| ZE411 | Agusta A109A (AE-331) | AAC No 8 Flt, Credenhill | |
| ZE412 | Agusta A109A | AAC No 8 Flt, Credenhill | |
| ZE413 | Agusta A109A | AAC No 8 Flt, Credenhill | |
| ZE418 | WS61 Sea King AEW7 [186/R] | RN No 849 Sqn, A Flt, Culdrose | |
| ZE420 | WS61 Sea King AEW7 [189] | RN No 849 Sqn, Culdrose | |
| ZE422 | WS61 Sea King AEW7 . | RN HMF, St Mawgan (conversion) | |
| ZE425 | WS61 Sea King HC4 [WR] | RN No 848 Sqn, Yeovilton | |
| ZE426 | WS61 Sea King HC4 [WX] | RN No 848 Sqn, Yeovilton | |
| ZE427 | WS61 Sea King HC4 [WZ] | RN No 848 Sqn, Yeovilton | |
| ZE428 | WS61 Sea King HC4 [VS] | RN No 846 Sqn, Yeovilton | |
| ZE432 | BAC 1-11/479FU (DQ-FBV) | DPA/ETPS, Boscombe Down | |
| ZE433 | BAC 1-11/479FU (DQ-FBQ) | DPA/AFD/QinetiQ, Boscombe Down | |
| ZE438 | BAe Jetstream T3 [76] | RN FONA/Heron Flight, Yeovilton | |
| ZE439 | BAe Jetstream T3 [77] | RN FONA/Heron Flight, Yeovilton | |
| ZE440 | BAe Jetstream T3 [78] | RN FONA/Heron Flight, Yeovilton | |
| ZE441 | BAe Jetstream T3 [79] | RN FONA/Heron Flight, Yeovilton | |
| ZE449 | SA330L Puma HC1 (9017M/PA-12) | RAF No 1563 Flt, Basrah, Iraq | |
| ZE477 | WS Lynx 3 | The Helicopter Museum, Weston-super-Mare | |
| ZE495 | Grob G103 Viking T1 (BGA3000) [VA] | RAF CGMF, stored Syerston | |
| ZE496 | Grob G103 Viking T1 (BGA3001) [VB] | RAF No 661 VGS, Kirknewton | |
| ZE498 | Grob G103 Viking T1 (BGA3003) [VC] | RAF CGMF, Syerston | |
| ZE499 | Grob G103 Viking T1 (BGA3004) [VD] | RAF No 615 VGS, Kenley | |
| ZE501 | Grob G103 Viking T1 (BGA3006) [VE] | Sold as BGA3006 | |
| ZE502 | Grob G103 Viking T1 (BGA3007) [VF] | RAF ACCGS/No 643 VGS, Syerston | |
| ZE503 | Grob G103 Viking T1 (BGA3008) [VG] | RAF No 625 VGS, Hullavington | |
| ZE504 | Grob G103 Viking T1 (BGA3009) [VH] | RAF No 621 VGS, Hullavington | |
| ZE520 | Grob G103 Viking T1 (BGA3010) [VJ] | RAF No 625 VGS, Hullavington | |
| ZE521 | Grob G103 Viking T1 (BGA3011) [VK] | RAF No 626 VGS, Predannack | |
| ZE522 | Grob G103 Viking T1 (BGA3012) [VL] | RAF No 621 VGS, Hullavington | |
| ZE524 | Grob G103 Viking T1 (BGA3014) [VM] | RAF No 625 VGS, Hullavington | |
| ZE526 | Grob G103 Viking T1 (BGA3016) [VN] | RAF No 662 VGS, Arbroath | |
| ZE527 | Grob G103 Viking T1 (BGA3017) [VP] | RAF No 626 VGS, Predannack | |
| ZE528 | Grob G103 Viking T1 (BGA3018) [VQ] | RAF No 614 VGS, Wethersfield | |
| ZE529 | Grob G103 Viking T1 (BGA3019) (comp ZE655) [VR] | RAF ACCGS/No 643 VGS, Syerston | |
| ZE530 | Grob G103 Viking T1 (BGA3020) [VS] | RAF No 611 VGS, Watton | |
| ZE531 | Grob G103 Viking T1 (BGA3021) [VT] | RAF No 615 VGS, Kenley | |
| ZE532 | Grob G103 Viking T1 (BGA3022) [VU] | RAF No 614 VGS, Wethersfield | |
| ZE533 | Grob G103 Viking T1 (BGA3023) [VV] | RAF No 622 VGS, Upavon | |
| ZE534 | Grob G103 Viking T1 (BGA3024) [VW] | Sold as BGA3024 | |
| ZE550 | Grob G103 Viking T1 (BGA3025) [VX] | RAF No 615 VGS, Kenley | |
| ZE551 | Grob G103 Viking T1 (BGA3026) [VY] | RAF No 614 VGS, Wethersfield | |
| ZE552 | Grob G103 Viking T1 (BGA3027) [VZ] | RAF No 621 VGS, Hullavington | |
| ZE553 | Grob G103 Viking T1 (BGA3028) [WA] | RAF No 615 VGS, Kenley | |
| ZE554 | Grob G103 Viking T1 (BGA3029) [WB] | RAF No 611 VGS, Watton | |

| Notes | Serial | Type (other identity) [code] | Owner/operator, location or fate |
|---|---|---|---|
| | ZE555 | Grob G103 Viking T1 (BGA3030) [WC] | RAF No 625 VGS, Hullavington |
| | ZE556 | Grob G103 Viking T1 (BGA3031) [WD] | RAF CGMF, Syerston (damaged) |
| | ZE557 | Grob G103 Viking T1 (BGA3032) [WE] | RAF No 622 VGS, Upavon |
| | ZE558 | Grob G103 Viking T1 (BGA3033) [WF] | RAF ACCGS/No 643 VGS, Syerston |
| | ZE559 | Grob G103 Viking T1 (BGA3034) [WG] | RAF No 661 VGS, Kirknewton |
| | ZE560 | Grob G103 Viking T1 (BGA3035) [WH] | RAF No 661 VGS, Kirknewton |
| | ZE561 | Grob G103 Viking T1 (BGA3036) [WJ] | RAF No 631 VGS, Sealand |
| | ZE562 | Grob G103 Viking T1 (BGA3037) [WK] | RAF No 626 VGS, Predannack |
| | ZE563 | Grob G103 Viking T1 (BGA3038) [WL] | RAF No 614 VGS, Wethersfield |
| | ZE564 | Grob G103 Viking T1 (BGA3039) [WN] | RAF 662 VGS, Arbroath |
| | ZE584 | Grob G103 Viking T1 (BGA3040) [WP] | RAF No 631 VGS, Sealand |
| | ZE585 | Grob G103 Viking T1 (BGA3041) [WQ] | RAF No 626 VGS, Predannack |
| | ZE586 | Grob G103 Viking T1 (BGA3042) [WR] | RAF No 631 VGS, Sealand |
| | ZE587 | Grob G103 Viking T1 (BGA3043) [WS] | RAF No 611 VGS, Watton |
| | ZE589 | Grob G103 Viking T1 (BGA3045) <ff> | To BGA3045 |
| | ZE590 | Grob G103 Viking T1 (BGA3046) [WT] | RAF No 661 VGS, Kirknewton |
| | ZE591 | Grob G103 Viking T1 (BGA3047) [WU] | RAF No 631 VGS, Sealand |
| | ZE592 | Grob G103 Viking T1 (BGA3048) [WV] | RAF ACCGS/No 643 VGS, Syerston |
| | ZE593 | Grob G103 Viking T1 (BGA3049) [WW] | RAF No 621 VGS, Hullavington |
| | ZE594 | Grob G103 Viking T1 (BGA3050) [WX] | RAF ACCGS/No 643 VGS, Syerston |
| | ZE595 | Grob G103 Viking T1 (BGA3051) [WY] | RAF No 622 VGS, Upavon |
| | ZE600 | Grob G103 Viking T1 (BGA3052) [WZ] | RAF No 622 VGS, Upavon |
| | ZE601 | Grob G103 Viking T1 (BGA3053) [XA] | RAF No 611 VGS, Watton |
| | ZE602 | Grob G103 Viking T1 (BGA3054) [XB] | RAF No 614 VGS, Wethersfield |
| | ZE603 | Grob G103 Viking T1 (BGA3055) [XC] | RAF ACCGS/No 643 VGS, Syerston |
| | ZE604 | Grob G103 Viking T1 (BGA3056) [XD] | RAF No 615 VGS, Kenley |
| | ZE605 | Grob G103 Viking T1 (BGA3057) [XE] | RAF ACCGS/No 643 VGS, Syerston |
| | ZE606 | Grob G103 Viking T1 (BGA3058) [XF] | RAF No 615 VGS, Kenley |
| | ZE607 | Grob G103 Viking T1 (BGA3059) [XG] | RAF No 614 VGS, Wethersfield |
| | ZE608 | Grob G103 Viking T1 (BGA3060) [XH] | RAF, stored CGMF Syerston |
| | ZE609 | Grob G103 Viking T1 (BGA3061) [XJ] | RAF No 622 VGS, Upavon |
| | ZE610 | Grob G103 Viking T1 (BGA3062) [XK] | RAF No 615 VGS, Kenley |
| | ZE611 | Grob G103 Viking T1 (BGA3063) [XL] | RAF No 611 VGS, Watton |
| | ZE613 | Grob G103 Viking T1 (BGA3065) [XM] | RAF No 662 VGS, Arbroath |
| | ZE614 | Grob G103 Viking T1 (BGA3066) [XN] | RAF No 614 VGS, Wethersfield |
| | ZE625 | Grob G103 Viking T1 (BGA3067) [XP] | RAF No 625 VGS, Hullavington |

| Serial | Type (other identity) [code] | Owner/operator, location or fate | Notes |
|--------|------------------------------|----------------------------------|-------|
| ZE626 | Grob G103 Viking T1 (BGA3068) [XQ] | RAF No 626 VGS, Predannack | |
| ZE627 | Grob G103 Viking T1 (BGA3069) [XR] | RAF No 631 VGS, Sealand | |
| ZE628 | Grob G103 Viking T1 (BGA3070) [XS] | RAF No 622 VGS, Upavon | |
| ZE629 | Grob G103 Viking T1 (BGA3071) [XT] | RAF No 662 VGS, Arbroath | |
| ZE630 | Grob G103 Viking T1 (BGA3072) [XU] | RAF No 662 VGS, Arbroath | |
| ZE631 | Grob G103 Viking T1 (BGA3073) [XV] | RAF No 662 VGS, Arbroath | |
| ZE632 | Grob G103 Viking T1 (BGA3074) [XW] | RAF No 631 VGS, Sealand | |
| ZE633 | Grob G103 Viking T1 (BGA3075) [XX] | RAF No 611 VGS, Watton | |
| ZE635 | Grob G103 Viking T1 (BGA3077) [XY] | To BGA3077 | |
| ZE636 | Grob G103 Viking T1 (BGA3078) [XZ] | RAF No 621 VGS, Hullavington | |
| ZE637 | Grob G103 Viking T1 (BGA3079) [YA] | RAF No 622 VGS, Upavon | |
| ZE650 | Grob G103 Viking T1 (BGA3080) [YB] | RAF No 622 VGS, Upavon | |
| ZE651 | Grob G103 Viking T1 (BGA3081) [YC] | RAF No 661 VGS, Kirknewton | |
| ZE652 | Grob G103 Viking T1 (BGA3082) [YD] | RAF ACCGS/No 643 VGS, Syerston | |
| ZE653 | Grob G103 Viking T1 (BGA3083) [YE] | RAF No 661 VGS, Kirknewton | |
| ZE656 | Grob G103 Viking T1 (BGA3086) [YH] | RAF No 625 VGS, Hullavington | |
| ZE657 | Grob G103 Viking T1 (BGA3087) [YJ] | RAF No 615 VGS, Kenley | |
| ZE658 | Grob G103 Viking T1 (BGA3088) [YK] | RAF No 614 VGS, Wethersfield | |
| ZE677 | Grob G103 Viking T1 (BGA3090) [YM] | RAF No 621 VGS, Hullavington | |
| ZE678 | Grob G103 Viking T1 (BGA3091) [YN] | RAF, stored CGMF Syerston | |
| ZE679 | Grob G103 Viking T1 (BGA3092) [YP] | RAF No 622 VGS, Upavon | |
| ZE680 | Grob G103 Viking T1 (BGA3093) [YQ] | RAF ACCGS/No 643 VGS, Syerston | |
| ZE681 | Grob G103 Viking T1 (BGA3094) [YR] | RAF CGMF, Syerston (damaged) | |
| ZE682 | Grob G103 Viking T1 (BGA3095) [YS] | RAF No 662 VGS, Arbroath | |
| ZE683 | Grob G103 Viking T1 (BGA3096) [YT] | RAF No 661 VGS, Kirknewton | |
| ZE684 | Grob G103 Viking T1 (BGA3097) [YU] | RAF ACCGS/No 643 VGS, Syerston | |
| ZE685 | Grob G103 Viking T1 (BGA3098) [YV] | RAF No 631 VGS, Sealand | |
| ZE686 | Grob G103 Viking T1 (BGA3099) | RAF CGMF, Syerston | |
| ZE690 | BAe Sea Harrier FA2 [003] | RN No 801 Sqn, Yeovilton | |
| ZE691 | BAe Sea Harrier FA2 | Privately owned, Sproughton | |
| ZE692 | BAe Sea Harrier FA2 [008] | RN No 801 Sqn, Yeovilton | |
| ZE693 | BAe Sea Harrier FA2 [717] | Privately owned, Dukinfield, Gr Manchester | |
| ZE694 | BAe Sea Harrier FA2 | Midland Air Museum, Coventry | |
| ZE695 | BAe Sea Harrier FA2 [718] | Privately owned, Sproughton | |
| ZE696 | BAe Sea Harrier FA2 [124/R] | Privately owned, Colsterworth, Leics | |
| ZE697 | BAe Sea Harrier FA2 [006] | Privately owned, Charlwood | |
| ZE698 | BAe Sea Harrier FA2 [001] | Privately owned, Charlwood | |
| ZE700 | BAe 146 CC2 (G-6-021) | RAF No 32(The Royal) Sqn, Northolt | |
| ZE701 | BAe 146 CC2 (G-6-029) | RAF No 32(The Royal) Sqn, Northolt | |
| ZE704 | Lockheed TriStar C2 (N508PA) | RAF No 216 Sqn, Brize Norton | |
| ZE705 | Lockheed TriStar C2 (N509PA) | RAF No 216 Sqn, Brize Norton | |
| ZE706 | Lockheed TriStar C2A (N503PA) | RAF No 216 Sqn, Brize Norton | |
| ZE728 | Panavia Tornado F3 (comp ZD903) [TH] | RAF No 25 Sqn, Leeming | |

| Notes | Serial | Type (other identity) [code] | Owner/operator, location or fate |
|---|---|---|---|
| | ZE729 | Panavia Tornado F3 (comp ZD933) [DH] | *Scrapped, November 2005* |
| | ZE730 | Panavia Tornado F3 (MM7204) | RAF/DARA, stored St Athan |
| | ZE731 | Panavia Tornado F3 [GP] | RAF No 43 Sqn, Leuchars |
| | ZE734 | Panavia Tornado F3 [DA] | RAF/DARA, St Athan |
| | ZE735 | Panavia Tornado F3 | RAF F3 OCU/No 56(R) Sqn, Leuchars |
| | ZE736 | Panavia Tornado F3 (comp ZD937) [WB] | RAF F3 OCU/No 56(R) Sqn, Leuchars |
| | ZE737 | Panavia Tornado F3 [GK] | RAF No 43 Sqn, Leuchars |
| | ZE755 | Panavia Tornado F3 [YL] | RAF No 25 Sqn, Leeming |
| | ZE756 | Panavia Tornado F3 | RAF/DARA, stored St Athan |
| | ZE757 | Panavia Tornado F3 [YJ] | RAF No 25 Sqn, Leeming |
| | ZE758 | Panavia Tornado F3 [DO] | RAF No 111 Sqn, Leuchars |
| | ZE760 | Panavia Tornado F3 (MM7206) [AP] | RAF Coningsby, on display |
| | ZE761 | Panavia Tornado F3 (MM7203) | DPA/BAE Systems, Warton |
| | ZE762 | Panavia Tornado F3 (MM7207) | RAF/DARA, stored St Athan |
| | ZE763 | Panavia Tornado F3 [DG] | RAF No 25 Sqn, Leeming |
| | ZE764 | Panavia Tornado F3 [YD] | RAF/DARA, St Athan |
| | ZE785 | Panavia Tornado F3 | RAF AWC/FJWOEU, Coningsby |
| | ZE786 | Panavia Tornado F3 (comp ZD934) [TF] | RAF F3 OCU/No 56(R) Sqn, Leuchars |
| | ZE787 | Panavia Tornado F3 (MM7205) | RAF/DARA, St Athan |
| | ZE788 | Panavia Tornado F3 [GL] | DPA/BAE Systems, Warton |
| | ZE790 | Panavia Tornado F3 [DK] | RAF No 111 Sqn, Leuchars |
| | ZE791 | Panavia Tornado F3 [HF] | RAF No 111 Sqn, Leuchars |
| | ZE792 | Panavia Tornado F3 (MM7211) | *Scrapped, January 2005* |
| | ZE793 | Panavia Tornado F3 (comp ZD935) [TE] | RAF No 25 Sqn, Leeming |
| | ZE794 | Panavia Tornado F3 [XW] | RAF No 25 Sqn, Leeming |
| | ZE808 | Panavia Tornado F3 | DPA/BAE Systems, Warton |
| | ZE810 | Panavia Tornado F3 [XU] | RAF No 43 Sqn, Leuchars |
| | ZE812 | Panavia Tornado F3 [XR] | RAF St Athan (wfu) |
| | ZE831 | Panavia Tornado F3 [XQ] | RAF No 25 Sqn, Leeming |
| | ZE832 | Panavia Tornado F3 (MM7202) [XP] | RAF St Athan (wfu) |
| | ZE834 | Panavia Tornado F3 [HD] | RAF No 111 Sqn, Leuchars |
| | ZE835 | Panavia Tornado F3 (MM7209) | RAF St Athan, Fire Section |
| | ZE837 | Panavia Tornado F3 (MM55057) [TD] | RAF Leuchars (wfu) |
| | ZE838 | Panavia Tornado F3 [GH] | RAF No 43 Sqn, Leuchars |
| | ZE839 | Panavia Tornado F3 [XK] | RAF Leeming (wfu) |
| | ZE887 | Panavia Tornado F3 [XI] | RAF Leeming (wfu) |
| | ZE888 | Panavia Tornado F3 [TC] | RAF/DARA, St Athan |
| | ZE889 | Panavia Tornado F3 [XH] | RAF ASF, Leuchars (wfu) |
| | ZE907 | Panavia Tornado F3 [DA] | RAF No 25 Sqn, Leeming |
| | ZE908 | Panavia Tornado F3 [TB] | RAF St Athan (wfu) |
| | ZE934 | Panavia Tornado F3 [TA] | Royal Scottish Mus'm of Flight, E Fortune |
| | ZE936 | Panavia Tornado F3 [HE] | RAF No 111 Sqn, Leuchars |
| | ZE941 | Panavia Tornado F3 [KT] | RAF Leuchars (wfu) |
| | ZE942 | Panavia Tornado F3 [DF] | RAF No 111 Sqn, Leuchars |
| | ZE961 | Panavia Tornado F3 [XD] | RAF No 25 Sqn, Leeming |
| | ZE962 | Panavia Tornado F3 [XC] | *Crashed 14 October 2005, North Sea* |
| | ZE963 | Panavia Tornado F3 [YT] | RAF F3 OCU/No 56(R) Sqn, Leuchars |
| | ZE964 | Panavia Tornado F3 [XT] | RAF F3 OCU/No 56(R) Sqn, Leuchars |
| | ZE965 | Panavia Tornado F3 [WT] | RAF F3 OCU/No 56(R) Sqn, Leuchars |
| | ZE966 | Panavia Tornado F3 [VT] | RAF St Athan (wfu) |
| | ZE967 | Panavia Tornado F3 [UT] | RAF Leuchars, at main gate |
| | ZE968 | Panavia Tornado F3 [HB] | RAF No 111 Sqn, Leuchars |
| | ZE969 | Panavia Tornado F3 [XA] | RAF No 25 Sqn, Leeming |
| | ZE982 | Panavia Tornado F3 [VV] | RAF No 25 Sqn, Leeming |
| | ZE983 | Panavia Tornado F3 [WY] | RAF No 111 Sqn, Leuchars |
| | ZF115 | WS61 Sea King HC4 (wreck) | RN, stored *HMS Sultan*, Gosport |
| | ZF116 | WS61 Sea King HC4 [WP] | RN No 848 Sqn, Yeovilton |
| | ZF117 | WS61 Sea King HC4 [VX] | RN No 846 Sqn, Yeovilton |
| | ZF118 | WS61 Sea King HC4 [K] | RN No 845 Sqn, Yeovilton |
| | ZF119 | WS61 Sea King HC4 [WY] | RN No 848 Sqn, Yeovilton |
| | ZF120 | WS61 Sea King HC4 [VZ] | RN No 846 Sqn, Yeovilton |
| | ZF121 | WS61 Sea King HC4 [T] | RN No 846 Sqn, Yeovilton |
| | ZF122 | WS61 Sea King HC4 [F] | RN No 845 Sqn, Yeovilton |
| | ZF123 | WS61 Sea King HC4 [WW] | RN No 848 Sqn, Yeovilton |
| | ZF124 | WS61 Sea King HC4 [L] | RN No 845 Sqn, Yeovilton |
| | ZF130 | BAe 125-60B (G-BLUW) [fuselage] | Electroworkz, Islington |

| Serial | Type (other identity) [code] | Owner/operator, location or fate | Notes |
|--------|------------------------------|----------------------------------|-------|
| ZF135 | Shorts Tucano T1 | RAF No 1 FTS, Linton-on-Ouse | |
| ZF136 | Shorts Tucano T1 | RAF, stored Shawbury | |
| ZF137 | Shorts Tucano T1 | RAF No 1 FTS/*207(R) Sqn*, Linton-on-Ouse | |
| ZF138 | Shorts Tucano T1 | RAF, stored Shawbury | |
| ZF139 | Shorts Tucano T1 | RAF No 1 FTS, Linton-on-Ouse | |
| ZF140 | Shorts Tucano T1 | RAF No 1 FTS/*207(R) Sqn*, Linton-on-Ouse | |
| ZF141 | Shorts Tucano T1 | *Withdrawn for sale, RAF Shawbury* | |
| ZF142 | Shorts Tucano T1 | RAF No 1 FTS, Linton-on-Ouse | |
| ZF143 | Shorts Tucano T1 | RAF No 1 FTS, Linton-on-Ouse | |
| ZF144 | Shorts Tucano T1 | RAF No 1 FTS, Linton-on-Ouse | |
| ZF145 | Shorts Tucano T1 | RAF No 1 FTS, Linton-on-Ouse | |
| ZF160 | Shorts Tucano T1 | RAF, stored Shawbury | |
| ZF161 | Shorts Tucano T1 | RAF No 1 FTS/*72(R) Sqn*, Linton-on-Ouse | |
| ZF162 | Shorts Tucano T1 | RAF, stored Shawbury | |
| ZF163 | Shorts Tucano T1 | RAF, stored Shawbury | |
| ZF164 | Shorts Tucano T1 | *Withdrawn for sale, RAF Shawbury* | |
| ZF165 | Shorts Tucano T1 | *Withdrawn for sale, RAF Shawbury* | |
| ZF166 | Shorts Tucano T1 | RAF, stored Shawbury | |
| ZF167 | Shorts Tucano T1 (fuselage) | Shorts, Belfast | |
| ZF168 | Shorts Tucano T1 | RAF, stored Shawbury | |
| ZF169 | Shorts Tucano T1 | RAF No 1 FTS/*72(R) Sqn*, Linton-on-Ouse | |
| ZF170 | Shorts Tucano T1 | RAF No 1 FTS, Linton-on-Ouse | |
| ZF171 | Shorts Tucano T1 | RAF No 1 FTS, Linton-on-Ouse | |
| ZF172 | Shorts Tucano T1 | RAF No 1 FTS, Linton-on-Ouse | |
| ZF200 | Shorts Tucano T1 | *Withdrawn for sale, RAF Shawbury* | |
| ZF201 | Shorts Tucano T1 | *Withdrawn for sale, RAF Shawbury* | |
| ZF202 | Shorts Tucano T1 | RAF, stored Shawbury | |
| ZF203 | Shorts Tucano T1 | RAF, stored Shawbury | |
| ZF204 | Shorts Tucano T1 | RAF No 1 FTS/*207(R) Sqn*, Linton-on-Ouse | |
| ZF205 | Shorts Tucano T1 | RAF No 1 FTS/*72(R) Sqn*, Linton-on-Ouse | |
| ZF206 | Shorts Tucano T1 | RAF, stored Shawbury | |
| ZF207 | Shorts Tucano T1 | RAF, stored Shawbury | |
| ZF208 | Shorts Tucano T1 | RAF, stored Shawbury | |
| ZF209 | Shorts Tucano T1 | RAF No 1 FTS/*72(R) Sqn*, Linton-on-Ouse | |
| ZF210 | Shorts Tucano T1 | RAF, stored Shawbury | |
| ZF211 | Shorts Tucano T1 | RAF, stored Shawbury | |
| ZF212 | Shorts Tucano T1 | RAF No 1 FTS, Linton-on-Ouse | |
| ZF238 | Shorts Tucano T1 | RAF, stored Shawbury | |
| ZF239 | Shorts Tucano T1 | RAF No 1 FTS, Linton-on-Ouse | |
| ZF240 | Shorts Tucano T1 | RAF No 1 FTS, Linton-on-Ouse | |
| ZF241 | Shorts Tucano T1 | RAF, stored Shawbury | |
| ZF242 | Shorts Tucano T1 | RAF No 1 FTS, Linton-on-Ouse | |
| ZF243 | Shorts Tucano T1 | RAF No 1 FTS, Linton-on-Ouse | |
| ZF244 | Shorts Tucano T1 | RAF No 1 FTS/*72(R) Sqn*, Linton-on-Ouse | |
| ZF245 | Shorts Tucano T1 | *Withdrawn for sale, RAF Shawbury* | |
| ZF263 | Shorts Tucano T1 | RAF, stored Shawbury | |
| ZF264 | Shorts Tucano T1 | RAF No 1 FTS, Linton-on-Ouse | |
| ZF265 | Shorts Tucano T1 | *Withdrawn for sale, RAF Shawbury* | |
| ZF266 | Shorts Tucano T1 | RAF, stored Shawbury | |
| ZF267 | Shorts Tucano T1 | *Withdrawn for sale, RAF Shawbury* | |
| ZF268 | Shorts Tucano T1 | RAF No 1 FTS, Linton-on-Ouse | |
| ZF269 | Shorts Tucano T1 | RAF No 1 FTS/*72(R) Sqn*, Linton-on-Ouse | |
| ZF284 | Shorts Tucano T1 | *Withdrawn for sale, RAF Shawbury* | |
| ZF285 | Shorts Tucano T1 | *Withdrawn for sale, RAF Shawbury* | |
| ZF286 | Shorts Tucano T1 | RAF No 1 FTS, Linton-on-Ouse | |
| ZF287 | Shorts Tucano T1 | RAF No 1 FTS/*72(R) Sqn*, Linton-on-Ouse | |
| ZF288 | Shorts Tucano T1 | RAF, stored Shawbury | |
| ZF289 | Shorts Tucano T1 | RAF No 1 FTS, Linton-on-Ouse | |
| ZF290 | Shorts Tucano T1 | RAF No 1 FTS/*72(R) Sqn*, Linton-on-Ouse | |
| ZF291 | Shorts Tucano T1 | RAF No 1 FTS, Linton-on-Ouse | |
| ZF292 | Shorts Tucano T1 | RAF No 1 FTS/*207(R) Sqn*, Linton-on-Ouse | |
| ZF293 | Shorts Tucano T1 | RAF No 1 FTS/*72(R) Sqn*, Linton-on-Ouse | |
| ZF294 | Shorts Tucano T1 | RAF, stored Shawbury | |
| ZF295 | Shorts Tucano T1 | RAF No 1 FTS, Linton-on-Ouse | |
| ZF315 | Shorts Tucano T1 | RAF No 1 FTS, Linton-on-Ouse | |
| ZF317 | Shorts Tucano T1 | RAF No 1 FTS, Linton-on-Ouse | |
| ZF318 | Shorts Tucano T1 | RAF, stored Shawbury | |
| ZF319 | Shorts Tucano T1 | RAF, stored Shawbury | |
| ZF320 | Shorts Tucano T1 | RAF, stored Shawbury | |

| Notes | Serial | Type (other identity) [code] | Owner/operator, location or fate |
|---|---|---|---|
| | ZF338 | Shorts Tucano T1 | RAF No 1 FTS, Linton-on-Ouse |
| | ZF339 | Shorts Tucano T1 | RAF No 1 FTS/*72(R) Sqn*, Linton-on-Ouse |
| | ZF340 | Shorts Tucano T1 | *Withdrawn for sale, RAF Shawbury* |
| | ZF341 | Shorts Tucano T1 | RAF No 1 FTS/*207(R) Sqn*, Linton-on-Ouse |
| | ZF342 | Shorts Tucano T1 | RAF No 1 FTS, Linton-on-Ouse |
| | ZF343 | Shorts Tucano T1 | RAF No 1 FTS, Linton-on-Ouse |
| | ZF344 | Shorts Tucano T1 | RAF No 1 FTS, Linton-on-Ouse |
| | ZF345 | Shorts Tucano T1 | RAF No 1 FTS/*207(R) Sqn*, Linton-on-Ouse |
| | ZF346 | Shorts Tucano T1 | RAF, stored Shawbury |
| | ZF347 | Shorts Tucano T1 | RAF No 1 FTS, Linton-on-Ouse |
| | ZF348 | Shorts Tucano T1 | RAF No 1 FTS, Linton-on-Ouse |
| | ZF349 | Shorts Tucano T1 | RAF No 1 FTS, Linton-on-Ouse |
| | ZF350 | Shorts Tucano T1 | RAF, stored Shawbury |
| | ZF372 | Shorts Tucano T1 | RAF, stored Shawbury |
| | ZF373 | Shorts Tucano T1 | *Withdrawn for sale, RAF Shawbury* |
| | ZF374 | Shorts Tucano T1 | RAF No 1 FTS/*72(R) Sqn*, Linton-on-Ouse |
| | ZF375 | Shorts Tucano T1 | RAF, stored Shawbury |
| | ZF376 | Shorts Tucano T1 | RAF, stored Shawbury |
| | ZF377 | Shorts Tucano T1 | RAF No 1 FTS, Linton-on-Ouse |
| | ZF378 | Shorts Tucano T1 | RAF No 1 FTS, Linton-on-Ouse |
| | ZF379 | Shorts Tucano T1 | RAF No 1 FTS, Linton-on-Ouse |
| | ZF380 | Shorts Tucano T1 | RAF, stored Shawbury |
| | ZF405 | Shorts Tucano T1 | RAF No 1 FTS, Linton-on-Ouse |
| | ZF406 | Shorts Tucano T1 | RAF No 1 FTS, Linton-on-Ouse |
| | ZF407 | Shorts Tucano T1 | RAF No 1 FTS, Linton-on-Ouse |
| | ZF408 | Shorts Tucano T1 | RAF, stored Shawbury |
| | ZF409 | Shorts Tucano T1 | RAF No 1 FTS, Linton-on-Ouse |
| | ZF410 | Shorts Tucano T1 | RAF No 1 FTS, Linton-on-Ouse |
| | ZF411 | Shorts Tucano T1 | *Withdrawn for sale, RAF Shawbury* |
| | ZF412 | Shorts Tucano T1 | RAF, stored Shawbury |
| | ZF413 | Shorts Tucano T1 | RAF, stored Shawbury |
| | ZF414 | Shorts Tucano T1 | RAF, stored Shawbury |
| | ZF415 | Shorts Tucano T1 | *Withdrawn for sale, RAF Shawbury* |
| | ZF416 | Shorts Tucano T1 | RAF No 1 FTS, Linton-on-Ouse |
| | ZF417 | Shorts Tucano T1 | RAF No 1 FTS/*207(R) Sqn*, Linton-on-Ouse |
| | ZF418 | Shorts Tucano T1 | RAF No 1 FTS, Linton-on-Ouse |
| | ZF445 | Shorts Tucano T1 | RAF, stored Shawbury |
| | ZF446 | Shorts Tucano T1 | RAF No 1 FTS, Linton-on-Ouse |
| | ZF447 | Shorts Tucano T1 | RAF, stored Shawbury |
| | ZF448 | Shorts Tucano T1 | RAF No 1 FTS, Linton-on-Ouse |
| | ZF449 | Shorts Tucano T1 | RAF, stored Shawbury |
| | ZF450 | Shorts Tucano T1 | *Withdrawn for sale, RAF Shawbury* |
| | ZF483 | Shorts Tucano T1 | RAF No 1 FTS/*72(R) Sqn*, Linton-on-Ouse |
| | ZF484 | Shorts Tucano T1 | RAF, stored Shawbury |
| | ZF485 | Shorts Tucano T1 (G-BULU) | RAF No 1 FTS, Linton-on-Ouse |
| | ZF486 | Shorts Tucano T1 | RAF, stored Shawbury |
| | ZF487 | Shorts Tucano T1 | RAF No 1 FTS, Linton-on-Ouse |
| | ZF488 | Shorts Tucano T1 | RAF, stored Shawbury |
| | ZF489 | Shorts Tucano T1 | RAF, stored Shawbury |
| | ZF490 | Shorts Tucano T1 | RAF, stored Shawbury |
| | ZF491 | Shorts Tucano T1 | RAF No 1 FTS, Linton-on-Ouse |
| | ZF492 | Shorts Tucano T1 | RAF No 1 FTS, Linton-on-Ouse |
| | ZF510 | Shorts Tucano T1 | DPA/AFD/QinetiQ, Boscombe Down |
| | ZF511 | Shorts Tucano T1 | DPA/AFD/QinetiQ, Boscombe Down |
| | ZF512 | Shorts Tucano T1 | RAF No 1 FTS, Linton-on-Ouse |
| | ZF513 | Shorts Tucano T1 | RAF No 1 FTS/*72(R) Sqn*, Linton-on-Ouse |
| | ZF514 | Shorts Tucano T1 | RAF No 1 FTS/*72(R) Sqn*, Linton-on-Ouse |
| | ZF515 | Shorts Tucano T1 | RAF No 1 FTS/*72(R) Sqn*, Linton-on-Ouse |
| | ZF516 | Shorts Tucano T1 | RAF, stored Shawbury |
| | ZF534 | BAe EAP | Loughborough University |
| | ZF537 | WS Lynx AH9 | AAC No 661 Sqn/1 Regt, Gütersloh |
| | ZF538 | WS Lynx AH9 | AAC No 659 Sqn/4 Regt, Wattisham |
| | ZF539 | WS Lynx AH9 | AAC No 661 Sqn/1 Regt, Gütersloh |
| | ZF540 | WS Lynx AH9 | AAC No 661 Sqn/1 Regt, Gütersloh |
| | ZF557 | WS Lynx HMA8 [318] | RN/DARA, Fleetlands |
| | ZF558 | WS Lynx HMA8 | DPA/Westland Helicopters, Yeovil |
| | ZF560 | WS Lynx HMA8 [338/CT] | RN No 815 Sqn, *Campbeltown* Flt, Yeovilton |
| | ZF562 | WS Lynx HMA8 [427] | RN No 815 Sqn, *St Albans* Flt, Yeovilton |
| | ZF563 | WS Lynx HMA8 [670] | RN No 815 Sqn OEU, Yeovilton |

| Serial | Type (other identity) [code] | Owner/operator, location or fate | Notes |
|--------|------------------------------|----------------------------------|-------|
| ZF573 | PBN 2T Islander CC2A (G-SRAY) | RAF Northolt Station Flight | |
| ZF579 | BAC Lightning F53 | Gatwick Aviation Museum, Charlwood | |
| ZF580 | BAC Lightning F53 | BAE Systems Samlesbury, at main gate | |
| ZF581 | BAC Lightning F53 | BAE Systems, Rochester, on display | |
| ZF582 | BAC Lightning F53 <ff> | Bournemouth Aviation Museum | |
| ZF583 | BAC Lightning F53 | Solway Aviation Society, Carlisle | |
| ZF584 | BAC Lightning F53 | Ferranti Ltd, South Syle, Edinburgh | |
| ZF587 | BAC Lightning F53 <ff> | Lashenden Air Warfare Museum, Headcorn | |
| ZF588 | BAC Lightning F53 [L] | East Midlands Airport Aeropark | |
| ZF590 | BAC Lightning F53 <rf> | Scrapped | |
| ZF592 | BAC Lightning F53 | Repainted in Saudi marks as 53-686, 2005 | |
| ZF593 | BAC Lightning F53 (fuselage) | Scrapped | |
| ZF594 | BAC Lightning F53 | North-East Aircraft Museum, Usworth | |
| ZF595 | BAC Lightning T55 (fuselage) | Privately owned, Grainthorpe, Lincs | |
| ZF596 | BAe North-West Heritage Group Warton <ff> | BAe North-West Heritage Group Warton | |
| ZF622 | Piper PA-31 Navajo Chieftain 350 (N3548Y) | DPA/AFD/QinetiQ, Boscombe Down | |
| ZF641 | EHI-101 [PP1] | SFDO, RNAS Culdrose | |
| ZF649 | EHI-101 Merlin [PP5] | RN AESS, HMS Sultan, Gosport | |
| | | | |
| ZG101 | EHI-101 (mock-up) [GB] | Westland Helicopters/Agusta, Yeovil | |
| ZG471 | BAe Harrier GR7A [61A] | RAF No 1 Sqn, Cottesmore | |
| ZG472 | BAe Harrier GR7A [62A] | RAF No 1 Sqn, Cottesmore | |
| ZG474 | BAe Harrier GR7 [64] | RAF No 4 Sqn, Cottesmore | |
| ZG477 | BAe Harrier GR9 [67] | DPA/AFD/QinetiQ, Boscombe Down | |
| ZG478 | BAe Harrier GR9A [68] | RAF AWC/FJWOEU, Coningsby | |
| ZG479 | BAe Harrier GR7 [69] | RAF HOCU/No 20(R) Sqn, Wittering | |
| ZG480 | BAe Harrier GR9 [70] | DPA/BAE Systems, Warton (conversion) | |
| ZG500 | BAe Harrier GR9 [71] | RAF JUMP, Cottesmore (conversion) | |
| ZG501 | BAe Harrier GR9 [72] | RAF AWC/FJWOEU, Coningsby | |
| ZG502 | BAe Harrier GR9 [73] | DPA/BAE Systems, Warton (conversion) | |
| ZG503 | BAe Harrier GR9 [74] | DPA/BAE Systems, Warton | |
| ZG504 | BAe Harrier GR9 [75] | DPA/BAE Systems, Warton (conversion) | |
| ZG505 | BAe Harrier GR9 [76] | RAF AWC/FJWOEU, Coningsby | |
| ZG506 | BAe Harrier GR7 [77] | RAF No 1 Sqn, Cottesmore | |
| ZG507 | BAe Harrier GR7 [78] | RAF HMF, Wittering (on rebuild) | |
| ZG508 | BAe Harrier GR7 [79] | RAF AWC/FJWOEU, Coningsby | |
| ZG509 | BAe Harrier GR7 [80] | RAF, Wittering | |
| ZG510 | BAe Harrier GR9 [81] | DPA/BAE Systems, Warton (conversion) | |
| ZG511 | BAe Harrier GR9 [82] | RAF No 1 Sqn, Cottesmore | |
| ZG512 | BAe Harrier GR9 [83] | RAF HOCU/No 20(R) Sqn, Wittering | |
| ZG530 | BAe Harrier GR7 [84] | RAF HOCU/No 20(R) Sqn, Wittering | |
| ZG531 | BAe Harrier GR9 [85] | RAF Cottesmore | |
| ZG705 | Panavia Tornado GR4A [J] | RAF No 13 Sqn, Marham | |
| ZG706 | Panavia Tornado GR1A [E] | RAF/DARA, stored St Athan | |
| ZG707 | Panavia Tornado GR4A [FJ] | RAF No 12 Sqn, Lossiemouth | |
| ZG709 | Panavia Tornado GR4A [V] | RAF No 14 Sqn, Lossiemouth | |
| ZG711 | Panavia Tornado GR4A [O] | RAF No 617 Sqn, Lossiemouth | |
| ZG712 | Panavia Tornado GR4A [F] | RAF Marham, WLT | |
| ZG713 | Panavia Tornado GR4A [G] | RAF No 13 Sqn, Marham | |
| ZG714 | Panavia Tornado GR4A [Q] | RAF No 13 Sqn, Marham | |
| ZG726 | Panavia Tornado GR4A [K] | RAF No 13 Sqn, Marham | |
| ZG727 | Panavia Tornado GR4A | RAF No 617 Sqn, Lossiemouth | |
| ZG728 | Panavia Tornado F3 (MM7229) | RAF St Athan, Fire Section | |
| ZG729 | Panavia Tornado GR4A [M] | DPA/BAE Systems, Warton | |
| ZG730 | Panavia Tornado F3 (MM7230) | Scrapped, January 2005 | |
| ZG731 | Panavia Tornado F3 | RAF AWC/FJWOEU, Coningsby | |
| ZG732 | Panavia Tornado F3 (MM7227) [WU] | RAF/DARA, stored St Athan | |
| ZG734 | Panavia Tornado F3 (MM7231) | RAF/DARA, stored St Athan | |
| ZG735 | Panavia Tornado F3 (MM7232) | RAF/DARA, stored St Athan | |
| ZG750 | Panavia Tornado GR4 [TX] | RAF No 15(R) Sqn, Lossiemouth | |
| ZG751 | Panavia Tornado F3 [D] | RAF No 1435 Flt, Mount Pleasant, FI | |
| ZG752 | Panavia Tornado GR4 [TTW] | RAF No 15(R) Sqn, Lossiemouth | |
| ZG753 | Panavia Tornado F3 [HH] | RAF No 111 Sqn, Leuchars | |
| ZG754 | Panavia Tornado GR4 [TP] | RAF No 15(R) Sqn, Lossiemouth | |
| ZG755 | Panavia Tornado F3 [DL] | RAF No 43 Sqn, Leuchars | |
| ZG756 | Panavia Tornado GR4 [BX] | RAF No 14 Sqn, Lossiemouth | |
| ZG757 | Panavia Tornado F3 [GN] | RAF No 43 Sqn, Leuchars | |
| ZG768 | Panavia Tornado F3 (MM7233) | RAF/DARA, stored St Athan | |
| ZG769 | Panavia Tornado GR4 | RAF/DARA, St Athan (damaged) | |
| ZG770 | Panavia Tornado F3 [WK] | RAF Leeming (wfu) | |
| ZG771 | Panavia Tornado GR4 [T] | RAF No 15(R) Sqn, Lossiemouth | |

| Notes | Serial | Type (other identity) [code] | Owner/operator, location or fate |
|---|---|---|---|
| | ZG772 | Panavia Tornado F3 [WJ] | RAF F3 OCU/No 56(R) Sqn, Leuchars |
| | ZG773 | Panavia Tornado GR4 | DPA/BAE Systems, Warton |
| | ZG774 | Panavia Tornado F3 [WK] | RAF F3 OCU/No 56(R) Sqn, Leuchars |
| | ZG775 | Panavia Tornado GR4 [FB] | RAF No 12 Sqn, Lossiemouth |
| | ZG776 | Panavia Tornado F3 [C] | RAF No 1435 Flt, Mount Pleasant, FI |
| | ZG777 | Panavia Tornado GR4 [TC] | RAF No 15(R) Sqn, Lossiemouth |
| | ZG778 | Panavia Tornado F3 [H] | RAF No 1435 Flt, Mount Pleasant, FI |
| | ZG779 | Panavia Tornado GR4 [N] | RAF No 2 Sqn, Marham |
| | ZG780 | Panavia Tornado F3 [XXV] | RAF No 25 Sqn, Leeming |
| | ZG791 | Panavia Tornado GR4 [P] | RAF No 13 Sqn, Marham |
| | ZG792 | Panavia Tornado GR4 [AJ-G] | RAF No 617 Sqn, Lossiemouth |
| | ZG793 | Panavia Tornado F3 [WM] | RAF F3 OCU/No 56(R) Sqn, Leuchars |
| | ZG794 | Panavia Tornado GR4 [TN] | RAF No 15(R) Sqn, Lossiemouth |
| | ZG795 | Panavia Tornado F3 [WD] | RAF Leeming (wfu) |
| | ZG796 | Panavia Tornado F3 | RAF Leeming (wfu) |
| | ZG797 | Panavia Tornado F3 [GF] | RAF No 43 Sqn, Leuchars |
| | ZG798 | Panavia Tornado F3 [F] | RAF No 1435 Flt, Mount Pleasant, FI |
| | ZG799 | Panavia Tornado F3 [HJ] | RAF No 111 Sqn, Leuchars |
| | ZG816 | WS61 Sea King HAS6 [014/L] | RN, stored HMS Sultan, Gosport |
| | ZG817 | WS61 Sea King HAS6 [702/PW] | RN AESS, HMS Sultan, Gosport |
| | ZG818 | WS61 Sea King HAS6 [707/PW] | RN, stored HMS Sultan, Gosport |
| | ZG819 | WS61 Sea King HAS6 [265/N] | RN AESS, HMS Sultan, Gosport |
| | ZG820 | WS61 Sea King HC4 [A] | RN No 845 Sqn, Yeovilton |
| | ZG821 | WS61 Sea King HC4 [G] | RN No 845 Sqn, Yeovilton |
| | ZG822 | WS61 Sea King HC4 [WS] | RN No 848 Sqn, Yeovilton |
| | ZG844 | PBN 2T Islander AL1 (G-BLNE) | AAC No 1 Flt/5 Regt, Aldergrove |
| | ZG845 | PBN 2T Islander AL1 (G-BLNT) | AAC No 1 Flt/5 Regt, Aldergrove |
| | ZG846 | PBN 2T Islander AL1 (G-BLNU) | AAC No 1 Flt/5 Regt, Aldergrove |
| | ZG847 | PBN 2T Islander AL1 (G-BLNV) | AAC No 1 Flt/5 Regt, Aldergrove |
| | ZG848 | PBN 2T Islander AL1 (G-BLNY) | AAC No 1 Flt/5 Regt, Aldergrove |
| | ZG857 | BAe Harrier GR9 | RAF JUMP, Cottesmore (conversion) |
| | ZG858 | BAe Harrier GR9 [90] | RAF JUMP, Cottesmore (conversion) |
| | ZG859 | BAe Harrier GR9 [91] | RAF Wittering, instructional use |
| | ZG860 | BAe Harrier GR9 | DPA/BAE Systems, Warton (conversion) |
| | ZG862 | BAe Harrier GR9 [94] | DPA/BAE Systems, Warton (conversion) |
| | ZG875 | WS61 Sea King HAS6 [013/L] | RN, stored HMS Sultan, Gosport (damaged) |
| | ZG879 | Powerchute Raider Mk 1 | DPA/Powerchute, Hereford |
| | ZG884 | WS Lynx AH9 | AAC No 661 Sqn/1 Regt, Gütersloh |
| | ZG885 | WS Lynx AH9 | AAC No 661 Sqn/1 Regt, Gütersloh |
| | ZG886 | WS Lynx AH9 | AAC No 661 Sqn/1 Regt, Gütersloh |
| | ZG887 | WS Lynx AH9 | AAC No 661 Sqn/1 Regt, Gütersloh |
| | ZG888 | WS Lynx AH9 | AAC No 661 Sqn/1 Regt, Gütersloh |
| | ZG889 | WS Lynx AH9 | AAC No 661 Sqn/1 Regt, Gütersloh |
| | ZG914 | WS Lynx AH9 | AAC No 661 Sqn/1 Regt, Gütersloh |
| | ZG915 | WS Lynx AH9 | AAC No 1 Regt, Gütersloh |
| | ZG916 | WS Lynx AH9 | AAC No 1 Regt, Gütersloh |
| | ZG917 | WS Lynx AH9 | AAC No 661 Sqn/1 Regt, Gütersloh |
| | ZG918 | WS Lynx AH9 | AAC No 1 Regt, Gütersloh |
| | ZG919 | WS Lynx AH9 | AAC No 661 Sqn/1 Regt, Gütersloh |
| | ZG920 | WS Lynx AH9 | AAC No 1 Regt, Gütersloh |
| | ZG921 | WS Lynx AH9 | AAC No 1 Regt, Gütersloh |
| | ZG922 | WS Lynx AH9 | AAC/DARA, stored Fleetlands |
| | ZG923 | WS Lynx AH9 | AAC No 661 Sqn/1 Regt, Gütersloh |
| | ZG969 | Pilatus PC-9 (HB-HQE) | BAE Systems Warton |
| | ZG989 | PBN 2T Islander ASTOR (G-DLRA) | DPA/PBN, Bembridge |
| | ZG993 | PBN 2T Islander AL1 (G-BOMD) | AAC No 1 Flight/5 Regt, Aldergrove |
| | ZG994 | PBN 2T Islander AL1 (G-BPLN) (fuselage) | Britten-Norman, stored Bembridge |
| | ZG995 | PBN 2T Defender AL1 (G-SURV) | RAF |
| | ZG996 | PBN 2T Defender AL1 (G-BWPR) | RAF |
| | ZG997 | PBN 2T Defender AL1 (G-BWPV) | RAF |
| | ZH101 | Boeing E-3D Sentry AEW1 | RAF No 8 Sqn/No 23 Sqn, Waddington |
| | ZH102 | Boeing E-3D Sentry AEW1 | RAF No 8 Sqn/No 23 Sqn, Waddington |
| | ZH103 | Boeing E-3D Sentry AEW1 | RAF No 8 Sqn/No 23 Sqn, Waddington |
| | ZH104 | Boeing E-3D Sentry AEW1 | RAF No 8 Sqn/No 23 Sqn, Waddington |
| | ZH105 | Boeing E-3D Sentry AEW1 | RAF No 8 Sqn/No 23 Sqn, Waddington |
| | ZH106 | Boeing E-3D Sentry AEW1 | RAF No 8 Sqn/No 23 Sqn, Waddington |
| | ZH107 | Boeing E-3D Sentry AEW1 | RAF No 8 Sqn/No 23 Sqn, Waddington |
| | ZH115 | Grob G109B Vigilant T1 [TA] | RAF No 635 VGS, Salmesbury |
| | ZH116 | Grob G109B Vigilant T1 [TB] | RAF No 618 VGS, Odiham |
| | ZH117 | Grob G109B Vigilant T1 [TC] | RAF No 642 VGS, Linton-on-Ouse |

| Serial | Type (other identity) [code] | Owner/operator, location or fate | Notes |
|--------|------------------------------|----------------------------------|-------|
| ZH118 | Grob G109B Vigilant T1 [TD] | RAF No 612 VGS, Abingdon | |
| ZH119 | Grob G109B Vigilant T1 [TE] | RAF No 632 VGS, Ternhill | |
| ZH120 | Grob G109B Vigilant T1 [TF] | RAF No 633 VGS, Cosford | |
| ZH121 | Grob G109B Vigilant T1 [TG] | RAF No 612 VGS, Abingdon | |
| ZH122 | Grob G109B Vigilant T1 [TH] | RAF No 664 VGS, Newtownards | |
| ZH123 | Grob G109B Vigilant T1 [TJ] | RAF No 637 VGS, Little Rissington | |
| ZH124 | Grob G109B Vigilant T1 [TK] | RAF No 642 VGS, Linton-on-Ouse | |
| ZH125 | Grob G109B Vigilant T1 [TL] | RAF No 613 VGS, Halton | |
| ZH126 | Grob G109B Vigilant T1 (D-KGRA) [TM] | RAF No 624 VGS, Chivenor RMB | |
| ZH127 | Grob G109B Vigilant T1 (D-KEEC) [TN] | RAF No 642 VGS, Linton-on-Ouse | |
| ZH128 | Grob G109B Vigilant T1 [TP] | RAF ACCGS/No 644 VGS, Syerston | |
| ZH129 | Grob G109B Vigilant T1 [TQ] | RAF No 635 VGS, Salmesbury | |
| ZH139 | BAe Harrier GR7 <R> (BAPC 191/ZD472) | RAF M&RU, Bottesford | |
| ZH141 | AS355F-1 Twin Squirrel (G-OILX) | RAF No 32(The Royal) Sqn, Northolt | |
| ZH144 | Grob G109B Vigilant T1 [TR] | RAF No 663 VGS, Kinloss | |
| ZH145 | Grob G109B Vigilant T1 [TS] | RAF ACCGS/No 644 VGS, Syerston | |
| ZH146 | Grob G109B Vigilant T1 [TT] | RAF No 664 VGS, Newtownards | |
| ZH147 | Grob G109B Vigilant T1 [TU] | RAF ACCGS/No 644 VGS, Syerston | |
| ZH148 | Grob G109B Vigilant T1 [TV] | RAF CGMF, Syerston | |
| ZH184 | Grob G109B Vigilant T1 [TW] | RAF No 632 VGS, Ternhill | |
| ZH185 | Grob G109B Vigilant T1 [TX] | RAF ACCGS/No 644 VGS, Syerston | |
| ZH186 | Grob G109B Vigilant T1 [TY] | RAF No 613 VGS, Halton | |
| ZH187 | Grob G109B Vigilant T1 [TZ] | RAF No 633 VGS, Cosford | |
| ZH188 | Grob G109B Vigilant T1 [UA] | RAF No 633 VGS, Cosford | |
| ZH189 | Grob G109B Vigilant T1 [UB] | RAF No 636 VGS, Aberporth | |
| ZH190 | Grob G109B Vigilant T1 [UC] | RAF ACCGS/No 644 VGS, Syerston | |
| ZH191 | Grob G109B Vigilant T1 [UD] | RAF No 645 VGS, Topcliffe | |
| ZH192 | Grob G109B Vigilant T1 [UE] | RAF No 635 VGS, Salmesbury | |
| ZH193 | Grob G109B Vigilant T1 [UF] | RAF No 633 VGS, Cosford | |
| ZH194 | Grob G109B Vigilant T1 [UG] | RAF ACCGS/No 644 VGS, Syerston | |
| ZH195 | Grob G109B Vigilant T1 [UH] | RAF No 642 VGS, Linton-on-Ouse | |
| ZH196 | Grob G109B Vigilant T1 [UJ] | RAF No 618 VGS, Odiham | |
| ZH197 | Grob G109B Vigilant T1 [UK] | RAF No 618 VGS, Odiham | |
| ZH200 | BAe Hawk 200 | BAE Systems Warton, Overseas Customer Training Centre | |
| ZH205 | Grob G109B Vigilant T1 [UL] | RAF No 634 VGS, St Athan | |
| ZH206 | Grob G109B Vigilant T1 [UM] | RAF No 635 VGS, Samlesbury | |
| ZH207 | Grob G109B Vigilant T1 [UN] | RAF No 632 VGS, Ternhill | |
| ZH208 | Grob G109B Vigilant T1 [UP] | RAF No 645 VGS, Topcliffe | |
| ZH209 | Grob G109B Vigilant T1 [UQ] | RAF No 634 VGS, St Athan | |
| ZH211 | Grob G109B Vigilant T1 [UR] | RAF No 636 VGS, Aberporth | |
| ZH247 | Grob G109B Vigilant T1 [US] | RAF No 618 VGS, Odiham | |
| ZH248 | Grob G109B Vigilant T1 [UT] | RAF No 637 VGS, Little Rissington | |
| ZH249 | Grob G109B Vigilant T1 [UU] | RAF No 633 VGS, Cosford | |
| ZH263 | Grob G109B Vigilant T1 [UV] | RAF No 632 VGS, Ternhill | |
| ZH264 | Grob G109B Vigilant T1 [UW] | RAF ACCGS/No 644 VGS, Syerston | |
| ZH265 | Grob G109B Vigilant T1 [UX] | RAF No 645 VGS, Topcliffe | |
| ZH266 | Grob G109B Vigilant T1 [UY] | RAF No 635 VGS, Samlesbury | |
| ZH267 | Grob G109B Vigilant T1 [UZ] | RAF No 645 VGS, Topcliffe | |
| ZH268 | Grob G109B Vigilant T1 [SA] | RAF No 612 VGS, Abingdon | |
| ZH269 | Grob G109B Vigilant T1 [SB] | RAF No 645 VGS, Topcliffe | |
| ZH270 | Grob G109B Vigilant T1 [SC] | RAF No 616 VGS, Henlow | |
| ZH271 | Grob G109B Vigilant T1 [SD] | RAF No 637 VGS, Little Rissington | |
| ZH278 | Grob G109B Vigilant T1 (D-KAIS) [SF] | RAF No 612 VGS, Abingdon | |
| ZH279 | Grob G109B Vigilant T1 (D-KNPS) [SG] | RAF No 613 VGS, Halton | |
| ZH536 | PBN 2T Islander CC2 (G-BSAH) | RAF Northolt Station Flight | |
| ZH540 | WS61 Sea King HAR3A [U] | RAF No 22 Sqn, B Flt, Wattisham | |
| ZH541 | WS61 Sea King HAR3A [V] | RAF No 22 Sqn, A Flt, Chivenor RMB | |
| ZH542 | WS61 Sea King HAR3A [W] | RAF No 22 Sqn, B Flt, Wattisham | |
| ZH543 | WS61 Sea King HAR3A [X] | DPA/Westland Helicopters, Yeovil | |
| ZH544 | WS61 Sea King HAR3A | RAF HMF, St Mawgan | |
| ZH545 | WS61 Sea King HAR3A [Z] | RAF No 22 Sqn, A Flt, Chivenor RMB | |
| ZH552 | Panavia Tornado F3 [ST] | RAF F3 OCU/No 56(R) Sqn, Leuchars | |
| ZH553 | Panavia Tornado F3 [DY] | RAF F3 OCU/No 56(R) Sqn, Leuchars | |
| ZH554 | Panavia Tornado F3 | RAF AWC/FJWOEU, Coningsby | |
| ZH555 | Panavia Tornado F3 [PT] | RAF No 43 Sqn, Leuchars | |
| ZH556 | Panavia Tornado F3 [HT] | RAF No 111 Sqn, Leuchars | |
| ZH557 | Panavia Tornado F3 [NT] | RAF F3 OCU/No 56(R) Sqn, Leuchars | |

| Notes | Serial | Type (other identity) [code] | Owner/operator, location or fate |
|---|---|---|---|
| | ZH559 | Panavia Tornado F3 [GT] | RAF F3 OCU/No 56(R) Sqn, Leuchars |
| | ZH588 | Eurofighter Typhoon (DA2) | DPA/BAE Systems, Warton |
| | ZH590 | Eurofighter Typhoon (DA4) | DPA/BAE Systems, Warton |
| | ZH653 | BAe Harrier T10 | DPA/BAE Systems, Warton |
| | ZH654 | BAe Harrier T10 | DPA/QinetiQ, stored Boscombe Down (wreck) |
| | ZH655 | BAe Harrier T10 [Q] | RAF, Wittering |
| | ZH656 | BAe Harrier T10 [104] | RAF HOCU/No 20(R) Sqn, Wittering |
| | ZH657 | BAe Harrier T10 [105] | RAF No 3 Sqn, Cottesmore |
| | ZH658 | BAe Harrier T10 [106] | RAF/DARA, St Athan |
| | ZH659 | BAe Harrier T10 [107] | RAF HOCU/No 20(R) Sqn, Wittering |
| | ZH660 | BAe Harrier T10 [108] | RAF HOCU/No 20(R) Sqn, Wittering |
| | ZH661 | BAe Harrier T10 [109] | RAF HOCU/No 20(R) Sqn, Wittering |
| | ZH662 | BAe Harrier T10 [110] | RAF HOCU/No 20(R) Sqn, Wittering |
| | ZH663 | BAe Harrier T12 [111] | DPA/BAE Systems, Warton (conversion) |
| | ZH664 | BAe Harrier T10 [112] | RAF HOCU/No 20(R) Sqn, Wittering |
| | ZH665 | BAe Harrier T10 [113] | DPA/BAE Systems, Warton |
| | ZH763 | BAC 1-11/539GL (G-BGKE) | DPA/AFD/QinetiQ, Boscombe Down |
| | ZH775 | B-V Chinook HC2 (N7424J) | RAF No 18 Sqn, Odiham |
| | ZH776 | B-V Chinook HC2 (N7424L) | RAF No 27 Sqn, Odiham |
| | ZH777 | B-V Chinook HC2 (N7424M) | RAF No 27 Sqn, Odiham |
| | ZH796 | BAe Sea Harrier FA2 [001] | RN No 801 Sqn, Yeovilton |
| | ZH797 | BAe Sea Harrier FA2 [000/L] | RN No 801 Sqn, Yeovilton |
| | ZH798 | BAe Sea Harrier FA2 [002/L] | RN, stored Shawbury |
| | ZH799 | BAe Sea Harrier FA2 [730] | Privately owned, Sproughton |
| | ZH800 | BAe Sea Harrier FA2 [011] | RN No 801 Sqn, Yeovilton |
| | ZH801 | BAe Sea Harrier FA2 [716/R] | RN SHOPS, Yeovilton |
| | ZH802 | BAe Sea Harrier FA2 [711] | RN SHOPS, Yeovilton |
| | ZH803 | BAe Sea Harrier FA2 [004/L] | RN No 801 Sqn, Yeovilton |
| | ZH804 | BAe Sea Harrier FA2 [007/L] | RN No 801 Sqn, Yeovilton |
| | ZH806 | BAe Sea Harrier FA2 [007] | Privately owned, Sproughton |
| | ZH807 | BAe Sea Harrier FA2 <ff> | Privately owned, Newport, Isle of Wight |
| | ZH808 | BAe Sea Harrier FA2 [003/N] | RN No 801 Sqn, Cyprus (wfu) |
| | ZH809 | BAe Sea Harrier FA2 | RN SHOPS, Yeovilton |
| | ZH810 | BAe Sea Harrier FA2 [125] | Privately owned, Sproughton |
| | ZH811 | BAe Sea Harrier FA2 [005/L] | RN No 801 Sqn, Yeovilton |
| | ZH812 | BAe Sea Harrier FA2 | RN SHOPS, Yeovilton |
| | ZH813 | BAe Sea Harrier FA2 [006/L] | RN No 801 Sqn, Yeovilton |
| | ZH814 | Bell 212HP (G-BGMH) | AAC No 7 Flt, Brunei |
| | ZH815 | Bell 212HP (G-BGCZ) | AAC No 7 Flt, Brunei |
| | ZH816 | Bell 212HP (G-BGMG) | AAC No 7 Flt, Brunei |
| | ZH821 | EHI-101 Merlin HM1 | DPA/Westland Helicopters, Yeovil |
| | ZH822 | EHI-101 Merlin HM1 | RN MDMF, Culdrose |
| | ZH823 | EHI-101 Merlin HM1 | DPA/Westland Helicopters, Yeovil |
| | ZH824 | EHI-101 Merlin HM1 | DPA/AFD/QinetiQ, Boscombe Down |
| | ZH825 | EHI-101 Merlin HM1 [583] | RN MDMF, Culdrose |
| | ZH826 | EHI-101 Merlin HM1 | RN MDMF, Culdrose |
| | ZH827 | EHI-101 Merlin HM1 | RN/DARA, stored Fleetlands |
| | ZH828 | EHI-101 Merlin HM1 [013/CU] | RN No 820 Sqn, Culdrose |
| | ZH829 | EHI-101 Merlin HM1 | RN/DARA, stored Fleetlands |
| | ZH830 | EHI-101 Merlin HM1 | DPA/AFD/QinetiQ, Boscombe Down |
| | ZH831 | EHI-101 Merlin HM1 [583] | RN No 824 Sqn, Culdrose |
| | ZH832 | EHI-101 Merlin HM1 | DPA/AFD/QinetiQ, Boscombe Down |
| | ZH833 | EHI-101 Merlin HM1 [500] | RN MDMF, Culdrose |
| | ZH834 | EHI-101 Merlin HM1 [538/CU] | RN No 700M OEU, Culdrose |
| | ZH835 | EHI-101 Merlin HM1 [580] | RN No 824 Sqn, Culdrose |
| | ZH836 | EHI-101 Merlin HM1 [268/CU] | RN No 814 Sqn, Culdrose |
| | ZH837 | EHI-101 Merlin HM1 [582/CU] | RN No 824 Sqn, Culdrose |
| | ZH838 | EHI-101 Merlin HM1 [539] | RN No 700M OEU, Culdrose |
| | ZH839 | EHI-101 Merlin HM1 [581/CU] | RN No 824 Sqn, Culdrose |
| | ZH840 | EHI-101 Merlin HM1 [537/CU] | RN No 700M OEU, Culdrose |
| | ZH841 | EHI-101 Merlin HM1 [012/CU] | RN No 820 Sqn, Culdrose |
| | ZH842 | EHI-101 Merlin HM1 [537/CU] | RN No 700M OEU, Culdrose |
| | ZH843 | EHI-101 Merlin HM1 | RN No 820 Sqn, Culdrose |
| | ZH844 | EHI-101 Merlin HM1 | RN FSAIU, Yeovilton (damaged) |
| | ZH845 | EHI-101 Merlin HM1 [535/CU] | DPA/Westland Helicopters, Yeovil |
| | ZH846 | EHI-101 Merlin HM1 [587/CU] | RN MDMF, Culdrose |
| | ZH847 | EHI-101 Merlin HM1 [585] | RN MDMF, Culdrose |
| | ZH848 | EHI-101 Merlin HM1 [500] | RN No 829 Sqn, Culdrose |
| | ZH849 | EHI-101 Merlin HM1 [584] | RN No 824 Sqn, Culdrose |
| | ZH850 | EHI-101 Merlin HM1 [462/WM] | RN No 829 Sqn, *Westminster* Flt, Culdrose |
| | ZH851 | EHI-101 Merlin HM1 [457] | RN No 829 Sqn, *Lancaster* Flt, Culdrose |

| Serial | Type (other identity) [code] | Owner/operator, location or fate | Notes |
|--------|------------------------------|----------------------------------|-------|
| ZH852 | EHI-101 Merlin HM1 [372/NL] | RN No 829 Sqn, *Northumberland* Flt, Culdrose | |
| ZH853 | EHI-101 Merlin HM1 | RN MDMF, Culdrose | |
| ZH854 | EHI-101 Merlin HM1 [580/CU] | RN MDMF, Culdrose | |
| ZH855 | EHI-101 Merlin HM1 [267/CU] | RN MDMF, Culdrose | |
| ZH856 | EHI-101 Merlin HM1 [266] | RN No 814 Sqn, Culdrose | |
| ZH857 | EHI-101 Merlin HM1 [415/MM] | RN No 829 Sqn, *Monmouth* Flt, Culdrose | |
| ZH858 | EHI-101 Merlin HM1 [415] | RN MDMF, Culdrose | |
| ZH860 | EHI-101 Merlin HM1 [269/CU] | RN No 814 Sqn, Culdrose | |
| ZH861 | EHI-101 Merlin HM1 [586] | RN No 824 Sqn, Culdrose | |
| ZH862 | EHI-101 Merlin HM1 [010/CU] | RN No 820 Sqn, Culdrose | |
| ZH863 | EHI-101 Merlin HM1 [270] | RN No 814 Sqn, Culdrose | |
| ZH864 | EHI-101 Merlin HM1 [011/CU] | RN No 820 Sqn, Culdrose | |
| ZH865 | Lockheed C-130J-30 Hercules C4 (N130JA) | DPA/AFD/QinetiQ, Boscombe Down | |
| ZH866 | Lockheed C-130J-30 Hercules C4 (N130JE) | RAF Lyneham Transport Wing | |
| ZH867 | Lockheed C-130J-30 Hercules C4 (N130JJ) | RAF Lyneham Transport Wing | |
| ZH868 | Lockheed C-130J-30 Hercules C4 (N130JN) | RAF Lyneham Transport Wing | |
| ZH869 | Lockheed C-130J-30 Hercules C4 (N130JV) | RAF Lyneham Transport Wing | |
| ZH870 | Lockheed C-130J-30 Hercules C4 (*N73235*/N78235) | RAF Lyneham Transport Wing | |
| ZH871 | Lockheed C-130J-30 Hercules C4 (N73238) | DPA/AFD/QinetiQ, Boscombe Down | |
| ZH872 | Lockheed C-130J-30 Hercules C4 (N4249Y) | RAF Lyneham Transport Wing | |
| ZH873 | Lockheed C-130J-30 Hercules C4 (N4242N) | RAF Lyneham Transport Wing | |
| ZH874 | Lockheed C-130J-30 Hercules C4 (N41030) | RAF Lyneham Transport Wing | |
| ZH875 | Lockheed C-130J-30 Hercules C4 (N4099R) | RAF Lyneham Transport Wing | |
| ZH876 | Lockheed C-130J-30 Hercules C4 (N4080M) | RAF Lyneham Transport Wing | |
| ZH877 | Lockheed C-130J-30 Hercules C4 (N4081M) | RAF Lyneham Transport Wing | |
| ZH878 | Lockheed C-130J-30 Hercules C4 (N73232) | RAF Lyneham Transport Wing | |
| ZH879 | Lockheed C-130J-30 Hercules C4 (N4080M) | RAF Lyneham Transport Wing | |
| ZH880 | Lockheed C-130J Hercules C5 (N73238) | DPA/AFD/QinetiQ, Boscombe Down | |
| ZH881 | Lockheed C-130J Hercules C5 (N4081M) | RAF Lyneham Transport Wing | |
| ZH882 | Lockheed C-130J Hercules C5 (N4099R) | RAF Lyneham Transport Wing | |
| ZH883 | Lockheed C-130J Hercules C5 (N4242N) | RAF Lyneham Transport Wing | |
| ZH884 | Lockheed C-130J Hercules C5 (N4249Y) | RAF Lyneham Transport Wing | |
| ZH885 | Lockheed C-130J Hercules C5 (N41030) | RAF Lyneham Transport Wing | |
| ZH886 | Lockheed C-130J Hercules C5 (N73235) | RAF Lyneham Transport Wing | |
| ZH887 | Lockheed C-130J Hercules C5 (N4187W) | RAF Lyneham Transport Wing | |
| ZH888 | Lockheed C-130J Hercules C5 (N4187) | RAF Lyneham Transport Wing | |
| ZH889 | Lockheed C-130J Hercules C5 (N4099R) | RAF Lyneham Transport Wing | |
| ZH890 | Grob G109B Vigilant T1 [SE] | RAF No 663 VGS, Kinloss | |
| ZH891 | B-V Chinook HC2A (N20075) | RAF No 18 Sqn, Odiham | |
| ZH892 | B-V Chinook HC2A (N2019V) [BL] | RAF No 18 Sqn, Odiham | |
| ZH893 | B-V Chinook HC2A (N2025L) [BM] | RAF No 27 Sqn, Odiham | |
| ZH894 | B-V Chinook HC2A (N2026E) | RAF No 18 Sqn, Odiham | |
| ZH895 | B-V Chinook HC2A (N2034K) | RAF No 18 Sqn, Odiham | |
| ZH896 | B-V Chinook HC2A (N2038G) | DPA/AFD/QinetiQ, Boscombe Down | |
| ZH897 | B-V Chinook HC3 (N2045G) | DPA/AFD/QinetiQ, Boscombe Down | |
| ZH898 | B-V Chinook HC3 (N2057Q) | DPA, stored Boscombe Down | |
| ZH899 | B-V Chinook HC3 (N2057R) | DPA, stored Boscombe Down | |

| Notes | Serial | Type (other identity) [code] | Owner/operator, location or fate |
|-------|--------|------------------------------|----------------------------------|
| | ZH900 | B-V Chinook HC3 (N2060H) | DPA, stored Boscombe Down |
| | ZH901 | B-V Chinook HC3 (N2060M) | DPA, stored Boscombe Down |
| | ZH902 | B-V Chinook HC3 (N2064W) | DPA, stored Boscombe Down |
| | ZH903 | B-V Chinook HC3 (N20671) | DPA, stored Boscombe Down |
| | ZH904 | B-V Chinook HC3 (N2083K) | Boeing, Philadelphia, for RAF |
| | ZJ100 | BAe Hawk 102D | BAE Systems Warton |
| | ZJ117 | EHI-101 Merlin HC3 | DPA/AFD/QinetiQ, Boscombe Down |
| | ZJ118 | EHI-101 Merlin HC3 [B] | RAF No 1419 Flt, Basrah, Iraq |
| | ZJ119 | EHI-101 Merlin HC3 [C] | RAF MDMF, RNAS Culdrose |
| | ZJ120 | EHI-101 Merlin HC3 [D] | RAF No 28 Sqn, Benson |
| | ZJ121 | EHI-101 Merlin HC3 [E] | RAF No 28 Sqn, Benson |
| | ZJ122 | EHI-101 Merlin HC3 [F] | RAF MDMF, RNAS Culdrose |
| | ZJ123 | EHI-101 Merlin HC3 [G] | RAF No 1419 Flt, Basrah, Iraq |
| | ZJ124 | EHI-101 Merlin HC3 [H] | RAF No 28 Sqn, Benson |
| | ZJ125 | EHI-101 Merlin HC3 [J] | RAF No 28 Sqn, Benson |
| | ZJ126 | EHI-101 Merlin HC3 [K] | RAF No 28 Sqn, Benson |
| | ZJ127 | EHI-101 Merlin HC3 [L] | RAF No 28 Sqn, Benson |
| | ZJ128 | EHI-101 Merlin HC3 [M] | RAF No 1419 Flt, Basrah, Iraq |
| | ZJ129 | EHI-101 Merlin HC3 [N] | RAF No 28 Sqn, Benson |
| | ZJ130 | EHI-101 Merlin HC3 [O] | RAF No 28 Sqn, Benson |
| | ZJ131 | EHI-101 Merlin HC3 [P] | RAF No 28 Sqn, Benson |
| | ZJ132 | EHI-101 Merlin HC3 [Q] | RAF MDMF, RNAS Culdrose |
| | ZJ133 | EHI-101 Merlin HC3 [R] | RAF No 1419 Flt, Basrah, Iraq |
| | ZJ134 | EHI-101 Merlin HC3 [S] | RAF MDMF, RNAS Culdrose |
| | ZJ135 | EHI-101 Merlin HC3 [T] | RAF No 28 Sqn, Benson |
| | ZJ136 | EHI-101 Merlin HC3 [U] | RAF MDMF, RNAS Culdrose |
| | ZJ137 | EHI-101 Merlin HC3 [W] | RAF No 28 Sqn, Benson |
| | ZJ138 | EHI-101 Merlin HC3 [X] | RAF No 28 Sqn, Benson |
| | ZJ139 | AS355F-1 Twin Squirrel (G-NUTZ) | RAF No 32(The Royal) Sqn, Northolt |
| | ZJ140 | AS355F-1 Twin Squirrel (G-FFHI) | RAF No 32(The Royal) Sqn, Northolt |
| | ZJ164 | AS365N-2 Dauphin 2 (G-BTLC) | RN/Bond Helicopters, Plymouth |
| | ZJ165 | AS365N-2 Dauphin 2 (G-NTOO) | RN/Bond Helicopters, Plymouth |
| | ZJ166 | WAH-64 Apache AH1 (N9219G) | DPA, stored Shawbury |
| | ZJ167 | WAH-64 Apache AH1 | AAC, stored Shawbury |
| | ZJ168 | WAH-64 Apache AH1 (N3123T) | DPA/Westland Helicopters, Yeovil |
| | ZJ169 | WAH-64 Apache AH1 (N3114H) | AAC No 673 Sqn/2 Regt, Middle Wallop |
| | ZJ170 | WAH-64 Apache AH1 (N3065U) | AAC, stored Shawbury |
| | ZJ171 | WAH-64 Apache AH1 (N3266T) | DPA/AFD/QinetiQ, Boscombe Down |
| | ZJ172 | WAH-64 Apache AH1 | AAC No 664 Sqn/9 Regt, Dishforth |
| | ZJ173 | WAH-64 Apache AH1 (N3266W) | AAC, stored Shawbury |
| | ZJ174 | WAH-64 Apache AH1 | AAC No 662 Sqn/3 Regt, Wattisham |
| | ZJ175 | WAH-64 Apache AH1 (N3218V) | AAC No 662 Sqn/3 Regt, Wattisham |
| | ZJ176 | WAH-64 Apache AH1 | AAC No 663 Sqn/3 Regt, Wattisham |
| | ZJ177 | WAH-64 Apache AH1 | DPA/Westland Helicopters, Yeovil |
| | ZJ178 | WAH-64 Apache AH1 | AAC No 663 Sqn/3 Regt, Wattisham |
| | ZJ179 | WAH-64 Apache AH1 | AAC No 663 Sqn/3 Regt, Wattisham |
| | ZJ180 | WAH-64 Apache AH1 | AAC No 662 Sqn/3 Regt, Wattisham |
| | ZJ181 | WAH-64 Apache AH1 | AAC No 662 Sqn/3 Regt, Wattisham |
| | ZJ182 | WAH-64 Apache AH1 | AAC No 662 Sqn/3 Regt, Wattisham |
| | ZJ183 | WAH-64 Apache AH1 | AAC No 664 Sqn/9 Regt, Dishforth |
| | ZJ184 | WAH-64 Apache AH1 | AAC No 662 Sqn/3 Regt, Wattisham |
| | ZJ185 | WAH-64 Apache AH1 | AAC No 664 Sqn/9 Regt, Dishforth |
| | ZJ186 | WAH-64 Apache AH1 | DPA/Westland Helicopters, Yeovil |
| | ZJ187 | WAH-64 Apache AH1 | AAC No 662 Sqn/3 Regt, Wattisham |
| | ZJ188 | WAH-64 Apache AH1 | DPA/Westland Helicopters, Yeovil |
| | ZJ189 | WAH-64 Apache AH1 | AAC, stored Shawbury |
| | ZJ190 | WAH-64 Apache AH1 | AAC No 662 Sqn/3 Regt, Wattisham |
| | ZJ191 | WAH-64 Apache AH1 | AAC No 673 Sqn/2 Regt, Middle Wallop |
| | ZJ192 | WAH-64 Apache AH1 | AAC No 663 Sqn/3 Regt, Wattisham |
| | ZJ193 | WAH-64 Apache AH1 | AAC No 664 Sqn/9 Regt, Dishforth |
| | ZJ194 | WAH-64 Apache AH1 | AAC No 662 Sqn/3 Regt, Wattisham |
| | ZJ195 | WAH-64 Apache AH1 | AAC, stored Shawbury |
| | ZJ196 | WAH-64 Apache AH1 | AAC No 664 Sqn/9 Regt, Dishforth |
| | ZJ197 | WAH-64 Apache AH1 | AAC, stored Shawbury |
| | ZJ198 | WAH-64 Apache AH1 | AAC, stored Shawbury |
| | ZJ199 | WAH-64 Apache AH1 | AAC, stored Shawbury |
| | ZJ200 | WAH-64 Apache AH1 | AAC, stored Shawbury |
| | ZJ202 | WAH-64 Apache AH1 | AAC, stored Shawbury |
| | ZJ203 | WAH-64 Apache AH1 | AAC No 663 Sqn/3 Regt, Wattisham |
| | ZJ204 | WAH-64 Apache AH1 | AAC No 656 Sqn/9 Regt, Dishforth |
| | ZJ205 | WAH-64 Apache AH1 | DPA/AFD/QinetiQ, Boscombe Down |
| | ZJ206 | WAH-64 Apache AH1 | AAC No 673 Sqn/2 Regt, Middle Wallop |

| Serial | Type (other identity) [code] | Owner/operator, location or fate | Notes |
|--------|------------------------------|----------------------------------|-------|
| ZJ207 | WAH-64 Apache AH1 | AAC No 673 Sqn/2 Regt, Middle Wallop | |
| ZJ208 | WAH-64 Apache AH1 | AAC No 656 Sqn/9 Regt, Dishforth | |
| ZJ209 | WAH-64 Apache AH1 | AAC No 664 Sqn/9 Regt, Dishforth | |
| ZJ210 | WAH-64 Apache AH1 | DPA/AFD/QinetiQ, Boscombe Down | |
| ZJ211 | WAH-64 Apache AH1 | AAC No 673 Sqn/2 Regt, Middle Wallop | |
| ZJ212 | WAH-64 Apache AH1 | AAC No 673 Sqn/2 Regt, Middle Wallop | |
| ZJ213 | WAH-64 Apache AH1 | AAC No 673 Sqn/2 Regt, Middle Wallop | |
| ZJ214 | WAH-64 Apache AH1 | AAC No 673 Sqn/2 Regt, Middle Wallop | |
| ZJ215 | WAH-64 Apache AH1 | AAC No 673 Sqn/2 Regt, Middle Wallop | |
| ZJ216 | WAH-64 Apache AH1 | AAC No 673 Sqn/2 Regt, Middle Wallop | |
| ZJ217 | WAH-64 Apache AH1 | AAC No 673 Sqn/2 Regt, Middle Wallop | |
| ZJ218 | WAH-64 Apache AH1 | AAC No 673 Sqn/2 Regt, Middle Wallop | |
| ZJ219 | WAH-64 Apache AH1 | AAC No 673 Sqn/2 Regt, Middle Wallop | |
| ZJ220 | WAH-64 Apache AH1 | AAC No 673 Sqn/2 Regt, Middle Wallop | |
| ZJ221 | WAH-64 Apache AH1 | AAC No 673 Sqn/2 Regt, Middle Wallop | |
| ZJ222 | WAH-64 Apache AH1 | AAC, stored Shawbury | |
| ZJ223 | WAH-64 Apache AH1 | AAC No 656 Sqn/9 Regt, Dishforth | |
| ZJ224 | WAH-64 Apache AH1 | AAC No 656 Sqn/9 Regt, Dishforth | |
| ZJ225 | WAH-64 Apache AH1 | AAC No 656 Sqn/9 Regt, Dishforth | |
| ZJ226 | WAH-64 Apache AH1 | DPA/Westland Helicopters, Yeovil | |
| ZJ227 | WAH-64 Apache AH1 | AAC No 656 Sqn/9 Regt, Dishforth | |
| ZJ228 | WAH-64 Apache AH1 | AAC No 656 Sqn/9 Regt, Dishforth | |
| ZJ229 | WAH-64 Apache AH1 | AAC No 656 Sqn/9 Regt, Dishforth | |
| ZJ230 | WAH-64 Apache AH1 | AAC No 664 Sqn/9 Regt, Dishforth | |
| ZJ231 | WAH-64 Apache AH1 | AAC No 664 Sqn/9 Regt, Dishforth | |
| ZJ232 | WAH-64 Apache AH1 | AAC No 664 Sqn/9 Regt, Dishforth | |
| ZJ233 | WAH-64 Apache AH1 | AAC No 656 Sqn/9 Regt, Dishforth | |
| ZJ234 | Bell 412EP Griffin HT1 (G-BWZR) [S] | DHFS No 60(R) Sqn, RAF Shawbury | |
| ZJ235 | Bell 412EP Griffin HT1 (G-BXBF) [I] | DHFS No 60(R) Sqn, RAF Shawbury | |
| ZJ236 | Bell 412EP Griffin HT1 (G-BXBE) [X] | DHFS No 60(R) Sqn, RAF Shawbury | |
| ZJ237 | Bell 412EP Griffin HT1 (G-BXFF) [T] | DHFS No 60(R) Sqn, RAF Shawbury | |
| ZJ238 | Bell 412EP Griffin HT1 (G-BXHC) [Y] | DHFS No 60(R) Sqn, RAF Shawbury | |
| ZJ239 | Bell 412EP Griffin HT1 (G-BXFH) [R] | DHFS No 60(R) Sqn, RAF Shawbury | |
| ZJ240 | Bell 412EP Griffin HT1 (G-BXIR) [U] | DHFS No 60(R) Sqn/SARTU, RAF Valley | |
| ZJ241 | Bell 412EP Griffin HT1 (G-BXIS) [L] | DHFS No 60(R) Sqn/SARTU, RAF Valley | |
| ZJ242 | Bell 412EP Griffin HT1 (G-BXDK) [E] | DHFS No 60(R) Sqn, RAF Shawbury | |
| ZJ243 | AS350BA Squirrel HT2 (G-BWZS) | DHFS, RAF Shawbury | |
| ZJ244 | AS350BA Squirrel HT2 (G-BXMD) | School of Army Aviation/No 670 Sqn, Middle Wallop | |
| ZJ245 | AS350BA Squirrel HT2 (G-BXME) | School of Army Aviation/No 670 Sqn, Middle Wallop | |
| ZJ246 | AS350BA Squirrel HT2 (G-BXMJ) | School of Army Aviation/No 670 Sqn, Middle Wallop | |
| ZJ247 | AS350BA Squirrel HT2 (G-BXNB) | School of Army Aviation/No 670 Sqn, Middle Wallop | |
| ZJ248 | AS350BA Squirrel HT2 (G-BXNE) | School of Army Aviation/No 670 Sqn, Middle Wallop | |
| ZJ249 | AS350BA Squirrel HT2 (G-BXNJ) | School of Army Aviation/No 670 Sqn, Middle Wallop | |
| ZJ250 | AS350BA Squirrel HT2 (G-BXNY) | School of Army Aviation/No 670 Sqn, Middle Wallop | |
| ZJ251 | AS350BA Squirrel HT2 (G-BXOG) | DHFS, RAF Shawbury | |
| ZJ252 | AS350BA Squirrel HT2 (G-BXOK) | School of Army Aviation/No 670 Sqn, Middle Wallop | |
| ZJ253 | AS350BA Squirrel HT2 (G-BXPG) | School of Army Aviation/No 670 Sqn, Middle Wallop | |
| ZJ254 | AS350BA Squirrel HT2 (G-BXPJ) | School of Army Aviation/No 670 Sqn, Middle Wallop | |
| ZJ255 | AS350BB Squirrel HT1 (G-BXAG) | DHFS, RAF Shawbury | |
| ZJ256 | AS350BB Squirrel HT1 (G-BXCE) | DHFS, RAF Shawbury | |
| ZJ257 | AS350BB Squirrel HT1 (G-BXDJ) | DHFS, RAF Shawbury | |
| ZJ259 | AS350BB Squirrel HT1 (G-BXFJ) | DHFS, RAF Shawbury | |
| ZJ260 | AS350BB Squirrel HT1 (G-BXGB) | DHFS, RAF Shawbury | |
| ZJ261 | AS350BB Squirrel HT1 (G-BXGJ) | DHFS, RAF Shawbury | |
| ZJ262 | AS350BB Squirrel HT1 (G-BXHB) | DHFS, RAF Shawbury | |
| ZJ263 | AS350BB Squirrel HT1 (G-BXHK) | DHFS, RAF Shawbury | |

| Notes | Serial | Type (other identity) [code] | Owner/operator, location or fate |
|---|---|---|---|
| | ZJ264 | AS350BB Squirrel HT1 (G-BXHW) | DHFS, RAF Shawbury |
| | ZJ265 | AS350BB Squirrel HT1 (G-BXHX) | DHFS, RAF Shawbury |
| | ZJ266 | AS350BB Squirrel HT1 (G-BXIL) | DHFS, RAF Shawbury |
| | ZJ267 | AS350BB Squirrel HT1 (G-BXIP) | DHFS, RAF Shawbury |
| | ZJ268 | AS350BB Squirrel HT1 (G-BXJE) | DHFS, RAF Shawbury |
| | ZJ269 | AS350BB Squirrel HT1 (G-BXJN) | DHFS, RAF Shawbury |
| | ZJ270 | AS350BB Squirrel HT1 (G-BXJR) | DHFS, RAF Shawbury |
| | ZJ271 | AS350BB Squirrel HT1 (G-BXKE) | DHFS, RAF Shawbury |
| | ZJ272 | AS350BB Squirrel HT1 (G-BXKN) | DHFS, RAF Shawbury |
| | ZJ273 | AS350BB Squirrel HT1 (G-BXKP) | DHFS, RAF Shawbury |
| | ZJ274 | AS350BB Squirrel HT1 (G-BXKR) | DHFS, RAF Shawbury |
| | ZJ275 | AS350BB Squirrel HT1 (G-BXLB) | DHFS, RAF Shawbury |
| | ZJ276 | AS350BB Squirrel HT1 (G-BXLE) | DHFS, RAF Shawbury |
| | ZJ277 | AS350BB Squirrel HT1 (G-BXLH) | DHFS, RAF Shawbury |
| | ZJ278 | AS350BB Squirrel HT1 (G-BXMB) | DHFS, RAF Shawbury |
| | ZJ279 | AS350BB Squirrel HT1 (G-BXMC) | DHFS, RAF Shawbury |
| | ZJ280 | AS350BB Squirrel HT1 (G-BXMI) | DHFS, RAF Shawbury |
| | ZJ514 | BAE Systems Nimrod MRA4 (XV251) [PA-4] | DPA/BAE Systems, Woodford (conversion) |
| | ZJ515 | BAE Systems Nimrod MRA4 (XV258) [PA-5] | DPA/BAE Systems, Woodford (conversion) |
| | ZJ516 | BAE Systems Nimrod MRA4 (XV247) [PA-1] | DPA/BAE Systems, Woodford |
| | ZJ517 | BAE Systems Nimrod MRA4 (XV242) [PA-3] | DPA/BAE Systems, Woodford |
| | ZJ518 | BAE Systems Nimrod MRA4 (XV234) [PA-2] | DPA/BAE Systems, Warton |
| | ZJ519 | BAE Systems Nimrod MRA4 (XZ284) [PA-6] | DPA/BAE Systems, Woodford (conversion) |
| | ZJ520 | BAE Systems Nimrod MRA4 (XV233) [PA-7] | DPA/BAE Systems, Woodford (conversion) |
| | ZJ521 | BAE Systems Nimrod MRA4 [PA-8] | BAE Systems, for RAF |
| | ZJ522 | BAE Systems Nimrod MRA4 [PA-9] | BAE Systems, for RAF |
| | ZJ523 | BAE Systems Nimrod MRA4 [PA-10] | BAE Systems, for RAF |
| | ZJ524 | BAE Systems Nimrod MRA4 [PA-11] | BAE Systems, for RAF |
| | ZJ525 | BAE Systems Nimrod MRA4 [PA-12] | BAE Systems, for RAF |
| | ZJ526 | BAE Systems Nimrod MRA4 [PA-13] | BAE Systems, for RAF |
| | ZJ527 | BAE Systems Nimrod MRA4 [PA-14] | BAE Systems, for RAF |
| | ZJ528 | BAE Systems Nimrod MRA4 [PA-15] | BAE Systems, for RAF |
| | ZJ529 | BAE Systems Nimrod MRA4 [PA-16] | BAE Systems, for RAF |
| | ZJ530 | BAE Systems Nimrod MRA4 [PA-17] | BAE Systems, for RAF |
| | ZJ531 | BAE Systems Nimrod MRA4 [PA-18] | BAE Systems, for RAF |
| | ZJ583 | Meteor Mirach | RN No 792 Sqn, Culdrose |
| | ZJ584 | Meteor Mirach | RN No 792 Sqn, Culdrose |
| | ZJ585 | Meteor Mirach | RN No 792 Sqn, Culdrose |
| | ZJ587 | Meteor Mirach | RN No 792 Sqn, Culdrose |
| | ZJ591 | Meteor Mirach | RN No 792 Sqn, Culdrose |
| | ZJ593 | Meteor Mirach | RN No 792 Sqn, Culdrose |
| | ZJ600 | Meteor Mirach | RN No 792 Sqn, Culdrose |
| | ZJ601 | Meteor Mirach | RN No 792 Sqn, Culdrose |
| | ZJ602 | Meteor Mirach | RN No 792 Sqn, Culdrose |
| | ZJ605 | Meteor Mirach | RN No 792 Sqn, Culdrose |
| | ZJ608 | Meteor Mirach | RN No 792 Sqn, Culdrose |
| | ZJ609 | Meteor Mirach | RN No 792 Sqn, Culdrose |
| | ZJ610 | Meteor Mirach | RN No 792 Sqn, Culdrose |
| | ZJ612 | Meteor Mirach | RN No 792 Sqn, Culdrose |
| | ZJ613 | Meteor Mirach | RN No 792 Sqn, Culdrose |
| | ZJ614 | Meteor Mirach | RN No 792 Sqn, Culdrose |
| | ZJ615 | Meteor Mirach | RN No 792 Sqn, Culdrose |
| | ZJ617 | Meteor Mirach | RN No 792 Sqn, Culdrose |
| | ZJ635 | AS355F-1 Twin Squirrel (G-NEXT) | DPA/ETPS, Boscombe Down |
| | ZJ645 | D-BD Alpha Jet (98+62) | DPA/ETPS, Boscombe Down |
| | ZJ646 | D-BD Alpha Jet (98+55) | DPA/AFD/QinetiQ, Boscombe Down |
| | ZJ647 | D-BD Alpha Jet (98+71) | DPA/ETPS, Boscombe Down |
| | ZJ648 | D-BD Alpha Jet (98+09) | DPA/AFD/QinetiQ, Boscombe Down |
| | ZJ649 | D-BD Alpha Jet (98+73) | DPA/AFD/QinetiQ, Boscombe Down |
| | ZJ650 | D-BD Alpha Jet (98+35) | DPA/AFD/QinetiQ, Boscombe Down |
| | ZJ651 | D-BD Alpha Jet (41+42) | DPA/ETPS, Boscombe Down |
| | ZJ652 | D-BD Alpha Jet (41+09) | DPA/QinetiQ Boscombe Down, spares use |
| | ZJ653 | D-BD Alpha Jet (40+22) | DPA/QinetiQ Boscombe Down, spares use |
| | ZJ654 | D-BD Alpha Jet (41+02) | DPA/QinetiQ Boscombe Down, spares use |
| | ZJ655 | D-BD Alpha Jet (41+19) | DPA/QinetiQ Boscombe Down, spares use |
| | ZJ656 | D-BD Alpha Jet (41+40) | DPA/QinetiQ Boscombe Down, spares use |

| Serial | Type (other identity) [code] | Owner/operator, location or fate | Notes |
|--------|------------------------------|----------------------------------|-------|
| ZJ657 | Meteor Mirach | RN No 792 Sqn, Culdrose | |
| ZJ658 | Meteor Mirach | RN No 792 Sqn, Culdrose | |
| ZJ659 | Meteor Mirach | RN No 792 Sqn, Culdrose | |
| ZJ660 | Meteor Mirach | RN No 792 Sqn, Culdrose | |
| ZJ661 | Meteor Mirach | RN No 792 Sqn, Culdrose | |
| ZJ662 | Meteor Mirach | RN No 792 Sqn, Culdrose | |
| ZJ668 | Intora Firebird | *Not built* | |
| ZJ669 | Intora Firebird | *Not built* | |
| ZJ690 | Bombardier Sentinel R1 (C-GJRG) | DPA/Raytheon, Chester | |
| ZJ691 | Bombardier Sentinel R1 (C-FZVM) | DPA/Raytheon, Chester | |
| ZJ692 | Bombardier Sentinel R1 (C-FZWW) | DPA/Raytheon, Chester | |
| ZJ693 | Bombardier Sentinel R1 (C-FZXC) | DPA/Raytheon, Chester | |
| ZJ694 | Bombardier Sentinel R1 (C-FZYL) | DPA/Raytheon, Chester | |
| ZJ699 | Eurofighter Typhoon (PT001) | DPA/BAE Systems, Warton | |
| ZJ700 | Eurofighter Typhoon (PS002) | DPA/BAE Systems, Warton | |
| ZJ703 | Bell 412EP Griffin HAR2 (G-CBST) [*Spades*,3] | RAF No 84 Sqn, Akrotiri | |
| ZJ704 | Bell 412EP Griffin HAR2 (G-CBWT) [*Clubs*,4] | RAF No 84 Sqn, Akrotiri | |
| ZJ705 | Bell 412EP Griffin HAR2 (G-CBXL) [*Hearts*, 5] | RAF No 84 Sqn, Akrotiri | |
| ZJ706 | Bell 412EP Griffin HAR2 (G-CBYR) [*Diamonds*, 6] | RAF No 84 Sqn, Akrotiri | |
| ZJ707 | Bell 412EP Griffin HT1 (G-CBUB) [O] | DHFS No 60(R) Sqn, RAF Shawbury | |
| ZJ708 | Bell 412EP Griffin HT1 (G-CBVP) [K] | DHFS No 60(R) Sqn, RAF Shawbury | |
| ZJ721 | Meteor Mirach | RN No 792 Sqn, Culdrose | |
| ZJ722 | Meteor Mirach | RN No 792 Sqn, Culdrose | |
| ZJ723 | Meteor Mirach | RN No 792 Sqn, Culdrose | |
| ZJ724 | Meteor Mirach | RN No 792 Sqn, Culdrose | |
| ZJ725 to ZJ776 | Meteor Mirach | DPA/QinetiQ/RN | |
| ZJ800 | Eurofighter Typhoon T1 [BC] | RAF No 29(R) Sqn, Coningsby | |
| ZJ801 | Eurofighter Typhoon T1 [BJ] | RAF No 29(R) Sqn, Coningsby | |
| ZJ802 | Eurofighter Typhoon T1 [BB] | RAF No 29(R) Sqn, Coningsby | |
| ZJ803 | Eurofighter Typhoon T1 [BA] | RAF No 29(R) Sqn, Coningsby | |
| ZJ804 | Eurofighter Typhoon T1 | DPA/BAE Systems, Warton | |
| ZJ805 | Eurofighter Typhoon T1 [BD] | RAF No 29(R) Sqn, Coningsby | |
| ZJ806 | Eurofighter Typhoon T1 [BE] | RAF No 29(R) Sqn, Coningsby | |
| ZJ807 | Eurofighter Typhoon T1 [BF] | RAF No 29(R) Sqn, Coningsby | |
| ZJ808 | Eurofighter Typhoon T1 [BG] | RAF No 29(R) Sqn, Coningsby | |
| ZJ809 | Eurofighter Typhoon T1 [BH] | RAF No 29(R) Sqn, Coningsby | |
| ZJ810 | Eurofighter Typhoon T1 [BI] | RAF No 29(R) Sqn, Coningsby | |
| ZJ811 | Eurofighter Typhoon T1A [AZ] | RAF No 17(R) Sqn, Coningsby | |
| ZJ812 | Eurofighter Typhoon T1A [BK] | RAF No 29(R) Sqn, Coningsby | |
| ZJ813 | Eurofighter Typhoon T1A [BL] | RAF No 29(R) Sqn, Coningsby | |
| ZJ814 | Eurofighter Typhoon T1A | DPA/BAE Systems, for RAF | |
| ZJ815 | Eurofighter Typhoon T1A | DPA/BAE Systems, for RAF | |
| ZJ910 | Eurofighter Typhoon F2 | DPA/BAE Systems, for RAF | |
| ZJ911 | Eurofighter Typhoon F2 [BZ] | RAF No 29(R) Sqn, Coningsby | |
| ZJ912 | Eurofighter Typhoon F2 [AB] | RAF No 17(R) Sqn, Coningsby | |
| ZJ913 | Eurofighter Typhoon F2 [AA] | RAF No 17(R) Sqn, Coningsby | |
| ZJ914 | Eurofighter Typhoon F2 [AC] | RAF No 17(R) Sqn, Coningsby | |
| ZJ915 | Eurofighter Typhoon F2 [BY] | RAF No 29(R) Sqn, Coningsby | |
| ZJ916 | Eurofighter Typhoon F2 [AD] | RAF No 17(R) Sqn, Coningsby | |
| ZJ917 | Eurofighter Typhoon F2 [AE] | RAF No 17(R) Sqn, Coningsby | |
| ZJ918 | Eurofighter Typhoon F2 | DPA/BAE Systems, for RAF | |
| ZJ919 | Eurofighter Typhoon F2 | DPA/BAE Systems, for RAF | |
| ZJ920 | Eurofighter Typhoon F2 [BX] | RAF No 29(R) Sqn, Coningsby | |
| ZJ921 | Eurofighter Typhoon F2 [BW] | RAF No 29(R) Sqn, Coningsby | |
| ZJ922 | Eurofighter Typhoon F2 | DPA/BAE Systems, for RAF | |
| ZJ923 | Eurofighter Typhoon F2 | DPA/BAE Systems, for RAF | |
| ZJ924 | Eurofighter Typhoon F2 | DPA/BAE Systems, for RAF | |
| ZJ925 | Eurofighter Typhoon F2 | DPA/BAE Systems, for RAF | |
| ZJ926 | Eurofighter Typhoon F2 | DPA/BAE Systems, for RAF | |
| ZJ927 | Eurofighter Typhoon F2 | DPA/BAE Systems, for RAF | |
| ZJ928 | Eurofighter Typhoon F2 | DPA/BAE Systems, for RAF | |
| ZJ929 | Eurofighter Typhoon F2 | DPA/BAE Systems, for RAF | |
| ZJ930 | Eurofighter Typhoon F2 | DPA/BAE Systems, for RAF | |
| ZJ931 | Eurofighter Typhoon F2 | DPA/BAE Systems, for RAF | |
| ZJ932 | Eurofighter Typhoon F2 | DPA/BAE Systems, for RAF | |

| Notes | Serial | Type (other identity) [code] | Owner/operator, location or fate |
|---|---|---|---|
| | ZJ933 | Eurofighter Typhoon F2 | DPA/BAE Systems, for RAF |
| | ZJ934 | Eurofighter Typhoon F2 | DPA/BAE Systems, for RAF |
| | ZJ935 | Eurofighter Typhoon F2 | DPA/BAE Systems, for RAF |
| | ZJ936 | Eurofighter Typhoon F2 | DPA/BAE Systems, for RAF |
| | ZJ937 | Eurofighter Typhoon F2 | DPA/BAE Systems, for RAF |
| | ZJ938 | Eurofighter Typhoon F2 | DPA/BAE Systems, for RAF |
| | ZJ939 | Eurofighter Typhoon F2 | DPA/BAE Systems, for RAF |
| | ZJ940 | Eurofighter Typhoon F2 | DPA/BAE Systems, for RAF |
| | ZJ941 | Eurofighter Typhoon F2 | DPA/BAE Systems, for RAF |
| | ZJ942 | Eurofighter Typhoon F2 | DPA/BAE Systems, for RAF |
| | ZJ943 | Eurofighter Typhoon F2 | DPA/BAE Systems, for RAF |
| | ZJ944 | Eurofighter Typhoon F2 | DPA/BAE Systems, for RAF |
| | ZJ945 | Eurofighter Typhoon F2 | DPA/BAE Systems, for RAF |
| | ZJ951 | BAE Systems Hawk 120D | BAE Systems, Warton |
| | ZJ954 | SA330H Puma HC1 (SAAF 144) | DPA/Westland Helicopters, Yeovil |
| | ZJ955 | SA330H Puma HC1 (SAAF 148) | DPA/Eurocopter, for RAF |
| | ZJ956 | SA330H Puma HC1 (SAAF 172) | DPA/Eurocopter, for RAF |
| | ZJ957 | SA330H Puma HC1 (SAAF 169) | DPA/Eurocopter, for RAF |
| | ZJ958 | SA330H Puma (SAAF 173) | DPA, stored DSDC Llangennech |
| | ZJ959 | SA330H Puma (SAAF 184) | DPA, stored DSDC Llangennech |
| | ZJ960 | Grob G109B Vigilant T1 (D-KSMU) [SH] | RAF No 663 VGS, Kinloss |
| | ZJ961 | Grob G109B Vigilant T1 (D-KLCW) [SJ] | RAF ACCGS/No 644 VGS, Syerston |
| | ZJ962 | Grob G109B Vigilant T1 (D-KBEU) [SK] | RAF No 613 VGS, Halton |
| | ZJ963 | Grob G109B Vigilant T1 (D-KMSN) [SL] | RAF No 616 VGS, Henlow |
| | ZJ964 | Bell 212HP (G-BJGV) [A] | AAC No 25 Flt, Belize |
| | ZJ965 | Bell 212HP (G-BJGU) [B] | AAC No 25 Flt, Belize |
| | ZJ966 | Bell 212HP (G-BJJO) [C] | AAC No 25 Flt, Belize |
| | ZJ967 | Grob G109B Vigilant T1 (G-DEWS) [SM] | RAF ACCGS/No 644 VGS, Syerston |
| | ZJ968 | Grob G109B Vigilant T1 (N109BT) [SN] | RAF No 616 VGS, Henlow |
| | ZJ969 | Bell 212 (G-BGLJ) | AAC No 671 Sqn/2 Regt, Middle Wallop |
| | ZJ972 | WS Lynx 120 | *To Oman as 758, 14 July 2005* |
| | ZJ978 | WS Lynx 120 | *To Oman as 764, 27 October 2004* |
| | ZJ979 | WS Lynx 120 | *To Oman as 765, 7 January 2005* |
| | ZJ980 | WS Lynx 120 | *To Oman as 766, 7 January 2005* |
| | ZJ981 | WS Lynx 120 | *To Oman as 767, 27 January 2005* |
| | ZJ982 | WS Lynx 120 | *To Oman as 768, 1 November 2005* |
| | ZJ983 | WS Lynx 120 | *To Oman as 769, 14 July 2005* |
| | ZJ984 | WS Lynx 120 | *To Oman as 770, 14 July 2005* |
| | ZJ985 | WS Lynx 120 | *To Oman as 771, 1 November 2005* |
| | ZJ986 | WS Lynx 120 | *To Oman as 772, 1 November 2005* |
| | ZJ987 | WS Lynx 110 | *To Thai Navy as 2313, December 2004* |
| | ZJ988 | WS Lynx 110 | *To Thai Navy as 2314, December 2004* |
| | ZJ990 | EHI-101 Merlin Mk512 | Westland Helicopters, for Denmark as M-501 |
| | ZJ991 | EHI-101 Merlin Mk512 | Westland Helicopters, for Denmark as M-502 |
| | ZJ992 | EHI-101 Merlin Mk512 | Westland Helicopters, for Denmark as M-503 |
| | ZJ993 | EHI-101 Merlin Mk512 | Westland Helicopters, for Denmark as M-504 |
| | ZJ994 | EHI-101 Merlin Mk512 | Westland Helicopters, for Denmark as M-505 |
| | ZJ995 | EHI-101 Merlin Mk512 | Westland Helicopters, for Denmark as M-506 |
| | ZJ996 | EHI-101 Merlin Mk512 | Westland Helicopters, for Denmark as M-507 |
| | ZJ997 | EHI-101 Merlin Mk512 | Westland Helicopters, for Denmark as M-508 |
| | ZJ998 | EHI-101 Merlin Mk512 | Westland Helicopters, for Denmark as M-509 |
| | ZJ999 | EHI-101 Merlin Mk512 | Westland Helicopters, for Denmark as M-510 |
| | ZK001 | EHI-101 Merlin Mk512 | Westland Helicopters, for Denmark as M-511 |
| | ZK002 | EHI-101 Merlin Mk512 | Westland Helicopters, for Denmark as M-512 |

| Serial | Type (other identity) [code] | Owner/operator, location or fate | Notes |
|--------|------------------------------|----------------------------------|-------|
| ZK003 | EHI-101 Merlin Mk512 | Westland Helicopters, for Denmark as M-513 | |
| ZK004 | EHI-101 Merlin Mk512 | Westland Helicopters, for Denmark as M-514 | |
| ZK005 | Grob G109B Vigilant T1 (OH-797) [SP] | RAF ACCGS/No 644 VGS, Syerston | |
| ZK010 | BAE Systems Hawk 128 | DPA/BAE Systems, Warton | |
| ZK011 | BAE Systems Hawk 128 | Reservation for RAF | |
| ZK012 | BAE Systems Hawk 128 | Reservation for RAF | |
| ZK013 | BAE Systems Hawk 128 | Reservation for RAF | |
| ZK014 | BAE Systems Hawk 128 | Reservation for RAF | |
| ZK015 | BAE Systems Hawk 128 | Reservation for RAF | |
| ZK016 | BAE Systems Hawk 128 | Reservation for RAF | |
| ZK017 | BAE Systems Hawk 128 | Reservation for RAF | |
| ZK018 | BAE Systems Hawk 128 | Reservation for RAF | |
| ZK019 | BAE Systems Hawk 128 | Reservation for RAF | |
| ZK020 | BAE Systems Hawk 128 | Reservation for RAF | |
| ZK021 | BAE Systems Hawk 128 | Reservation for RAF | |
| ZK022 | BAE Systems Hawk 128 | Reservation for RAF | |
| ZK023 | BAE Systems Hawk 128 | Reservation for RAF | |
| ZK024 | BAE Systems Hawk 128 | Reservation for RAF | |
| ZK025 | BAE Systems Hawk 128 | Reservation for RAF | |
| ZK026 | BAE Systems Hawk 128 | Reservation for RAF | |
| ZK027 | BAE Systems Hawk 128 | Reservation for RAF | |
| ZK028 | BAE Systems Hawk 128 | Reservation for RAF | |
| ZK029 | BAE Systems Hawk 128 | Reservation for RAF | |
| ZK030 | BAE Systems Hawk 128 | Reservation for RAF | |
| ZK031 | BAE Systems Hawk 128 | Reservation for RAF | |
| ZK032 | BAE Systems Hawk 128 | Reservation for RAF | |
| ZK033 | BAE Systems Hawk 128 | Reservation for RAF | |
| ZK034 | BAE Systems Hawk 128 | Reservation for RAF | |
| ZK035 | BAE Systems Hawk 128 | Reservation for RAF | |
| ZK036 | BAE Systems Hawk 128 | Reservation for RAF | |
| ZK037 | BAE Systems Hawk 128 | Reservation for RAF | |
| ZK038 | BAE Systems Hawk 128 | Reservation for RAF | |
| ZK039 | BAE Systems Hawk 128 | Reservation for RAF | |
| ZK040 | BAE Systems Hawk 128 | Reservation for RAF | |
| ZK041 | BAE Systems Hawk 128 | Reservation for RAF | |
| ZK042 | BAE Systems Hawk 128 | Reservation for RAF | |
| ZK043 | BAE Systems Hawk 128 | Reservation for RAF | |
| ZK044 | BAE Systems Hawk 128 | Reservation for RAF | |
| ZK105* | Boeing Scan Eagle UAV | DPA/RN, Boscombe Down | |
| ZK106 | BAE Systems Hawk 129 | BAE Systems, for Bahrain | |
| ZK107 | BAE Systems Hawk 129 | BAE Systems, for Bahrain | |
| ZK108 | BAE Systems Hawk 129 | BAE Systems, for Bahrain | |
| ZK109 | BAE Systems Hawk 129 | BAE Systems, for Bahrain | |
| ZK110 | BAE Systems Hawk 129 | BAE Systems, for Bahrain | |
| ZK111 | BAE Systems Hawk 129 | BAE Systems, for Bahrain | |
| ZK112 | EHI-101 Merlin Mk518 | Westland Helicopters, for Japan MSDF | |
| ZK113 | Panavia Tornado IDS | DPA/BAE Systems, Warton (R.Saudi AF 6606) | |
| ZK115 | WS Super Lynx 300 | Westland Helicopters, for South Africa | |
| ZK116 | WS Super Lynx 300 | Westland Helicopters, for South Africa | |
| ZK117 | WS Super Lynx 300 | Westland Helicopters, for South Africa | |
| ZK118 | WS Super Lynx 300 | Westland Helicopters, for South Africa | |
| ZK119 | Pilatus PC-9 (HB-HQU/RSAF2204) | BAE Systems, Warton | |
| ZK450 | Beech Super King Air B200 (G-RAFJ) | SERCO/RAF No 3 FTS/45(R) Sqn, Cranwell | |
| ZK451 | Beech Super King Air B200 (G-RAFK) | SERCO/RAF No 3 FTS/45(R) Sqn, Cranwell | |
| ZK452 | Beech Super King Air B200 (G-RAFL) | SERCO/RAF No 3 FTS/45(R) Sqn, Cranwell | |
| ZK453 | Beech Super King Air B200 (G-RAFM) | SERCO/RAF No 3 FTS/45(R) Sqn, Cranwell | |
| ZK454 | Beech Super King Air B200 (G-RAFN) | SERCO/RAF No 3 FTS/45(R) Sqn, Cranwell | |
| ZK455 | Beech Super King Air B200 (G-RAFO) | SERCO/RAF No 3 FTS/45(R) Sqn, Cranwell | |
| ZK456 | Beech Super King Air B200 (G-RAFP) | SERCO/RAF No 3 FTS/45(R) Sqn, Cranwell | |
| ZK531 | BAe Hawk T53 (LL-5306) | DPA/BAE Systems, Warton | |
| ZK532 | BAe Hawk T53 (LL-5315) | DPA/BAE Systems, Warton | |
| ZK533 | BAe Hawk T53 (LL-5317) | DPA/BAE Systems, Warton | |

| Notes | Serial | Type (other identity) [code] | Owner/operator, location or fate |
|---|---|---|---|
| | ZK534 | BAe Hawk T53 (LL-5319) | BAE Systems, Brough |
| | ZK535 | BAe Hawk T53 (LL-5320) | DPA/BAE Systems, Warton |
| | | | |
| | ZM400 | Airbus A400M | Reservation for RAF |
| | ZM401 | Airbus A400M | Reservation for RAF |
| | ZM402 | Airbus A400M | Reservation for RAF |
| | ZM403 | Airbus A400M | Reservation for RAF |
| | ZM404 | Airbus A400M | Reservation for RAF |
| | ZM405 | Airbus A400M | Reservation for RAF |
| | ZM406 | Airbus A400M | Reservation for RAF |
| | ZM407 | Airbus A400M | Reservation for RAF |
| | ZM408 | Airbus A400M | Reservation for RAF |
| | ZM409 | Airbus A400M | Reservation for RAF |
| | ZM410 | Airbus A400M | Reservation for RAF |
| | ZM411 | Airbus A400M | Reservation for RAF |
| | ZM412 | Airbus A400M | Reservation for RAF |
| | ZM413 | Airbus A400M | Reservation for RAF |
| | ZM414 | Airbus A400M | Reservation for RAF |
| | ZM415 | Airbus A400M | Reservation for RAF |
| | ZM416 | Airbus A400M | Reservation for RAF |
| | ZM417 | Airbus A400M | Reservation for RAF |
| | ZM418 | Airbus A400M | Reservation for RAF |
| | ZM419 | Airbus A400M | Reservation for RAF |
| | ZM420 | Airbus A400M | Reservation for RAF |
| | ZM421 | Airbus A400M | Reservation for RAF |
| | ZM422 | Airbus A400M | Reservation for RAF |
| | ZM423 | Airbus A400M | Reservation for RAF |
| | ZM424 | Airbus A400M | Reservation for RAF |
| | | | |
| | ZR321 | Agusta A.109E Power Elite | Agusta, for RAF |
| | ZR322 | Agusta A.109E Power Elite | Agusta, for RAF |
| | ZR323 | Agusta A.109E Power Elite | Agusta, for RAF |
| | | | |
| | ZT800 | WS Super Lynx Mk 300 | DPA/Westland Helicopters, Yeovil |
| | | | |
| | ZZ171 | Boeing C-17A Globemaster III (00-201/N171UK) | RAF No 99 Sqn, Brize Norton |
| | ZZ172 | Boeing C-17A Globemaster III (00-202/N172UK) | RAF No 99 Sqn, Brize Norton |
| | ZZ173 | Boeing C-17A Globemaster III (00-203/N173UK) | RAF No 99 Sqn, Brize Norton |
| | ZZ174 | Boeing C-17A Globemaster III (00-204/N174UK) | RAF No 99 Sqn, Brize Norton |
| | ZZ175 | Boeing C-17A Globemaster III | Reservation for RAF |

Peter Vacher's recently restored Hawker Hurricane I R4118 is a Battle of Britain veteran. *Daniel J. March*

The Fighter Collection's unique Hawker Nimrod I S1581 is based at Duxford.

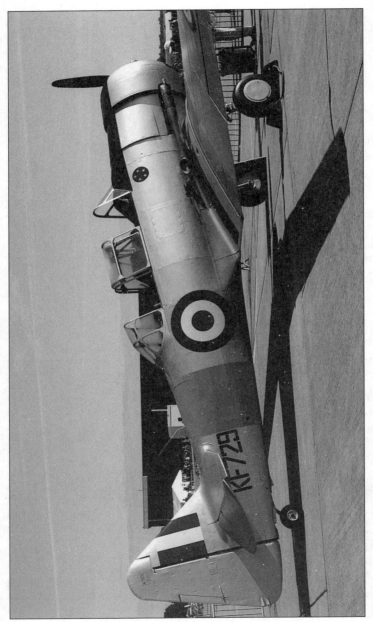

CCF T-6J Texan/Harvard IIB KF729, restored at Thruxton, was flown for the first time last summer.

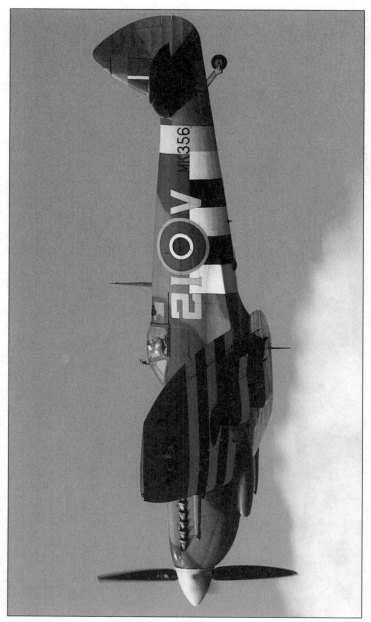

Battle of Britain Memorial Flight Spitfire LF.IXC MK356 has the code 2I-V of No 443 Squadron in 1944.

Air Atlantique Historic Flight operates Anson T21 WD413 from its Coventry base.

Boeing Chinook HC2 ZA707 of No 27 Squadron at RAF Odiham was flown at airshows in 2005. *Daniel J. March*

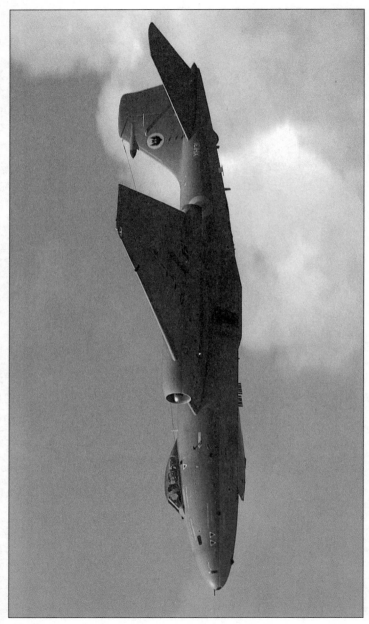

Canberra PR9 XH131 of No 39 (1PRU) Squadron at RAF Marham, is to be retired in July.

This former Swiss AF de Havilland Vampire T55 is painted as XJ771 with the Air Atlantique Classic Flight.

DH82A Tiger Moth II XL716 is operated from Compton Abbas, Dorset.

The Britannia Preservation Society at Kemble maintains Bristol Britannia C1 XM496 .

WS Scout AH1 XT626/Q is displayed by the AAC Historic Flight at Middle Wallop.

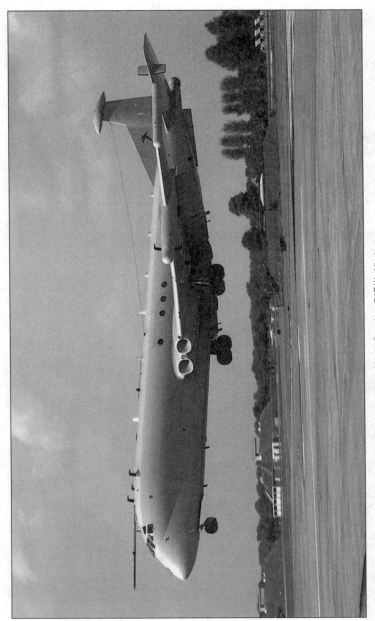

A rare visitor to RIAT 2005 at RAF Fairford was HS Nimrod R1 XW664 of No 51 Squadron, RAF Waddington.

Painted black overall Jet Provost T5A XW333 is owned by Global Aviation at Humberside.

With a special 'Firebirds 2005' colour scheme, Tornado F3 ZG772/WJ was used by the F3 display team last year.

BAe 125 CC3 ZE395 of No 32 (The Royal) Squadron is painted in the Northolt-based squadron's new colour scheme.

Shorts Tucano T1 ZF244 of No 1 FTS/72(R) Squadron at RAF Linton-on-Ouse carries the name *Moshoeshoe* on its nose.

Marking 90 years of service by No 8 Squadron, Boeing E-3D Sentry ZH103 acquired new tail flashes last year.

Eurofighter Typhoon T1 ZJ809/BH is on the strength of No 29(R) Squadron at RAF Coningsby.

# Aircraft in UK Military Service with Civil Registrations

| Serial | Type (other identity) [code] | Owner/operator, location or fate | Notes |
|--------|------------------------------|----------------------------------|-------|
| G-BONT | Slingsby T.67M Firefly 2 | HCS/DEFTS, Middle Wallop | |
| G-BUUA | Slingsby T.67M Firefly 2 | HCS/DEFTS, Middle Wallop | |
| G-BUUB | Slingsby T.67M Firefly 2 | HCS/DEFTS, Middle Wallop | |
| G-BUUC | Slingsby T.67M Firefly 2 | HCS/DEFTS, Middle Wallop | |
| G-BUUK | Slingsby T.67M Firefly 2 | HCS/DEFTS, Middle Wallop | |
| G-BWXA | Slingsby T.67M Firefly 260 | HCS/DEFTS, Barkston Heath | |
| G-BWXB | Slingsby T.67M Firefly 260 | HCS/DEFTS, Barkston Heath | |
| G-BWXC | Slingsby T.67M Firefly 260 | HCS/DEFTS, Barkston Heath | |
| G-BWXD | Slingsby T.67M Firefly 260 | HCS/DEFTS, Barkston Heath | |
| G-BWXE | Slingsby T.67M Firefly 260 | HCS/DEFTS, Barkston Heath | |
| G-BWXF | Slingsby T.67M Firefly 260 | HCS/DEFTS, Barkston Heath | |
| G-BWXG | Slingsby T.67M Firefly 260 | HCS/DEFTS, Barkston Heath | |
| G-BWXH | Slingsby T.67M Firefly 260 | HCS/DEFTS, Barkston Heath | |
| G-BWXI | Slingsby T.67M Firefly 260 | HCS/DEFTS, Barkston Heath | |
| G-BWXJ | Slingsby T.67M Firefly 260 | HCS/DEFTS, Barkston Heath | |
| G-BWXK | Slingsby T.67M Firefly 260 | HCS/DEFTS, Barkston Heath | |
| G-BWXL | Slingsby T.67M Firefly 260 | HCS/DEFTS, Barkston Heath | |
| G-BWXM | Slingsby T.67M Firefly 260 | HCS/DEFTS, Barkston Heath | |
| G-BWXN | Slingsby T.67M Firefly 260 | HCS/DEFTS, Barkston Heath | |
| G-BWXO | Slingsby T.67M Firefly 260 | HCS/DEFTS, Barkston Heath | |
| G-BWXR | Slingsby T.67M Firefly 260 | HCS/DEFTS, Barkston Heath | |
| G-BWXS | Slingsby T.67M Firefly 260 | HCS/DEFTS, Barkston Heath | |
| G-BWXT | Slingsby T.67M Firefly 260 | HCS/DEFTS, Barkston Heath | |
| G-BWXU | Slingsby T.67M Firefly 260 | HCS/DEFTS, Barkston Heath | |
| G-BWXV | Slingsby T.67M Firefly 260 | HCS/DEFTS, Barkston Heath | |
| G-BWXW | Slingsby T.67M Firefly 260 | HCS/DEFTS, Barkston Heath | |
| G-BWXX | Slingsby T.67M Firefly 260 | HCS/DEFTS, Barkston Heath | |
| G-BWXY | Slingsby T.67M Firefly 260 | HCS/DEFTS, Barkston Heath | |
| G-BWXZ | Slingsby T.67M Firefly 260 | HCS/DEFTS, Barkston Heath | |
| G-BYUA | Grob G.115E Tutor | Bombardier/Cambridge UAS/ University of London AS, Wyton | |
| G-BYUB | Grob G.115E Tutor | Bombardier/CFS/East Midlands Universities AS, Cranwell | |
| G-BYUC | Grob G.115E Tutor | Bombardier/CFS/East Midlands Universities AS, Cranwell | |
| G-BYUD | Grob G.115E Tutor | Bombardier/Universities of Glasgow & Strathclyde AS, Glasgow | |
| G-BYUE | Grob G.115E Tutor | Bombardier/CFS/East Midlands Universities AS, Cranwell | |
| G-BYUF | Grob G.115E Tutor | Bombardier/University of Birmingham AS, Cosford | |
| G-BYUG | Grob G.115E Tutor | Bombardier/Universities of Glasgow & Strathclyde AS, Glasgow | |
| G-BYUH | Grob G.115E Tutor | Bombardier/Bristol UAS, Colerne | |
| G-BYUI | Grob G.115E Tutor | Bombardier/Liverpool UAS/Manchester and Salford Universities AS, Woodvale | |
| G-BYUJ | Grob G.115E Tutor | Bombardier/Southampton UAS, Boscombe Down | |
| G-BYUK | Grob G.115E Tutor | Bombardier/University of Birmingham AS, Cosford | |
| G-BYUL | Grob G.115E Tutor | Bombardier/Southampton UAS, Boscombe Down | |
| G-BYUM | Grob G.115E Tutor | Bombardier/Southampton UAS, Boscombe Down | |
| G-BYUN | Grob G.115E Tutor | Bombardier/University of Wales AS, St Athan | |
| G-BYUO | Grob G.115E Tutor | Bombardier/University of London AS, Wyton | |
| G-BYUP | Grob G.115E Tutor | Bombardier/East Lowlands UAS/Aberdeen, Dundee & St Andrews UAS, Leuchars | |
| G-BYUR | Grob G.115E Tutor | Bombardier//East Lowlands UAS/Aberdeen, Dundee &  St Andrews UAS, Leuchars | |
| G-BYUS | Grob G.115E Tutor | Bombardier/University of Wales AS, St Athan | |

## Civil Registered Aircraft in UK Military Service

| Notes | Serial | Type (other identity) [code] | Owner/operator, location or fate |
|-------|--------|------------------------------|----------------------------------|
| | G-BYUT | Grob G.115E Tutor | Bombardier/University of Wales AS, St Athan |
| | G-BYUU | Grob G.115E Tutor | Bombardier/East Lowlands UAS/Aberdeen, Dundee & St Andrews UAS, Leuchars |
| | G-BYUV | Grob G.115E Tutor | Bombardier/Oxford UAS, Benson |
| | G-BYUW | Grob G.115E Tutor | Bombardier/East Lowlands UAS/Aberdeen, Dundee & St Andrews UAS, Leuchars |
| | G-BYUX | Grob G.115E Tutor | Bombardier/Liverpool UAS/Manchester and Salford Universities AS, Woodvale |
| | G-BYUY | Grob G.115E Tutor | Bombardier/East Lowlands UAS/Aberdeen, Dundee & St Andrews UAS, Leuchars |
| | G-BYUZ | Grob G.115E Tutor | Bombardier/Liverpool UAS/Manchester and Salford Universities AS, Woodvale |
| | G-BYVA | Grob G.115E Tutor | Bombardier/CFS/East Midlands Universities AS, Cranwell |
| | G-BYVB | Grob G.115E Tutor | Bombardier/East Lowlands UAS/Aberdeen, Dundee & St Andrews UAS, Leuchars |
| | G-BYVC | Grob G.115E Tutor | Bombardier/Cambridge UAS/University of London AS, Wyton |
| | G-BYVD | Grob G.115E Tutor | Bombardier/Cambridge UAS/University of London AS, Wyton |
| | G-BYVE | Grob G.115E Tutor | Bombardier/Cambridge UAS/University of London AS, Wyton |
| | G-BYVF | Grob G.115E Tutor | Bombardier/RN No 727 Sqn, Plymouth |
| | G-BYVG | Grob G.115E Tutor | Bombardier/Yorkshire Universities AS, Church Fenton |
| | G-BYVH | Grob G.115E Tutor | Bombardier/East Lowlands UAS/Aberdeen, Dundee & St Andrews UAS, Leuchars |
| | G-BYVI | Grob G.115E Tutor | Bombardier/Universities of Glasgow & Strathclyde AS, Glasgow |
| | G-BYVJ | Grob G.115E Tutor | Bombardier/University of Birmingham AS, Cosford |
| | G-BYVK | Grob G.115E Tutor | Bombardier/RN No 727 Sqn, Plymouth |
| | G-BYVL | Grob G.115E Tutor | Bombardier/Oxford UAS, Benson |
| | G-BYVM | Grob G.115E Tutor | Bombardier/Universities of Glasgow & Strathclyde AS, Glasgow |
| | G-BYVN | Grob G.115E Tutor | Bombardier/Bristol UAS, Colerne |
| | G-BYVO | Grob G.115E Tutor | Bombardier/Cambridge UAS/University of London AS, Wyton |
| | G-BYVP | Grob G.115E Tutor | Bombardier/Oxford UAS, Benson |
| | G-BYVR | Grob G.115E Tutor | Bombardier/CFS/East Midlands Universities AS, Cranwell |
| | G-BYVS | Grob G.115E Tutor | Bombardier/Northumbrian Universities AS, Leeming |
| | G-BYVT | Grob G.115E Tutor | Bombardier/Cambridge UAS/University of London AS, Wyton |
| | G-BYVU | Grob G.115E Tutor | Bombardier/Oxford UAS, Benson |
| | G-BYVV | Grob G.115E Tutor | Bombardier/Northumbrian Universities AS, Leeming |
| | G-BYVW | Grob G.115E Tutor | Bombardier/University of Wales AS, St Athan |
| | G-BYVX | Grob G.115E Tutor | Bombardier/Yorkshire Universities AS, Church Fenton |
| | G-BYVY | Grob G.115E Tutor | Bombardier/University of Birmingham AS, Cosford |
| | G-BYVZ | Grob G.115E Tutor | Bombardier/Yorkshire Universities AS, Church Fenton |
| | G-BYWA | Grob G.115E Tutor | Bombardier/Oxford UAS, Benson |
| | G-BYWB | Grob G.115E Tutor | Bombardier/CFS/East Midlands Universities AS, Cranwell |
| | G-BYWC | Grob G.115E Tutor | Bombardier/Bristol UAS, Colerne |
| | G-BYWD | Grob G.115E Tutor | Bombardier/Liverpool UAS/Manchester and Salford Universities AS, Woodvale |
| | G-BYWE | Grob G.115E Tutor | Bombardier/Bristol UAS, Colerne |
| | G-BYWF | Grob G.115E Tutor | Bombardier/CFS/East Midlands Universities AS, Cranwell |
| | G-BYWG | Grob G.115E Tutor | Bombardier/Bristol UAS, Colerne |

| Serial | Type (other identity) [code] | Owner/operator, location or fate | Notes |
|---|---|---|---|
| G-BYWH | Grob G.115E Tutor | Bombardier/Northumbrian Universities AS, Leeming | |
| G-BYWI | Grob G.115E Tutor | Bombardier/Cambridge UAS/University of London AS, Wyton | |
| G-BYWJ | Grob G.115E Tutor | Bombardier/Liverpool UAS/Manchester and Salford Universities AS, Woodvale | |
| G-BYWK | Grob G.115E Tutor | Bombardier/Bristol UAS, Colerne | |
| G-BYWL | Grob G.115E Tutor | Bombardier/Liverpool UAS/Manchester and Salford Universities AS, Woodvale | |
| G-BYWM | Grob G.115E Tutor | Bombardier/RN No 727 Sqn, Plymouth | |
| G-BYWN | Grob G.115E Tutor | Bombardier/Liverpool UAS/Manchester and Salford Universities AS, Woodvale | |
| G-BYWO | Grob G.115E Tutor | Bombardier/Yorkshire Universities AS, Church Fenton | |
| G-BYWP | Grob G.115E Tutor | Bombardier/Yorkshire Universities AS, Church Fenton | |
| G-BYWR | Grob G.115E Tutor | Bombardier/Cambridge UAS/University of London AS, Wyton | |
| G-BYWS | Grob G.115E Tutor | Bombardier/Yorkshire Universities AS, Church Fenton | |
| G-BYWT | Grob G.115E Tutor | Bombardier/Northumbrian Universities AS, Leeming | |
| G-BYWU | Grob G.115E Tutor | Bombardier/Cambridge UAS/University of London AS, Wyton | |
| G-BYWV | Grob G.115E Tutor | Bombardier/Yorkshire Universities AS, Church Fenton | |
| G-BYWW | Grob G.115E Tutor | Bombardier/CFS/East Midlands Universities AS, Cranwell | |
| G-BYWX | Grob G.115E Tutor | Bombardier/Bristol UAS, Colerne | |
| G-BYWY | Grob G.115E Tutor | Bombardier/CFS/East Midlands Universities AS, Cranwell | |
| G-BYWZ | Grob G.115E Tutor | Bombardier/CFS/East Midlands Universities AS, Cranwell | |
| G-BYXA | Grob G.115E Tutor | Bombardier/Liverpool UAS/Manchester and Salford Universities AS, Woodvale | |
| G-BYXB | Grob G.115E Tutor | Bombardier/Southampton UAS, Boscombe Down | |
| G-BYXC | Grob G.115E Tutor | Bombardier/CFS/East Midlands Universities AS, Cranwell | |
| G-BYXD | Grob G.115E Tutor | Bombardier/CFS/East Midlands Universities AS, Cranwell | |
| G-BYXE | Grob G.115E Tutor | Bombardier/Yorkshire Universities AS, Church Fenton | |
| G-BYXF | Grob G.115E Tutor | Bombardier/University of Birmingham AS, Cosford | |
| G-BYXG | Grob G.115E Tutor | Bombardier/Cambridge UAS/University of London AS, Wyton | |
| G-BYXH | Grob G.115E Tutor | Bombardier/Bristol UAS, Colerne | |
| G-BYXI | Grob G.115E Tutor | Bombardier/Liverpool UAS/Manchester and Salford Universities AS, Woodvale | |
| G-BYXJ | Grob G.115E Tutor | Bombardier/Southampton UAS, Boscombe Down | |
| G-BYXK | Grob G.115E Tutor | Bombardier/RN No 727 Sqn, Plymouth | |
| G-BYXL | Grob G.115E Tutor | Bombardier/University of Birmingham AS, Cosford | |
| G-BYXM | Grob G.115E Tutor | Bombardier/Southampton UAS, Boscombe Down | |
| G-BYXN | Grob G.115E Tutor | Bombardier/CFS/East Midlands Universities AS, Cranwell | |
| G-BYXO | Grob G.115E Tutor | Bombardier/University of Birmingham AS, Cosford | |
| G-BYXP | Grob G.115E Tutor | Bombardier/Cambridge UAS/University of London AS, Wyton | |
| G-BYXR | Grob G.115E Tutor | Bombardier/Oxford UAS, Benson | |
| G-BYXS | Grob G.115E Tutor | Bombardier/RN No 727 Sqn, Plymouth | |
| G-BYXT | Grob G.115E Tutor | Bombardier/Cambridge UAS/University of London AS, Wyton | |
| G-BYXX | Grob G.115E Tutor | Bombardier/Liverpool UAS/Manchester and Salford Universities AS, Woodvale | |
| G-BYXY | Grob G.115E Tutor | Bombardier/Cambridge UAS/University of London AS, Wyton | |
| G-BYXZ | Grob G.115E Tutor | Bombardier/CFS/East Midlands Universities AS, Cranwell | |

## Civil Registered Aircraft in UK Military Service

| Notes | Serial | Type (other identity) [code] | Owner/operator, location or fate |
|-------|--------|------------------------------|----------------------------------|
| | G-BYYA | Grob G.115E Tutor | Bombardier/Northumbrian Universities AS, Leeming |
| | G-BYYB | Grob G.115E Tutor | Bombardier/CFS/East Midlands Universities AS, Cranwell |
| | G-FFRA | Dassault Falcon 20DC (N902FR) | FR Aviation, Bournemouth |
| | G-FRAF | Dassault Falcon 20E (N911FR) | FR Aviation, Bournemouth |
| | G-FRAH | Dassault Falcon 20DC (N900FR) | FR Aviation, Durham/Tees Valley |
| | G-FRAI | Dassault Falcon 20E (N901FR) | FR Aviation, Durham/Tees Valley |
| | G-FRAJ | Dassault Falcon 20E (N903FR) | FR Aviation, Durham/Tees Valley |
| | G-FRAK | Dassault Falcon 20DC (N905FR) | FR Aviation, Bournemouth |
| | G-FRAL | Dassault Falcon 20DC (N904FR) | FR Aviation, Durham/Tees Valley |
| | G-FRAO | Dassault Falcon 20DC (N906FR) | FR Aviation, Bournemouth |
| | G-FRAP | Dassault Falcon 20DC (N908FR) | FR Aviation, Bournemouth |
| | G-FRAR | Dassault Falcon 20DC (N909FR) | FR Aviation, Bournemouth |
| | G-FRAS | Dassault Falcon 20C (117501) | FR Aviation, Durham/Tees Valley |
| | G-FRAT | Dassault Falcon 20C (117502) | FR Aviation, Durham/Tees Valley |
| | G-FRAU | Dassault Falcon 20C (117504) | FR Aviation, Durham/Tees Valley |
| | G-FRAW | Dassault Falcon 20ECM (117507) | FR Aviation, Durham/Tees Valley |
| | G-FRBA | Dassault Falcon 20C | FR Aviation, Bournemouth |

# RAF Maintenance Command/ Support Command/Logistics Command 'M' number Cross-reference

| | | | |
|---|---|---|---|
| 1764M/K4972 | 7533M/WT680 | 7865M/TX226 | 8054BM/XM417 |
| 2015M/K5600 | 7544M/WN904 | 7866M/XH278 | 8055AM/XM402 |
| 2292M/K8203 | 7548M/PS915 | 7868M/WZ736 | 8055BM/XM404 |
| 2361M/K6035 | 7556M/WK584 | 7869M/WK935 | 8056M/XG337 |
| 3118M/H5199/(BK892) | 7564M/XE982 | 7872M/*WZ826*/(XD826) | 8057M/XR243 |
| 3858M/X7688 | 7570M/XD674 | 7881M/WD413 | 8063M/WT536 |
| 4354M/BL614 | 7582M/WP190 | 7882M/XD525 | 8070M/EP120 |
| 4552M/T5298 | 7583M/WP185 | 7883M/XT150 | 8072M/PK624 |
| 5377M/EP120 | 7602M/WE600 | 7891M/XM693 | 8073M/TB252 |
| 5405M/LF738 | 7605M/WS692 | 7894M/XD818 | 8075M/RW382 |
| 5466M/*BN230*/(LF751) | 7606M/WV562 | 7895M/WF784 | 8078M/XM351 |
| 5690M/MK356 | 7607M/TJ138 | 7898M/XP854 | 8080M/XM480 |
| 5718M/BM597 | 7615M/WV679 | 7900M/WA576 | 8081M/XM468 |
| 5758M/DG202 | 7616M/WW388 | 7906M/WH132 | 8082M/XM409 |
| 6457M/ML427 | 7618M/WW442 | 7917M/WA591 | 8084M/XM369 |
| 6490M/LA255 | 7622M/WV606 | 7920M/WL360 | 8086M/TB752 |
| 6640M/RM694 | 7631M/VX185 | 7923M/XT133 | 8092M/WK654 |
| 6850M/TE184 | 7641M/XA634 | 7928M/XE849 | 8094M/WT520 |
| 6944M/RW386 | 7645M/WD293 | 7930M/WH301 | 8101M/WH984 |
| 6946M/RW388 | 7648M/XF785 | 7931M/RD253 | 8102M/WT486 |
| 6948M/DE673 | 7673M/WV332 | 7932M/WZ744 | 8103M/WR985 |
| 6960M/MT847 | 7689M/*WW421*/(WW450) | 7933M/XR220 | 8106M/WR982 |
| 7008M/EE549 | 7693M/WV483 | 7937M/WS843 | 8114M/WL798 |
| 7014M/N6720 | 7694M/WV486 | 7938M/XH903 | 8117M/WR974 |
| 7015M/NL985 | 7696M/WV493 | 7939M/XD596 | 8118M/WZ549 |
| 7035M/*K2567*/(DE306) | 7698M/WV499 | 7940M/XL764 | 8119M/WR971 |
| 7060M/VF301 | 7704M/TW536 | 7955M/XH767 | 8121M/XM474 |
| 7090M/EE531 | 7705M/WL505 | 7957M/XF545 | 8124M/WZ572 |
| 7118M/LA198 | 7706M/WB584 | 7959M/WS774 | 8128M/WH775 |
| 7119M/LA226 | 7709M/WT933 | 7960M/WS726 | 8131M/WT507 |
| 7150M/PK683 | 7711M/PS915 | 7961M/WS739 | 8140M/XJ571 |
| 7154M/WB188 | 7712M/WK281 | 7964M/WS760 | 8142M/XJ560 |
| 7174M/VX272 | 7715M/XK724 | 7965M/WS792 | 8147M/XR526 |
| 7175M/VV106 | 7716M/WS776 | 7967M/WS788 | 8151M/WV795 |
| 7200M/VT812 | 7718M/WA577 | 7971M/XK699 | 8153M/WV903 |
| 7241M/TE311/*(MK178* | 7719M/WK277 | 7973M/WS807 | 8154M/WV908 |
| 7243M/TE462 | 7737M/XD602 | 7976M/XK418 | 8155M/WV797 |
| 7245M/RW382 | 7741M/VZ477 | 7979M/XM529 | 8156M/XE339 |
| 7246M/TD248 | 7750M/*WK864*/(WL168) | 7980M/XM561 | 8158M/XE369 |
| 7256M/TB752 | 7751M/WL131 | 7982M/XH892 | 8160M/XD622 |
| 7257M/TB252 | 7755M/WG760 | 7983M/XD506 | 8161M/XE993 |
| 7279M/TB752 | 7758M/PM651 | 7984M/XN597 | 8162M/WM913 |
| 7281M/TB252 | 7759M/PK664 | 7986M/WG777 | 8163M/XP919 |
| 7288M/PK724 | 7761M/XH318 | 7988M/XL149 | 8164M/*WN105*/(WF299) |
| 7293M/RW393 | 7762M/XE670 | 7990M/XD452 | 8165M/WH791 |
| 7323M/VV217 | 7764M/XH318 | 7997M/XG452 | 8169M/WH364 |
| 7325M/R5868 | 7770M/*XF506*/(WT746) | 7998M/*XM515*/(XD515) | 8173M/XN685 |
| 7326M/VN485 | 7793M/XG523 | 8005M/WG768 | 8176M/WH791 |
| 7362M/475081/(VP546) | 7796M/WJ676 | 8009M/XG518 | 8177M/*WM311*/(WM224) |
| 7416M/WN907 | 7798M/XH783 | 8010M/XG547 | 8179M/XN928 |
| 7421M/WT660 | 7806M/TA639 | 8012M/VS562 | 8183M/*XN972*/(XN962) |
| 7422M/WT684 | 7809M/XA699 | 8016M/XT677 | 8184M/WT520 |
| 7428M/WK198 | 7816M/WG763 | 8017M/XL762 | 8186M/WR977 |
| 7432M/WZ724 | 7817M/TX214 | 8018M/XN344 | 8187M/WH791 |
| 7438M/*18671*/(WP905) | 7825M/WK991 | 8021M/XL824 | 8189M/*WD615* (WD646) |
| 7443M/WX853 | 7827M/XA917 | 8022M/XN341 | 8190M/XJ918 |
| 7458M/WX905 | 7829M/XH992 | 8027M/XM555 | 8192M/XR658 |
| 7464M/XA564 | 7839M/WV781 | 8032M/XH837 | 8196M/XE920 |
| 7470M/XA553 | 7841M/WV783 | 8033M/XD382 | 8198M/WT339 |
| 7473M/XE946 | 7851M/WZ706 | 8034M/XL703 | 8203M/XD377 |
| 7491M/WT569 | 7854M/XM191 | 8041M/XF690 | 8205M/XN819 |
| 7496M/WT612 | 7855M/XK416 | 8043M/XF836 | 8206M/WG419 |
| 7499M/WT555 | 7859M/XP283 | 8046M/XL770 | 8208M/WG303 |
| 7510M/WT694 | 7860M/XL738 | 8049M/WE168 | 8209M/WG418 |
| 7525M/WT619 | 7862M/XR246 | 8050M/XG329 | 8210M/WG471 |
| 7530M/WT648 | 7863M/*XP248* | 8052M/WH166 | 8211M/WK570 |
| 7532M/WT651 | 7864M/XP244 | 8054AM/XM410 | 8213M/WK626 |

111

# RAF Maintenance Cross-reference

| | | | |
|---|---|---|---|
| 8215M/WP869 | 8468M/MM5701/(BT474) | 8645M/XD163 | 8807M/XL587 |
| 8216M/WP927 | 8470M/584219 | 8648M/XK526 | 8810M/XJ825 |
| 8229M/XM355 | 8471M/701152 | 8653M/XS120 | 8816M/XX734 |
| 8230M/XM362 | 8472M/120227/(VN679) | 8655M/XN126 | 8818M/XK527 |
| 8234M/XN458 | 8473M/WP190 | 8656M/XP405 | 8820M/VP952 |
| 8235M/XN549 | 8474M/494083 | 8657M/VZ634 | 8821M/XX115 |
| 8236M/XP573 | 8475M/360043/(PJ876) | 8661M/XJ727 | 8822M/VP957 |
| 8237M/XS179 | 8476M/24 | 8662M/XR458 | 8828M/XS587 |
| 8238M/XS180 | 8477M/4101/(DG200) | 8666M/XE793 | 8830M/XF515 |
| 8344M/WH960 | 8478M/10639 | 8668M/WJ821 | 8831M/XG160 |
| 8350M/WH840 | 8479M/730301 | 8671M/XJ435 | 8832M/*XG168*/(XG172) |
| 8352M/XN632 | 8481M/191614 | 8672M/XP351 | 8833M/XL569 |
| 8355M/KN645 | 8482M/112372/(VK893) | 8673M/XD165 | 8834M/*XL571* |
| 8357M/WK576 | 8483M/420430 | 8676M/XL577 | 8836M/XL592 |
| 8359M/WF825 | 8484M/5439 | 8679M/XF526 | 8838M/*34037*/(429356) |
| 8361M/WB670 | 8485M/997 | 8680M/XF527 | 8839M/*69*/(XG194) |
| 8362M/WG477 | 8486M/BAPC 99 | 8681M/XG164 | 8840M/XG252 |
| 8364M/WG464 | 8487M/J-1172 | 8682M/XP404 | 8841M/XE606 |
| 8365M/XK421 | 8488M/WL627 | 8687M/XJ639 | 8847M/XX344 |
| 8366M/XG454 | 8491M/WJ880 | 8693M/WH863 | 8848M/XZ135 |
| 8367M/XG474 | 8493M/XR571 | 8696M/WH773 | 8852M/XV337 |
| 8368M/XF926 | 8494M/XP557 | 8700M/ZD234 | 8853M/XT277 |
| 8369M/WE139 | 8495M/XR672 | 8702M/XG196 | 8855M/XT284 |
| 8370M/N1671 | 8501M/XP640 | 8703M/VW453 | 8857M/XW544 |
| 8371M/XA847 | 8502M/XP686 | 8706M/XF383 | 8858M/XW541 |
| 8372M/K8042 | 8507M/XS215 | 8708M/XF509 | 8863M/XG154 |
| 8373M/P2617 | 8508M/XS218 | 8709M/XG209 | 8867M/XK532 |
| 8375M/NX611 | 8509M/XT141 | 8710M/XG274 | 8868M/WH775 |
| 8376M/RF398 | 8514M/XS176 | 8711M/XG290 | 8869M/WH957 |
| 8377M/R9125 | 8535M/XN776 | 8713M/XG225 | 8870M/WH964 |
| 8378M/*T9707* | 8538M/XN781 | 8718M/XX396 | 8871M/WJ565 |
| 8379M/DG590 | 8545M/XN726 | 8719M/XT257 | 8873M/XR453 |
| 8380M/Z7197 | 8546M/XN728 | 8722M/WJ640 | 8874M/XE597 |
| 8382M/VR930 | 8548M/WT507 | 8724M/XW923 | 8875M/XE624 |
| 8383M/K9942 | 8549M/WT534 | 8726M/XP299 | 8876M/*VM791*/(XA312) |
| 8384M/X4590 | 8554M/TG511 | 8727M/XR486 | 8880M/XF435 |
| 8385M/N5912 | 8561M/XS100 | 8728M/WT532 | 8881M/XG254 |
| 8386M/NV778 | 8563M/*XX822*/(XW563) | 8729M/WJ815 | 8883M/XX946 |
| 8387M/T6296 | 8565M/*WT720*/(E-408) | 8733M/XL318 | 8884M/VX275 |
| 8388M/XL993 | 8566M/XV279 | 8736M/XF375 | 8885M/XW922 |
| 8389M/VX573 | 8570M/XR954 | 8739M/XH170 | 8886M/XA243 |
| 8392M/SL674 | 8573M/XM708 | 8740M/WE173 | 8888M/XA231 |
| 8394M/WG422 | 8575M/XP542 | 8741M/XW329 | 8889M/XN239 |
| 8395M/WF408 | 8576M/XP502 | 8743M/WD790 | 8890M/WT532 |
| 8396M/XK740 | 8578M/XR534 | 8746M/XH171 | 8892M/XL618 |
| 8399M/WR539 | 8582M/XE874 | 8749M/XH537 | 8895M/XX746 |
| 8401M/XP686 | 8583M/BAPC 94 | 8751M/XT255 | 8896M/XX821 |
| 8406M/XP831 | 8585M/XE670 | 8753M/WL795 | 8897M/XX969 |
| 8407M/XP585 | 8586M/XE643 | 8762M/WH740 | 8898M/XX119 |
| 8408M/XS186 | 8588M/XR681 | 8763M/WH665 | 8899M/XX756 |
| 8409M/XS209 | 8589M/XR700 | 8764M/XP344 | 8900M/XZ368 |
| 8410M/XR662 | 8590M/XM191 | 8767M/XX635 | 8901M/XZ383 |
| 8413M/XM192 | 8591M/XA813 | 8768M/A-522 | 8902M/XX739 |
| 8414M/XM173 | 8595M/XH278 | 8769M/A-528 | 8903M/XX747 |
| 8417M/XM144 | 8598M/WP270 | 8770M/XL623 | 8904M/XX966 |
| 8422M/XM169 | 8600M/XX761 | 8771M/XM602 | 8905M/XX975 |
| 8427M/XM172 | 8602M/*PF179*/(XR541) | 8772M/WR960 | 8906M/XX976 |
| 8429M/XH592 | 8604M/XS104 | 8777M/XX914 | 8907M/XZ371 |
| 8434M/XM411 | 8606M/XP530 | 8778M/XM598 | 8908M/XZ382 |
| 8436M/XN554 | 8608M/XP540 | 8779M/XM607 | 8909M/XV784 |
| 8437M/WG362 | 8610M/XL502 | 8780M/WK102 | 8910M/XL160 |
| 8439M/WZ846 | 8611M/WF128 | 8781M/WE982 | 8911M/XH673 |
| 8440M/WD935 | 8618M/*XS111*/(XP504) | 8782M/XH136 | 8918M/XX109 |
| 8442M/XP411 | 8620M/XP534 | 8783M/XW272 | 8920M/XT469 |
| 8453M/XP745 | 8621M/XR538 | 8785M/XS642 | 8921M/XT466 |
| 8458M/XP672 | 8624M/*XR991*/(XS102) | 8789M/XK970 | 8922M/XT467 |
| 8459M/XR650 | 8627M/XP558 | 8792M/XP345 | 8923M/XX819 |
| 8460M/XP680 | 8628M/XJ380 | 8793M/XP346 | 8924M/XP701 |
| 8462M/XX477 | 8630M/WG362 | 8794M/XP398 | 8925M/XP706 |
| 8463M/XP355 | 8631M/XR574 | 8796M/XK943 | 8931M/XV779 |
| 8464M/XJ758 | 8633M/3W-17/MK732 | 8797M/XX947 | 8932M/XR718 |
| 8465M/W1048 | 8634M/WP314 | 8799M/WV787 | 8934M/XR749 |
| 8466M/L-866 | 8640M/XR977 | 8800M/XG226 | 8935M/XR713 |
| 8467M/WP912 | 8642M/XR537 | 8805M/XT772 | 8937M/XX751 |

| | | | |
|---|---|---|---|
| 8938M/WV746 | 9056M/XS488 | 9174M/XZ131 | 9273M/XS726 |
| 8941M/XT456 | 9059M/ZE360 | 9175M/P1344 | 9274M/XS738 |
| 8942M/XN185 | 9061M/XW335 | 9176M/XW430 | 9275M/XS729 |
| 8943M/XE799 | 9062M/XW351 | 9177M/XW328 | 9276M/XS733 |
| 8944M/WZ791 | 9066M/XV582 | 9179M/XW309 | 9277M/XT601 |
| 8945M/XX818 | 9067M/XV586 | 9180M/XW311 | 9278M/XS643 |
| 8946M/XZ389 | 9070M/XV581 | 9181M/XW358 | 9279M/XT681 |
| 8947M/XX726 | 9072M/XW768 | 9185M/XZ987 | 9280M/XV804 |
| 8948M/XX757 | 9073M/XW924 | 9187M/XW405 | 9281M/XZ146 |
| 8949M/XX743 | 9075M/XV752 | 9188M/XW364 | 9282M/XZ101 |
| 8950M/XX956 | 9076M/XV808 | 9189M/ZD350 | 9283M/XZ322 |
| 8951M/XX727 | 9078M/XV753 | 9190M/XW318 | 9284M/ZA267 |
| 8952M/XX730 | 9079M/XZ130 | 9191M/XW416 | 9285M |
| 8953M/XX959 | 9080M/ZE350 | 9192M/XW361 | 9286M |
| 8954M/XZ384 | 9086M/ZE352 | 9193M/XW367 | 9287M |
| 8955M/XX110 | 9087M/XX753 | 9194M/XW420 | 9288M/XX520 |
| 8957M/XN582 | 9090M/XW353 | 9195M/XW330 | 9289M/XX665 |
| 8961M/XS925 | 9091M/XW434 | 9196M/XW370 | 9290M/XX626 |
| 8967M/XV263 | 9092M/XH669 | 9197M/*XX530*/(XX637) | 9291M/XX686 |
| 8969M/XR753 | 9093M/WK124 | 9198M/XS641 | 9292M/XW892 |
| 8972M/XR754 | 9095M/XW547 | 9199M/XW290 | 9293M/ |
| 8973M/XS922 | 9096M/WV322 | 9200M/XW425 | 9294M/ |
| 8974M/XM473 | 9097M/XW366 | 9201M/ZD667 | 9295M/ |
| 8975M/XW917 | 9098M/XV406 | 9203M/*3066* | 9296M/ |
| 8976M/XZ630 | 9103M/XV411 | 9205M/*E449* | 9297M/XX141 |
| 8978M/XX837 | 9109M/XW312 | 9206M/F6314 | 9298M/ZE340 |
| 8983M/XM478 | 9110M/XX736 | 9207M/8417/18 | 9299M |
| 8984M/XN551 | 9111M/XW421 | 9208M/F938 | 9300M/XX431 |
| 8985M/WK127 | 9113M/*XV498* | 9210M/MF628 | 9301M |
| 8986M/XV261 | 9115M/XV863 | 9211M/733682 | 9302M/ZD462 |
| 8987M/XM358 | 9117M/XV161 | 9212M/*KL216*/(45-49295) | 9303M/XV709 |
| 8990M/XM419 | 9118M/XV253 | 9213M/N5182 | 9304M |
| 8995M/XM425 | 9119M/XW303 | 9215M/XL164 | 9305M |
| 8996M/XM414 | 9120M/XW419 | 9216M/XL190 | 9306M/XX979 |
| 8998M/XT864 | 9122M/XZ997 | 9218M/XL563 | 9307M |
| 9002M/XW763 | 9123M/XT773 | 9219M/XZ971 | 9308M |
| 9003M/XZ390 | 9124M/XW427 | 9221M/XZ966 | 9309M |
| 9004M/XZ370 | 9125M/XW410 | 9222M/XZ968 | 9310M |
| 9005M/XZ374 | 9126M/XW413 | 9224M/XL568 | 9311M |
| 9006M/XX967 | 9127M/XW432 | 9225M/XX885 | 9312M |
| 9007M/XX968 | 9128M/XW292 | 9226M/XV865 | 9313M |
| 9008M/XX140 | 9129M/XW294 | 9227M/XB812 | 9314M/ZA320 |
| 9009M/XX763 | 9130M/XW327 | 9229M/ZA678 | 9315M |
| 9010M/XX764 | 9131M/*DD931* | 9230M/ZA676 | 9316M |
| 9011M/XM412 | 9132M/XX977 | 9233M/XZ431 | 9317M/ZA450 |
| 9012M/XN494 | 9133M/*413573* | 9234M/XV864 | 9318M |
| 9014M/XN584 | 9134M/XT288 | 9236M/WV318 | 9319M |
| 9015M/XW320 | 9136M/XT891 | 9237M/XF445 | 9320M |
| 9017M/ZE449 | 9137M/XN579 | 9238M/ZA717 | 9321M |
| 9018M/XW365 | 9139M/XV863 | 9239M/7198/18 | 9322M |
| 9019M/XX824 | 9140M/XZ287 | 9241M/XS639 | 9323M |
| 9020M/XX825 | 9141M/XV118 | 9242M/XH672 | 9324M/XV659 |
| 9021M/XX826 | 9143M/XN589 | 9246M/XS714 | 9325M/XV710 |
| 9022M/XX958 | 9144M/XV353 | 9248M/WB627 | 9326M/XV653 |
| 9026M/XP629 | 9145M/XV863 | 9249M/WV396 | 9327M |
| 9027M/XP556 | 9146M/XW299 | 9251M/XX746 | 9328M |
| 9028M/XP563 | 9147M/XW301 | 9253M/ZA254 | 9329M |
| 9029M/XS217 | 9148M/XW436 | 9254M/XX965 | 9330M |
| 9032M/XR673 | 9149M/XW375 | 9255M/XZ375 | 9331M/XW852 |
| 9033M/XS181 | 9150M/*FX760* | 9257M/XX962 | 9332M/XZ935 |
| 9036M/XM350 | 9151M/XT907 | 9258M/XW265 | 9333M |
| 9038M/XV810 | 9152M/XV424 | 9259M/XS710 | 9334M/ZA322 |
| 9039M/XN586 | 9153M/XW360 | 9260M/XS734 | 9335M/ZA375 |
| 9040M/XZ138 | 9154M/XW321 | 9261M/*W2068* | 9336M/ZA407 |
| 9041M/XW763 | 9155M/WL679 | 9262M/XZ358 | 9337M |
| 9042M/XL954 | 9162M/XZ991 | 9263M/XW267 | 9338M |
| 9044M/XS177 | 9163M/XV415 | 9264M/XS735 | 9339M |
| 9045M/XN636 | 9166M/XW323 | 9265M/WK585 | 9340M |
| 9046M/XM349 | 9167M/XV744 | 9266M/XZ119 | 9341M |
| 9047M/XW409 | 9168M/XZ132 | 9267M/XW269 | 9342M/XR498 |
| 9048M/XM403 | 9169M/XW547 | 9268M/XR529 | 9343M/XR506 |
| 9049M/XW404 | 9170M/XZ994 | 9269M/XT914 | |
| 9052M/WJ717 | 9172M/XW304 | 9270M/XZ145 | |
| 9055M/XT770 | 9173M/XW418 | 9272M/XS486 | |

# RN Landing Platform and Shore Station Code-letters

| Code | Deck Letters | Vessel Name & Pennant No | Vessel Type & Unit |
|------|------|------|------|
| — | AB | HMS *Albion* (L14) | Assault |
| — | AS | RFA *Argus* (A135) | Aviation Training ship |
| 365/6 | AY | HMS *Argyll* (F231) | Type 23 (815 Sqn) |
| — | BD | RFA *Sir Bedivere* (L3004) | Landing ship |
| — | BV | RFA *Black Rover* (A273) | Fleet tanker |
| 335 | CF | HMS *Cardiff* (D108) | Type 42 (815 Sqn) |
| 350/1 | CL | HMS *Cumberland* (F85) | Type 22 (815 Sqn) |
| 348 | CM | HMS *Chatham* (F87) | Type 22 (815 Sqn) |
| 388 | CT | HMS *Campbeltown* (F86) | Type 22 (815 Sqn) |
| — | CU | RNAS Culdrose (HMS *Seahawk*) | |
| 412/3 | CW | HMS *Cornwall* (F99) | Type 22 (815 Sqn) |
| — | DC | HMS *Dumbarton Castle* (P265) | Fishery protection |
| — | DG | RFA *Diligence* (A132) | Maintenance |
| 411 | EB | HMS *Edinburgh* (D97) | Type 42 (815 Sqn) |
| 434/5 | EE | HMS *Endurance* (A171) | Ice Patrol (815 Sqn) |
| 420 | EX | HMS *Exeter* (D89) | Type 42 (815 Sqn) |
| — | FA | RFA *Fort Austin* (A386) | Support ship |
| — | FE | RFA *Fort Rosalie* (A385) | Support ship |
| — | FL | DARA Fleetlands | |
| — | FS | HMS *Fearless* (L10) | Assault |
| 410 | GC | HMS *Gloucester* (D96) | Type 42 (815 Sqn) |
| — | GD | RFA *Sir Galahad* (L3005) | Landing ship |
| 437 | GT | HMS *Grafton* (F80) | Type 23 (815 Sqn) |
| — | GV | RFA *Gold Rover* (A271) | Fleet tanker |
| — | GY | RFA *Grey Rover* (A269) | Fleet tanker |
| 404 | IR | HMS *Iron Duke* (F234) | Type 23 (815 Sqn) |
| 425 | KT | HMS *Kent* (F78) | Type 23 (815 Sqn) |
| — | L | HMS *Illustrious* (R06) | Carrier |
| 457 | LA | HMS *Lancaster* (F229) | Type 23 (829 Sqn) |
| — | LC | HMS *Leeds Castle* (P258) | Fishery protection |
| 332 | LP | HMS *Liverpool* (D92) | Type 42 (815 Sqn) |
| 363/4 | MA | HMS *Marlborough* (F233) | Type 23 (815 Sqn) |
| 360 | MC | HMS *Manchester* (D95) | Type 42 (815 Sqn) |
| 415 | MM | HMS *Monmouth* (F235) | Type 23 (829 Sqn) |
| 444 | MR | HMS *Montrose* (F236) | Type 23 (815 Sqn) |
| — | N | HMS *Invincible* (R05) | Carrier |
| 361/2 | NF | HMS *Norfolk* (F230) | Type 23 (815 Sqn) |
| 372 | NL | HMS *Northumberland* (F238) | Type 23 (829 Sqn) |
| 417 | NM | HMS *Nottingham* (D91) | Type 42 (815 Sqn) |
| — | O | HMS *Ocean* (L12) | Helicopter carrier |
| 426 | PD | HMS *Portland* (F79) | Type 23 (815 Sqn) |
| — | PV | RFA *Sir Percivale* (L3036) | Landing ship |
| — | R | HMS *Ark Royal* (R07) | Carrier |
| 474 | RM | HMS *Richmond* (F239) | Type 23 (815 Sqn) |
| 427 | SB | HMS *St Albans* (F83) | Type 23 (815 Sqn) |
| 375 | SM | HMS *Somerset* (F82) | Type 23 (815 Sqn) |
| 334 | SN | HMS *Southampton* (D90) | Type 42 (815 Sqn) |
| 422 | SU | HMS *Sutherland* (F81) | Type 23 (815 Sqn) |
| — | TM | RFA *Sir Tristram* (L3505) | Landing ship |
| — | VL | RNAS Yeovilton (HMS *Heron*) | |
| 462 | WM | HMS *Westminster* (F237) | Type 23 (829 Sqn) |
| 407 | YK | HMS *York* (D98) | Type 42 (815 Sqn) |
| — | — | HMS *Bulwark* (L15) | Assault |
| — | — | HMS *Daring* | Type 45 |
| — | — | HMS *Dauntless* | Type 45 |
| — | — | HMS *Diamond* | Type 45 |
| — | — | RFA *Cardigan Bay* | Landing ship |
| — | — | RFA *Fort Victoria* (A387) | Auxiliary Oiler |
| — | — | RFA *Fort George* (A388) | Auxiliary Oiler |
| — | — | RFA *Largs Bay* | Landing ship |
| — | — | RFA *Lyme Bay* | Landing ship |
| — | — | RFA *Mounts Bay* | Landing ship |
| — | — | RFA *Wave Knight* (A389) | Fleet tanker |
| — | — | RFA *Wave Ruler* (A390) | Fleet tanker |

# Ships' Numeric Code – Deck Letters Analysis

|     | 0  | 1  | 2  | 3  | 4  | 5  | 6  | 7  | 8  | 9 |
|-----|----|----|----|----|----|----|----|----|----|---|
| 33  |    |    | LP |    | SN | CF |    |    |    |   |
| 34  |    |    |    |    |    |    |    |    | CM |   |
| 35  | CL | CL |    |    |    |    |    |    |    |   |
| 36  | MC | NF | NF | MA | MA | AY | AY |    |    |   |
| 37  |    |    | NL |    |    | SM |    |    |    |   |
| 38  |    |    |    |    |    |    |    |    | CT |   |
| 40  |    |    |    |    | IR |    |    | YK |    |   |
| 41  | GC | EB | CW | CW |    | MM |    | NM |    |   |
| 42  | EX |    | SU |    |    | KT | PD | SB |    |   |
| 43  |    |    |    |    | EE | EE |    | GT |    |   |
| 44  |    |    |    |    | MR |    |    |    |    |   |
| 45  |    |    |    |    |    |    |    | LA |    |   |
| 46  |    |    | WM |    |    |    |    |    |    |   |
| 47  |    |    |    |    | RM |    |    |    |    |   |

# RN Code – Squadron – Base – Aircraft Cross-check

| Deck/Base Code Numbers | Letters | Unit | Location | Aircraft Type(s) |
|---|---|---|---|---|
| 000 — 006 | L | 801 Sqn | Yeovilton | Sea Harrier FA2 |
| 010 — 020 | CU | 820 Sqn | Culdrose | Merlin HM1 |
| 180 — 182 | CU | 849 Sqn HQ Flt | Culdrose | Sea King AEW7 |
| 183 — 185 | L | 849 Sqn B Flt | Culdrose | Sea King AEW7 |
| 186 — 188 | R | 849 Sqn A Flt | Culdrose | Sea King AEW7 |
| 264 — 274 | R | 814 Sqn | Culdrose | Merlin HM1 |
| 300 — 308 | VL | 815 Sqn | Yeovilton | Lynx HAS3/HMA8 |
| 318 — 319 | VL | 815 Sqn OEU | Yeovilton | Lynx HMA8 |
| 332 — 479 | * | 815 Sqn | Yeovilton | Lynx HAS3/HMA8 |
| 500 — 515 | CU | 829 Sqn | Culdrose | Merlin HM1 |
| 535 — 541 | CU | 700M OEU | Culdrose | Merlin HM1 |
| 560 — 573 | CU | 750 Sqn | Culdrose | Jetstream T2 |
| 576 — 579 | - | FONA | Yeovilton | Jetstream T3 |
| 580 — 585 | CU | 824 Sqn | Culdrose | Merlin HM1 |
| 630 — 648 | VL | 702 Sqn | Yeovilton | Lynx HAS3 |
| 670 — 676 | VL | 702 Sqn | Yeovilton | Lynx HMA8 |
| 700 — 709 | PW | 771 Sqn | Prestwick | Sea King HAS6 |
| 820 — 831 | CU | 771 Sqn | Culdrose | Sea King HU5/HAS6 |

*See foregoing separate ships' Deck Letters Analysis
Note that only the 'last two' digits of the Code are worn by some aircraft types, especially helicopters.

# Royal Air Force Squadron Markings

This table gives brief details of the markings worn by aircraft of RAF squadrons. While this may help to identify the operator of a particular machine, it may not always give the true picture. For example, from time to time aircraft are loaned to other units while others (such as those with No 4 FTS at Valley) wear squadron marks but are actually operated on a pool basis. Squadron badges are usually located on the front fuselage.

| Squadron | Type(s) operated | Base(s) | Distinguishing marks & other comments |
|---|---|---|---|
| No 1 Sqn | Harrier GR7/GR7A/GR9/T10 | RAF Cottesmore | Badge: A red & white winged number 1 on a white diamond. Tail fin has a red stripe with the badge repeated on it. |
| No 2 Sqn | Tornado GR4/GR4A | RAF Marham | Badge: A wake knot on a white circular background flanked on either side by black and white triangles. Tail fin has a black stripe with white triangles and the badge repeated on it. Codes are single letters inside a white triangle on the tail. |
| No 3 Sqn | Harrier GR7/GR7A/T10* | RAF Cottesmore* | Badge: A blue cockatrice on a white circular background flanked by two green bars edged with yellow. Tail fin has a green stripe edged with yellow. (* until 31 March 2006) |
| No 3 Sqn | Typhoon T1/F2** | RAF Coningsby** | (** from 01 April 2006) |
| No 4 Sqn | Harrier GR7/GR7A/T10 | RAF Cottesmore | Badge: A yellow lightning flash inside a red and black circle flanked by bars on either side repeating this design. Tail fin has a yellow lightning flash on a red and black stripe. |
| No 6 Sqn | Jaguar GR3A/T4 | RAF Coltishall* | Badge: A red winged can opener inside a circle edged in red. Tail has a light blue bar with red diagonal lines. Aircraft are coded E+.(* until 31 March 2006) |
| No 6 Sqn | Jaguar GR3A/T4 | RAF Coningsby** | (** from 01 April 2006) |
| No 7 Sqn | Chinook HC2/ Gazelle AH1 | RAF Odiham | Badge (on tail): A blue badge containing the seven stars of Ursa Major ('The Plough') in yellow. Aircraft are coded E+. Aircraft pooled with No 18 Sqn and No 27 Sqn. |
| No 8 Sqn | Sentry AEW1 | RAF Waddington | Badge (on tail): A grey, sheathed, Arabian dagger. Aircraft pooled with No 23 Sqn and No 54(R) Sqn. |
| No 9 Sqn | Tornado GR4 | RAF Marham | Badge: A green bat on a black circular background, flanked by yellow and green horizontal stripes. The green bat also appears on the tail, edged in yellow. Aircraft are coded A+. |
| No 12 Sqn | Tornado GR4 | RAF Lossiemouth | Roundel is superimposed on a green chevron. Tail fin has a black & white horizontal stripe with the squadron badge, a fox's head on a white circle, in the middle. Aircraft are coded F+. |
| No 13 Sqn | Tornado GR4/GR4A | RAF Marham | A yellow lightning flash on a green and blue background on the nose. Badge (on tail): A lynx's head over a dagger on a white shield. |

| Squadron | Type(s) operated | Base(s) | Distinguishing marks & other comments |
|---|---|---|---|
| No 14 Sqn | Tornado GR4 | RAF Lossiemouth | Badge: A red cross on a white circle, with wings either side, flanked by blue diamonds on a white background. The blue diamonds are repeated horizontally across the tail. Aircraft are coded B+. |
| No 15(R) Sqn [NTOCU] | Tornado GR4 | RAF Lossiemouth | Roman numerals XV appear in white on the tail. Aircraft are either coded T* or TA*. |
| No 17(R) Sqn | Typhoon T1/F2 | Coningsby | Badge (on tail): A gauntlet on a black shield. Roundel is flanked by two white bars which have a pair of jagged black lines running along them horizontally. Aircraft are coded A*. |
| No 18 Sqn | Chinook HC2 | RAF Odiham | Badge (on tail): A red winged horse on a black circle. Aircraft are coded B*. Aircraft pooled with No 7 Sqn and No 27 Sqn. |
| No 19(R) Sqn | Hawk T1/T1A/T1W | RAF Valley | Badge (on tail): A fish flanked by two wings on a yellow circle. Aircraft also carry black and white checks either side of the roundel on the fuselage. Aircraft pooled with No 208(R) Sqn; part of No 4 FTS. |
| No 20(R) Sqn [HOCU] | Harrier GR7/GR7A/GR9/T10 | RAF Wittering | Badge: An eagle in a white circle flanked by a white stripe on a blue background. On the tail is a stripe made up of black, yellow, green and red triangles. |
| No 22 Sqn | Sea King HAR3/HAR3A | A Flt: RMB Chivenor B Flt: Wattisham C Flt: RAF Valley | Badge: A black pi symbol in front of a white Maltese cross on a red circle. |
| No 23 Sqn | Sentry AEW1 | RAF Waddington | Badge (on tail): A red eagle preying on a yellow falcon. Aircraft pooled with No 8 Sqn and No 54(R) Sqn. |
| No 24 Sqn | Hercules C1/C3/C4/C5 | RAF Lyneham | No squadron markings carried. Aircraft pooled with No 30 Sqn, No 47 Sqn and No 70 Sqn. |
| No 25 Sqn | Tornado F3 | RAF Leeming | Badge (on tail): A hawk on a gauntlet. |
| No 27 Sqn | Chinook HC2 | RAF Odiham | Badge (on tail): An dark green elephant on a green circle, flanked by green and dark green stripes. Aircraft pooled with No 7 Sqn and No 18 Sqn. |
| No 28 Sqn | Merlin HC3 | RAF Benson | Badge: A winged horse above two white crosses on a red shield. |
| No 29(R) Sqn | Typhoon T1/F2 | Coningsby | Badge (on tail): An eagle in flight, preying on a buzzard, with three red Xs across the top. The roundel is flanked by two white bars outlined by a red line, each containing three red Xs. Aircraft are coded B*. |
| No 30 Sqn | Hercules C1/C3/C4/C5 | RAF Lyneham | No squadron markings carried. Aircraft pooled with No 24 Sqn, No 47 Sqn, No 57(R) Sqn and No 70 Sqn. |
| No 31 Sqn | Tornado GR4 | RAF Marham | Badge: A gold, five-pointed star on a yellow circle flanked by yellow and green checks. The star is repeated on the tail. Aircraft are coded D*. |

# RAF Squadron Markings

| Squadron | Type(s) operated | Base(s) | Distinguishing marks & other comments |
|---|---|---|---|
| No 32(The Royal) Sqn | BAe 125 CC3/146 CC2/ Twin Squirrel HCC1 | RAF Northolt | No squadron markings carried but aircraft carry a distinctive livery with a blue flash along the middle of the fuselage and a red tail. |
| No 33 Sqn | Puma HC1 | RAF Benson | Badge: A stag's head. |
| No 39(1 PRU) Sqn | Canberra PR9 | RAF Marham | Badge (on tail): A winged bomb on a light blue circle. Aircraft are coded A*. [Disbands 31-07-06] |
| No 41 Sqn | Jaguar GR3A/T4* | RAF Coltishall* | Badge: A red, double armed cross, flanked by red and white horizontal stipes. Stripes repeated on tail. Aircraft are coded F*. (*until 31 March 2006) |
| No 41(R) Sqn | Tornado F3/GR4 Harrier GR7A/GR9** | RAF Coningsby** | (**from 01 April 2006) |
| No 42(R) Sqn [NOCU] | Nimrod MR2 | RAF Kinloss | No squadron markings usually carried. Aircraft pooled with No 120 Sqn, No 201 Sqn and No 206 Sqn. |
| No 43 Sqn | Tornado F3 | RAF Leuchars | Badge (on tail): A black and red gamecock in a band of black and white squares. |
| No 45(R) Sqn | Raytheon Beech Super King Air 200 | RAF Cranwell | No squadron markings usually carried. Part of No 3 FTS. |
| No 47 Sqn | Hercules C1/C3/C4/C5 | RAF Lyneham | No squadron markings usually carried. Aircraft pooled with No 24 Sqn, 30 Sqn and No 70 Sqn. |
| No 51 Sqn | Nimrod R1 | RAF Waddington | Badge (on tail): A red goose in flight. |
| No 54(R) Sqn [ISTAR OCU] | Sentry AEW1/Nimrod R1 | RAF Waddington | Based aircraft as required. |
| No 55(R) Sqn | Dominie T1 | RAF Cranwell | Badge (on tail): A blue fist holding an arrow on a white circle. Part of No 3 FTS. |
| No 56(R) Sqn [F3OCU] | Tornado F3 | RAF Leuchars | Badge (on tail): A gold phoenix rising from red flames. The tail fin has a stripe made up of red and white checks. |
| No 60(R) Sqn | Griffin HT1 | RAF Shawbury [DHFS] &RAF Valley [SARTU] | No squadron markings usually carried. |
| No 70 Sqn | Hercules C1/C3/C4/C5 | RAF Lyneham | No squadron markings usually carried. Aircraft pooled with No 24 Sqn, No 30 Sqn and No 47 Sqn. |
| No 72(R) Sqn | Tucano T1 | RAF Linton-on-Ouse | Badge: A black swift in flight on a red disk, flanked by blue bars edged with red. The blue bars edged with red also flank the roundel on the fuselage; part of No 1 FTS |
| No 78 Sqn | Chinook HC2/ Sea King HAR3 | RAF Mount Pleasant | Badge: A yellow, heraldic tiger with two tails, on a black circle. The badge appears on the tail of the Chinook and by the cockpit on the Sea King. |
| No 84 Sqn | Griffin HAR2 | RAF Akrotiri | Badge (on tail): A scorpion on a playing card symbol (diamonds, clubs etc.). Aircraft carry a vertical blue stripe through the roundel on the fuselage. |

| Squadron | Type(s) operated | Base(s) | Distinguishing marks & other comments |
|----------|------------------|---------|----------------------------------------|
| No 99 Sqn | Globemaster III | RAF Brize Norton | Badge (on tail): A black puma leaping. |
| No 100 Sqn | Hawk T1/T1A | RAF Leeming | Badge (on tail): A skull in front of two bones crossed. Aircraft are usually coded C*. Incorporates the Joint Forward Air Control Training and Standards Unit (JFACTSU) |
| No 101 Sqn | VC10 C1K/K3/K4 | RAF Brize Norton | Badge (on tail): A lion behind a castle turret. |
| No 111 Sqn | Tornado F3 | RAF Leuchars | Badge (on tail): A cross in front of crossed swords on a light grey circle, flanked by a stripe of darker grey. |
| No 120 Sqn | Nimrod MR2 | RAF Kinloss | No squadron markings usually carried. Aircraft pooled with No 42(R) Sqn, No 201 Sqn and No 206 Sqn. |
| No 201 Sqn | Nimrod MR2 | RAF Kinloss | No squadron markings usually carried. Aircraft pooled with No 42(R) Sqn, No 120 Sqn and No 206 Sqn. |
| No 202 Sqn | Sea King HAR3 | A Flt: RAF Boulmer D Flt: RAF Lossiemouth E Flt: RAF Leconfield | Badge: A mallard alighting on a white circle. |
| No 203(R) Sqn | Sea King HAR3 | RAF St Mawgan | Badge: A green sea horse on a white circle. |
| No 207(R) Sqn | Tucano T1 | RAF Linton-on-Ouse | Badge: A red winged lion on a white disk. The roundel on the fuselage is flanked by red bars edged with yellow; part of No 1 FTS |
| No 208(R) Sqn | Hawk T1/T1A/T1W | RAF Valley | Badge (on tail): A Sphinx inside a white circle, flanked by flashes of yellow. Aircraft also carry blue and yellow bars either side of the roundel on the fuselage and a blue and yellow chevron on the nose. Aircraft pooled with No 19(R) Sqn; part of No 4 FTS. |
| No 216 Sqn | Tristar K1/KC1/C2/C2A | RAF Brize Norton | Badge (on tail): An eagle in flight with a bomb in its claws. |
| No 230 Sqn | Puma HC1 | RAF Aldergrove | Badge: A tiger in front of a palm tree on a black pentagon. |
| No 617 Sqn | Tornado GR4 | RAF Lossiemouth | Badge: Dam breached, flanked on either side by red lightning flashes on a black background. Tail fin is black with a red lightning flash. Aircraft are coded AJ-*. |
| No 1310 Flt | Chinook HC2 | Basrah, Iraq | No markings carried. Part of Joint Helicopter Force (Iraq). |
| No 1312 Flt | VC10 K3/K4 (101 Sqn) Hercules (LTW) | RAF Mount Pleasant | Badge (on tail): A red Maltese cross on a white circle, flanked by red and white horizontal bars. |
| No 1419 Flt | Merlin HC3 | Basrah, Iraq | No markings carried. Part of Joint Helicopter Force (Iraq). |
| No 1435 Flt | Tornado F3 | RAF Mount Pleasant | Badge (on tail): A red Maltese cross on a white circle, flanked by red and white horizontal bars. |
| No 1563 Flt | Puma HC1 | Basrah, Iraq | No markings carried. Part of Joint Helicopter Force (Iraq). |

# University Air Squadrons/ Air Experience Flights*

UAS aircraft carry squadron badges and markings, usually on the tail. Squadron crests all consist of a white circle surrounded by a blue circle, topped with a red crown and having a yellow scroll beneath. Each differs by the motto on the scroll, the UAS name running around the blue circle & by the contents at the centre and it is the latter which are described below. All AEFs come under the administration of local UASs and these are listed here.

| UAS | Base(s) | Marks |
|---|---|---|
| Aberdeen, Dundee & St Andrews UAS | RAF Leuchars | A red lion holding a stone turret between its paws above a crown. |
| University of Birmingham AS/ No 8 AEF | RAF Cosford | A blue griffon with two heads. |
| Bristol UAS/ No 3 AEF | RAF Colerne | A sailing ship on water. |
| Cambridge UAS/ No 5 AEF | RAF Wyton | A heraldic lion in front of a red badge. |
| East Lowlands UAS/ No 12 AEF | RAF Leuchars | An open book in front of a white diagonal cross edged in blue. |
| East Midlands Universities AS/No 7 AEF | RAF Cranwell | A yellow quiver, full of arrows. |
| Universities of Glasgow and Strathclyde AS/ No 4 AEF | Glasgow | A bird of prey in flight, holding a branch in its beak, in front of an upright sword. |
| Liverpool UAS | RAF Woodvale | A bird atop an open book, holding a branch in its beak. |
| University of London AS/ No 6 AEF | RAF Wyton | A globe superimposed over an open book. |
| Manchester and Salford Universities AS/ No 10 AEF | RAF Woodvale | A bird of prey with a green snake in its beak. |
| Northumbrian Universities AS/ No 11 AEF | RAF Leeming | A white cross on a blue background. |
| Oxford UAS | RAF Benson | An open book in front of crossed swords. |
| Southampton UAS/ No 2 AEF | Boscombe Down | A red stag in front of a stone pillar. |
| University of Wales AS/ No 1 AEF | DARA St Athan | A red Welsh dragon in front of an open book, clasping a sword. Some aircraft have the dragon in front of white and green squares. |
| Yorkshire Universities AS/ No 9 AEF | RAF Church Fenton | An open book in front of a Yorkshire rose with leaves. |

* Note: University Air Squadrons and Air Experience Flights are being re-organised in 2006. This will change the names of units, bases and the allocation of aircraft.

# Fleet Air Arm Squadron Markings

This table gives brief details of the markings worn by aircraft of FAA squadrons. Squadron badges, when worn, are usually located on the front fuselage. All FAA squadron badges comprise a crown atop a circle edged in gold braid and so the badge details below list only what appears in the circular part.

| Squadron | Type(s) operated | Base(s) | Distinguishing marks & other comments |
|---|---|---|---|
| No 700M OEU | Merlin HM1 | RNAS Culdrose | Badge: A pair of gold scales on a background of blue and white waves, flanked by two bees. |
| No 702 Sqn | Lynx HAS3/HMA8 | RNAS Yeovilton | Badge: A Lynx rearing up in front of a circle comprising alternate dark blue and white sectors. |
| No 727 Sqn | Heron | Plymouth | Badge: The head of Britannia wearing a gold helmet on a background of blue and white waves. |
| No 750 Sqn | Jetstream T2 | RNAS Culdrose | Badge: A Greek runner bearing a torch & sword on a background of blue and white waves. |
| No 771 Sqn | Sea King HU5/HAS6 | RNAS Culdrose & Prestwick | Badge: Three bees on a background of blue and white waves. |
| No 792 Sqn | Mirach | RNAS Culdrose | Badge: (Not worn) A panther's head on a gold background. |
| No 801 Sqn | Sea Harrier FA2 | RNAS Yeovilton | Badge: A winged trident on a white background. On the tail is a white winged trident and there are black & white checks upon the rudder. |
| No 814 Sqn | Merlin HM1 | RNAS Culdrose | Badge: A winged tiger mask on a background of dark blue and white waves. |
| No 815 Sqn | Lynx HAS3/HMA8 | RNAS Yeovilton | Badge: A winged, gold harpoon on a background of blue and white waves. |
| No 820M Sqn | Merlin HM1 | RNAS Culdrose | Badge: A flying fish on a background of blue and white waves. |
| No 824 Sqn | Merlin HM1 | RNAS Culdrose | Badge: A heron on a background of blue and white waves. |
| No 829 Sqn | Merlin HM1 | RNAS Culdrose | Badge: A kingfisher hovering on a background of blue and white waves. |
| No 845 Sqn | Sea King HC4 | RNAS Yeovilton | Badge: A dragonfly on a background of blue and white waves. |
| No 846 Sqn | Sea King HC4 | RNAS Yeovilton | Badge: A swordsman riding a winged horse whilst attacking a serpent on a background of blue and white waves. Aircraft are usually coded V*. |
| No 847 Sqn | Gazelle AH1 & Lynx AH7 | RNAS Yeovilton | Badge: A gold sea lion on a blue background. |
| No 848 Sqn | Sea King HC4 | RNAS Yeovilton | Badge: Inside a red circle, a hawk in flight with a torpedo in its claws above white and blue waves. Aircraft are usually coded W*. |
| No 849 Sqn | Sea King AEW7 | RNAS Culdrose | Badge: A winged streak of lightning with an eye in front on a background of blue and white waves. |

Some *historic, classic and warbird* aircraft carry the markings of overseas air arms and can be seen in the UK, mainly preserved in museums and collections or taking part in air shows.

| Notes | Serial | Type (other identity) | Owner/operator, location |
|---|---|---|---|
| | | **ARGENTINA** | |
| | - | Bell UH-1H Iroquois (AE-406/*998-8888*) [Z] | RAF Valley, instructional use |
| | 0729 | Beech T-34C Turbo Mentor | FAA Museum, stored RNAS Yeovilton |
| | 0767 | Aermacchi MB339AA | Rolls-Royce Heritage Trust, stored Derby |
| | A-515 | FMA IA58 Pucara (ZD485) | RAF Museum, Cosford |
| | A-517 | FMA IA58 Pucara (G-BLRP) | Privately owned, Channel Islands |
| | A-522 | FMA IA58 Pucara (8768M) | FAA Museum, at NE Aircraft Museum, Usworth |
| | A-528 | FMA IA58 Pucara (8769M) | Norfolk & Suffolk Avn Museum, Flixton |
| | A-533 | FMA IA58 Pucara (ZD486) <ff> | Boscombe Down Museum |
| | A-549 | FMA IA58 Pucara (ZD487) | Imperial War Museum, Duxford |
| | AE-409 | Bell UH-1H Iroquois [656] | Museum of Army Flying, Middle Wallop |
| | AE-422 | Bell UH-1H Iroquois | FAA Museum, stored RNAS Yeovilton |
| | | **AUSTRALIA** | |
| | A2-4 | Supermarine Seagull V (VH-ALB) | RAF Museum, Hendon |
| | A16-199 | Lockheed Hudson IIIA (G-BEOX) [SF-R] | RAF Museum, Hendon |
| | A17-48 | DH82A Tiger Moth (G-BPHR) | Privately owned, Netherthorpe |
| | *A19-144* | Bristol 156 Beaufighter XIc (JM135/A8-324) | The Fighter Collection, Duxford |
| | A79-808 | DH115 Vampire T33 | De Havilland Aviation, Swansea |
| | A92-480 | GAF Jindivik 4A (A92-LLAN-1) | QinetiQ Llanbedr, on display |
| | A92-664 | GAF Jindivik 4A | Privately owned, Llanbedr |
| | A92-708 | GAF Jindivik 4A | Bristol Aero Collection, stored Kemble |
| | N6-766 | DH115 Sea Vampire T22 (XG766/G-SPDR) | De Havilland Aviation, Swansea |
| | | **BELGIUM** | |
| | FT-36 | Lockheed T-33A | Dumfries & Galloway Avn Mus, Dumfries |
| | *H-50* | Noorduyn AT-16 Harvard IIB (OO-DAF) | Privately owned, Brasschaat, Belgium |
| | HD-75 | Hanriot HD1 (G-AFDX) | RAF Museum, Hendon |
| | IF-68 | Hawker Hunter F6 <ff> | Privately owned, Market Drayton |
| | K-16 | Douglas C-53D Skytrooper (OT-CWG/N49G) | Air Dakota, Brussels, Belgium |
| | L-44 | Piper L-18C Super Cub (OO-SPQ) | Royal Aéro Para Club de Spa, Belgium |
| | L-47 | Piper L-18C Super Cub (OO-SPG) | Aeroclub Braaschaat VZW, Braaschaat, Belgium |
| | L-156 | Piper L-18C Super Cub (OO-LGB) | Aeroclub Braaschaat VZW, Braaschaat, Belgium |
| | V-18 | SNCAN Stampe SV-4B (OO-GWD) | Antwerp Stampe Centre, Antwerp-Deurne, Belgium |
| | V-29 | SNCAN Stampe SV-4B (OO-GWB) | Antwerp Stampe Centre, Antwerp-Deurne, Belgium |
| | | **BOLIVIA** | |
| | FAB184 | SIAI-Marchetti SF.260W (G-SIAI) | Privately owned, Booker |
| | | **BOTSWANA** | |
| | OJ1 | BAC Strikemaster 83 (ZG805/G-BXFU) | Global Aviation, Humberside |
| | | **BRAZIL** | |
| | 1317 | Embraer T-27 Tucano | Shorts, Belfast (engine test bed) |
| | | **BURKINA FASO** | |
| | BF-8431 | SIAI-Marchetti SF.260 (G-NRRA) [31] | Privately owned, Oaksey Park |

| Serial | Type (other identity) | Owner/operator, location | Notes |
|--------|----------------------|--------------------------|-------|
| **CANADA** | | | |
| 622 | Piasecki HUP-3 Retriever (51-16622/N6699D) | The Helicopter Museum, Weston-super-Mare | |
| 920 | VS Stranraer (CF-BXO) [Q-N] | RAF Museum, Hendon | |
| 3349 | NA64 Yale (G-BYNF) | Privately owned, Duxford | |
| 5403 | Hawker Hurricane X (G-HRLO) | Hawker Restorations Ltd, Milden | |
| 5450 | Hawker Hurricane XII (G-TDTW) | Hawker Restorations Ltd, Milden | |
| 5487 | Hawker Hurricane II (G-CBOE) | Privately owned, Thruxton | |
| *9754* | Consolidated PBY-5A Catalina (VP-BPS) [P] | Privately owned, Lee-on-Solent | |
| 9893 | Bristol 149 Bolingbroke IVT | Imperial War Museum store, Duxford | |
| 9940 | Bristol 149 Bolingbroke IVT | Royal Scottish Mus'm of Flight, E Fortune | |
| 15195 | Fairchild PT-19A Cornell | RAF Museum Reserve Collection, Stafford | |
| *16693* | Auster J/1N Alpha (G-BLPG) [693] | Privately owned, Clacton | |
| 18393 | Avro Canada CF-100 Canuck 4B (G-BCYK) | Imperial War Museum, Duxford | |
| *18671* | DHC1 Chipmunk 22 (WP905/7438M/G-BNZC) [671] | Privately owned, Old Warden | |
| *20249* | Noorduyn AT-16 Harvard IIB (PH-KLU) [XS-249] | Privately owned, Texel, The Netherlands | |
| *20310* | CCF T-6J Harvard IV (G-BSBG) [310] | Privately owned, Tatenhill | |
| *21261* | Lockheed T-33A-N Silver Star (G-TBRD) | Golden Apple Operations/ARC, Duxford | |
| 21417 | Canadair CT-133 Silver Star | Yorkshire Air Museum, Elvington | |
| 23140 | Canadair CL-13 Sabre [AX] <rf> | Midland Air Museum, Coventry | |
| 23380 | Canadair CL-13 Sabre <rf> | RAF Millom Museum, Haverigg | |
| *FJ777* | Boeing-Stearman PT-17D Kaydet(41-8689/G-BIXN) | Privately owned, Rendcomb | |
| | | | |
| **CHINA** | | | |
| 2632016 | Nanchang CJ-6A Chujiao (G-BXZB) (also wears *2632019*) | Privately owned, Hibaldstow | |
| 2751219 | Nanchang CJ-6A Chujiao (G-BVVG) [68] | Privately owned, Fishburn | |
| | | | |
| **CROATIA** | | | |
| *8110* | Avia FL.3 (G-AGFT) | Privately owned, Breighton | |
| | | | |
| **CZECH REPUBLIC** | | | |
| 3677 | Letov S-102 (MiG-15) (613677) | Royal Scottish Mus'm of Flight, E Fortune | |
| 3794 | Letov S-102 (MiG-15) (623794) | Imperial War Museum, stored Duxford | |
| 9147 | Mil Mi-4 | The Helicopter Museum, Weston-super-Mare | |
| | | | |
| **DENMARK** | | | |
| A-011 | SAAB A-35XD Draken | Privately owned, Grainthorpe, Lincs | |
| AR-107 | SAAB S-35XD Draken | Newark Air Museum, Winthorpe | |
| E-402 | Hawker Hunter F51 | Farnborough Air Sciences Trust, Farnborough | |
| E-419 | Hawker Hunter F51 | North-East Aircraft Museum, Usworth | |
| E-420 | Hawker Hunter F51 (G-9-442) | Privately owned, Walton-on-Thames | |
| E-421 | Hawker Hunter F51 | Brooklands Museum, Weybridge | |
| E-423 | Hawker Hunter F51 (G-9-444) | SWWAPS, Lasham | |
| E-424 | Hawker Hunter F51 (G-9-445) | Aeroventure, Doncaster | |
| ET-272 | Hawker Hunter T7 <ff> | Boulton Paul Association, Wolverhampton | |
| ET-273 | Hawker Hunter T7 <ff> | Aeroventure, Doncaster | |
| K-682 | Douglas C-47A Skytrain (OY-BPB) | Foreningen For Flyvende Mus, Vaerløse, Denmark | |
| L-866 | Consolidated PBY-6A Catalina (8466M) | RAF Museum, Cosford | |
| R-756 | Lockheed F-104G Starfighter | Midland Air Museum, Coventry | |
| S-881 | Sikorsky S-55C | The Helicopter Museum, Weston-super-Mare | |
| S-882 | Sikorsky S-55C | Paintball Adventure West, Lulsgate | |
| S-887 | Sikorsky S-55C | Privately owned, Marksbury, Somerset | |
| | | | |
| **ECUADOR** | | | |
| *FAE259* | BAC Strikemaster 80 (G-UPPI) [T59] | Gower Jets Ltd, Swansea | |
| | | | |
| **EGYPT** | | | |
| 764 | Mikoyan MiG-21SPS <ff> | Privately owned, Northampton | |

125

# Historic Aircraft

| Notes | Serial | Type (other identity) | Owner/operator, location |
|---|---|---|---|
| | 771 | WS61 Sea King 47 (WA.826) | RN AESS, *HMS Sultan*, Gosport |
| | 773 | WS61 Sea King 47 (WA.823) | RN AESS, *HMS Sultan*, Gosport |
| | 774 | WS61 Sea King 47 (WA.822) | RN AESS, *HMS Sultan*, Gosport |
| | 775 | WS61 Sea King 47 (WA.824) | RN AESS, *HMS Sultan*, Gosport |
| | 776 | WS61 Sea King 47 (WA.825) | RN AESS, *HMS Sultan*, Gosport |
| | 0446 | Mikoyan MiG-21UM <ff> | Thameside Aviation Museum, Tilbury |
| | 7907 | Sukhoi Su-7 <ff> | Robertsbridge Aviation Society, Mayfield |
| | **FINLAND** | | |
| | *GN-101* | Folland Gnat F1 (XK741) | Midland Air Museum, Coventry |
| | VI-3 | Valtion Viima 2 (OO-EBL) | Privately owned, Brasschaat, Belgium |
| | **FRANCE** | | |
| | *1/4513* | Spad XIII <R> (G-BFYO/*S3398*) | American Air Museum, Duxford |
| | 20 | MH1521C1 Broussard (G-BWGG) [315-SQ] | Privately owned, Rednal |
| | 37 | Nord 3400 (G-ZARA) [MAB] | Privately owned, Boston |
| | 57 | Dassault Mystère IVA [8-MT] | Imperial War Museum, Duxford |
| | 67 | SNCAN 1101 Noralpha (F-GMCY) [CY] | Privately owned, la Ferté-Alais, France |
| | 70 | Dassault Mystère IVA | Midland Air Museum, Coventry |
| | 78 | Nord 3202B-1 (G-BIZK) | Privately owned, Little Snoring |
| | 79 | Dassault Mystère IVA [2-EG] | Norfolk & Suffolk Avn Museum, Flixton |
| | 82 | Curtiss Hawk 75 (G-CCVH) | The Fighter Collection, Duxford |
| | 82 | NA T-28D Fennec (F-AZKG) [CD-113] | Privately owned, Strasbourg, France |
| | 83 | Dassault Mystère IVA [8-MS] | Newark Air Museum, Winthorpe |
| | 83 | Morane-Saulnier MS.733 Alcyon (F-AZKS) | Privately owned, Montlucon, France |
| | 84 | Dassault Mystère IVA [8-NF] | Lashenden Air Warfare Museum, Headcorn |
| | 85 | Dassault Mystère IVA [8-MV] | Cold War Jets Collection, Bruntingthorpe |
| | 101 | Dassault Mystère IVA [8-MN] | Bomber County Aviation Museum, Hemswell |
| | 104 | MH1521M Broussard (F-GHFG) [307-FG] | Privately owned, France |
| | 105 | Nord N2501F Noratlas (F-AZVM) [62-SI] | Le Noratlas de Provence, Marseilles, France |
| | 121 | Dassault Mystère IVA | City of Norwich Aviation Museum |
| | 128 | Morane-Saulnier MS.733 Alcyon (F-BMMY) | Privately owned, St Cyr, France |
| | 143 | Morane-Saulnier MS733 Alcyon (G-MSAL) | The Squadron, North Weald |
| | 146 | Dassault Mystère IVA [8-MC] | North-East Aircraft Museum, Usworth |
| | 156 | SNCAN Stampe SV-4B (G-NIFE) | Privately owned, Gloucester |
| | 185 | MH1521M Broussard (G-BWLR) | Privately owned, Glos |
| | 282 | Dassault MD311 Flamant (F-AZFX) [316-KY] | Memorial Flt Association, la Ferté-Alais, France |
| | 290 | Dewoitine D27 (F-AZJD) | Amicale J-B Salis, la Ferté-Alais, France |
| | 316 | MH1521M Broussard (F-GGKR) [315-SN] | Privately owned, Lognes, France |
| | 318 | Dassault Mystère IVA [8-NY] | Dumfries & Galloway Avn Mus, Dumfries |
| | 319 | Dassault Mystère IVA [8-ND] | Rebel Air Museum, Andrewsfield |
| | 354 | Morane-Saulnier MS315E-D2 (G-BZNK) | Privately owned, Hemswell |
| | 394 | SNCAN Stampe SV-4C (G-BIMO) | Privately owned, Dunsfold |
| | 538 | Dassault Mirage IIIE [3-QH] | Yorkshire Air Museum, Elvington |
| | 1058 | SO1221 Djinn (FR108) [CDL] | The Helicopter Museum, Weston-super-Mare |
| | 17473 | Lockheed T-33A | Midland Air Museum, Coventry |
| | 42157 | NA F-100D Super Sabre [11-ML] | North-East Aviation Museum, Usworth |
| | 54439 | Lockheed T-33A (55-4439) [WI] | North-East Aircraft Museum, Usworth |
| | 63938 | NA F-100F Super Sabre [11-MU] | Lashenden Air Warfare Museum, Headcorn |
| | 121748 | Grumman F8F-2P Bearcat (F-AZRJ) [5834/P] | Privately owned, Anemasse, France |
| | 125716 | Douglas AD-4N Skyraider (F-AZFN) [22-DG] | Privately owned, Mélun, France |
| | *133704* | CV F4U-7 Corsair (125541/F-AZYS) | Les Ailes de l'Aéro, Cuers, France |
| | 141406 | Douglas C-47A Skytrain (F-AZTE) [E] | Privately owned, la Ferté-Alais, France |
| | 517692 | NA T-28S Fennec (G-TROY) [142] | Privately owned, Duxford |
| | *18-5395* | Piper L-18C Super Cub (52-2436/G-CUBJ) [CDG] | Privately owned, Breighton |
| | 51-7545 | NA T-28S Fennec (N14113) | Privately owned, Duxford |

126

# Historic Aircraft

| Serial | Type (other identity) | Owner/operator, location | Notes |
|---|---|---|---|
| C850 | Salmson 2A2 <R> | Barton Aviation Heritage Society, Barton | |
| MS824 | Morane-Saulnier Type N <R> (G-AWBU) | Flying Aces Museum, Compton Abbas | |
| TE184 | VS361 Spitfire LF XVIE (6850M/G-MXVI) [D] | Privately owned, Duxford | |

**GERMANY**

| Serial | Type (other identity) | Owner/operator, location | Notes |
|---|---|---|---|
| - | Fieseler Fi103R-IV (V-1) (BAPC 91) | Lashenden Air Warfare Museum, Headcorn | |
| - | Focke-Achgelis Fa330A-1 (8469M) | RAF Museum, Cosford | |
| - | Fokker Dr1 Dreidekker <R> (BAPC 88) | FAA Museum, RNAS Yeovilton | |
| - | Messerschmitt Bf109 <R> (6357/BAPC 74) [6] | Kent Battle of Britain Museum, Hawkinge | |
| 1 | Hispano HA 1.112M1L Buchon (C4K-102/G-BWUE) | Privately owned, Breighton | |
| 2 | Messerschmitt Bf109G-10 (151591/D-FDME) | Messerschmitt Stiftung, Manching, Germany | |
| 3 | SNCAN 1101 Noralpha (G-BAYV) | Barton Aviation Heritage Society, Barton | |
| 6 | Messerschmitt Bf109G-2/Trop (10639/8478M/G-USTV) | RAF Museum, Hendon | |
| 7 | Messerschmitt Bf109G-4 (D-FWME) | Messerschmitt Aircraft Co, Albstadt, Germany | |
| 8 | Focke Wulf Fw190 <R> (G-WULF) | Privately owned, Halfpenny Green | |
| 9 | Focke Wulf Fw190 <R> (G-CCFW) | Privately owned, Kemble | |
| 14 | Messerschmitt Bf109 <R> (BAPC 67) | Kent Battle of Britain Museum, Hawkinge | |
| 14 | SNCAN 1101 Noralpha (G-BSMD) | Privately owned, Prestwick | |
| 152/17 | Fokker Dr1 Dreidekker (BAPC 239) <R> (G-ATJM) | Privately owned, East Garston, Bucks | |
| 157/18 | Fokker D.VIII <R> | Norfolk & Suffolk Air Museum, Flixton | |
| 210/16 | Fokker EIII (BAPC 56) | Science Museum, South Kensington | |
| 422/15 | Fokker EIII <R> (G-AVJO) | Privately owned, Compton Abbas | |
| 425/17 | Fokker Dr1 Dreidekker <R> (BAPC 133) | Kent Battle of Britain Museum, Hawkinge | |
| 450/17 | Fokker Dr1 Dreidekker <R> (G-BVGZ) | Privately owned, Breighton | |
| 626/8 | Fokker DVII <R> (N6268) | Privately owned, Booker | |
| 764 | Mikoyan MiG-21SPS <ff> | Privately owned, Booker | |
| 959 | Mikoyan MiG-21SPS | Midland Air Museum, Coventry | |
| 1190 | Messerschmitt Bf109E-3 [4] | Imperial War Museum, Duxford | |
| 1342 | Messerschmitt Bf109E-3 (N342FH) | Privately owned, Wattisham | |
| 1480 | Messerschmitt Bf109 <R> (BAPC 66) [6] | Kent Battle of Britain Museum, Hawkinge | |
| 1801/18 | Bowers Fly Baby 1A (G-BNPV) | Privately owned, Chessington | |
| 1803/18 | Bowers Fly Baby 1A (G-BUYU) | Privately owned, Chessington | |
| 1983 | Messerschmitt Bf109E-3 (G-EMIL) | Privately owned, Surrey | |
| 2088 | Fieseler Fi156A Storch (G-STCH) | Privately owned, Surrey | |
| 2100 | Focke-Wulf Fw189A-1 (G-BZKY) [V7+1H] | Privately owned, Sandown | |
| 3523 | Messerschmitt Bf109E-7 | Privately owned, Lancing | |
| 4034 | Messerschmitt Bf109E (G-CDII) | Privately owned, Duxford | |
| 4101 | Messerschmitt Bf109E-3 (DG200/8477M) [12] | RAF Museum, Hendon | |
| 4477 | CASA 1.131E Jungmann (G-RETA) [GD+EG] | The Shuttleworth Collection, Old Warden | |
| 6234 | Junkers Ju87R-4 (G-STUK) | Privately owned, Surrey | |
| 7198/18 | LVG CVI (G-AANJ/9239M) | RAF Museum, Hendon | |
| 7485 | Messerschmitt Bf109F-4 | Charleston Aviation Services, Colchester | |
| 8147 | Messerschmitt Bf109F-4 | Charleston Aviation Services, Colchester | |
| 8417/18 | Fokker DVII (9207M) | RAF Museum, Hendon | |
| 12802 | Antonov An-2T (D-FOFM) | Historische Flugzeuge, Grossenhain, Germany | |
| 15458 | Messerschmitt Bf109F-4 | Charleston Aviation Services, Colchester | |
| 100143 | Focke-Achgelis Fa330A-1 | Imperial War Museum, Duxford | |
| 100502 | Focke-Achgelis Fa330A-1 | The Real Aeroplane Company, Breighton | |
| 100509 | Focke-Achgelis Fa330A-1 | Science Museum, stored Wroughton | |
| 100545 | Focke-Achgelis Fa330A-1 | Fleet Air Arm Museum, stored RNAS Yeovilton | |
| 100549 | Focke-Achgelis Fa330A-1 | Lashenden Air Warfare Museum, Headcorn | |
| 110451 | Fieseler Fi156D Storch (G-STOR) | Privately owned, Surrey | |

## Historic Aircraft

| Notes | Serial | Type (other identity) | Owner/operator, location |
|---|---|---|---|
| | 112372 | Messerschmitt Me262A-2a (AM.51/VK893/8482M) [4] | RAF Museum, Hendon |
| | 120227 | Heinkel He162A-2 Salamander (VN679/AM.65/8472M) [2] | RAF Museum, Hendon |
| | 120235 | Heinkel He162A-1 Salamander (AM.68) | Imperial War Museum, Lambeth |
| | 191316 | Messerschmitt Me163B Komet | Science Museum, South Kensington |
| | *191454* | Messerschmitt Me163B Komet <R> (BAPC 271) | The Shuttleworth Collection, Old Warden |
| | 191614 | Messerschmitt Me163B Komet (8481M) | RAF Museum Restoration Centre, Cosford |
| | 191659 | Messerschmitt Me163B Komet (8480M) [15] | Royal Scottish Mus'm of Flight, E Fortune |
| | 211028 | Focke Wulf Fw190D-9 (G-DORA) | Privately owned, Surrey |
| | 280020 | Flettner Fl282/B-V20 Kolibri (frame only) | Midland Air Museum, Coventry |
| | 360043 | Junkers Ju88R-1 (PJ876/8475M) [D5+EV] | RAF Museum, Hendon |
| | 420430 | Messerschmitt Me410A-1/U2 (AM.72/8483M) [3U+CC] | RAF Museum, Cosford |
| | 475081 | Fieseler Fi156C-7 Storch ] (VP546/AM.101/7362M)[GM+AK] | RAF Museum, Cosford |
| | 494083 | Junkers Ju87D-3 (8474M) [RI+JK] | RAF Museum, Hendon |
| | 584219 | Focke Wulf Fw190F-8/U1 (AM.29/8470M) [38] | RAF Museum, Hendon |
| | 701152 | Heinkel He111H-23 (8471M) [NT+SL] | RAF Museum, Hendon |
| | 730301 | Messerschmitt Bf110G-4 (AM.34/8479M) [D5+RL] | RAF Museum, Hendon |
| | 733682 | Focke Wulf Fw190A-8/R7 (AM.75/9211M) | Imperial War Museum, Lambeth |
| | *2+1* | Focke Wulf Fw190 <R> (G-SYFW) [7334] | Privately owned, Guernsey, CI |
| | *17+TF* | Bücker Bü133C Jungmeister (G-BZTJ) | Privately owned, Turweston |
| | *22+35* | Lockheed F-104G Starfighter | SWWAPS, Lasham |
| | *22+57* | Lockheed F-104G Starfighter | Privately owned, Grainthorpe, Lincs |
| | *23.02* | Albatros B.II <R> (D-EKGH) | Historischer Flugzeugbau, Fürstenwalde, Germany |
| | *28+08* | Aero L-39ZO Albatros (142/28+04) | Privately owned, Long Stratton, Norfolk |
| | *2E+RA* | Fieseler Fi-156C-3 Storch (F-AZRA) | Amicale J-B Salis, la Ferté-Alais, France |
| | *4+1* | Focke Wulf Fw190 <R> (G-BSLX) | Privately owned, Norwich |
| | *4V+GH* | Amiot AAC1/Ju52 (Port.AF 6316) [9] | Imperial War Museum, Duxford |
| | *6G+ED* | Slepcev Storch (G-BZOB) [5447] | Privately owned, Croydon, Cambs |
| | *58+89* | Dornier Do28D-2 Skyservant (D-ICDY) | Privately owned, Uetersen, Germany |
| | *96+21* | Mil Mi-24D (406) | Imperial War Museum, Duxford |
| | *96+26* | Mil Mi-24D (429) | The Helicopter Museum, Weston-super-Mare |
| | *97+04* | Putzer Elster B (G-APVF) | Privately owned, Breighton |
| | *98+14* | Sukhoi Su-22M-4 | Hawker Hunter Aviation Ltd, stored Scampton |
| | *99+24* | NA OV-10B Bronco (F-AZKM) | Privately owned, Montelimar, France |
| | *99+32* | NA OV-10B Bronco (G-BZGK) | Privately owned, Duxford |
| | *AZ+JU* | CASA 3.52L (F-AZJU) | Amicale J-B Salis, la Ferté-Alais, France |
| | *BU+CC* | CASA 1.131E Jungmann (G-BUCC) | Privately owned, Sandown |
| | *BU+CK* | CASA 1.131E Jungmann (G-BUCK) | Privately owned, White Waltham |
| | *CC+43* | Pilatus P-2 (G-CJCI) | Privately owned, Norwich |
| | *CF+HF* | Morane-Saulnier MS502 (EI-AUY) | Imperial War Museum, Duxford |
| | *CW+BG* | CASA 1.131E Jungmann (G-BXBD) [50,483] | Privately owned, Duxford |
| | *D5397/17* | Albatros DVA <R> (G-BFXL) | FAA Museum, RNAS Yeovilton |
| | *ES+BH* | Messerschmitt Bf108B-2 (D-ESBH) | Messerschmitt Stiftung, Manching, Germany |
| | *FI+S* | Morane-Saulnier MS505 (G-BIRW) | Royal Scottish Mus'm of Flight, E Fortune |
| | *FM+BB* | Messerschmitt Bf109G-6 (D-FMBB) | Messerschmitt Stiftung, Manching, Germany |
| | *FW+WC* | Flug Werk FW190A-8/N (D-FWWC) | Flug Werk, Manching, Germany |
| | *GL+SU* | Bücker Bü1181B-1 Bestmann (G-GLSU) | Privately owned, Surrey |
| | *JA+120* | Canadair CL-13 Sabre 4 (MM19607) | *Currently not known* |
| | *KG+EM* | Nord 1002 (G-ETME) | Privately owned, White Waltham |

| Serial | Type (other identity) | Owner/operator, location | Notes |
|--------|----------------------|--------------------------|-------|
| LG+01 | Bücker Bü133C Jungmeister (G-AYSJ) | The Fighter Collection, Duxford | |
| LG+03 | Bücker Bü133C Jungmeister (G-AEZX) | Privately owned, Milden | |
| NJ+C11 | Nord 1002 (G-ATBG) | Privately owned, Booker | |
| S4+A07 | CASA 1.131E Jungmann (G-BWHP) | Privately owned, Yarcombe, Devon | |
| S5+B06 | CASA 1.131E Jungmann 2000 (G-BSFB) | Privately owned, Old Buckenham | |
| TA+RC | Morane-Saulnier MS505 (G-BPHZ) | Historic Aircraft Collection, Duxford | |

**GHANA**

| | | | |
|--------|----------------------|--------------------------|-------|
| G-102 | SA122 Bulldog | Privately owned, stored Salisbury | |
| G-108 | SA122 Bulldog (G-BCUP) | Privately owned, stored Salisbury | |

**GREECE**

| | | | |
|--------|----------------------|--------------------------|-------|
| 51-6171 | NA F-86D Sabre | North-East Aircraft Museum, Usworth | |
| 52-6541 | Republic F-84F Thunderflash [541] | North-East Aircraft Museum, Usworth | |
| 63-8418 | Northrop F-5A | Martin-Baker Ltd, Chalgrove, Fire Section | |

**HONG KONG**

| | | | |
|--------|----------------------|--------------------------|-------|
| HKG-5 | SA128 Bulldog (G-BULL) | Privately owned, Old Sarum | |
| HKG-6 | SA128 Bulldog (G-BPCL) | Privately owned, North Weald | |
| HKG-11 | Slingsby T.67M Firefly 200 (G-BYRY) | Privately owned, Tibenham | |
| HKG-13 | Slingsby T.67M Firefly 200 (G-BXKW) | Privately owned, Tibenham | |

**HUNGARY**

| | | | |
|--------|----------------------|--------------------------|-------|
| 501 | Mikoyan MiG-21PF | Imperial War Museum, Duxford | |

**INDIA**

| | | | |
|--------|----------------------|--------------------------|-------|
| Q497 | EE Canberra T4 (WE191) (fuselage) | Dumfries & Galloway Avn Mus, Dumfries | |

**INDONESIA**

| | | | |
|--------|----------------------|--------------------------|-------|
| LL-5313 | BAe Hawk T53 | BAE Systems, Brough, on display | |

**IRAQ**

| | | | |
|--------|----------------------|--------------------------|-------|
| 333 | DH115 Vampire T55 <ff> | Aeroventure, Doncaster | |

**ITALY**

| | | | |
|--------|----------------------|--------------------------|-------|
| MM5701 | Fiat CR42 (BT474/8468M) [13-95] | RAF Museum, Hendon | |
| MM52801 | Fiat G46-3B (G-BBII) [4-97] | Privately owned, Sandown | |
| MM53692 | CCF T-6G Texan | RAeS Medway Branch, Rochester | |
| MM53774 | Fiat G59-4B (I-MRSV) [181] | Privately owned, Parma, Italy | |
| MM54099 | NA T-6G Texan (G-BRBC) [RR-56] | Privately owned, Chigwell | |
| MM54-2372 | Piper L-21B Super Cub | Privately owned, Kesgrave, Suffolk | |

**JAPAN**

| | | | |
|--------|----------------------|--------------------------|-------|
| - | Yokosuka MXY 7 Ohka II (BAPC 159) | Defence School, Chattenden | |
| 24 | Kawasaki Ki100-1B (8476M/BAPC 83) | RAF Museum, Hendon | |
| 997 | Yokosuka MXY 7 Ohka II (8485M/BAPC 98) | Gr Manchester Mus of Science & Industry | |
| 5439 | Mitsubishi Ki46-III (8484M/BAPC 84) | RAF Museum, Cosford | |
| 15-1585 | Yokosuka MXY 7 Ohka II (BAPC 58) | Science Museum, at FAA Museum, RNAS Yeovilton | |
| I-13 | Yokosuka MXY 7 Ohka II (8486M/BAPC 99) | RAF Museum, Cosford | |
| Y2-176 | Mitsubishi A6M3-2 Zero (3685) [76] | Imperial War Museum, Duxford | |

**JORDAN**

| | | | |
|--------|----------------------|--------------------------|-------|
| 408 | SA125 Bulldog (G-BDIN) | Privately owned, Lasham | |
| 417 | SA125A Bulldog (G-CCZE) | Privately owned, Lasham | |
| 418 | SA125A Bulldog (G-CCZF) | Privately owned, Lasham | |

**MEXICO**

| | | | |
|--------|----------------------|--------------------------|-------|
| EPC-152 | Mudry/CAARP CAP-10B (G-CCXC) [52] | Privately owned, Hatch | |

**MYANMAR**

| | | | |
|--------|----------------------|--------------------------|-------|
| UB424 | VS361 Spitfire IX (UB425) | Historic Flying Ltd, Duxford | |
| UB441 | VS361 Spitfire IX (ML119) | Privately owned, Sedlescombe, E Sussex | |

## Historic Aircraft

| Notes | Serial | Type (other identity) | Owner/operator, location |
|-------|--------|----------------------|--------------------------|
| | **NETHERLANDS** | | |
| | *16-218* | Consolidated PBY-5A Catalina (2459/PH-PBY) | Neptune Association, Lelystad, The Netherlands |
| | *174* | Fokker S-11 Instructor (E-31/G-BEPV) | Privately owned, Spanhoe |
| | 204 | Lockheed SP-2H Neptune [V] | RAF Museum, Cosford |
| | *A-12* | DH82A Tiger Moth (PH-TYG) | Privately owned, Gilze-Rijen, The Netherlands |
| | B-64 | Noorduyn AT-16 Harvard IIB (PH-LSK) | KLu Historic Flt, Gilze-Rijen, The Netherlands |
| | B-71 | Noorduyn AT-16 Harvard IIB (PH-MLM) | KLu Historic Flt, Gilze-Rijen, The Netherlands |
| | B-118 | Noorduyn AT-16 Harvard IIB (PH-IIB) | KLu Historic Flt, Gilze-Rijen, The Netherlands |
| | E-14 | Fokker S-11 Instructor (PH-AFS) | Privately owned, Lelystad, The Netherlands |
| | E-15 | Fokker S-11 Instructor (G-BIYU) | Privately owned, Bagby |
| | E-18 | Fokker S-11 Instructor (PH-HTC) | Duke of Brabant AF, Eindhoven, The Netherlands |
| | E-20 | Fokker S-11 Instructor (PH-GRB) | Privately owned, Gilze-Rijen, The Netherlands |
| | E-27 | Fokker S-11 Instructor (PH-HOL) | Privately owned, Lelystad, The Netherlands |
| | E-32 | Fokker S-11 Instructor (PH-HOl) | Privately owned, Gilze-Rijen, The Netherlands |
| | E-36 | Fokker S-11 Instructor (PH-ACG) | Privately owned, Lelystad, The Netherlands |
| | E-39 | Fokker S-11 Instructor (PH-HOG) | Privately owned, Lelystad, The Netherlands |
| | *G-29* | Beech D18S (PH-KHV) | KLu Historic Flt, Gilze-Rijen, The Netherlands |
| | MK732 | VS 361 Spitfire LF IXC (8633M/PH-OUQ) [3W-17] | KLu Historic Flt, Gilze-Rijen, The Netherlands |
| | N-202 | Hawker Hunter F6 [10] <ff> | Privately owned, Eaglescott |
| | N-250 | Hawker Hunter F6 (G-9-185) <ff> | Imperial War Museum, Duxford |
| | N-268 | Hawker Hunter FGA78 (Qatar QA-10) | Yorkshire Air Museum, Elvington |
| | N-315 | Hawker Hunter T7 (XM121) | Jet Avn Preservation Grp, Long Marston |
| | *N5-149* | NA B-25J Mitchell (44-29507/HD346/N320SQ) [232511] | Duke of Brabant AF, Gilze-Rijen, The Netherlands |
| | R-55 | Piper L-18C Super Cub (52-2466/G-BLMI) | Privately owned, White Waltham |
| | R-109 | Piper L-21B Super Cub (54-2337/PH-GAZ) | KLu Historic Flt, Gilze-Rijen, The Netherlands |
| | R-122 | Piper L-21B Super Cub (54-2412/PH-PPW) | KLu Historic Flt, Gilze-Rijen, The Netherlands |
| | R-137 | Piper L-21B Super Cub (54-2427/PH-PSC) | Privately owned, Gilze-Rijen, The Netherlands |
| | R-151 | Piper L-21B Super Cub (54-2441/G-BIYR) | Privately owned, Dunkeswell |
| | R-156 | Piper L-21B Super Cub (54-2446/G-ROVE) | Privately owned, Headcorn |
| | R-163 | Piper L-21B Super Cub (54-2453/G-BIRH) | Privately owned, Hinton-in-the-Hedges |
| | R-167 | Piper L-21B Super Cub (54-2457/G-LION) | Privately owned, Turweston, Bucks |
| | R-177 | Piper L-21B Super Cub (54-2467/PH-KNR) | KLu Historic Flt, Gilze-Rijen, The Netherlands |
| | R-181 | Piper L-21B Super Cub (54-2471/PH-GAU) | Privately owned, Gilze-Rijen, The Netherlands |
| | *R-345* | Piper J-3C Cub (PH-UCS) | Privately owned, The Netherlands |
| | S-9 | DHC2 L-20A Beaver (55-4585/PH-DHC) | KLu Historic Flt, Gilze-Rijen, The Netherlands |
| | **NEW ZEALAND** | | |
| | NZ3909 | WS Wasp HAS1 (XT782) | Kennet Aviation, North Weald |
| | *NZ6361* | BAC Strikemaster 87 (OJ5/G-BXFP) | Privately owned, Chalgrove |
| | **NORTH KOREA** | | |
| | - | WSK Lim-2 (MiG-15) (01420/G-BMZF) | FAA Museum, RNAS Yeovilton |
| | **NORTH VIETNAM** | | |
| | 1211 | WSK Lim-5 (MiG-17F) (G-MIGG) | Privately owned, Bournemouth |

| Serial | Type (other identity) | Owner/operator, location | Notes |
|--------|----------------------|--------------------------|-------|
| **NORWAY** | | | |
| *423/427* | Gloster Gladiator I (L8032/G-AMRK/*N2308*) | The Shuttleworth Collection, Old Warden | |
| 848 | Piper L-18C Super Cub (LN-ACL) [FA-N] | Privately owned, Norway | |
| 56321 | SAAB S91B Safir (G-BKPY) [U-AB] | Newark Air Museum, Winthorpe | |
| **OMAN** | | | |
| 425 | BAC Strikemaster 82A (G-SOAF) | Privately owned, Hawarden | |
| 801 | Hawker Hunter T66B | Privately owned, Exeter | |
| 853 | Hawker Hunter FR10 (XF426) | RAF Museum, Hendon | |
| **POLAND** | | | |
| 05 | WSK SM-2 (Mi-2) (1005) | The Helicopter Museum, Weston-super-Mare | |
| 309 | WSK SBLim-2A (MiG-15UTI) <ff> | Royal Scottish Mus'm of Flight, E Fortune | |
| 408 | WSK-PZL Mielec TS-11 Iskra (1H-0408) | Midland Air Museum, Coventry | |
| 1018 | WSK-PZL Mielec TS-11 Iskra (1H-1018/G-ISKA) | Cold War Jets Collection, Bruntingthorpe | |
| 1120 | WSK Lim-2 (MiG-15bis) | RAF Museum, Cosford | |
| **PORTUGAL** | | | |
| *85* | Isaacs Fury II (G-BTPZ) | Privately owned, Ormskirk | |
| 1360 | OGMA/DHC1 Chipmunk T20 (G-BYYU) (fuselage) | Privately owned, Little Staughton | |
| 1365 | OGMA/DHC1 Chipmunk T20 (G-DHPM) | Privately owned, Sywell | |
| 1372 | OGMA/DHC1 Chipmunk T20 (HB-TUM) | Privately owned, Switzerland | |
| *1377* | DHC1 Chipmunk 22 (G-BARS) | Privately owned, Yeovilton | |
| 1741 | CCF Harvard IV (G-HRVD) | Privately owned, Bruntingthorpe | |
| 1747 | CCF T-6J Harvard IV (*20385*/G-BGPB) | The Aircraft Restoration Co, Duxford | |
| **QATAR** | | | |
| QA12 | Hawker Hunter FGA78 <ff> | Privately owned, Cwmbran | |
| QP30 | WS Lynx Mk 28 (G-BFDV/TD 013) | Army SEAE, Arborfield | |
| QP31 | WS Lynx Mk 28 | DARA Fleetlands Apprentice School | |
| QP32 | WS Lynx Mk 28 (TD 016) | AAC Stockwell Hall, Middle Wallop | |
| **RUSSIA (& FORMER SOVIET UNION)** | | | |
| - | Mil Mi-24V (3532424810853) | Privately owned, Hawarden | |
| - | Mil Mi-24D (3532464505029) | Midland Air Museum, Coventry | |
| *1* | SPP Yak C-11 (G-BZMY) | Privately owned, North Weald | |
| *01* | Yakovlev Yak-52 (9311709/G-YKSZ) | Privately owned, White Waltham | |
| *02* | Yakovlev Yak-52 (888615/G-CBLJ) | Privately owned, North Weald | |
| *2* | Yakovlev Yak-18T (RA-02933) | Privately owned, Wickenby | |
| *03* | Mil Mi-24D (3532461715415) | Privately owned, Hawarden | |
| *03* | Yakovlev Yak-9UM (0470403/F-AZYJ) | Privately owned, Stadtlohn, Germany | |
| *03* | Yakovlev Yak-52 (899803/G-YAKR) | Privately owned, North Weald | |
| *04* | Yakovlev Yak-52 (9211612/RA-22521) | Privately owned, Wellesbourne Mountford | |
| 05 | Yakovlev Yak-50 (832507/YL-CBH) | Privately owned, Hawarden | |
| *07* | Mikoyan MiG-23ML (024003607) | Newark Air Museum, Winthorpe | |
| *07* | WSK SM-1 (Mi-1) (Polish AF 2007) | The Helicopter Museum, Weston-super-Mare | |
| *07* | Yakovlev Yak-18M (G-BMJY) | Privately owned, East Garston, Bucks | |
| *09* | Yakovlev Yak-52 (9411809/G-BVMU) | Privately owned, Shipdham | |
| *9* | Polikarpov Po-2 (ZK-POZ) | The Shuttleworth Collection, Old Warden | |
| *9* | SPP Yak C-11 (G-OYAK) | Privately owned, Little Gransden | |
| *10* | Yakovlev Yak-50 (801810/G-BTZB) | Privately owned, Lee-on-Solent | |
| *10* | Yakovlev Yak-52 (822710/G-CBMD) | Privately owned, Headcorn | |
| *11* | SPP Yak C-11 (G-YCII) | Privately owned, Woodchurch, Kent | |
| 12 | LET L-29 Delfin (194555/ES-YLM/G-DELF) | Privately owned, Manston | |
| *12* | Yakovlev Yak-3M (0470107/D-FJAK) | MDM Aviation, Freiburg, Germany | |
| *14* | Yakovlev Yak-52 (899404/G-CCCP) | Privately owned, Navestock | |
| *15* | SPP Yak C-11 (170103/D-FYAK) | Classic Aviation Company, Hannover, Germany | |
| 18 | LET L-29S Delfin (591771/YL-PAF) | Privately owned, Hawarden | |

131

# Historic Aircraft

| Notes | Serial | Type (other identity) | Owner/operator, location |
|---|---|---|---|
| *19* | Polikarpov I-15bis <R> (4439/FLARF-02089) | Privately owned, Duxford |
| 19 | Yakovlev Yak-52 (811202/YL-CBI) | Privately owned, Hawarden |
| 20 | Lavochkin La-11 | The Fighter Collection, Duxford |
| 20 | Yakovlev Yak-52 (790404/YL-CBJ) | Privately owned, Hawarden |
| 23 | Bell P-39Q Airacobra (44-2911) | Privately owned, Sussex |
| 23 | Mikoyan MiG-27D (83712515040) | Privately owned, Hawarden |
| *26* | Yakovlev Yak-52 (9111306/G-BVXK) | Privately owned, White Waltham |
| *27* | Yakovlev Yak-3UTI-PW (9/04623/F-AZIM) | Capel Aviation, la Ferté-Alais, France |
| 27 | Yakovlev Yak-52 (9111307/G-YAKX) | Privately owned, Popham |
| 31 | Yakovlev Yak-52 (9111311/G-YAKV) | Privately owned, Rendcomb |
| *33* | Yakovlev Yak-50 (853206/G-YAKZ) | Privately owned, Compton Abbas |
| 35 | Sukhoi Su-17M-3 (25102) | Privately owned, Hawarden |
| *36* | SPP/Yak C-11 (G-KYAK) | Privately owned, North Weald |
| *36* | SPP Yak C-11 (G-IYAK) | Privately owned, Sleap |
| 42 | Yakovlev Yak-52 (833901/G-LENA) | Privately owned, Compton Abbas |
| *42* | Yakovlev Yak-52 (888911/G-CBRU) | Privately owned, Rochester |
| 43 | Yakovlev Yak-52 (877601/G-BWSV) | Privately owned, North Weald |
| *46* | Yakovlev Yak-50 (825905/G-GYAK) | Privately owned, North Weald |
| 48 | Yakovlev Yak-52 (9111413/G-CBSN) | Privately owned, Manston |
| *49* | Yakovlev Yak-50 (822305/G-YAKU) | Privately owned, Compton Abbas |
| *50* | Yakovlev Yak-50 (812101/G-CBPM) | Privately owned, High Cross |
| 50 | Yakovlev Yak-52 (9111415/G-CBRW) | Privately owned, White Waltham |
| 51 | LET L-29S Delfin (491273/YL-PAG) | Privately owned, Breighton |
| 52 | Yakovlev Yak-52 (800708/G-CBPY) | Privately owned, Sherburn-in-Elmet |
| 52 | Yakovlev Yak-52 (878202/G-BWVR) | Privately owned, Barton |
| 54 | Sukhoi Su-17M (69004) | Privately owned, Hawarden |
| 55 | Yakovlev Yak-52 (9111505/G-BVOK) | Intrepid Aviation, North Weald |
| 56 | Yakovlev Yak-52 (811504) | Privately owned, Hawarden |
| 56 | Yakovlev Yak-52 (9111506/RA-44516) | Privately owned, White Waltham |
| *61* | Yakovlev Yak-50 (842710/G-YAKM) | Privately owned, Compton Abbas |
| *66* | Yakovlev Yak-52 (855905/G-YAKN) | Privately owned, Compton Abbas |
| *67* | Yakovlev Yak-52 (822013/G-CBSL) | Privately owned, Leicester |
| *69* | Hawker Hunter FGA9 (8839M/XG194) | RAF North Luffenham Training Area |
| 69 | Yakovlev Yak-52 (855509/LY-ALS) | Privately owned, Little Gransden |
| 69 | Yakovlev Yak-52 (888712/G-CCSU) | Privately owned, Germany |
| *69* | Yakovlev Yak-52 (899413/G-XYAK) | Privately owned, Duxford |
| 71 | Mikoyan MiG-27M (61912507006) | Newark Air Museum, Winthorpe |
| *72* | Yakovlev Yak-52 (9111608/G-BXAV) | Privately owned, Wolverhampton |
| 74 | Yakovlev Yak-52 (877404/G-LAOK) [JA-74, IV-62] | Privately owned, Tollerton |
| 74 | Yakovlev Yak-52 (888802/G-BXID) | Privately owned, Kemble |
| *93* | Yakovlev Yak-50 (853001/G-JYAK) | Privately owned, North Weald |
| 96 | Yakovlev Yak-55M (901103/G-YKSS) | Privately owned, Headcorn |
| 100 | Yakovlev Yak-52 (866904/G-YAKI) | Privately owned, Popham |
| *101* | Yakovlev Yak-52 (866915/G-CDBW) | Privately owned, Rochester |
| 112 | Yakovlev Yak-52 (822610/LY-AFB) | Privately owned, Little Gransden |
| 139 | Yakovlev Yak-52 (833810/G-BWOD) | Privately owned, Sywell |
| *503* | Mikoyan MiG-21SMT (G-BRAM) | Farnborough Air Sciences Trust, Farnborough |
| 1342 | Yakovlev Yak-1 (G-BTZD) | Privately owned, St Leonards-on-Sea |
| 1870710 | Ilyushin Il-2 (G-BZVW) | Privately owned, Sandtoft |
| 1878576 | Ilyushin Il-2 (G-BZVX) | Privately owned, Sandtoft |
| *1-12* | Yakovlev Yak-52 (9011013/RA-02293) | Privately owned, Halfpenny Green |
| (RK858) | VS361 Spitfire LF IX | The Fighter Collection, Duxford |
| (SM639) | VS361 Spitfire LF IX | Privately owned, Catfield |

## SAUDI ARABIA

| Notes | Serial | Type (other identity) | Owner/operator, location |
|---|---|---|---|
| 1104 | BAC Strikemaster 80 (G-SMAS) | Privately owned, Hawarden |
| 1107 | BAC Strikemaster 80 | Privately owned, Shoreham |
| 1112 | BAC Strikemaster 80 (G-FLYY) | Privately owned, Hawarden |
| 1120 | BAC Strikemaster 80A (G-RSAF) | Privately owned, Hawarden |
| 1125 | BAC Strikemaster 80A | Privately owned, Bentwaters |
| 1130 | BAC Strikemaster 80A (G-CDHB) | Privately owned, Humberside |
| 1133 | BAC Strikemaster 80A (G-BESY) | Imperial War Museum, Duxford |
| 53-686 | BAC Lightning F53 (ZF592) | City of Norwich Aviation Museum |
| 55-713 | BAC Lightning T55 (ZF598) | Midland Air Museum, Coventry |

| Serial | Type (other identity) | Owner/operator, location | Notes |
|--------|----------------------|--------------------------|-------|
| **SOUTH AFRICA** | | | |
| 91 | Westland Wasp HAS1 (pod) | Privately owned, Oaksey Park | |
| 92 | Westland Wasp HAS1 (G-BYCX) | Privately owned, Chiseldon | |
| 221 | DH115 Vampire T55 <ff> | Privately owned, Hemel Hempstead | |
| 6130 | Lockheed Ventura II (AJ469) | RAF Museum, stored Cosford | |
| 7429 | NA AT-6D Harvard III (D-FASS) | Privately owned, Aachen, Germany | |
| | | | |
| **SOUTH VIETNAM** | | | |
| 24550 | Cessna L-19E Bird Dog (G-PDOG) [GP] | Privately owned, Lincs | |
| | | | |
| **SPAIN** | | | |
| B.2I-27 | CASA 2.111B (He111H-16) (B.2I-103) | Imperial War Museum, stored Duxford | |
| C.4E-88 | Messerschmitt Bf109E | Privately owned, East Garston, Bucks | |
| E.3B-114 | CASA 1.131E Jungmann (G-BJAL) | Privately owned, Breighton | |
| E.3B-143 | CASA 1.131E Jungmann (G-JUNG) | Privately owned, White Waltham | |
| E.3B-153 | CASA 1.131E Jungmann (G-BPTS) [781-75] | Privately owned, Duxford | |
| E.3B-350 | CASA 1.131E Jungmann (G-BHPL) [05-97] | Privately owned, Compton Abbas | |
| (E.3B-369) | CASA 1.131E Jungmann (G-BPDM) [781-32] | Privately owned, Heighington | |
| E.3B-494 | CASA 1.131E Jungmann (G-CDLC) [81-47] | Privately owned, Kemble | |
| E.3B-521 | CASA 1.131E Jungmann [781-3] | RAF Museum, Hendon | |
| E.18-2 | Piper PA-31P Navajo 425 | Bentwaters Cold War Museum | |
| EM-01 | DH60G Moth (G-AAOR) | Privately owned, Rendcomb | |
| ES.1-4 | Bücker Bü133C Jungmeister (G-BUTX) | Privately owned, Breighton | |
| ES.1-16 | CASA 1.133L Jungmeister | Privately owned, Stretton, Cheshire | |
| | | | |
| **SWEDEN** | | | |
| - | Thulin A/Bleriot XI (SE-XMC) | Privately owned, Loberod, Sweden | |
| 081 | CFM 01 Tummelisa <R> (SE-XIL) | Privately owned, Loberod, Sweden | |
| 05108 | DH60 Moth | Privately owned, Langham | |
| 17239 | SAAB B-17A (SE-BYH) [7-J] | Flygvapenmuseum, Linköping, Sweden | |
| 28693 | DH100 Vampire FB6 (J-1184/SE-DXY) [9-G] | Scandinavian Historic Flight, Oslo, Norway | |
| 29640 | SAAB J-29F [20-08] | Midland Air Museum, Coventry | |
| 29670 | SAAB J-29F (SE-DXB) [10-R] | Flygvapenmuseum/F10 Wing, Angelholm, Sweden | |
| 32028 | SAAB 32A Lansen (G-BMSG) | Privately owned, Cranfield | |
| 34066 | Hawker Hunter F58 (J-4089/SE-DXA) [9-G] | Scandinavian Historic Flight, Oslo, Norway | |
| 35075 | SAAB J-35J Draken [40] | Dumfries & Galloway Aviation Museum | |
| 35515 | SAAB J-35F Draken [49] | Irvin-GQ, Llangeinor | |
| 37918 | SAAB AJSH-37 Viggen [57] | Newark Air Museum, Winthrop | |
| | | | |
| **SWITZERLAND** | | | |
| A-10 | CASA 1.131E Jungmann (G-BECW) | Privately owned, Rochester | |
| A-12 | Bücker Bu131B Jungmann (G-CCHY) | Privately owned, Booker | |
| A-50 | CASA 1.131E Jungmann (G-CBCE) | Privately owned, Breighton | |
| A-57 | CASA 1.131E Jungmann (G-BECT) | Privately owned, Goodwood | |
| A-125 | Pilatus P-2 (G-BLKZ) | Privately owned, Duxford | |
| A-701 | Junkers Ju52/3m (HB-HOS) | Ju-Air, Dubendorf, Switzerland | |
| A-702 | Junkers Ju52/3m (HB-HOT) | Ju-Air, Dubendorf, Switzerland | |
| A-703 | Junkers Ju52/3m (HB-HOP) | Ju-Air, Dubendorf, Switzerland | |
| A-806 | Pilatus P3-03 (G-BTLL) | Privately owned, stored Headcorn | |
| C-552 | EKW C-3605 (G-DORN) | Privately owned, Bournemouth | |
| C-558 | EKW C-3605 | Privately owned, Spanhoe | |
| J-1008 | DH100 Vampire FB6 | Mosquito Aircraft Museum, London Colney | |
| J-1172 | DH100 Vampire FB6 (8487M) | RAF Museum Reserve Collection, Stafford | |
| J-1573 | DH112 Venom FB50 (G-VICI) | Source Classic Jet Flight, Bournemouth | |
| J-1605 | DH112 Venom FB50 (G-BLID) | Gatwick Aviation Museum, Charlwood, Surrey | |
| J-1629 | DH112 Venom FB50 | Air Atlantique Classic Flight, Coventry | |
| J-1649 | DH112 Venom FB50 | Air Atlantique Classic Flight, Coventry | |
| J-1704 | DH112 Venom FB54 | RAF Museum, Cosford | |
| J-1712 | DH112 Venom FB54 <ff> | North West Aviation Heritage, Hooton Park | |
| J-1758 | DH112 Venom FB54 (N203DM) | Privately owned, stored North Weald | |

## Historic Aircraft

| Notes | Serial | Type (other identity) | Owner/operator, location |
|---|---|---|---|
| | J-1790 | DH112 Venom FB50 (J-1632/G-VNOM) | Mosquito Aircraft Museum, London Colney |
| | J-4015 | Hawker Hunter F58 (J-4040/HB-RVS) | Privately owned, St Stephan, Switzerland |
| | J-4021 | Hawker Hunter F58 (G-HHAC) | Hawker Hunter Aviation Ltd, Scampton |
| | J-4031 | Hawker Hunter F58 (G-BWFR) | Hawker Hunter Aviation Ltd, Scampton |
| | J-4058 | Hawker Hunter F58 (G-HHAD) | Hawker Hunter Aviation Ltd, Scampton |
| | J-4064 | Hawker Hunter F58 (HB-RVQ) | Fliegermuseum Altenrhein, Switzerland |
| | J-4066 | Hawker Hunter F58 (G-HHAE) | Hawker Hunter Aviation Ltd, Scampton |
| | J-4072 | Hawker Hunter F58 (G-HHAB) | Hawker Hunter Aviation Ltd, Scampton |
| | J-4081 | Hawker Hunter F58 (G-HHAF) | Hawker Hunter Aviation Ltd, Scampton |
| | J-4083 | Hawker Hunter F58 (G-EGHH) | Privately owned, Exeter |
| | J-4086 | Hawker Hunter F58 (HB-RVU) | Privately owned, Altenrhein, Switzerland |
| | J-4090 | Hawker Hunter F58 (G-SIAL) | The Old Flying Machine Company, Scampton |
| | J-4091 | Hawker Hunter F58 | British Aviation Heritage, Bruntingthorpe |
| | J-4201 | Hawker Hunter T68 (HB-RVR) | Amici dell'Hunter, Sion, Switzerland |
| | J-4205 | Hawker Hunter T68 (HB-RVP) | Fliegermuseum Altenrhein, Switzerland |
| | U-80 | Bücker Bü133D Jungmeister (G-BUKK) | Privately owned, Kendford |
| | U-95 | Bücker Bü133C Jungmeister (G-BVGP) | Privately owned, Booker |
| | U-99 | Bücker Bü133C Jungmeister (G-AXMT) | Privately owned, Breighton |
| | U-110 | Pilatus P-2 (G-PTWO) | Privately owned, Earls Colne |
| | V-54 | SE3130 Alouette II (G-BVSD) | Privately owned, Glos |
| **USA** | | | |
| | - | Noorduyn AT-16 Harvard IIB (KLu B-168) | American Air Museum, Duxford |
| | 001 | Ryan ST-3KR Recruit (G-BYPY) | Privately owned, Duxford |
| | 14 | Boeing-Stearman A75N-1 Kaydet (G-ISDN) | Privately owned, Kemble |
| | 23 | Fairchild PT-23 (N49272) | Privately owned, DCAE Cosford |
| | 27 | NA SNJ-7 Texan (90678/G-BRVG) | Privately owned, Goodwood |
| | 43 | Noorduyn AT-16 Harvard IIB (43-13064/G-AZSC) [SC] | Privately owned, North Weald |
| | 44 | Boeing-Stearman D75N-1 Kaydet (42-15852/G-RJAH) | Privately owned, Rendcomb |
| | 49 | Curtiss P-40M Kittyhawk (43-5802/G-KITT/*P8196*) | The Fighter Collection, Duxford |
| | 85 | WAR P-47 Thunderbolt <R> (G-BTBI) | Privately owned, Perth |
| | 112 | Boeing-Stearman PT-13D Kaydet (42-17397/G-BSWC) | Privately owned, Staverton |
| | 379 | Boeing-Stearman PT-13D Kaydet (42-14865/G-ILLE) | Privately owned, Tibenham |
| | 399 | Boeing-Stearman N2S-5 Kaydet (38495/N67193) | Privately owned, Gelnhausen, Germany |
| | 441 | Boeing-Stearman N2S-4 Kaydet (30010/G-BTFG) | Privately owned, Manston |
| | 540 | Piper L-4H Grasshopper (43-29877/G-BCNX) | Privately owned, Monewden |
| | 578 | Boeing-Stearman N2S-5 Kaydet (N1364V) | Privately owned, North Weald |
| | 628 | Beech D17S (44-67761/N18V) | Privately owned, stored East Garston, Bucks |
| | 669 | Boeing-Stearman A75N-1 Kaydet (37869/G-CCXA) | Privately owned, Old Buckenham |
| | 699 | Boeing-Stearman N2S-3 Kaydet (38233/G-CCXB) | Privately owned, Old Buckenham |
| | 718 | Boeing-Stearman PT-13D Kaydet (42-17555/N5345N) | Privately owned, Tibenham |
| | 744 | Boeing-Stearman A75N-1 Kaydet (42-16532/OO-USN) | Privately owned, Wevelgem, Belgium |
| | 854 | Ryan PT-22 Recruit (42-17378/G-BTBH) | Privately owned, Old Warden |
| | 855 | Ryan PT-22 Recruit (41-15510/N56421) | Privately owned, DCAE Cosford |
| | 897 | Aeronca 11AC Chief (G-BJEV) [E] | Privately owned, English Bicknor, Glos |
| | 1102 | Boeing-Stearman N2S-5 Kaydet (G-AZLE) [102] | Privately owned, Tongham |

| Serial | Type (other identity) | Owner/operator, location | Notes |
|--------|----------------------|--------------------------|-------|
| 1164 | Beech D18S (G-BKGL) | The Aircraft Restoration Co, Duxford | |
| 1180 | Boeing-Stearman N2S-3 Kaydet (3403/G-BRSK) | Privately owned, Morley | |
| 2807 | NA T-6G Texan (49-3072/G-TEXN) [V-103] | Privately owned, Shoreham | |
| 3397 | Boeing-Stearman N2S-3 Kaydet (G-OBEE) [174] | Privately owned, Old Buckenham | |
| 4406 | Naval Aircraft Factory N3N-3 (G-ONAF) [12] | Privately owned, Sandown | |
| 6136 | Boeing-Stearman A75N-1 Kaydet (42-16136/G-BRUJ) [205] | Privately owned, Liverpool | |
| 6771 | Republic F-84F Thunderstreak (BAF FU-6) | RAF Museum, stored Cosford | |
| 7797 | Aeronca L-16A (47-0797/G-BFAF) | Privately owned, Finmere | |
| 8084 | NA AT-6D Harvard III (42-85068/LN-AMY) | The Old Flying Machine Company, Duxford | |
| 8178 | NA F-86A Sabre (48-0178/G-SABR) [FU-178] | Golden Apple Operations/ARC, Duxford | |
| 8242 | NA F-86A Sabre (48-0242) [FU-242] | Midland Air Museum, Coventry | |
| 01532 | Northrop F-5E Tiger II <R> | RAF Alconbury on display | |
| 02538 | Fairchild PT-19B (N33870) | Privately owned, Greenham Common | |
| 07539 | Boeing-Stearman N2S-3 Kaydet (N63590) [143] | Privately owned, Billericay | |
| 14286 | Lockheed T-33A (51-4286) | American Air Museum, Duxford | |
| O-14419 | Lockheed T-33A (51-4419) | Midland Air Museum, Coventry | |
| 14863 | NA AT-6D Harvard III (41-33908/G-BGOR) | Privately owned, Rednal | |
| 15154 | Bell OH-58A Kiowa (70-15154) | R. Military College of Science, Shrivenham | |
| 15445 | Piper L-18C Super Cub (51-15445/G-BLGT) | Privately owned, Dunkeswell | |
| 15990 | Bell AH-1F Hueycobra (67-19590) | Museum of Army Flying, stored Middle Wallop | |
| 16445 | Bell AH-1F Hueycobra (69-16445) | R. Military College of Science, Shrivenham | |
| 16506 | Hughes OH-6A Cayuse (67-16506) | The Helicopter Museum, Weston-super-Mare | |
| 16579 | Bell UH-1H Iroquois (66-16579) | The Helicopter Museum, Weston-super-Mare | |
| 16718 | Lockheed T-33A (51-6718) | City of Norwich Aviation Museum | |
| 17962 | Lockheed SR-71A (61-7962) | American Air Museum, Duxford | |
| 18263 | Boeing-Stearman PT-17 Kaydet (41-8263/N38940) [822] | Privately owned, Tibenham | |
| 19252 | Lockheed T-33A (51-9252) | Tangmere Military Aviation Museum | |
| 21509 | Bell UH-1H Iroquois (72-21509/NX41574) | Privately owned, Blackpool | |
| 21605 | Bell UH-1H Iroquois (72-21605) | American Air Museum, Duxford | |
| 21714 | Grumman F8F-2P Bearcat (121714/G-RUMM) [201-B] | The Fighter Collection, Duxford | |
| 24538 | Kaman HH-43F Huskie (62-4535) | Midland Air Museum, Coventry | |
| 24541 | Cessna L-19E Bird Dog (N134TT) | Privately owned, Yarcombe | |
| 24568 | Cessna L-19E Bird Dog (LN-WNO) | Army Aviation Norway, Kjeller, Norway | |
| 28521 | CCF Harvard IV (G-TVIJ) [TA-521] | Privately owned, Woodchurch, Kent | |
| 30861 | NA TB-25J Mitchell (44-30861/N9089Z) | Privately owned, North Weald | |
| 31145 | Piper L-4B Grasshopper (43-1145/G-BBLH) [26-G] | Privately owned, Biggin Hill | |
| 31171 | NA B-25J Mitchell (44-31171/N7614C) | American Air Museum, Duxford | |
| 31430 | Piper L-4B Grasshopper (43-1430/G-BHVV) | Privately owned, Rochester | |
| 31952 | Aeronca O-58B Defender (G-BRPR) | Privately owned, Earls Colne | |
| 34037 | NA TB-25N Mitchell (44-29366/N9115Z/8838M) | RAF Museum, Hendon | |
| 37414 | McD F-4C Phantom (63-7414) | Midland Air Museum, Coventry | |
| 39624 | Wag Aero Sport Trainer (G-BVMH) [39-D] | Privately owned, Temple Bruer | |
| 40467 | Grumman F6F-5K Hellcat (80141/G-BTCC) [19] | The Fighter Collection, Duxford | |
| 41386 | Thomas-Morse S4 Scout <R> (G-MJTD) | Privately owned, Lutterworth | |
| 42165 | NA F-100D Super Sabre (54-2165) [VM] | American Air Museum, Duxford | |
| 42174 | NA F-100D Super Sabre (54-2174) [UH] | Midland Air Museum, Coventry | |

# Historic Aircraft

| Notes | Serial | Type (other identity) | Owner/operator, location |
|-------|--------|----------------------|--------------------------|
| | 42196 | NA F-100D Super Sabre (54-2196) | Norfolk & Suffolk Avn Museum, Flixton |
| | *46214* | Grumman TBM-3E Avenger (69327/CF-KCG) [X-3] | American Air Museum, Duxford |
| | 48846 | Boeing B-17G Flying Fortress (44-8846/F-AZDX) [DS-M] | Assoc Fortresse Toujours Volant, Paris, France |
| | 53319 | Grumman TBM-3R Avenger (G-BTDP) [319-RB] | Privately owned, North Weald |
| | 54433 | Lockheed T-33A (55-4433) | Norfolk & Suffolk Avn Museum, Flixton |
| | 54884 | Piper L-4J Grasshopper (45-4884/N61787) [57-D] | Privately owned, Chiseldon |
| | 56498 | Douglas C-54Q Skymaster (N44914) | Privately owned, stored North Weald |
| | 58811 | NA B-25J Mitchell (45-8811/F-AZID) [HD] | Privately owned, Athens, Greece |
| | 60312 | McD F-101F Voodoo (56-0312) | Midland Air Museum, Coventry |
| | 60689 | Boeing B-52D Stratofortress (56-0689) | American Air Museum, Duxford |
| | *63000* | NA F-100D Super Sabre (54-2212) [FW-000] | USAF Croughton, Oxon, at gate |
| | *63319* | NA F-100D Super Sabre (54-2269) [FW-319] | RAF Lakenheath, on display |
| | *63428* | Republic F-105G Thunderchief (62-4428) | USAF Croughton, Oxon, at gate |
| | 66692 | Lockheed U-2CT (56-6692) | American Air Museum, Duxford |
| | 70270 | McD F-101B Voodoo (57-270) (fuselage) | Midland Air Museum, Coventry |
| | 80425 | Grumman F7F-3P Tigercat (N7235C/G-RUMT) [WT-14] | The Fighter Collection, Duxford |
| | *80995* | Cessna 337D Super Skymaster (F-BRPQ) | Privately owned, Strasbourg, France |
| | 82062 | DHC U-6A Beaver (58-2062) | Midland Air Museum, Coventry |
| | 91822 | Republic F-105D Thunderchief (59-1822) | Imperial War Museum, Duxford |
| | *93542* | CCF Harvard IV (G-BRLV) [LTA-542] | Privately owned, North Weald |
| | 96995 | CV F4U-4 Corsair (OE-EAS) [BR-37] | Flying Bulls, Salzburg, Austria |
| | 97264 | CV F4U-4 Corsair (F-AZVJ) [403] | Corsair Warbird, Dijon, France |
| | *111836* | NA AT-6C Harvard IIA (41-33262/G-TSIX) [JZ-6] | Privately owned, Tatemhill |
| | 111989 | Cessna L-19A Bird Dog (51-11989/N33600) | Museum of Army Flying, Middle Wallop |
| | 114700 | NA T-6G Texan (51-14700/G-TOMC) | Privately owned, Netherthorpe |
| | 115042 | NA T-6G Texan (51-15042/G-BGHU) [TA-042] | Privately owned, Headcorn |
| | 115227 | NA T-6G Texan (51-15227/G-BKRA) | Privately owned, Staverton |
| | 115302 | Piper L-18C Super Cub (51-15302/G-BJTP) [TP] | Privately owned, Defford |
| | 115684 | Piper L-21A Super Cub (51-15684/G-BKVM) [DC] | Privately owned, Strubby |
| | 124143 | Douglas AD-4NA Skyraider (F-AZDP) [205-RM] | Amicale J-B Salis, la Ferté-Alais, France |
| | *124485* | Boeing B-17G Flying Fortress (44-85784/G-BEDF)[DF-A] | B-17 Preservation Ltd, Duxford |
| | 124724 | CV F4U-5NL Corsair (F-AZEG) [22] | Amicale J-B Salis, la Ferté-Alais, France |
| | 126922 | Douglas AD-4NA Skyraider (G-RADR) [402-AK] | Kennet Aviation, North Weald |
| | 126956 | Douglas AD-4NA Skyraider (F-AZDQ) [3-RM] | Aéro Retro, St Rambert d'Albon, France |
| | 127002 | Douglas AD-4NA Skyraider (F-AZHK) [618-G] | Privately owned, Cuers, France |
| | *133704* | CV F4U-5NL Corsair (124541/F-AZYS) [14.F.6] | Privately owned, Le Castellet, France |
| | *134076* | NA AT-6D Harvard III (41-34671/F-AZSC) [TA076] | Privately owned, Yvetot, France |
| | 138179 | NA T-28A Trojan (OE-ESA) [BA] | The Flying Bulls, Salzburg, Austria |
| | 138266 | NA T-28B Trojan (HB-RCT) [266-CT] | Jet Alpine Fighter, Sion, Switzerland |
| | 140547 | NA T-28C Trojan (F-AZHN) [IF-28] | Privately owned, Toussus le Noble, France |
| | 140566 | NA T-28C Trojan (N556EB) [252] | Privately owned, la Ferté-Alais, France |
| | 146289 | NA T-28C Trojan (N99153) [2W] | Norfolk & Suffolk Aviation Museum, Flixton |
| | *150225* | WS58 Wessex 60 (G-AWOX) [123] | Privately owned, Lulsgate |
| | 155529 | McD F-4J(UK) Phantom (ZE359) [AJ-114] | American Air Museum, Duxford |
| | 155848 | McD F-4S Phantom [WT-11] | Royal Scottish Mus'm of Flight, E Fortune |
| | 159233 | HS AV-8A Harrier [CG-33] | Imperial War Museum North, Salford Quays |

| Serial | Type (other identity) | Owner/operator, location | Notes |
|--------|----------------------|--------------------------|-------|
| 162071 | McD AV-8B Harrier II (fuselage) | Rolls-Royce, Filton | |
| 162737 | McD AV-8B Harrier II (fuselage) | RAF/DARA, St Athan | |
| 162958 | McD AV-8B Harrier II (fuselage) | QinetiQ, Boscombe Down | |
| 162964 | McD AV-8B Harrier II <ff> | RAF Wittering | |
| 162964 | McD AV-8B Harrier II <rf> | BAE Systems, Brough | |
| 163177 | McD AV-8B Harrier II (fuselage) | BAE Systems, Warton | |
| 163205 | McD AV-8B Harrier II (fuselage) | RAF/DARA, St Athan | |
| 212540 | Noorduyn AT-16 Harvard IIB (42-12540/G-BBHK) [RD-40] | Privately owned, Kemble | |
| *217786* | Boeing-Stearman PT-17 Kaydet (41-8169/CF-EQS) [25] | American Air Museum, Duxford | |
| 219993 | Bell P-39Q Airacobra (42-19993/N793QG) | The Fighter Collection, Duxford | |
| *224319* | Douglas C-47B Skytrain (44-77047/G-AMSN) <ff> | Privately owned, Sussex | |
| *226413* | Republic P-47D Thunderbolt (45-49192/N47DD) [ZU-N] | American Air Museum, Duxford | |
| *226671* | Republic P-47M Thunderbolt (G-THUN) [MX-X] | The Fighter Collection, Duxford | |
| *231983* | Boeing B-17G Flying Fortress (44-83735/F-BDRS) [IY-G] | The Fighter Collection, Duxford | |
| 234539 | Fairchild PT-19B Cornell (42-34539/N50429) [63] | Privately owned, Dunkeswell | |
| 236657 | Piper L-4A Grasshopper (42-36657/G-BGSJ) [72-D] | Privately owned, Langport | |
| *237123* | Waco CG-4A Hadrian (BAPC 157) (fuselage) | Yorkshire Air Museum, Elvington | |
| 238410 | Piper L-4A Grasshopper (42-38410/G-BHPK) [44-A] | Privately owned, Tibenham | |
| 241079 | Waco CG-4A <R> | Assault Glider Association, Shawbury | |
| *243809* | Waco CG-4A Hadrian (BAPC 185) | Museum of Army Flying, Middle Wallop | |
| 252983 | Schweizer TG-3A (42-52983/N66630) | Imperial War Museum, stored Duxford | |
| 314887 | Fairchild Argus III (43-14887/G-AJPI) | Privately owned, Eelde, The Netherlands | |
| 315211 | Douglas C-47A (43-15211/N1944A) [J8-Z] | Privately owned, Kemble | |
| 315509 | Douglas C-47A (43-15509/G-BHUB) [W7-S] | American Air Museum, Duxford | |
| 325147 | NA P-51C Mustang (43-25147/G-PSIC) [HO-W] | The Fighter Collection, Duxford | |
| 329405 | Piper L-4A Grasshopper (43-29405/G-BCOB) [23-A] | Privately owned, South Walsham | |
| *329417* | Piper L-4A Grasshopper (42-38400/G-BDHK) | Privately owned, English Bicknor | |
| 329471 | Piper L-4H Grasshopper (43-29471/G-BGXA) [44-F] | Privately owned, Martley, Worcs | |
| 329601 | Piper L-4H Grasshopper (43-29601/G-AXHR) [44-D] | Privately owned, Nayland | |
| 329854 | Piper L-4H Grasshopper (43-29854/G-BMKC) [44-R] | Privately owned, Newtownards | |
| 329934 | Piper L-4H Grasshopper (43-29934/G-BCPH) [72-B] | Privately owned, Thatcham | |
| 330238 | Piper L-4H Grasshopper (43-30238/G-LIVH) [24-A] | Privately owned, Barton | |
| 330485 | Piper L-4H Grasshopper (43-30485/G-AJES) [44-C] | Privately owned, Shifnal | |
| *343251* | Boeing-Stearman N2S-5 Kaydet (43517/G-NZSS) [27] | Privately owned, Kidlington | |
| *411622* | NA P-51D Mustang (44-74427/F-AZSB) [G4-C] | Amicale J-B Salis, la Ferté-Alais, France | |
| *413317* | NA P-51D Mustang (44-74409/N51RT) [VF-B] | RAF Museum, Hendon | |
| *413573* | NA P-51D Mustang (44-73415/9133M/N6526D) [B6-V] | RAF Museum, Cosford | |
| *413704* | NA P-51D Mustang (44-73149/G-BTCD) [B7-H] | The Old Flying Machine Company, Duxford | |
| *414151* | NA P-51D Mustang (44-73140/NL314BG) [HO-M] | Privately owned, Greenham Common | |
| *414419* | NA P-51D Mustang (45-15118/G-MSTG) [LH-F] | Privately owned, Hardwick, Norfolk | |
| *414450* | NA P-51D Mustang (44-73877/N167F) [B6-S] | Scandinavian Historic Flight, Oslo, Norway | |

## Historic Aircraft

| Notes | Serial | Type (other identity) | Owner/operator, location |
|---|---|---|---|
| | *433915* | Consolidated PBY-5A Catalina (G-PBYA) | Plane Sailing, Duxford |
| | 434602 | Douglas A-26B Invader (44-34602/N167B) [B] | Scandinavian Historic Flight, Oslo, Norway |
| | 435710 | Douglas A-26C Invader (44-35710/OO-INV) | Historic Invader Avn, Schiphol, The Netherlands |
| | *442268* | Noorduyn AT-16 Harvard IIB (KF568/LN-TEX) [TA-268] | Scandinavian Historic Flight, Oslo, Norway |
| | 454467 | Piper L-4J Grasshopper (45-4467/G-BILI) [44-J] | Privately owned, White Waltham |
| | 454537 | Piper L-4J Grasshopper (45-4537/G-BFDL) [04-J] | Privately owned, Shempston Farm, Lossiemouth |
| | 455811 | NA T-28B Trojan (45-8811/HB-RDE) [SB] | Jet Alpine Fighter, Sion, Switzerland |
| | 461748 | Boeing B-29A Superfortress (44-61748/G-BHDK) [Y] | American Air Museum, Duxford |
| | *463209* | NA P-51D Mustang <R> (BAPC 255) [WZ-S] | American Air Museum, Duxford |
| | 463864 | NA P-51D Mustang (44-63864/G-CBNM) [HL-W] | The Fighter Collection, Duxford |
| | 472035 | NA P-51D Mustang (44-72035/G-SIJJ) | Privately owned, North Weald |
| | 472216 | NA P-51D Mustang (44-72216/G-BIXL) [HO-M] | Privately owned, East Garston, Bucks |
| | *472218* | CAC-18 Mustang 22 (A68-192/G-HAEC) [WZ-I] | Privately owned, Woodchurch, Kent |
| | *472218* | NA P-51D Mustang (44-73979) [WZ-I] | Imperial War Museum, Lambeth |
| | 472773 | NA P-51D Mustang (44-72773/G-CDHI) [QP-M] | Privately owned, Breighton |
| | 474425 | NA P-51D Mustang (44-74425/PH-PSI) [OC-G] | Privately owned, Lelystad, The Netherlands |
| | 474923 | NA P-51D Mustang (44-74923/N6395) | Privately owned, Lelystad, The Netherlands |
| | 479744 | Piper L-4H Grasshopper (44-79744/G-BGPD) [49-M] | Privately owned, Marsh, Bucks |
| | 479766 | Piper L-4H Grasshopper (44-79766/G-BKHG) [63-D] | Privately owned, Frogland Cross |
| | 480015 | Piper L-4H Grasshopper (44-80015/G-AKIB) [44-M] | Privately owned, Bodmin |
| | 480133 | Piper L-4J Grasshopper (44-80133/G-BDCD) [44-B] | Privately owned, Slinfold |
| | 480321 | Piper L-4J Grasshopper (44-80321/G-FRAN) [44-H] | Privately owned, Rayne, Essex |
| | 480480 | Piper L-4J Grasshopper (44-80480/G-BECN) [44-E] | Privately owned, Rayne, Essex |
| | 480551 | Piper L-4J Grasshopper (44-80551/LN-KLT) [43-S] | Scandinavian Historic Flight, Oslo, Norway |
| | 480636 | Piper L-4J Grasshopper (44-80636/G-AXHP) [58-A] | Privately owned, Spanhoe |
| | 480723 | Piper L-4J Grasshopper (44-80723/G-BFZB) [E5-J] | Privately owned, Egginton |
| | 480752 | Piper L-4J Grasshopper (44-80752/G-BCXJ) [39-E] | Privately owned, Old Sarum |
| | 483868 | Boeing B-17G Flying Fortress (44-83868/N5237V) [A-N] | RAF Museum, Hendon |
| | 493209 | NA T-6G Texan (49-3209/G-DDMV/*41*) | Privately owned, Rochester |
| | 511701A | Beech C-45H (51-11701/G-BSZC) [AF258] | Privately owned, Bryngwyn Bach |
| | *607327* | PA-18 Super Cub 95 (G-ARAO) [09-L] | Privately owned, Denham |
| | 00195700 | Cessna F.150G (G-OIDW) | Privately owned, Halfpenny Green |
| | 3-1923 | Aeronca O-58B Defender (43-1923/G-BRHP) | Privately owned, Chiseldon |
| | *18-2001* | Piper L-18C Super Cub (52-2401/G-BIZV) | Privately owned, Croydon, Cambs |
| | 39-139 | Beech YC-43 Traveler (N295BS) | Duke of Brabant AF, Eindhoven, The Netherlands |
| | 41-33275 | NA AT-6C Texan (G-BICE) [CE] | Privately owned, Monewden |
| | 42-12417 | Noorduyn AT-16 Harvard IIB (Klu. B-163) | Covert Forces Museum, Harrington, Northants |
| | 42-35870 | Talyorcraft DCO-65 (G-BWLJ) [129] | Privately owned, Nayland |

| Serial | Type (other identity) | Owner/operator, location | Notes |
|--------|----------------------|--------------------------|-------|
| 42-58678 | Taylorcraft DF-65 (G-BRIY) [IY] | Privately owned, Carlisle | |
| *42-78044* | Aeronca 11AC Chief (G-BRXL) | Privately owned, Thurrock | |
| 42-84555 | NA AT-6D Harvard III (FAP.1662/G-ELMH) [EP-H] | Privately owned, Hardwick, Norfolk | |
| 42-93510 | Douglas C-47A Skytrain [CM] <ff> | Privately owned, Kew | |
| 43-9628 | Douglas A-20G Havoc <ff> | Privately owned, Hinckley, Leics | |
| 44-4315 | Bell P-63C Kingcobra | Privately owned, Redhill | |
| 44-4368 | Bell P-63C Kingcobra | Privately owned, Redhill | |
| 44-13954 | NA P-51D Mustang (G-UAKE) | Mustang Restoration Co Ltd, Coventry | |
| 44-14574 | NA P-51D Mustang (fuselage) | East Essex Aviation Museum, Clacton | |
| *44-42914* | Douglas DC-4 (N31356) | Privately owned, stored North Weald | |
| 44-51228 | Consolidated B-24M Liberator [RE-N] | American Air Museum, Duxford | |
| 44-79609 | Piper L-4H Grasshopper (G-BHXY) [PR] | Privately owned, Bodmin | |
| 44-80594 | Piper L-4J Grasshopper (G-BEDJ) | Privately owned, White Waltham | |
| 44-80647 | Piper L-4J Grasshopper (D-EGAF) | The Vintage Aircraft Co, Fürstenwalde, Germany | |
| 44-83184 | Fairchild UC-61K Argus III (G-RGUS) | Privately owned, Snitterby | |
| *46-11042* | Wolf WII <R> (G-BMZX) [7] | Privately owned, Kilrush, Eire | |
| 51-9036 | Lockheed T-33A | Newark Air Museum, Winthorpe | |
| 51-15319 | Piper L-18C Super Cub (G-FUZZ) [A-319] | Privately owned, Elvington | |
| 51-15555 | Piper L-18C Super Cub (G-OSPS) | Privately owned, Weston, Eire | |
| *54-005* | NA F-100D Super Sabre (54-2163) | Dumfries & Galloway Avn Mus, Dumfries | |
| 54-223 | NA F-100D Super Sabre (54-2223) | Newark Air Museum, Winthorpe | |
| 54-2447 | Piper L-21B Super Cub (G-SCUB) | Privately owned, Anwick | |
| 63-699 | McD F-4C Phantom (63-7699) [CG] | Midland Air Museum, Coventry | |
| 64-17657 | Douglas A-26A Invader (N99218) <ff> | Privately owned, Catfield | |
| *65-777* | McD F-4C Phantom (63-7419) [LN] | RAF Lakenheath, on display | |
| 67-120 | GD F-111E Aardvark (67-0120) [UH] | American Air Museum, Duxford | |
| 68-0060 | GD F-111E Aardvark <ff> | Dumfries & Galloway Avn Mus, Dumfries | |
| 72-1447 | GD F-111E Aardvark <ff> | American Air Museum, Duxford | |
| *72-448* | GD F-111E Aardvark (68-0011) [LN] | RAF Lakenheath, on display | |
| 74-0177 | GD F-111F Aardvark [CC] | RAF Museum, Cosford | |
| 76-020 | McD F-15A Eagle (76-0020) [BT] | American Air Museum, Duxford | |
| 76-124 | McD F-15B Eagle (76-0124) [LN] | RAF Lakenheath, instructional use | |
| 77-259 | Fairchild A-10A Thunderbolt (77-0259) [AR] | American Air Museum, Duxford | |
| 80-219 | Fairchild GA-10A Thunderbolt (80-0219) [AR] | RAF Alconbury, on display | |
| *92-048* | McD F-15A Eagle (74-0131) [LN] | RAF Lakenheath, on display | |
| *146-11083* | Wolf WII <R> (G-BNAI) [5] | Privately owned, Haverfordwest | |
| *H-57* | Piper L-4A Grasshopper (42-36375/G-AKAZ) | Privately owned, Duxford | |

**YUGOSLAVIA**

| | | | |
|--------|----------------------|--------------------------|-------|
| 23194 | Soko G-2A Galeb (YU-YAG) | Privately owned, Biggin Hill | |
| 23196 | Soko G-2A Galeb (YU-YAC) | Privately owned, Biggin Hill | |
| 30139 | Soko P-2 Kraguj [139] | Privately owned, Biggin Hill | |
| 30140 | Soko P-2 Kraguj (G-RADA) [140] | Privately owned, Biggin Hill | |
| 30146 | Soko P-2 Kraguj (G-BSXD) [146] | Privately owned, Elstree | |
| 30149 | Soko P-2 Kraguj (G-SOKO) [149] | Privately owned, Bournemouth | |
| 30151 | Soko P-2 Kraguj [151] | Privately owned, Sopley, Hants | |

The Fighter Collection's rare Curtiss Hawk 75 82/G-CCVH is painted in original French Air Force markings.

This Polikarpov I-15 bis (R) 4439 is based with The Fighter Collection at Duxford.

A privately owned Piper L-4H Grasshopper 329601 that is based at Nayland.

Bell P-39Q Airacobra 42-19993/N793QG *Brooklyn Bum-2nd* is flown by The Fighter Collection at Duxford.

A formation flypast at Duxford by P-51C Mustang 325147 and P-51D 463864.

# Irish Military Aircraft Markings

| Serial | Type (other identity) | Owner/operator, location | Notes |
|--------|----------------------|--------------------------|-------|
| 34 | Miles M14A Magister (N5392) | IAC Museum, Baldonnel | |
| 141 | Avro 652A Anson C19 | IAC Museum, Baldonnel | |
| 161 | VS509 Spitfire T9 (G-CCCA) | Historic Flying Ltd, Duxford | |
| 164 | DHC1 Chipmunk T20 | IAC Museum, Baldonnel | |
| 168 | DHC1 Chipmunk T20 | IAC Museum, Baldonnel | |
| 172 | DHC1 Chipmunk T20 | IAC, stored Baldonnel | |
| 173 | DHC1 Chipmunk T20 | South East Aviation Enthusiasts, Dromod | |
| 176 | DH104 Dove 4 (VP-YKF) | South East Aviation Enthusiasts, Waterford | |
| 177 | Percival P56 Provost T51 (G-BLIW) | Privately owned, Shoreham | |
| 181 | Percival P56 Provost T51 | Privately owned, Thatcham | |
| 183 | Percival P56 Provost T51 | IAC Museum, Baldonnel | |
| 184 | Percival P56 Provost T51 | South East Aviation Enthusiasts, Dromod | |
| 187 | DH115 Vampire T55 | South East Aviation Enthusiasts, Waterford | |
| 191 | DH115 Vampire T55 | IAC Museum, Baldonnel | |
| 192 | DH115 Vampire T55 | South East Aviation Enthusiasts, Dromod | |
| 195 | Sud SA316 Alouette III (F-WJDH) | IAC No 302 Sqn/3 Operations Wing, Baldonnel | |
| 196 | Sud SA316 Alouette III (F-WKQB) | IAC No 302 Sqn/3 Operations Wing, Baldonnel | |
| 197 | Sud SA316 Alouette III | IAC No 302 Sqn/3 Operations Wing, Baldonnel | |
| 198 | DH115 Vampire T11 (XE977) | IAC Museum, Baldonnel | |
| 199 | DHC1 Chipmunk T22 | IAC, stored Baldonnel | |
| 202 | Sud SA316 Alouette III | IAC Museum, Baldonnel | |
| 203 | Reims-Cessna FR172H | IAC No 104 Sqn/1 Operations Wing, Baldonnel | |
| 205 | Reims-Cessna FR172H | IAC No 104 Sqn/1 Operations Wing, Baldonnel | |
| 206 | Reims-Cessna FR172H | IAC No 104 Sqn/1 Operations Wing, Baldonnel | |
| 207 | Reims-Cessna FR172H | IAC, stored Waterford | |
| 208 | Reims-Cessna FR172H | IAC No 104 Sqn/1 Operations Wing, Baldonnel | |
| 210 | Reims-Cessna FR172H | IAC No 104 Sqn/1 Operations Wing, Baldonnel | |
| 211 | Sud SA316 Alouette III | IAC, stored Baldonnel | |
| 212 | Sud SA316 Alouette III | IAC No 302 Sqn/3 Operations Wing, Baldonnel | |
| 213 | Sud SA316 Alouette III | IAC, stored Baldonnel | |
| 214 | Sud SA316 Alouette III | IAC No 302 Sqn/3 Operations Wing, Baldonnel | |
| 215 | Fouga CM170 Super Magister | IAC Baldonnel, on display | |
| 216 | Fouga CM170 Super Magister | Carlow Institute of Technology, instructional use | |
| 217 | Fouga CM170 Super Magister (F-WVKO) | To Austria, 2005 | |
| 218 | Fouga CM170 Super Magister | IAC, stored Baldonnel | |
| 219 | Fouga CM170 Super Magister | IAC Museum, Baldonnel | |
| 220 | Fouga CM170 Super Magister | Cork University, instructional use | |
| 222 | SIAI SF-260WE Warrior | IAC, stored Baldonnel | |
| 225 | SIAI SF-260WE Warrior | IAC, stored Baldonnel | |
| 226 | SIAI SF-260WE Warrior | IAC, stored Baldonnel | |
| 227 | SIAI SF-260WE Warrior | IAC, stored Baldonnel | |
| 229 | SIAI SF-260WE Warrior | IAC Museum, Baldonnel | |
| 230 | SIAI SF-260WE Warrior | IAC, stored Baldonnel | |
| 231 | SIAI SF-260WE Warrior | IAC, stored Baldonnel | |
| 240 | Beech Super King Air 200MR | IAC No 102 Sqn/1 Operations Wing, Baldonnel | |
| 241 | Aérospatiale SA342L Gazelle | IAC No 303 Sqn/3 Operations Wing, Baldonnel | |
| 244 | Aérospatiale SA365F Dauphin II (F-ZKBZ) | IAC, stored Baldonnel | |
| 245 | Aérospatiale SA365F Dauphin II (F-ZKBJ) | IAC, stored Baldonnel | |
| 246 | Aérospatiale SA365F Dauphin II (F-ZKBP) | IAC No 301 Sqn/3 Operations Wing, Baldonnel | |

## Irish Military Aircraft Markings

| Notes | Serial | Type (other identity) | Owner/operator, location |
|---|---|---|---|
| | 247 | Aérospatiale SA365F Dauphin II (F-ZKBW) | IAC, stored Baldonnel |
| | 251 | Grumman G1159C Gulfstream IV (N17584) | IAC No 102 Sqn/1 Operations Wing, Baldonnel |
| | 252 | Airtech CN.235 MPA Persuader | IAC No 101 Sqn/1 Operations Wing, Baldonnel |
| | 253 | Airtech CN.235 MPA Persuader | IAC No 101 Sqn/1 Operations Wing, Baldonnel |
| | 254 | PBN-2T Defender 4000 (G-BWPN) | IAC No 106 Sqn/1 Operations Wing, Baldonnel |
| | 255 | AS355N Twin Squirrel (G-BXEV) | IAC No 106 Sqn/1 Operations Wing, Baldonnel |
| | 256 | Eurocopter EC135T-1 (G-BZRM) | IAC No 106 Sqn/1 Operations Wing, Baldonnel |
| | 258 | Gates Learjet 45 (N5009T) | IAC No 102 Sqn/1 Operations Wing, Baldonnel |
| | 260 | Pilatus PC-9M (HB-HQS) | IAC Flying Training School, Baldonnel |
| | 261 | Pilatus PC-9M (HB-HQT) | IAC Flying Training School, Baldonnel |
| | 262 | Pilatus PC-9M (HB-HQU) | IAC Flying Training School, Baldonnel |
| | 263 | Pilatus PC-9M (HB-HQV) | IAC Flying Training School, Baldonnel |
| | 264 | Pilatus PC-9M (HB-HQW) | IAC Flying Training School, Baldonnel |
| | 265 | Pilatus PC-9M (HB-HQX) | IAC Flying Training School, Baldonnel |
| | 266 | Pilatus PC-9M (HB-HQY) | IAC Flying Training School, Baldonnel |
| | 267 | Pilatus PC-9M (HB-HQZ) | IAC Flying Training School, Baldonnel |
| | 268 | Pilatus PC-9M | IAC (option) |
| | 269 | Pilatus PC-9M | IAC (option) |
| | 270 | Eurocopter EC135P-2 | IAC No 302 Sqn/3 Operations Wing, Baldonnel |
| | 271 | Eurocopter EC135P-2 | IAC No 302 Sqn/3 Operations Wing, Baldonnel |
| | 272 | Agusta AB.139 | IAC, on order |
| | 273 | Agusta AB.139 | IAC, on order |
| | 274 | Agusta AB.139 | IAC, on order |
| | 275 | Agusta AB.139 | IAC, on order |
| | 276 | Agusta AB.139 | IAC (option) |
| | 277 | Agusta AB.139 | IAC (option) |

Plane Sailing's Consolidated PBY-5A Catalina 433915/G-PBYA is operated on a Group basis.

# Overseas Military Aircraft Markings

Aircraft included in this section are a selection of those likely to be seen visiting UK civil and military airfields on transport flights, exchange visits, exercises and for air shows. It is not a comprehensive list of *all* aircraft operated by the air arms concerned.

**ALGERIA**
**Force Aérienne Algérienne/**
**Al Quwwat al Jawwiya al**
**Jaza'eriya**
**Lockheed**
**C-130H Hercules**
| | |
|---|---|
| 7T-WHE | (4935) |
| 7T-WHF | (4934) |
| 7T-WHI | (4930) |
| 7T-WHJ | (4928) |
| 7T-WHQ | (4926) |
| 7T-WHR | (4924) |
| 7T-WHS | (4912) |
| 7T-WHT | (4911) |
| 7T-WHY | (4913) |
| 7T-WHZ | (4914) |

**Lockheed**
**C-130H-30 Hercules**
| | |
|---|---|
| 7T-WHA | (4997) |
| 7T-WHB | (5224) |
| 7T-WHD | (4987) |
| 7T-WHL | (4989) |
| 7T-WHM | (4919) |
| 7T-WHN | (4894) |
| 7T-WHO | (4897) |
| 7T-WHP | (4921) |

**Grumman**
**G.1159C Gulfstream IVSP**
Ministry of Defence, Boufarik
| | |
|---|---|
| 7T-VPC | (1418) |
| 7T-VPM | (1421) |
| 7T-VPR | (1288) |
| 7T-VPS | (1291) |

**Gulfstream Aerospace**
**Gulfstream V**
Ministry of Defence, Boufarik
7T-VPG (617)

**AUSTRALIA**
**Royal Australian Air Force**
**Boeing 707-338C/368C\***
33 Sqn, Amberley
A20-261\*
A20-623
A20-624
A20-629

**Boeing 737-7DT**
34 Sqn, Canberra
A36-001
A36-002

**Canadair**
**CL.604 Challenger**
34 Sqn, Canberra
A37-001
A37-002
A37-003

**Lockheed**
**C-130H Hercules**
36 Sqn, Richmond, NSW
A97-001
A97-002
A97-003
A97-004
A97-005
A97-006
A97-007
A97-008
A97-009
A97-010
A97-011
A97-012

**Lockheed**
**C-130J-30 Hercules II**
37 Sqn, Richmond, NSW
A97-440
A97-441
A97-442
A97-447
A97-448
A97-449
A97-450
A97-464
A97-465
A97-466
A97-467
A97-468

**Lockheed**
**P-3 Orion**
10/11 Sqns, Maritime Patrol
Group, Edinburgh, NSW
| | | |
|---|---|---|
| A9-656 | AP-3C | 11 Sqn |
| A9-657 | P-3W | 11 Sqn |
| A9-658 | P-3W | 10 Sqn |
| A9-659 | P-3W | 11 Sqn |
| A9-660 | AP-3C | 10 Sqn |
| A9-661 | AP-3C | 10 Sqn |
| A9-662 | AP-3C | 11 Sqn |
| A9-663 | P-3W | 11 Sqn |
| A9-664 | P-3W | 11 Sqn |
| A9-665 | AP-3C | 10 Sqn |
| A9-751 | P-3C | 11 Sqn |
| A9-752 | AP-3C | 10 Sqn |
| A9-753 | P-3C | 10 Sqn |
| A9-755 | P-3C | 10 Sqn |
| A9-756 | P-3C | 11 Sqn |
| A9-757 | P-3C | 10 Sqn |
| A9-758 | P-3C | 11 Sqn |
| A9-759 | AP-3C | 10 Sqn |
| A9-760 | AP-3C | 10 Sqn |

**AUSTRIA**
**Österreichische**
**Luftstreitkräfte**
**Agusta-Bell**
**AB.206A JetRanger**

Fliegerregiment I
2 Hubschrauberstaffel,
Tulln
3C-JA
3C-JB
3C-JC
3C-JD
3C-JE
3C-JF
3C-JG
3C-JH
3C-JI
3C-JJ
3C-JM

**Agusta-Bell**
**AB.212/Bell 212\***
Fliegerregiment III
1 & 2 Hubschrauberstaffel,
Linz
5D-HB
5D-HC
5D-HD
5D-HF
5D-HG
5D-HH
5D-HI
5D-HJ
5D-HK
5D-HL
5D-HN
5D-HO
5D-HP
5D-HQ
5D-HR
5D-HS
5D-HT
5D-HU
5D-HV
5D-HW
5D-HX
5D-HY\*
5D-HZ

**Bell**
**OH-58B Kiowa**
Fliegerregiment I
3 Hubschrauberstaffel,
Tulln
3C-OA
3C-OB
3C-OC
3C-OD
3C-OE
3C-OG
3C-OH
3C-OI
3C-OJ
3C-OK
3C-OL

**Lockheed**
**C-130K Hercules**
Fliegerregiment III
 Transportstaffel, Linz
8T-CA
8T-CB
8T-CC

**Northrop F-5E Tiger II**
Fliegerregiment II
 2 Staffel/Uberwg, Graz
J-3004
J-3005
J-3014
J-3030
J-3033
J-3036
J-3038
J-3041
J-3052
J-3056
J-3057
J-3065

**Pilatus**
**PC-6B/B2-H2 Turbo Porter/**
**PC-6B/B2-H4 Turbo Porter\***
Fliegerregiment I
 Flachenstaffel, Tulln
3G-EA
3G-EB
3G-EC
3G-ED
3G-EE
3G-EF
3G-EG
3G-EH
3G-EJ
3G-EK
3G-EL
3G-EM
3G-EN\*

**Pilatus PC-7**
**Turbo Trainer**
Fliegerschule, Zeltweg
3H-FA
3H-FB
3H-FC
3H-FD
3H-FE
3H-FF
3H-FG
3H-FH
3H-FI
3H-FJ
3H-FK
3H-FL
3H-FM
3H-FN
3H-FO
3H-FP

**SAAB 105ÖE**
Fliegerregiment III
 Dusenstaffel, Linz
(yellow)
| | |
|---|---|
| B | (105402) |
| D | (105404) |
| E | (105405) |
| G | (105407) |
| I | (105409) |
| J | (105410) |

(green)
| | |
|---|---|
| B | (105412) |
| D | (105414) |
| GF-16 | (105416) |
| GG-17 | (105417) |

(red)
| | |
|---|---|
| B | (105422) |
| C | (105423) |
| D | (105424) |
| E | (105425) |
| F | (105426) |
| G | (105427) |
| H | (105428) |
| I | (105429) |
| J | (105430) |

(blue)
| | |
|---|---|
| A | (105431) |
| B | (105432) |
| C | (105433) |
| D | (105434) |
| E | (105435) |
| F | (105436) |
| G | (105437) |
| I | (105439) |
| J | (105440) |

**Short SC7**
**Skyvan 3M**
Fliegerregiment I
 Flachenstaffel, Tulln
5S-TA
5S-TB

**Sikorsky S-70A**
Fliegerregiment I
 1 Hubschrauberstaffel,
 Tulln
6M-BA
6M-BB
6M-BC
6M-BD
6M-BE
6M-BF
6M-BG
6M-BH
6M-BI

**BAHRAIN**
**BAE RJ.85/RJ.100\***
Bahrain Defence Force
A9C-BDF\*
A9C-HWR

**Boeing 747SP-21**
Bahrain Amiri Flt
A9C-HMH

**Boeing 747-4P8**
Bahrain Amiri Flt
A9C-HMK

**Grumman**
**G.1159 Gulfstream IITT/**
**G.1159C Gulfstream IV-SP**
Govt of Bahrain
A9C-BAH Gulfstream IV-SP
A9C-BG Gulfstream IITT

**BELGIUM**
**Composante Aérienne**
**Belge/Belgische**
**Luchtcomponent**
**D-BD Alpha Jet E**
7/11 Smaldeel (1 Wg),

Bevekom
AT-01
AT-02
AT-03
AT-05
AT-06
AT-08
AT-10
AT-11
AT-12
AT-13
AT-14
AT-15
AT-17
AT-18
AT-19
AT-20
AT-21
AT-22
AT-23
AT-24
AT-25
AT-26
AT-27
AT-28
AT-29
AT-30
AT-31
AT-32
AT-33

**Airbus A.310-322**
21 Smaldeel (15 Wg),
 Melsbroek
CA-01
CA-02

**Dassault**
**Falcon 900B**
21 Smaldeel (15 Wg),
 Melsbroek
CD-01

**Embraer**
**ERJ.135LR/ERJ.145LR\***
21 Smaldeel (15 Wg),
 Melsbroek
CE-01
CE-02
CE-03\*
CE-04\*

**Lockheed**
**C-130H Hercules**
20 Smaldeel (15 Wg),
 Melsbroek
CH-01
CH-02
CH-03
CH-04
CH-05
CH-07
CH-08
CH-09
CH-10
CH-11
CH-12

**Dassault**
**Falcon 20E**
21 Smaldeel (15 Wg),
 Melsbroek
CM-01
CM-02

## General Dynamics
## F-16 MLU
1,350 Smaldeel (2 Wg),
Florennes [FS];
31,349 Smaldeel, OCU(10 Wg),
Kleine-Brogel [BL]

| | | |
|---|---|---|
| FA-56 | F-16A | 2 Wg |
| FA-57 | F-16A | 2 Wg |
| FA-67 | F-16A | 2 Wg |
| FA-68 | F-16A | 2 Wg |
| FA-69 | F-16A | 2 Wg |
| FA-70 | F-16A | 10 Wg |
| FA-71 | F-16A | 2 Wg |
| FA-72 | F-16A | 2 Wg |
| FA-77 | F-16A | 10 Wg |
| FA-81 | F-16A | 10 Wg |
| FA-82 | F-16A | 10 Wg |
| FA-83 | F-16A | 10 Wg |
| FA-84 | F-16A | 2 Wg |
| FA-86 | F-16A | 10 Wg |
| FA-87 | F-16A | 10 Wg |
| FA-89 | F-16A | 2 Wg |
| FA-91 | F-16A | 2 Wg |
| FA-92 | F-16A | 2 Wg |
| FA-94 | F-16A | 10 Wg |
| FA-95 | F-16A | 10 Wg |
| FA-97 | F-16A | 10 Wg |
| FA-98 | F-16A | 10 Wg |
| FA-99 | F-16A | 10 Wg |
| FA-100 | F-16A | 10 Wg |
| FA-101 | F-16A | 2 Wg |
| FA-102 | F-16A | 2 Wg |
| FA-103 | F-16A | 2 Wg |
| FA-104 | F-16A | 2 Wg |
| FA-106 | F-16A | 10 Wg |
| FA-107 | F-16A | 2 Wg |
| FA-108 | F-16A | 2 Wg |
| FA-109 | F-16A | 2 Wg |
| FA-110 | F-16A | 10 Wg |
| FA-111 | F-16A | 10 Wg |
| FA-114 | F-16A | 10 Wg |
| FA-115 | F-16A | 2 Wg |
| FA-116 | F-16A | 10 Wg |
| FA-117 | F-16A | 2 Wg |
| FA-118 | F-16A | 10 Wg |
| FA-119 | F-16A | 10 Wg |
| FA-120 | F-16A | 2 Wg |
| FA-121 | F-16A | 2 Wg |
| FA-123 | F-16A | 10 Wg |
| FA-124 | F-16A | 10 Wg |
| FA-125 | F-16A | 2 Wg |
| FA-126 | F-16A | 2 Wg |
| FA-127 | F-16A | 2 Wg |
| FA-128 | F-16A | 2 Wg |
| FA-129 | F-16A | 10 Wg |
| FA-130 | F-16A | 2 Wg |
| FA-131 | F-16A | 2 Wg |
| FA-132 | F-16A | 2 Wg |
| FA-133 | F-16A | 10 Wg |
| FA-134 | F-16A | 10 Wg |
| FA-135 | F-16A | 2 Wg |
| FA-136 | F-16A | 2 Wg |
| FB-01 | F-16B | 2 Wg |
| FB-02 | F-16B | OCU |
| FB-04 | F-16B | 10 Wg |
| FB-05 | F-16B | 10 Wg |
| FB-08 | F-16B | 10 Wg |
| FB-09 | F-16B | 2 Wg |
| FB-10 | F-16B | 2 Wg |
| FB-12 | F-16B | 2 Wg |
| FB-14 | F-16B | 10 Wg |
| FB-15 | F-16B | OCU |
| FB-17 | F-16B | OCU |
| FB-18 | F-16B | 2 Wg |
| FB-20 | F-16B | 10 Wg |
| FB-21 | F-16B | 2 Wg |
| FB-22 | F-16B | OCU |
| FB-23 | F-16B | 10 Wg |
| FB-24 | F-16B | OCU |

## Fouga CM170 Magister
Fouga Flight/7 Smaldeel
(1 Wg), Bevekom

MT-04
MT-13
MT-14
MT-26
MT-34
MT-35
MT-37
MT-40
MT-48

## Westland Sea
## King Mk48/48A*
40 Smaldeel, Koksijde

RS-01
RS-02
RS-03*
RS-04
RS-05

## SIAI Marchetti
## SF260M/SF260D*
Ecole de Pilotage
Elementaire (5 Sm/1 Wg),
Bevekom

ST-02
ST-03
ST-04
ST-06
ST-12
ST-15
ST-16
ST-17
ST-18
ST-19
ST-20
ST-22
ST-23
ST-24
ST-25
ST-26
ST-27
ST-30
ST-31
ST-32
ST-34
ST-35
ST-36
ST-40*
ST-41*
ST-42*
ST-43*
ST-44*
ST-45*
ST-46*
ST-47*
ST-48*

## Composante Terrestre
## Belge/
## Belgische Landcomponent
## Sud
## SA318C/SE3130* Alouette II
Liaison Flight, Bierset;
SLV, Brasschaat

| | |
|---|---|
| A-22* | Liaison Flt |

| | |
|---|---|
| A-43 | SLV |
| A-44 | SLV |
| A-47 | Liaison Flt |
| A-49 | Liaison Flt |
| A-50 | Liaison Flt |
| A-53 | Liaison Flt |
| A-55 | SLV |
| A-57 | Liaison Flt |
| A-59 | Liaison Flt |
| A-61 | SLV |
| A-64 | Liaison Flt |
| A-65 | SLV |
| A-66 | Liaison Flt |
| A-68 | Liaison Flt |
| A-69 | Liaison Flt |
| A-70 | SLV |
| A-72 | SLV |
| A-74 | Liaison Flt |
| A-77 | SLV |
| A-78 | SLV |
| A-79 | SLV |
| A-80 | SLV |

## Britten-Norman
## BN-2A/BN-2B-21* Islander
SLV, Brasschaat

| | |
|---|---|
| B-01 | LA |
| B-02* | LB |
| B-04* | LD |
| B-08* | LH |
| B-09* | LI |
| B-10* | LJ |
| B-12 | LL |

## Agusta A109HA/HO*
16 Smaldeel MRH, Bierset;
17 Smaldeel MRH, Bierset;
18 Smaldeel MRH, Bierset;
SLV, Brasschaat

| | |
|---|---|
| H-01* | SLV |
| H-02* | 18 Sm MRH |
| H-04* | SLV |
| H-05* | 18 Sm MRH |
| H-06* | 17 Sm MRH |
| H-07* | 17 Sm MRH |
| H-11* | 18 Sm MRH |
| H-20 | 18 Sm MRH |
| H-21 | 18 Sm MRH |
| H-22 | 17 Sm MRH |
| H-24 | 17 Sm MRH |
| H-25 | 18 Sm MRH |
| H-26 | 18 Sm MRH |
| H-27 | 18 Sm MRH |
| H-28 | 17 Sm MRH |
| H-29 | 18 Sm MRH |
| H-30 | 18 Sm MRH |
| H-31 | 18 Sm MRH |
| H-32 | 18 Sm MRH |
| H-33 | 18 Sm MRH |
| H-35 | 18 Sm MRH |
| H-36 | 17 Sm MRH |
| H-37 | 18 Sm MRH |
| H-38 | 17 Sm MRH |
| H-39 | 18 Sm MRH |
| H-40 | 18 Sm MRH |
| H-41 | SLV |
| H-42 | SLV |
| H-43 | 17 Sm MRH |
| H-44 | 17 Sm MRH |
| H-45 | 17 Sm MRH |
| H-46 | 17 Sm MRH |

## Belgium – Canada

**Composante Marine Belge/
Belgische
Marinecomponent**
Koksijde Heli Flight
| | |
|---|---|
| M-1 | (OT-ZPA) |
| M-2 | (OT-ZPB) |
| M-3 | (OT-ZPC) |

**Police Fédérale/Federal
Politie**
**Cessna 182 Skylane**
Luchsteundetachment,
Melsbroek
| | |
|---|---|
| G-01 | C.182Q |
| G-04 | C.182R |

**MDH
MD.520N**
Luchsteundetachment,
Melsbroek
G-14
G-15

**MDH
MD.900 Explorer**
Luchsteundetachment,
Melsbroek
G-10
G-11
G-12

**Cadets de l'Air/
Luchtcadetten**
**Piper L-21B Super Cub**
Bases: Florennes,
Goetsenhoeven & Zoersel
LB-01
LB-02
LB-03
LB-05
LB-06

## BOTSWANA
**Botswana Defence Force**
**Grumman**
**G.1159C Gulfstream IV**
VIP Sqn, Sir Seretse
Kharma IAP
OK1

**Lockheed**
**C-130B Hercules**
Z10 Sqn, Thebephatshwa
OM-1
OM-2
OM-3

## BRAZIL
**Força Aérea Brasileira**
**Boeing KC-137**
2° GT 2° Esq, Galeæo
2401
2402
2403
2404

**Lockheed**
**C-130 Hercules**
1° GT, 1° Esq, Galeæo;
1° GTT, 1° Esq, Afonsos
| | | |
|---|---|---|
| 2451 | C-130E | 1° GTT |
| 2453 | C-130E | 1° GTT |
| 2454 | C-130E | 1° GTT |
| 2456 | C-130E | 1° GTT |

| | | |
|---|---|---|
| 2458 | SC-130E | 1° GT |
| 2459 | SC-130E | 1° GT |
| 2461 | KC-130H | 1° GT |
| 2462 | KC-130H | 1° GT |
| 2463 | C-130H | 1° GT |
| 2464 | C-130H | 1° GT |
| 2465 | C-130H | 1° GT |
| 2466 | C-130H | 1° GT |
| 2467 | C-130H | 1° GT |
| 2470 | C-130H | 1° GT |
| 2471 | C-130H | 1° GT |
| 2472 | C-130H | 1° GT |
| 2473 | C-130H | |
| 2474 | C-130H | 1° GT |
| 2475 | C-130H | 1° GT |
| 2476 | C-130H | |
| 2477 | C-130H | 1° GT |
| 2478 | C-130H | 1° GT |
| 2479 | C-130H | 1° GT |

## BRUNEI
**Airbus A.340-212**
Brunei Govt, Bandar Seri
Bergawan
V8-BKH A.340-212

**Boeing 747-430**
Brunei Govt, Bandar Seri
Bergawan
V8-ALI

**Boeing 767-27GER**
Brunei Govt, Bandar Seri
Bergawan
V8-MHB

**Gulfstream Aerospace
Gulfstream V**
Brunei Govt, Bandar Seri
Bergawan
V8-001

## BULGARIA
**Bulgarsky
Voenno-Vazdushni Sily**
**Antonov An-30**
16 TAP, Sofia/Dobroslavtzi
055

**Pilatus PC.XII/45**
16 TAP, Sofia/Dobroslavtzi
020

**Bulgarian Govt
Boeing 737-548**
Bulgarian Govt, Sofia
LZ-BOR

**Dassault Falcon 2000**
Bulgarian Govt, Sofia
LZ-OOI

**Tupolev Tu-134A-3**
Bulgarian Govt, Sofia
LZ-TUG

**Tupolev Tu-154M**
Bulgarian Govt, Sofia
LZ-BTZ

## BURKINA FASO
**Boeing 727-14/727-282***
Govt of Burkina Faso,

Ouagadougou
XT-BBE
XT-BFA*

## CAMEROON
**Grumman**
**G.1159A Gulfstream III**
Govt of Cameroon, Yaounde
TJ-AAW

## CANADA
**Canadian Forces**
**Lockheed**
**CC-130 Hercules**
**CC-130E/CC-130E(SAR)***
413 Sqn, Greenwood (SAR)
(14 Wing);
424 Sqn, Trenton (SAR)
(8 Wing);
426 Sqn, Trenton (8 Wing);
435 Sqn, Winnipeg
(17 Wing);
436 Sqn, Trenton (8 Wing)
| | |
|---|---|
| 130305* | 8 Wing |
| 130306* | 14 Wing |
| 130307 | 8 Wing |
| 130308* | 8 Wing |
| 130310* | 8 Wing |
| 130311* | 8 Wing |
| 130313 | 8 Wing |
| 130314* | 14 Wing |
| 130315* | 14 Wing |
| 130316 | 8 Wing |
| 130317 | 8 Wing |
| 130319 | 8 Wing |
| 130320 | 8 Wing |
| 130323 | 8 Wing |
| 130324* | 8 Wing |
| 130325 | 8 Wing |
| 130326 | 8 Wing |
| 130327 | 8 Wing |
| 130328 | 8 Wing |

**CC-130H/CC-130H(T)***
| | |
|---|---|
| 130332 | 17 Wing |
| 130333 | 17 Wing |
| 130334 | 8 Wing |
| 130335 | 8 Wing |
| 130336 | 17 Wing |
| 130337 | 8 Wing |
| 130338* | 17 Wing |
| 130339* | 17 Wing |
| 130340* | 17 Wing |
| 130341* | 17 Wing |
| 130342* | 17 Wing |

**CC-130H-30**
| | |
|---|---|
| 130343 | 8 Wing |
| 130344 | 8 Wing |

**Lockheed**
**CP-140 Aurora/
CP-140A Arcturus***
404 Sqn, Greenwood
(14 Wing);
405 Sqn, Greenwood
(14 Wing);
407 Sqn, Comox (19 Wing)
| | |
|---|---|
| 140101 | 407 Sqn |
| 140102 | 407 Sqn |
| 140103 | 407 Sqn |
| 140104 | 14 Wing |
| 140105 | 407 Sqn |
| 140106 | 14 Wing |
| 140107 | 14 Wing |
| 140108 | 14 Wing |

| | |
|---|---|
| 140109 | 14 Wing |
| 140110 | 14 Wing |
| 140111 | 14 Wing |
| 140112 | 14 Wing |
| 140113 | 407 Sqn |
| 140114 | 14 Wing |
| 140115 | 14 Wing |
| 140116 | 407 Sqn |
| 140117 | 14 Wing |
| 140118 | 14 Wing |
| 140120* | 14 Wing |
| 140121* | 14 Wing |

**De Havilland Canada**
**CT-142**
402 Sqn, Winnipeg
  (17 Wing)

| | |
|---|---|
| 142803 | CT-142 |
| 142804 | CT-142 |
| 142805 | CT-142 |
| 142806 | CT-142 |

**Canadair**
**CC-144 Challenger**
412 Sqn, Ottawa (8 Wing)

| | |
|---|---|
| 144601 | CC-144A |
| 144614 | CC-144B |
| 144615 | CC-144B |
| 144616 | CC-144B |
| 144617 | CC-144C |
| 144618 | CC-144C |

**Airbus**
**CC-150 Polaris**
**(A310-304/A310-304F*)**
437 Sqn, Trenton (8 Wing)

| | |
|---|---|
| 15001 | 216 |
| 15002* | 212 |
| 15003* | 202 |
| 15004* | 205 |
| 15005* | 204 |

**CHILE**
**Fuerza Aérea de Chile**
**Boeing 707**
Grupo 10, Santiago

| | |
|---|---|
| 902 | 707-351C |
| 903 | 707-330B |
| 904 | 707-358C |

**Boeing 737**
Grupo 10, Santiago

| | |
|---|---|
| 921 | 737-58N |
| 922 | 737-330 |

**Extra EA-300L**
*Los Halcones*

| | |
|---|---|
| 132 | [6] |
| 145 | [2] |
| 146 | [3] |
| 147 | [4] |
| 148 | [5] |
| 149 | [1] |

**Grumman**
**G.1159C Gulfstream IV**
Grupo 10, Santiago
911

**Lockheed**
**C-130B/H Hercules**
Grupo 10, Santiago

| | |
|---|---|
| 994 | C-130B |
| 995 | C-130H |
| 996 | C-130H |
| 997 | C-130B |
| 998 | C-130B |

**CROATIA**
**Canadair**
**CL.601 Challenger**
Croatian Govt, Zagreb
9A-CRO
9A-CRT

**CZECH REPUBLIC**
**Ceske Vojenske Letectvo**
**Aero L-39/L-59 Albatros**
221.TL/22.zL, Námest;
CLV, Pardubice

| | | |
|---|---|---|
| 0103 | L-39C | CLV |
| 0106 | L-39C | CLV |
| 0107 | L-39C | CLV |
| 0108 | L-39C | CLV |
| 0113 | L-39C | CLV |
| 0115 | L-39C | CLV |
| 0440 | L-39C | CLV |
| 0441 | L-39C | CLV |
| 0444 | L-39C | CLV |
| 0445 | L-39C | CLV |
| 0448 | L-39C | CLV |
| 2341 | L-39ZA | 221.TL/22.zL |
| 2344 | L-39ZA | 221.TL/22.zL |
| 2347 | L-39ZA | 221.TL/22.zL |
| 2350 | L-39ZA | 221.TL/22.zL |
| 2415 | L-39ZA | 221.TL/22.zL |
| 2418 | L-39ZA | 221.TL/22.zL |
| 2421 | L-39ZA | 221.TL/22.zL |
| 2424 | L-39ZA | 221.TL/22.zL |
| 2427 | L-39ZA | 221.TL/22.zL |
| 2430 | L-39ZA | 221.TL/22.zL |
| 2433 | L-39ZA | 221.TL/22.zL |
| 2436 | L-39ZA | 221.TL/22.zL |
| 3903 | L-39ZA | 221.TL/22.zL |
| 5013 | L-39ZA | 221.TL/22.zL |
| 5015 | L-39ZA | 221.TL/22.zL |
| 5017 | L-39ZA | 221.TL/22.zL |
| 5019 | L-39ZA | 221.TL/22.zL |

**Aero L-159A ALCA/L-159B***
212.TL/21.zTL, Cáslav;
LZO, Praha/Kbely

| | |
|---|---|
| 5831* | LZO |
| 5832* | LZO |
| 6001 | 212.TL/21.zTL |
| 6002 | 212.TL/21.zTL |
| 6003 | 212.TL/21.zTL |
| 6004 | 212.TL/21.zTL |
| 6005 | 212.TL/21.zTL |
| 6006 | 212.TL/21.zTL |
| 6007 | 212.TL/21.zTL |
| 6008 | 212.TL/21.zTL |
| 6009 | 212.TL/21.zTL |
| 6010 | 212.TL/21.zTL |
| 6011 | 212.TL/21.zTL |
| 6012 | 212.TL/21.zTL |
| 6013 | 212.TL/21.zTL |
| 6014 | 212.TL/21.zTL |
| 6015 | 212.TL/21.zTL |
| 6016 | 212.TL/21.zTL |
| 6017 | 212.TL/21.zTL |
| 6018 | 212.TL/21.zTL |
| 6019 | 212.TL/21.zTL |
| 6020 | 212.TL/21.zTL |
| 6021 | 212.TL/21.zTL |
| 6022 | 212.TL/21.zTL |
| 6023 | 212.TL/21.zTL |
| 6024 | 212.TL/21.zTL |
| 6025 | 212.TL/21.zTL |
| 6026 | 212.TL/21.zTL |
| 6027 | 212.TL/21.zTL |
| 6028 | 212.TL/21.zTL |
| 6029 | 212.TL/21.zTL |
| 6030 | 212.TL/21.zTL |
| 6031 | 212.TL/21.zTL |
| 6032 | 212.TL/21.zTL |
| 6033 | 212.TL/21.zTL |
| 6034 | 212.TL/21.zTL |
| 6035 | 212.TL/21.zTL |
| 6036 | 212.TL/21.zTL |
| 6037 | 212.TL/21.zTL |
| 6038 | 212.TL/21.zTL |
| 6039 | 212.TL/21.zTL |
| 6040 | 212.TL/21.zTL |
| 6041 | 212.TL/21.zTL |
| 6042 | 212.TL/21.zTL |
| 6043 | |
| 6044 | |
| 6045 | |
| 6046 | 212.TL/21.zTL |
| 6047 | 212.TL/21.zTL |
| 6048 | 212.TL/21.zTL |
| 6049 | 212.TL/21.zTL |
| 6050 | 212.TL/21.zTL |
| 6051 | 212.TL/21.zTL |
| 6052 | 212.TL/21.zTL |
| 6053 | 212.TL/21.zTL |
| 6054 | |
| 6055 | 212.TL/21.zTL |
| 6057 | 212.TL/21.zTL |
| 6058 | 212.TL/21.zTL |
| 6059 | 212.TL/21.zTL |
| 6060 | 212.TL/21.zTL |
| 6061 | 212.TL/21.zTL |
| 6062 | 212.TL/21.zTL |
| 6063 | 212.TL/21.zTL |
| 6064 | |
| 6065 | |
| 6066 | |
| 6067 | 212.TL/21.zTL |
| 6068 | 212.TL/21.zTL |
| 6069 | 212.TL/21.zTL |
| 6070 | 212.TL/21.zTL |
| 6071 | 212.TL/21.zTL |
| 6072 | 212.TL/21.zTL |
| 6073* | |

**Antonov An-24V**
241.dlt/24.zDL, Praha/Kbely
7110

**Antonov An-26/An-26Z-1M***
241.dlt/24.zDL, Praha/Kbely

| |
|---|
| 2408 |
| 2409 |
| 2507 |
| 3209* |
| 4201 |

**Antonov An-30FG**
241.dlt/24.zDL, Praha/Kbely
1107

**Canadair**
**CL.601-3A Challenger**
241.dlt/24.zDL, Praha/Kbely
5105

**LET 410 Turbolet**
241.dlt/24.zDL, Praha/Kbely

| | |
|---|---|
| 0503 | L-410MA |
| 0712 | L-410UVP-S |

| | |
|---|---|
| 0731 | L-410UVP |
| 0926 | L-410UVP-T |
| 0928 | L-410UVP-T |
| 0929 | L-410UVP-T |
| 1132 | L-410UVP-T |
| 1134 | L-410UVP |
| 1504 | L-410UVP |
| 1523 | L-410FG |
| 1525 | L-410FG |
| 1526 | L-410FG |
| 2312 | L-410UVP-E |
| 2601 | L-410UVP-E |
| 2602 | L-410UVP-E |
| 2710 | L-410UVP-E |

**Mil Mi-17/**
**Mi-171Sh***
232.vrl/23.zVrL, Prerov

| |
|---|
| 0803 |
| 0805 |
| 0809 |
| 0811 |
| 0816 |
| 0818 |
| 0819 |
| 0822 |
| 0825 |
| 0828 |
| 0830 |
| 0831 |
| 0832 |
| 0833 |
| 0834 |
| 0835 |
| 0836 |
| 0837 |
| 0839 |
| 0840 |
| 0848 |
| 0849 |
| 0850 |
| 9767* |
| 9774* |
| 9781* |
| 9799* |
| 9806* |
| 9813* |
| 9873* |
| 9887* |
| 9892* |

**Mil Mi-24/Mi-35**
231.lbvr/23.zVrL, Prerov

| | |
|---|---|
| 0103 | Mi-24D |
| 0214 | Mi-24D |
| 0217 | Mi-24D |
| 0218 | Mi-24D |
| 0219 | Mi-24D |
| 0701 | Mi-24V1 |
| 0702 | Mi-24V1 |
| 0703 | Mi-24V1 |
| 0705 | Mi-24V1 |
| 0709 | Mi-24V1 |
| 0710 | Mi-24V1 |
| 0788 | Mi-24V1 |
| 0789 | Mi-24V1 |
| 0790 | Mi-24V1 |
| 0812 | Mi-24V1 |
| 0815 | Mi-24V1 |
| 0816 | Mi-24V1 |
| 0834 | Mi-24V2 |
| 0835 | Mi-24V2 |
| 0836 | Mi-24V2 |
| 0837 | Mi-24V2 |

| | |
|---|---|
| 0838 | Mi-24V2 |
| 0839 | Mi-24V2 |
| 0981 | Mi-24V2 |
| 3361 | Mi-35 |
| 3362 | Mi-35 |
| 3365 | Mi-35 |
| 3366 | Mi-35 |
| 3367 | Mi-35 |
| 3368 | Mi-35 |
| 4010 | Mi-24D |
| 4011 | Mi-24D |
| 6050 | Mi-24DU |
| 7353 | Mi-35 |
| 7354 | Mi-35 |
| 7355 | Mi-35 |
| 7356 | Mi-35 |
| 7357 | Mi-35 |
| 7358 | Mi-35 |
| 7360 | Mi-35 |

**SAAB Gripen**
211.TL/21.zTL, Cáslav
**JAS 39C**

| |
|---|
| 9234 |
| 9235 |
| 9236 |
| 9237 |
| 9238 |
| 9239 |
| 9240 |
| 9241 |
| 9242 |
| 9243 |
| 9244 |
| 9245 |

**JAS 39D**

| |
|---|
| 9819 |
| 9820 |

**Tupolev Tu-154M**
241.dlt/24.zDL, Praha/Kbely

| |
|---|
| 1003 |
| 1016 |

**Yakovlev Yak-40**
241.dlt/24.zDL, Praha/Kbely

| | |
|---|---|
| 0260 | Yak-40 |
| 1257 | Yak-40K |

**DENMARK**
**Flyvevåbnet**
**Lockheed**
**C-130J-30 Hercules II**
Eskadrille 721, Aalborg

| |
|---|
| B-536 |
| B-537 |
| B-538 |

**Canadair**
**CL.604 Challenger**
Eskadrille 721, Aalborg

| |
|---|
| C-080 |
| C-168 |
| C-172 |

**General Dynamics**
**F-16 MLU**
Eskadrille 726, Aalborg;
Eskadrille 727, Skrydstrup;
Eskadrille 730, Skrydstrup

| | | |
|---|---|---|
| E-004 | F-16A | Esk 730 |
| E-005 | F-16A | Esk 726 |
| E-007 | F-16A | Esk 727 |
| E-008 | F-16A | Esk 726 |

| | | |
|---|---|---|
| E-011 | F-16A | Esk 727 |
| E-016 | F-16A | Esk 726 |
| E-017 | F-16A | Esk 730 |
| E-018 | F-16A | Esk 730 |
| E-024 | F-16A | Esk 730 |
| E-070 | F-16A | Esk 726 |
| E-074 | F-16A | Esk 730 |
| E-075 | F-16A | Esk 730 |
| E-107 | F-16A | Esk 726 |
| E-180 | F-16A | Esk 730 |
| E-182 | F-16A | Esk 730 |
| E-184 | F-16A | Esk 727 |
| E-187 | F-16A | Esk 730 |
| E-188 | F-16A | Esk 727 |
| E-189 | F-16A | Esk 726 |
| E-190 | F-16A | Esk 727 |
| E-191 | F-16A | Esk 730 |
| E-192 | F-16A | Esk 730 |
| E-193 | F-16A | Esk 727 |
| E-194 | F-16A | Esk 730 |
| E-195 | F-16A | Esk 726 |
| E-196 | F-16A | Esk 727 |
| E-197 | F-16A | Esk 730 |
| E-198 | F-16A | Esk 726 |
| E-199 | F-16A | Esk 730 |
| E-200 | F-16A | Esk 727 |
| E-202 | F-16A | Esk 730 |
| E-203 | F-16A | Esk 730 |
| E-596 | F-16A | Esk 730 |
| E-597 | F-16A | Esk 730 |
| E-598 | F-16A | Esk 727 |
| E-599 | F-16A | Esk 727 |
| E-600 | F-16A | Esk 730 |
| E-601 | F-16A | Esk 726 |
| E-602 | F-16A | Esk 730 |
| E-603 | F-16A | Esk 726 |
| E-604 | F-16A | Esk 726 |
| E-605 | F-16A | Esk 730 |
| E-606 | F-16A | Esk 726 |
| E-607 | F-16A | Esk 730 |
| E-608 | F-16A | Esk 726 |
| E-609 | F-16A | Esk 726 |
| E-610 | F-16A | Esk 730 |
| E-611 | F-16A | Esk 726 |
| ET-022 | F-16B | Esk 726 |
| ET-197 | F-16B | Esk 727 |
| ET-198 | F-16B | Esk 727 |
| ET-199 | F-16B | Esk 726 |
| ET-204 | F-16B | Esk 726 |
| ET-206 | F-16B | Esk 730 |
| ET-207 | F-16B | Esk 726 |
| ET-208 | F-16B | Esk 730 |
| ET-210 | F-16B | Esk 727 |
| ET-612 | F-16B | Esk 726 |
| ET-613 | F-16B | Esk 727 |
| ET-614 | F-16B | Esk 726 |
| ET-615 | F-16B | Esk 726 |

**Aérospatiale**
**AS.550C-2 Fennec**
Eskadrille 724, Vandel

| |
|---|
| P-090 |
| P-234 |
| P-254 |
| P-275 |
| P-276 |
| P-287 |
| P-288 |
| P-319 |
| P-320 |
| P-339 |
| P-352 |
| P-369 |

**SAAB**
**T-17 Supporter**
Eskadrille 721, Aalborg;
Flyveskolen, Karup (FLSK)

| | |
|---|---|
| T-401 | FLSK |
| T-402 | Esk 721 |
| T-403 | FLSK |
| T-404 | FLSK |
| T-405 | FLSK |
| T-407 | Esk 721 |
| T-408 | FLSK |
| T-409 | FLSK |
| T-410 | FLSK |
| T-411 | FLSK |
| T-412 | FLSK |
| T-413 | FLSK |
| T-414 | Esk 721 |
| T-415 | FLSK |
| T-417 | FLSK |
| T-418 | Esk 721 |
| T-419 | FLSK |
| T-420 | FLSK |
| T-421 | FLSK |
| T-423 | FLSK |
| T-425 | FLSK |
| T-426 | FLSK |
| T-427 | FLSK |
| T-428 | FLSK |
| T-429 | FLSK |
| T-430 | FLSK |
| T-431 | Esk 721 |
| T-432 | FLSK |

**Sikorsky S-61A Sea King**
Eskadrille 722, Vaerløse
Detachments at:
Aalborg, Ronne, Skrydstrup
U-240
U-275
U-276
U-277
U-278
U-279
U-280
U-481

**Søvaernets**
**Flyvetjaeneste**
**(Navy)**
**Westland Lynx**
**Mk 80/90B**
Eskadrille 728, Karup

| | |
|---|---|
| S-134 | Mk 90B |
| S-142 | Mk 90B |
| S-170 | Mk 90B |
| S-175 | Mk 80 |
| S-181 | Mk 90B |
| S-191 | Mk 90B |
| S-249 | Mk 90B |
| S-256 | Mk 90B |

**EGYPT**
**Al Quwwat al-Jawwiya**
**il Misriya**
**Lockheed**
**C-130H/C-130H-30***
**Hercules**
16 Sqn, Cairo West
1271/SU-BAB
1272/SU-BAC
1273/SU-BAD
1274/SU-BAE
1275/SU-BAF
1277/SU-BAI

1278/SU-BAJ
1279/SU-BAK
1280/SU-BAL
1281/SU-BAM
1282/SU-BAN
1283/SU-BAP
1284/SU-BAQ
1285/SU-BAR
1286/SU-BAS
1287/SU-BAT
1288/SU-BAU
1289/SU-BAV
1290/SU-BEW
1291/SU-BEX
1292/SU-BEY
1293/SU-BKS*
1294/SU-BKT*
1295/SU-BKU*
1296
1297
1298

**Egyptian Govt**
**Airbus A.340-211**
Egyptian Govt, Cairo
SU-GGG

**Grumman**
**G.1159A Gulfstream III/**
**G.1159C Gulfstream IV/**
**G.1159C Gulfream IV-SP/**
**Gulfstream 400**
Egyptian Air Force/Govt,
Cairo

| | |
|---|---|
| SU-BGM | Gulfstream IV |
| SU-BGU | Gulfstream III |
| SU-BGV | Gulfstream III |
| SU-BNC | Gulfstream IV |
| SU-BND | Gulfstream IV |
| SU-BNO | Gulfstream IV-SP |
| SU-BNP | Gulfstream IV-SP |
| SU-BPE | Gulfstream 400 |
| SU-BPF | Gulfstream 400 |

**FINLAND**
**Suomen Ilmavoimat**
**BAe Hawk 51/51A**
Hävittäjälentolaivue 11,
Rovoniemi;
Hävittäjälentolaivue 21,
Tampere/Pirkkala;
Hävittäjälentolaivue 31,
Kuopio/Rissala;
Hävittäjälentolaivue 41,
Kauhava

| | |
|---|---|
| HW-301 | HavLLv 41 |
| HW-303 | HavLLv 41 |
| HW-304 | HavLLv 41 |
| HW-306 | HavLLv 21 |
| HW-307 | HavLLv 21 |
| HW-308 | HavLLv 41 |
| HW-309 | HavLLv 21 |
| HW-310 | HavLLv 21 |
| HW-311 | HavLLv 31 |
| HW-312 | HavLLv 31 |
| HW-314 | HavLLv 41 |
| HW-315 | HavLLv 41 |
| HW-316 | HavLLv 31 |
| HW-318 | HavLLv 41 |
| HW-319 | HavLLv 41 |
| HW-320 | HavLLv 41 |
| HW-321 | HavLLv 41 |
| HW-322 | HavLLv 31 |
| HW-326 | HavLLv 41 |

| | |
|---|---|
| HW-327 | HavLLv 21 |
| HW-328 | HavLLv 41 |
| HW-329 | HavLLv 21 |
| HW-330 | HavLLv 21 |
| HW-331 | HavLLv 21 |
| HW-332 | HavLLv 41 |
| HW-333 | HavLLv 41 |
| HW-334 | HavLLv 31 |
| HW-335 | HavLLv 41 |
| HW-336 | HavLLv 41 |
| HW-337 | HavLLv 41 |
| HW-338 | HavLLv 31 |
| HW-339 | HavLLv 41 |
| HW-340 | HavLLv 41 |
| HW-341 | HavLLv 31 |
| HW-342 | HavLLv 21 |
| HW-343 | HavLLv 31 |
| HW-344 | HavLLv 41 |
| HW-345 | HavLLv 21 |
| HW-346 | HavLLv 41 |
| HW-347 | HavLLv 31 |
| HW-348 | HavLLv 21 |
| HW-349 | HavLLv 41 |
| HW-350 | HavLLv 41 |
| HW-351* | HavLLv 41 |
| HW-352* | HavLLv 41 |
| HW-353* | HavLLv 21 |
| HW-354* | HavLLv 21 |
| HW-355* | HavLLv 21 |
| HW-356* | HavLLv 31 |
| HW-357* | HavLLv 31 |

**Fokker**
**F.27 Friendship**
Tukilentolaivue,
Jyväskylä/Tikkakoski

| | |
|---|---|
| FF-1 | F.27-100 |
| FF-3 | F.27-400M |

**Gates**
**Learjet 35A**
Tukilentolaivue,
Jyväskylä/Tikkakoski;
Tukilentolaivue (Det.),
Kuopio/Rissala*
LJ-1*
LJ-2
LJ-3

**McDonnell Douglas**
**F-18 Hornet**
Hävittäjälentolaivue 11,
Roveniemi;
Hävittäjälentolaivue 21,
Tampere/Pirkkala;
Hävittäjälentolaivue 31,
Kuopio/Rissala;
Koelentokeskus,
Halli
**F-18C Hornet**

| | |
|---|---|
| HN-401 | HavLLv 31 |
| HN-402 | HavLLv 21 |
| HN-403 | HavLLv 31 |
| HN-404 | KoelntK |
| HN-405 | HavLLv 31 |
| HN-406 | HavLLv 31 |
| HN-407 | HavLLv 31 |
| HN-408 | HavLLv 31 |
| HN-409 | HavLLv 21 |
| HN-410 | HavLLv 31 |
| HN-411 | HavLLv 21 |
| HN-412 | HavLLv 11 |
| HN-413 | HavLLv 21 |
| HN-414 | KoelntK |

## Finland – France

| | | | | | |
|---|---|---|---|---|---|
| HN-415 | HavLLv 31 | 13 | 315-UL | 98 | 315-XO |
| HN-416 | HavLLv 21 | 14 | 315-XP | 99 | 315-XP |
| HN-417 | HavLLv 21 | 15 | 315-UN | 100 | 315-XQ |
| HN-418 | HavLLv 21 | 16 | 315-UO | 101 | F-SEXR [1]* |
| HN-419 | HavLLv 11 | 17 | 315-UP | 102 | F-SEXS [2]* |
| HN-420 | HavLLv 11 | 19 | 315-UR | 103 | 315-XT |
| HN-421 | HavLLv 21 | 20 | 315-US | 104 | 315-XU |
| HN-422 | HavLLv 31 | 21 | 315-UT | 105 | F-SEXV [4]* |
| HN-423 | HavLLv 21 | 24 | 315-UW | 106 | 315-XW |
| HN-424 | HavLLv 31 | 25 | 315-UX | 107 | 315-XX |
| HN-425 | HavLLv 11 | 26 | 315-UY | 108 | 315-XY |
| HN-426 | HavLLv 31 | 27 | 315-UZ | 109 | 315-XZ |
| HN-427 | HavLLv 21 | 28 | 315-VA | 110 | 315-YA |
| HN-428 | HavLLv 31 | 29 | 315-VB | 111 | 315-YB |
| HN-429 | HavLLv 11 | 30 | 315-VC | 112 | 315-YC |
| HN-431 | HavLLv 31 | 31 | 315-VD | 113 | 315-YD |
| HN-432 | HavLLv 31 | 32 | 315-VE | 114 | 315-YE |
| HN-433 | HavLLv 21 | 33 | 315-VF | 115 | 315-YF |
| HN-434 | HavLLv 11 | 34 | 315-VG | 116 | 315-YG |
| HN-435 | HavLLv 21 | 35 | 315-VH | 117 | F-SEYH [3]* |
| HN-436 | HavLLv 21 | 36 | 315-VI | 118 | 315-YI |
| HN-437 | HavLLv 11 | 37 | 315-VJ | 119 | 315-YJ |
| HN-438 | HavLLv 21 | 38 | 315-VK | 120 | 315-YK |
| HN-439 | HavLLv 31 | 39 | 315-VL | 121 | 315-YL |
| HN-440 | HavLLv 11 | 40 | 315-VM | 122 | 315-YM |
| HN-441 | HavLLv 21 | 41 | 315-VN | 123 | 315-YN |
| HN-442 | HavLLv 11 | 42 | 315-VO | 124 | 315-YO |
| HN-443 | HavLLv 21 | 43 | 315-VP | 125 | 315-YP |
| HN-444 | HavLLv 31 | 44 | 315-VQ | 126 | 315-YQ |
| HN-445 | HavLLv 11 | 45 | 315-VR | 127 | 315-YR |
| HN-446 | HavLLv 31 | 46 | 315-VS | 128 | 315-YS |
| HN-447 | HavLLv 11 | 47 | 315-VT | 129 | 315-YT |
| HN-448 | HavLLv 31 | 48 | 315-VU | 130 | 315-YU |
| HN-449 | HavLLv 21 | 50 | 315-VW | 131 | 315-YV |
| HN-450 | HavLLv 21 | 52 | 315-VX | 132 | 315-YW |
| HN-451 | HavLLv 11 | 54 | 315-VZ | 133 | 315-YX |
| HN-452 | HavLLv 31 | 56 | 315-WA | 134 | 315-YY |
| HN-453 | HavLLv 21 | 57 | F-ZVLB | 135 | 315-YZ |
| HN-454 | HavLLv 31 | 61 | 315-WD | 136 | 315-ZA |
| HN-455 | HavLLv 31 | 62 | 315-WE | 137 | 315-ZB |
| HN-456 | HavLLv 21 | 63 | 315-WF | 138 | 315-ZC |
| HN-457 | HavLLv 11 | 64 | 315-WG | 139 | 315-ZD |
| **F-18D Hornet** | | 65 | 315-WH | 140 | 315-ZE |
| HN-461 | KoelntK | 66 | 315-WI | 141 | 315-ZF |
| HN-462 | KoelntK | 67 | 315-WJ | 142 | 315-ZG |
| HN-463 | HavLLv 21 | 68 | 315-WK | 143 | 315-ZH |
| HN-464 | HavLLv 11 | 69 | 315-WL | 144 | 315-ZI |
| HN-465 | HavLLv 21 | 70 | 315-WM | 145 | 315-ZJ |
| HN-466 | HavLLv 11 | 72 | 315-WO | 146 | 315-ZK |
| HN-467 | HavLLv 31 | 73 | 315-WP | 149 | 315-ZM |
| | | 74 | 315-WQ | 150 | 315-ZN |
| | | 75 | 315-WR | 152 | 315-ZO |
| **FRANCE** | | 76 | 315-WS | 153 | 315-ZP |
| **Armée de l'Air** | | 77 | 315-WT | 154 | 315-ZQ |
| **Aérospatiale** | | 78 | 315-WU | 155 | 315-ZR |
| **TB-30 Epsilon** | | 79 | 315-WV | 158 | 315-ZS |
| *Cartouche Dorée,* | | 80 | 315-WW | 159 | 315-ZT |
| (EPAA 00.315) Cognac; | | 81 | 315-WX | | |
| EPAA 00.315, Cognac; | | 82 | 315-WY | | |
| SOCATA, Tarbes | | 83 | 315-WZ | **Airbus A.310-304** | |
| Please note: A large number | | 84 | 315-XA | ET 03.060 *Esterel,* | |
| of these machines are kept | | 85 | 315-XB | Paris/Charles de Gaulle | |
| in temporary storage at | | 86 | 315-XC | 418 | F-RADC |
| Chateaudun | | 87 | 315-XD | 421 | F-RADA |
| 1 | 315-UA | 88 | 315-XE | 422 | F-RADB |
| 2 | 315-UB | 89 | 315-XF | | |
| 3 | FZ     SOCATA | 90 | 315-XG | **Airbus A.319CJ-115** | |
| 4 | 315-UC | 91 | 315-XH | ETEC 00.065, Villacoublay | |
| 5 | 315-UD | 92 | 315-XI | 1485 | F-RBFA |
| 6 | 315-UE | 93 | 315-XJ | 1556 | F-RBFB |
| 7 | 315-UF | 94 | 315-XK | | |
| 8 | 315-UG | 95 | 315-XL | **Airbus A.340-212** | |
| 9 | 315-UH | 96 | 315-XM | ET 03.060 *Esterel,* | |
| 10 | 315-UI | 97 | 315-XN | Paris/Charles de Gaulle | |
| 12 | 315-UK | | | 075 (on order) | |

081 (on order)

**Airtech CN-235M-200**
ET 00.042 *Ventoux*,
  Mont-de-Marsan;
ETL 01.062 *Vercours*, Creil;
ETOM 00.052 *La Tontouta*,
  Noumea;
ETOM 00.082 *Maine*,
  Faaa-Tahiti

| | | |
|---|---|---|
| 045 | 62-IB | 01.062 |
| 065 | 82-IC | 00.082 |
| 066 | 52-ID | 00.052 |
| 071 | 62-IE | 01.062 |
| 072 | 82-IF | 00.082 |
| 105 | 52-IG | 00.052 |
| 107 | 52-IH | 00.052 |
| 111 | 62-II | 01.062 |
| 114 | 62-IJ | 01.062 |
| 123 | 62-IM | 01.062 |
| 128 | 62-IK | 00.042 |
| 129 | 62-IL | 01.062 |
| 137 | 62-IN | 01.062 |
| 141 | 62-IO | 01.062 |
| 152 | 62-IP | 01.062 |
| 156 | 62-IQ | 01.062 |
| 158 | 62-IR | 01.062 |
| 160 | 62-IS | 01.062 |
| 165 | 62-IT | 01.062 |

**Boeing C-135 Stratotanker**
GRV 00.093 *Bretagne*,
  Istres

| | | |
|---|---|---|
| 470 | C-135FR | 93-CA |
| 471 | C-135FR | 93-CB |
| 472 | C-135FR | 93-CC |
| 474 | C-135FR | 93-CE |
| 475 | C-135FR | 93-CF |
| 497 | KC-135R | 93-CM |
| 525 | KC-135R | 93-CN |
| 574 | KC-135R | 93-CP |
| 735 | C-135FR | 93-CG |
| 736 | C-135FR | 93-CH |
| 737 | C-135FR | 93-CI |
| 738 | C-135FR | 93-CJ |
| 739 | C-135FR | 93-CK |
| 740 | C-135FR | 93-CL |

**Boeing E-3F Sentry**
EDCA 00.036, Avord

| | |
|---|---|
| 201 | 36-CA |
| 202 | 36-CB |
| 203 | 36-CC |
| 204 | 36-CD |

**CASA 212-300 Aviocar**
CEV, Cazaux & Istres

| | |
|---|---|
| 377 | MO |
| 378 | MP |
| 386 | MQ |

**Cessna 310**
CEV, Cazaux & Istres

| | | |
|---|---|---|
| 187 | 310N | BJ |
| 190 | 310N | BL |
| 193 | 310N | BG |
| 194 | 310N | BH |
| 242 | 310K | AW |
| 513 | 310N | BE |
| 693 | 310N | BI |
| 820 | 310Q | CL |
| 981 | 310Q | BF |

**D-BD Alpha Jet**
AMD-BA, Istres;
CEAM (EC 02.330),
  Mont-de-Marsan;
CEV, Cazaux & Istres;
CITac 00.339 *Aquitaine*,
  Luxeuil;
EAC 00.314, Tours;
EC 01.002 *Cicogne*, Dijon;
EC 01.007 *Provence* &
  EC 02.007 *Argonne*,
  St Dizier;
EPNER, Istres;
ERS 01.091 *Gascogne*,
  Mont-de-Marsan;
ETO 01.008 *Saintonge* &
  ETO 02.008 *Nice*,
  Cazaux;
GE 00.312, Salon de
  Provence;
*Patrouille de France (PDF)*
  (EPAA 20.300),
  Salon de Provence

| | | |
|---|---|---|
| 01 | F-ZJTS | CEV |
| E1 | | CEV |
| E3 | | |
| E4 | | CEV |
| E5 | 314-LV | 00.314 |
| E7 | 7-PF | 02.007 |
| E8 | | CEV |
| E9 | | |
| E10 | 314-LK | 00.314 |
| E11 | | |
| E12 | | CEV |
| E13 | | |
| E14 | 314-TP | 00.314 |
| E15 | 8-NO | 02.008 |
| E17 | 314-LW | 00.314 |
| E18 | 8-NN | 02.008 |
| E19 | 314-UJ | 00.314 |
| E20 | 8-MS | 01.008 |
| E21 | 330-AL | CEAM |
| E22 | 314-LS | 00.314 |
| E23 | 314-UG | 00.314 |
| E24 | 8-MP | 01.008 |
| E25 | 314-TJ | 00.314 |
| E26 | | |
| E28 | 330-AJ | CEAM |
| E29 | 314-TM | 00.314 |
| E30 | | |
| E31 | F-TERK | PDF [9] |
| E32 | | |
| E33 | 8-MZ | 01.008 |
| E34 | 8-MF | 01.008 |
| E35 | 8-MJ | 01.008 |
| E36 | 314-UF | 00.314 |
| E37 | 8-NL | 02.008 |
| E38 | 8-MQ | 01.008 |
| E41 | F-TERA | PDF [1] |
| E42 | 314-TA | 00.314 |
| E43 | 314-LI | 00.314 |
| E44 | 314-LP | 00.314 |
| E45 | 314-TF | 00.314 |
| E46 | 314-TN | PDF [4] |
| E47 | 314-TR | 00.314 |
| E48 | 8-MH | 01.008 |
| E49 | 314-LB | 00.314 |
| E51 | 314-TH | 00.314 |
| E52 | | |
| E53 | 314-TC | 00.314 |
| E55 | 314-UC | 00.314 |
| E58 | 314-TK | 00.314 |
| E59 | 314-LY | 00.314 |
| E60 | | EPNER |

| | | |
|---|---|---|
| E61 | | |
| E63 | 312-RV | 00.312 |
| E64 | 314-TL | 00.314 |
| E65 | 7-PV | 02.007 |
| E66 | 8-ME | 01.008 |
| E67 | 314-TB | 00.314 |
| E68 | 339-DK | 00.339 |
| E69 | 314-TO | 00.314 |
| E72 | 314-LA | 00.314 |
| E73 | | |
| E74 | 8-MI | 01.008 |
| E75 | F-TERW | PDF [5] |
| E76 | 312-RU | 00.312 |
| E79 | 330-AH | CEAM |
| E80 | | CEV |
| E81 | | |
| E82 | 8-NB | 02.008 |
| E83 | 314-TZ | 00.314 |
| E84 | 314-UK | 00.314 |
| E85 | 8-MT | 01.008 |
| E86 | 8-NS | 02.008 |
| E87 | | |
| E88 | 314-LL | 00.314 |
| E89 | 314-LM | 00.314 |
| E90 | 330-AI | CEAM |
| E91 | 2-EL | 01.002 |
| E92 | 330-AK | CEAM |
| E93 | 314-LG | 00.314 |
| E94 | F-TERH | PDF [7] |
| E95 | 7-PZ | 02.007 |
| E96 | 314-LC | 00.314 |
| E97 | 8-NT | 02.008 |
| E98 | 314-TT | 00.314 |
| E99 | 330-AH | CEAM |
| E100 | | EPNER |
| E101 | 8-NQ | 02.008 |
| E102 | 8-MY | 01.008 |
| E103 | 314-UA | 00.314 |
| E104 | 314-LQ | 00.314 |
| E105 | 8-NU | 02.008 |
| E106 | 8-NA | 02.008 |
| E107 | 7-PY | 02.007 |
| E108 | | |
| E109 | 8-NJ | 02.008 |
| E110 | 8-NG | 02.008 |
| E112 | DA | 01.091 |
| E113 | | |
| E114 | 314-TU | 00.314 |
| E115 | 91-DA | 01.091 |
| E116 | 7-PW | 02.007 |
| E117 | F-TERI | PDF |
| E118 | 339-DN | 00.339 |
| E119 | 7-PX | 02.007 |
| E120 | F-TERG | PDF |
| E121 | 8-NE | 02.008 |
| E122 | F-TERD | PDF [6] |
| E123 | 8-ML | 01.008 |
| E124 | 314-TE | 00.314 |
| E125 | | |
| E126 | 312-RT | 00.312 |
| E127 | 314-TV | 00.314 |
| E128 | | |
| E129 | 314-UB | 00.314 |
| E130 | F-TERP | PDF [0] |
| E131 | | |
| E132 | 314-LZ | 00.314 |
| E133 | 8-MN | 01.008 |
| E134 | F-TERM | PDF [3] |
| E135 | F-TERX | PDF [8] |
| E136 | 314-TN | 00.314 |
| E137 | 314-LJ | 00.314 |
| E138 | 314-LT | 00.314 |
| E139 | 8-ND | 02.008 |
| E140 | 314-UD | 00.314 |

# France

| | | |
|---|---|---|
| E141 | 7-PJ | 02.007 |
| E142 | | |
| E143 | 312-RS | 00.312 |
| E144 | | |
| E145 | | |
| E146 | 314-LX | 00.314 |
| E147 | 8-NH | 02.008 |
| E148 | 8-MG | 01.008 |
| E149 | 8-MO | 01.008 |
| E150 | 8-NC | 02.008 |
| E151 | 8-MC | 01.008 |
| E152 | 314-LO | 00.314 |
| E153 | 314-TG | 00.314 |
| E154 | 8-NR | 02.008 |
| E155 | 8-NP | 02.008 |
| E156 | 314-TI | 00.314 |
| E157 | | |
| E158 | F-TERF | PDF [2] |
| E159 | 7-PP | 02.007 |
| E160 | F-TERC | PDF |
| E162 | | |
| E163 | F-TERB | PDF [7] |
| E164 | 8-MB | 01.008 |
| E165 | F-TERE | PDF |
| E166 | 314-TX | 00.314 |
| E167 | 314-UH | 00.314 |
| E168 | 314-TS | 00.314 |
| E169 | 314-LE | 00.314 |
| E170 | 314-UN | 00.314 |
| E171 | 314-LR | 00.314 |
| E173 | 314-LH | 00.314 |
| E176 | 8-MA | 01.008 |

**Dassault**
**Falcon 20**
CEV, Cazaux & Istres;
CITac 00.339 *Aquitaine*,
Luxeuil;
ETEC 00.065, Villacoublay

| | | |
|---|---|---|
| 22 | CS | CEV |
| 79 | CT | CEV |
| 86 | CG | CEV |
| 93 | F-RAED | 00.065 |
| 96 | CB | CEV |
| 104 | CW | CEV |
| 124 | CC | CEV |
| 131 | CD | CEV |
| 138 | CR | CEV |
| 167 | (F-RAEB) | 00.065 |
| 182 | 339-JA | 00.339 |
| 188 | CX | CEV |
| 252 | CA | CEV |
| 263 | CY | CEV |
| 288 | CV | CEV |
| 291 | 65-EG | 00.065 |
| 342 | F-RAEC | 00.065 |
| 375 | CZ | CEV |
| 422 | F-RAEH | 00.065 |
| 451 | 339-JC | 00.339 |
| 483 | 339-JI | 00.339 |

**Dassault**
**Falcon 50**
ETEC 00.065, Villacoublay

| | | |
|---|---|---|
| 5 | F-RAFI | |
| 27 | (F-RAFK) | |
| 34 | (F-RAFL) | |
| 78 | F-RAFJ | |

**Dassault**
**Falcon 900**
ETEC 00.065, Villacoublay

| | | |
|---|---|---|
| 02 | (F-RAFP) | |
| 004 | (F-RAFQ) | |

**Dassault**
**Mirage F.1**
CEAM (EC 02.330),
 Mont-de-Marsan;
CEV, Cazaux & Istres;
EC 01.030 *Alsace* &
 EC 02.030 *Normandie
 Niemen*, Colmar;
ER 01.033 *Belfort*,
 & ER 02.033 *Savoie*,
 Reims;
**Mirage F.1CT**

| | | |
|---|---|---|
| 219 | 30-SP | 01.030 |
| 220 | 30-QK | 02.030 |
| 221 | | |
| 223 | 30-QX | 02.030 |
| 225 | | |
| 226 | 30-SY | 01.030 |
| 227 | 330-AP | CEAM |
| 228 | 30-QT | 02.030 |
| 229 | | |
| 230 | 30-QB | 02.030 |
| 231 | | |
| 232 | 33-FK | 02.033 |
| 233 | 30-QT | 02.030 |
| 234 | 30-SI | 01.030 |
| 235 | | |
| 236 | 30-SB | 01.030 |
| 237 | | |
| 238 | | |
| 239 | 30-QP | 02.030 |
| 241 | | |
| 242 | 30-QA | 02.030 |
| 243 | 30-QJ | 02.030 |
| 244 | 30-QH | 02.030 |
| 245 | 30-SX | 01.030 |
| 246 | | |
| 248 | | |
| 251 | | |
| 252 | | |
| 253 | 30-SJ | 01.030 |
| 254 | 330-AF | CEAM |
| 255 | | |
| 256 | 30-SH | 01.030 |
| 257 | 30-SF | 01.030 |
| 258 | 33-FO | 03.033 |
| 259 | 30-QZ | 02.030 |
| 260 | 30-SR | 01.030 |
| 261 | 30-QY | 02.030 |
| 262 | | |
| 264 | | |
| 265 | | |
| 267 | 30-QC | 02.030 |
| 268 | 30-SM | 01.030 |
| 271 | 30-QQ | 02.030 |
| 272 | 30-QL | 02.030 |
| 273 | | |
| 274 | 30-QR | 02.030 |
| 275 | 30-QN | 02.030 |
| 278 | 30-SG | 01.030 |
| 279 | 30-SC | 01.030 |
| 280 | 30-QD | 02.030 |
| 281 | 30-QV | 02.030 |
| 283 | | |

**Mirage F.1B**

| | | |
|---|---|---|
| 501 | | |
| 502 | | |
| 504 | | |
| 505 | | |
| 507 | 30-SE | 01.030 |
| 509 | | |
| 510 | | |
| 511 | | |
| 512 | 30-SU | 01.030 |

| | | |
|---|---|---|
| 513 | 30-SV | 01.030 |
| 514 | | |
| 516 | | |
| 517 | | |
| 518 | | |
| 519 | 30-SK | 01.030 |
| 520 | 30-SO | 01.030 |

**Mirage F.1CR**

| | | |
|---|---|---|
| 602 | | CEV |
| 603 | 33-CB | 01.033 |
| 604 | 33-CF | 01.033 |
| 605 | 33-CO | 01.033 |
| 606 | 33-NP | 02.033 |
| 607 | 33-ND | 02.033 |
| 608 | 33-NG | 02.033 |
| 610 | 33-CI | 01.033 |
| 611 | 33-CN | 01.033 |
| 612 | 33-NJ | 02.033 |
| 613 | 33-CC | 01.033 |
| 614 | 33-CR | 01.033 |
| 615 | 33-CR | 01.033 |
| 616 | 33-NM | 02.033 |
| 617 | 33-NO | 02.033 |
| 620 | 33-CT | 01.033 |
| 622 | 33-NH | 02.033 |
| 623 | 33-CM | 01.033 |
| 624 | 33-NY | 02.033 |
| 627 | 33-NT | 02.033 |
| 628 | 33-NB | 02.033 |
| 630 | 33-CU | 01.033 |
| 631 | 33-NS | 02.033 |
| 632 | 33-CL | 01.033 |
| 634 | 33-CK | 01.033 |
| 635 | 33-CG | 01.033 |
| 636 | 33-NL | 02.033 |
| 637 | 33-CP | 01.033 |
| 638 | 33-NX | 02.033 |
| 640 | 33-NV | 02.033 |
| 641 | 33-NI | 02.033 |
| 642 | 33-NC | 02.033 |
| 643 | | |
| 645 | 33-CH | 01.033 |
| 646 | 33-NW | 02.033 |
| 647 | 33-CQ | 01.033 |
| 648 | 33-CE | 01.033 |
| 649 | 330-AB | CEAM |
| 650 | 33-CJ | 01.033 |
| 651 | 33-NB | 02.033 |
| 653 | 33-CV | 01.033 |
| 654 | 33-CK | 01.033 |
| 655 | 33-NG | 02.033 |
| 656 | 33-NK | 02.033 |
| 657 | | |
| 658 | 33-NQ | 02.033 |
| 659 | 33-CA | 01.033 |
| 660 | 33-CY | 01.033 |
| 661 | 33-NE | 02.033 |
| 662 | 33-NA | 02.033 |

**Dassault**
**Mirage 2000B**
AMD-BA, Istres;
CEAM (EC 02.330),
 Mont-de-Marsan;
CEV, Cazaux & Istres;
EC 02.002 *Côte d'Or*, Dijon;
EC 01.005 *Vendée* &
 EC 02.005 *Ile de France*,
 Orange;
EC 01.012 *Cambrésis* &
 EC 02.012 *Picardie*,
 Cambrai;

| | | |
|---|---|---|
| 501 | (BX1) | CEV |
| 502 | | |

| No. | Code | Unit |
|---|---|---|
| 504 | | CEV |
| 505 | 5-OY | 02.005 |
| 506 | 5-OD | 02.005 |
| 507 | 5-OR | 02.005 |
| 508 | 5-OP | 02.005 |
| 509 | 5-OK | 02.005 |
| 510 | 5-OQ | 02.005 |
| 512 | 5-OU | 02.005 |
| 513 | | |
| 514 | 5-OE | 02.005 |
| 515 | 5-OG | 02.005 |
| 516 | 5-OL | 02.005 |
| 518 | 5-OM | 02.005 |
| 519 | 5-OW | 02.005 |
| 520 | 5-OS | 02.005 |
| 521 | 5-ON | 02.005 |
| 522 | 5-OV | 02.005 |
| 523 | 5-OA | 02.005 |
| 524 | 330-AM | CEAM |
| 525 | 12-YP | 01.012 |
| 526 | 12-KO | 02.012 |
| 527 | 5-OB | 02.005 |
| 528 | 12-KO | 02.012 |
| 529 | 12-KJ | 02.012 |
| 530 | 12-YM | 01.012 |

**Dassault**
**Mirage 2000C/2000-5F\***
CEAM (EC 02.330),
 Mont-de-Marsan;
CEV, Istres;
EC 01.002 *Cigognes* &
 EC 02.002 *Côte
 d'Or*, Dijon;
EC 01.005 *Vendée* &
 EC 02.005 *Ile de France*,
 Orange;
EC 01.012 *Cambrésis* &
 EC 02.012 *Picardie*,
 Cambrai;
EC 04.033 *Vexin*, Djibouti

| No. | Code | Unit |
|---|---|---|
| 01* | | CEV |
| 1 | 5-NC | 01.005 |
| 2 | | CEV |
| 3 | 5-NN | 01.005 |
| 4 | 5-NT | 01.005 |
| 5 | 5-NI | 01.005 |
| 8 | 5-OO | 02.005 |
| 9 | 5-NH | 01.005 |
| 11 | 5-NJ | 01.005 |
| 12 | 5-NV | 01.005 |
| 13 | 5-NM | 01.005 |
| 14 | 5-NW | 01.005 |
| 15 | 5-NA | 01.005 |
| 16 | 5-OX | 02.005 |
| 17 | 5-OZ | 02.005 |
| 18 | 5-NP | 01.005 |
| 19 | 5-NE | 01.005 |
| 20 | 5-NQ | 01.005 |
| 21 | 5-NG | 01.005 |
| 22 | 5-ND | 01.005 |
| 25 | 5-NU | 01.005 |
| 27 | 5-OH | 02.005 |
| 28 | | |
| 29 | 5-NO | 01.005 |
| 30 | 5-OF | 02.005 |
| 32 | 5-NS | 01.005 |
| 34 | 5-OJ | 02.005 |
| 35 | 5-NL | 01.005 |
| 36 | 5-OC | 02.005 |
| 37 | 5-NF | 01.005 |
| 38* | 2-FK | 02.002 |
| 40* | 2-FG | 02.002 |
| 41* | 2-FZ | 02.002 |
| 42* | | |
| 43* | | |
| 44* | 2-EQ | 01.002 |
| 45* | 2-EF | 01.002 |
| 46* | 2-EN | 01.002 |
| 47* | 2-EP | 01.002 |
| 48* | 2-FX | 02.002 |
| 49* | 330-AN | CEAM |
| 51* | 330-AS | CEAM |
| 52* | 2-FC | 02.002 |
| 53* | 2-FA | 02.002 |
| 54* | 2-FY | 02.002 |
| 55* | 2-FR | 02.002 |
| 56* | 2-EG | 01.002 |
| 57* | 2-ET | 01.002 |
| 58* | 2-FO | 02.002 |
| 59* | 2-EV | 01.002 |
| 61* | 2-EM | 01.002 |
| 62* | 2-ED | 01.002 |
| 63* | 2-FQ | 02.002 |
| 64 | 330-AQ | CEAM |
| 65* | 2-EK | 01.002 |
| 66* | 2-FD | 02.002 |
| 67* | 2-FL | 02.002 |
| 68* | 2-FP | 02.002 |
| 69* | 2-FE | 02.002 |
| 70* | 2-EH | 01.002 |
| 71* | 2-FB | 02.002 |
| 72* | 2-EE | 01.002 |
| 73* | 2-ES | 01.002 |
| 74* | 2-EU | 01.002 |
| 76* | 2-EB | 01.002 |
| 77* | 330-AX | CEAM |
| 78* | 2-EC | 01.002 |
| 79 | 12-KS | 02.012 |
| 80 | 12-YJ | 01.012 |
| 81 | 12-KP | 02.012 |
| 82 | | |
| 83 | 33-LD | 04.033 |
| 85 | 12-YL | 01.012 |
| 86 | 12-KA | 02.012 |
| 87 | 12-KN | 02.012 |
| 88 | 12-YC | 01.012 |
| 89 | 12-YQ | 01.012 |
| 90 | 12-YS | 01.012 |
| 91 | 12-KL | 02.012 |
| 92 | 330-AW | CEAM |
| 93 | 12-KK | 02.012 |
| 94 | 12-YI | 01.012 |
| 95 | 12-KM | 02.012 |
| 96 | 12-YB | 01.012 |
| 97 | 12-YT | 01.012 |
| 98 | 12-YU | 01.012 |
| 99 | | |
| 100 | 12-YG | 01.012 |
| 101 | 12-KE | 02.012 |
| 102 | 12-KR | 02.012 |
| 103 | 12-YN | 01.012 |
| 104 | 12-KG | 02.012 |
| 105 | 12-YF | 01.012 |
| 106 | 12-KF | 02.012 |
| 107 | 33-LJ | 04.033 |
| 108 | 12-KV | 02.012 |
| 109 | 33-LB | 04.033 |
| 111 | 12-KN | 02.012 |
| 112 | 12-YC | 01.012 |
| 113 | 12-YO | 01.012 |
| 114 | 12-YK | 01.012 |
| 115 | 12-KH | 02.012 |
| 116 | 12-YD | 01.012 |
| 117 | 12-KQ | 02.012 |
| 118 | 12-YE | 01.012 |
| 119 | 12-KD | 02.012 |
| 120 | 33-LC | 04.033 |
| 121 | 12-KC | 02.012 |
| 122 | 12-YA | 01.012 |
| 123 | 12-YH | 01.012 |
| 124 | 12-KB | 02.012 |
| X7 | | CEV |

**Dassault**
**Mirage 2000D**
AMD-BA, Istres;
CEAM (EC 02.330),
 Mont-de-Marsan;
CEV, Istres;
EC 01.003 *Navarre*,
 EC 02.003 *Champagne* &
 EC 03.003 *Ardennes*,
 Nancy;
EC 04.033 *Vexin*, Djibouti

| No. | Code | Unit |
|---|---|---|
| 601 | 3-IS | 01.003 |
| 602 | 3-XJ | 03.003 |
| 603 | 3-IM | 01.003 |
| 604 | 3-IN | 01.003 |
| 605 | 3-XE | 03.003 |
| 606 | 3-JC | 02.003 |
| 607 | | CEV |
| 609 | 3-JP | 02.003 |
| 610 | 3-JW | 02.003 |
| 611 | 3-JG | 02.003 |
| 612 | 3-JK | 02.003 |
| 613 | 3-XU | 03.003 |
| 614 | 3-JB | 02.003 |
| 615 | 3-JY | 02.003 |
| 616 | 3-XH | 03.003 |
| 617 | 3-XA | 03.003 |
| 618 | | |
| 619 | 3-JE | 02.003 |
| 620 | | |
| 622 | | |
| 623 | 3-IB | 01.003 |
| 624 | 3-IW | 01.003 |
| 625 | | |
| 626 | 3-XH | 03.003 |
| 627 | 3-JL | 02.003 |
| 628 | | |
| 629 | 3-XO | 03.003 |
| 630 | 3-XD | 03.003 |
| 631 | 3-JO | 02.003 |
| 632 | 33-LG | 04.033 |
| 634 | 3-IL | 01.003 |
| 635 | 3-XP | 03.003 |
| 636 | 3-JJ | 02.003 |
| 637 | 3-XC | 03.003 |
| 638 | 3-IJ | 01.003 |
| 639 | 330-AV | CEAM |
| 640 | 3-IR | 01.003 |
| 641 | | |
| 642 | 3-JF | 02.003 |
| 643 | 3-JD | 02.003 |
| 644 | 3-IU | 01.003 |
| 645 | 3-XL | 03.003 |
| 646 | 3-IC | 01.003 |
| 647 | 3-IO | 01.003 |
| 648 | 3-XJ | 03.003 |
| 649 | | |
| 650 | 3-IA | 01.003 |
| 651 | 3-JV | 02.003 |
| 652 | 3-XN | 03.003 |
| 653 | 3-IE | 01.003 |
| 654 | 3-IT | 01.003 |
| 655 | | |
| 657 | 3-JM | 02.003 |
| 658 | 3-JN | 02.003 |
| 659 | 3-XR | 03.003 |
| 660 | 3-ID | 01.003 |
| 661 | 3-IH | 01.003 |

# France

| | | |
|---|---|---|
| 662 | 330-AA | CEAM |
| 664 | 3-JU | 02.003 |
| 665 | 3-XF | 03.003 |
| 666 | 3-IK | 01.003 |
| 667 | 3-JX | 02.003 |
| 668 | 330-AR | CEAM |
| 669 | 3-XV | 03.003 |
| 670 | 3-IQ | 01.003 |
| 671 | 3-XK | 03.003 |
| 672 | 3-JQ | 02.003 |
| 673 | | CEV |
| 674 | 3-IR | 01.003 |
| 675 | 3-JI | 02.003 |
| 676 | | CEV |
| 677 | 3-JT | 01.003 |
| 678 | 3-JA | 02.003 |
| 679 | 3-JX | 01.003 |
| 680 | 3-XM | 03.003 |
| 681 | 3-IG | 01.003 |
| 682 | 3-JR | 02.003 |
| 683 | 3-IV | 01.003 |
| 684 | 3-IF | 01.003 |
| 685 | 3-XZ | 03.003 |
| 686 | 3-JH | 02.003 |

**Dassault**
**Mirage 2000N**
CEAM (EC 02.330),
 Mont-de-Marsan;
CEV, Istres;
EC 01.004 *Dauphiné* &
 EC 02.004 *Lafayette*,
 Luxeuil;
EC 03.004 *Limousin*, Istres

| | | |
|---|---|---|
| 301 | | CEV |
| 303 | 4-CL | 03.004 |
| 304 | 4-CK | 03.004 |
| 305 | 4-CS | 03.004 |
| 306 | 4-BL | 02.004 |
| 307 | 4-CH | 03.004 |
| 309 | 4-AO | 01.004 |
| 310 | 4-CE | 03.004 |
| 311 | 4-AF | 01.004 |
| 312 | 4-CN | 03.004 |
| 313 | 4-CR | 03.004 |
| 314 | 4-AX | 01.004 |
| 315 | 4-BF | 02.004 |
| 316 | 4-BH | 02.004 |
| 317 | 4-BP | 02.004 |
| 319 | 4-AC | 01.004 |
| 320 | 4-CD | 03.004 |
| 322 | 4-CP | 03.004 |
| 323 | 4-CV | 03.004 |
| 324 | 4-CX | 03.004 |
| 325 | 4-CC | 03.004 |
| 326 | 4-AS | 01.004 |
| 327 | 4-CJ | 03.004 |
| 329 | 4-AU | 01.004 |
| 330 | 4-AT | 01.004 |
| 331 | 4-BO | 02.004 |
| 332 | 4-BN | 02.004 |
| 333 | 4-AB | 01.004 |
| 334 | 330-AV | CEAM |
| 335 | 4-CI | 03.004 |
| 336 | 4-BI | 02.004 |
| 337 | 4-AK | 01.004 |
| 338 | 4-CG | 03.004 |
| 339 | 4-AD | 01.004 |
| 340 | 4-AA | 01.004 |
| 341 | | |
| 342 | 4-BA | 02.004 |
| 343 | 4-AH | 01.004 |
| 344 | 4-BV | 02.004 |
| 345 | 4-BU | 02.004 |

| | | |
|---|---|---|
| 348 | 4-AL | 01.004 |
| 349 | 4-BM | 02.004 |
| 350 | 4-AJ | 01.004 |
| 351 | 4-AQ | 01.004 |
| 353 | 4-AM | 01.004 |
| 354 | 4-BJ | 02.004 |
| 355 | 4-AE | 01.004 |
| 356 | 4-BX | 02.004 |
| 357 | 4-CO | 03.004 |
| 358 | 4-BQ | 02.004 |
| 359 | 4-BG | 02.004 |
| 360 | 4-CB | 03.004 |
| 361 | 4-CA | 03.004 |
| 362 | 4-CU | 03.004 |
| 363 | 4-BK | 02.004 |
| 364 | 4-BB | 02.004 |
| 365 | 4-BE | 02.004 |
| 366 | 4-BC | 02.004 |
| 367 | 4-AS | 01.004 |
| 368 | 4-AR | 01.004 |
| 369 | 4-AG | 01.004 |
| 370 | 4-CA | 03.004 |
| 371 | 4-AV | 01.004 |
| 372 | 4-CM | 03.004 |
| 373 | 4-CF | 03.004 |
| 374 | 4-BS | 02.004 |
| 375 | 4-CL | 03.004 |

**Dassault**
**Rafale-B**
AMD-BA, Istres;
CEAM (EC 02.330),
 Mont-de-Marsan;
CEV, Istres

| | | |
|---|---|---|
| 301 | | CEV |
| 302 | 330-AC | CEAM |
| 303 | 330-EA | CEAM |
| 304 | 330-EB | CEAM |
| 305 | 330-EC | CEAM |
| 306 | 330-ED | CEAM |
| 307 | 330-EE | CEAM |
| 308 | | |
| 309 | | |
| 310 | | |
| 311 | | |
| B01 | | CEV |

**Dassault**
**Rafale-C**
AMD-BA, Istres;
CEV, Istres

| | | |
|---|---|---|
| 101 | | CEV |
| 102 | 330-EF | CEAM |
| 103 | | |
| 104 | | |
| C01 | | CEV |

**DHC-6 Twin Otter 200/300***
ET 00.042 *Ventoux*,
 Mont-de-Marsan;
GAM 00.056
 *Vaucluse*, Evreux

| | | |
|---|---|---|
| 292 | CC | 00.056 |
| 298 | CD | 00.056 |
| 300 | CE | 00.056 |
| 730* | CA | 00.042 |
| 742* | CB | 00.042 |
| 745* | CV | 00.042 |
| 790* | CW | 00.042 |

**Embraer**
**EMB.121AA/AN* Xingu**
EAT 00.319, Avord

| | |
|---|---|
| 054 | YX |

| | |
|---|---|
| 055* | YZ |
| 064 | YY |
| 066* | ZA |
| 69* | |
| 070* | ZC |
| 072 | YA |
| 073 | YB |
| 075 | YC |
| 076 | YD |
| 77* | ZD |
| 078 | YE |
| 080 | YF |
| 082 | YG |
| 083* | ZE |
| 084 | YH |
| 086 | YI |
| 089 | YJ |
| 090* | ZF |
| 091 | YK |
| 092 | YL |
| 095 | YM |
| 096 | YN |
| 098 | YO |
| 099 | YP |
| 101 | YR |
| 102 | YS |
| 103 | YT |
| 105 | YU |
| 107 | YV |
| 108 | YW |
| 111 | YQ |

**Embraer**
**EMB.312F Tucano**
GE 00.312, Salon de
 Provence

| | |
|---|---|
| 438 | 312-UW |
| 439 | 312-UY |
| 456 | 312-JA |
| 457 | 312-JB |
| 458 | 312-JC |
| 459 | 312-JD |
| 460 | 312-JE |
| 461 | 312-JF |
| 462 | 312-JG |
| 463 | 312-JH |
| 464 | 312-JI |
| 466 | 312-JK |
| 467 | 312-JL |
| 468 | 312-JM |
| 469 | 312-JN |
| 470 | 312-JO |
| 471 | 312-JP |
| 472 | 312-JQ |
| 473 | 312-JR |
| 474 | 312-JS |
| 475 | 312-JT |
| 477 | 312-JU |
| 478 | 312-JV |
| 479 | 312-JX |
| 480 | 312-JY |
| 481 | 312-JZ |
| 483 | 312-UB |
| 484 | 312-UC |
| 485 | 312-UD |
| 486 | 312-UE |
| 487 | 312-UF |
| 488 | 312-UG |
| 489 | 312-UH |
| 490 | 312-UI |
| 491 | 312-UJ |
| 492 | 312-UK |
| 493 | 312-UL |
| 494 | 312-UM |

| | |
|---|---|
| 495 | 312-UN |
| 496 | 312-UO |
| 497 | 312-UP |
| 498 | 312-UQ |
| 499 | 312-UR |
| 500 | 312-US |
| 501 | 312-UT |
| 503 | 312-UV |
| 504 | 312-UX |

**Eurocopter**
**AS.332 Super Puma/**
**AS.532 Cougar/**
**EC.725A-2 Cougar**
EH 03.067 *Parisis*,
Villacoublay;
EH 05.067 *Alpilles*,
Aix-en-Provence;
ETOM 00.082 *Maine*,
Faaa-Tahiti;
GAM 00.056 *Vaucluse*,
Evreux;
CEAM, Mont-de-Marsan

| | | | |
|---|---|---|---|
| 2014 | AS.332C | PN | 05.067 |
| 2057 | AS.332C | PO | 00.082 |
| 2093 | AS.332L | PP | 05.067 |
| 2233 | AS.332L-1 | 67-FY | 03.067 |
| 2235 | AS.332L-1 | 67-FZ | 03.067 |
| 2244 | AS.332C | PM | 00.082 |
| 2342 | AS.532UL | FX | 00.056 |
| 2369 | AS.532UL | FW | 00.056 |
| 2375 | AS.532UL | FV | 00.056 |
| 2377 | AS.332L-1 | 67-FU | 03.067 |
| 2461 | EC.725A-2 | 330-SA | CEAM |
| 2549 | EC.725A-2 | 330-SB | CEAM |
| 2619 | EC.725A-2 | 330-SC | CEAM |

**Lockheed**
**C-130H/C-130H-30* Hercules**
ET 02.061 *Franche-Comté*,
Orléans

| | |
|---|---|
| 4588 | 61-PM |
| 4589 | 61-PN |
| 5114 | 61-PA |
| 5116 | 61-PB |
| 5119 | 61-PC |
| 5140 | 61-PD |
| 5142* | 61-PE |
| 5144* | 61-PF |
| 5150* | 61-PG |
| 5151* | 61-PH |
| 5152* | 61-PI |
| 5153* | 61-PJ |
| 5226* | 61-PK |
| 5227* | 61-PL |

**SOCATA TBM 700**
CEV, Cazaux & Istres;
ETM 01.040 *Moselle*, Metz;
ETM 02.040 *Médoc*,
Bordeaux;

ETEC 00.065, Villacoublay;
EdC 00.070, Chateaudun

| | | |
|---|---|---|
| 33 | XA | 02.040 |
| 35 | XB | 02.040 |
| 70 | XC | 02.040 |
| 77 | XD | 01.040 |
| 78 | XE | |
| 80 | XF | 01.040 |
| 93 | XL | 02.040 |
| 94 | 65-XG | 00.070 |
| 95 | 65-XH | 00.065 |
| 103 | XI | 011.040 |
| 104 | XJ | |
| 105 | XK | 00.065 |
| 106 | MN | CEV |
| 110 | XP | 01.040 |
| 111 | XM | 00.065 |
| 117 | XN | 01.040 |
| 125 | XO | 00.065 |
| 131 | XQ | 00.065 |
| 146 | XR | 00.065 |
| 147 | XS | 00.065 |

**Transall**
**C-160F/C-160NG**
**GABRIEL*/C-160R**
CEAM (EET 06.330),
Mont-de-Marsan;
CEV, Cazaux & Istres;
EET 01.054 *Dunkerque*,
Metz;
ET 01.061 *Touraine* &
ET 03.061 *Poitou*, Orléans;
ET 01.064 *Béarn* &
ET 02.064 *Anjou*, Evreux;
ETOM 00.050 *Réunion*,
St Denis;
ETOM 00.055 *Ouessant*,
Dakar;
ETOM 00.058 *Guadeloupe*,
Pointe-à-Pitre;
ETOM 00.088 *Larzac*,
Djibouti

| | | | |
|---|---|---|---|
| RA02 | C-160R | 61-MI | 01.061 |
| RA04 | C-160R | 61-MS | 01.061 |
| RA06 | C-160R | 61-ZB | 03.061 |
| R1 | C-160R | 61-MA | 01.061 |
| R2 | C-160R | 61-MB | 01.061 |
| R3 | C-160R | 61-MC | 00.058 |
| R4 | C-160R | 61-MD | 01.061 |
| R11 | C-160R | 61-MF | 01.061 |
| R12 | C-160R | 61-MG | 01.061 |
| R13 | C-160R | 61-MH | 00.050 |
| R15 | C-160R | 61-MJ | 01.061 |
| R17 | C-160R | 61-ML | 01.061 |
| R18 | C-160R | 61-MM | 01.061 |
| R42 | C-160R | 61-MN | 01.061 |
| R43 | C-160R | 61-MO | 01.061 |
| R44 | C-160R | 61-MP | 01.061 |
| R45 | C-160R | 61-MQ | 01.061 |
| R46 | C-160R | 61-MR | 01.061 |
| R48 | C-160R | 61-MT | 01.061 |
| R49 | C-160R | 59-MU | CEV |
| R51 | C-160R | 61-MW | 01.061 |
| R52 | C-160R | 61-MX | 01.061 |
| R53 | C-160R | 61-MY | 01.061 |
| R54 | C-160R | 61-MZ | 01.061 |
| R55 | C-160R | 61-ZC | 03.061 |
| R86 | C-160R | 61-ZD | 03.061 |
| R87 | C-160R | 61-ZE | 00.050 |
| R88 | C-160R | 61-ZF | 03.061 |
| R89 | C-160R | 61-ZG | 03.061 |
| R90 | C-160R | 61-ZH | 03.061 |
| R91 | C-160R | 61-ZI | 03.061 |
| R92 | C-160R | 61-ZJ | 03.061 |
| R93 | C-160R | 61-ZK | 03.061 |
| R94 | C-160R | 61-ZL | 03.061 |
| R95 | C-160R | 61-ZM | 03.061 |
| R96 | C-160R | 61-ZN | 03.061 |
| R97 | C-160R | 61-ZA | 03.061 |
| R98 | C-160R | 61-ZP | 03.061 |
| R99 | C-160R | 61-ZQ | 03.061 |
| R100 | C-160R | 61-ZR | 03.061 |
| R153 | C-160R | 61-ZS | 03.061 |
| R154 | C-160R | 61-ZT | 03.061 |
| R157 | C-160R | 61-ZW | 03.061 |
| R158 | C-160R | 61-ZX | 03.061 |
| R159 | C-160R | 61-ZY | 03.061 |
| R160 | C-160R | 61-ZZ | 03.061 |
| R201 | C-160R | 64-GA | 01.064 |
| R202 | C-160R | 64-GB | 02.064 |
| R203 | C-160R | 64-GC | 01.064 |
| R204 | C-160R | 64-GD | 02.064 |
| R205 | C-160R | 64-GE | 01.064 |
| R206 | C-160R | 64-GF | 02.064 |

# France

R207 C-160R 64-GG  
01.064  
R208 C-160R 64-GH  
02.064  
R210 C-160R 64-GJ  
02.064  
R211 C-160R 64-GK  
01.064  
R212 C-160R 64-GL  
02.064  
R213 C-160R 64-GM  
01.064  
R214 C-160R 64-GN  
02.064  
R215 C-160R 64-GO  
01.064  
F216 C-160NG* 54-GT  
01.054  
R217 C-160R 64-GQ  
01.064  
R218 C-160R 64-GR  
02.064  
F221 C-160NG* GS  
01.054  
R223 C-160R 64-GW  
01.064  
R224 C-160R 64-GX  
02.064  
R225 C-160R 64-GY  
01.064  
R226 C-160R 64-GZ  
02.064  

**Aéronavale/Marine**
**Aérospatiale**
**SA.321G Super Frelon**
32 Flottille,  
 Hyères & Lanvéoc/Poulmic  
101  
106  
118  
134  
137  
144  
148  
160  
162  
163  
165  

**Dassault-Breguet**
**Atlantique 2**
21 Flottille,  
 Nimes/Garons;  
23 Flottille,  
 Lorient/Lann Bihoué  

| | |
|---|---|
| 1 | 21F |
| 2 | 23F |
| 3 | 21F |
| 4 | 21F |
| 5 | 23F |
| 6 | 23F |
| 7 | 21F |
| 8 | 23F |
| 9 | 21F |
| 10 | 21F |
| 11 | 23F |
| 12 | 23F |
| 13 | 21F |
| 14 | 23F |
| 15 | 21F |
| 16 | 23F |
| 17 | 21F |
| 18 | 21F |
| 19 | 23F |
| 20 | 21F |
| 21 | 21F |
| 22 | 23F |
| 23 | 21F |
| 24 | 21F |
| 25 | 21F |
| 26 | 21F |
| 27 | 23F |
| 28 | 21F |

**Dassault**
**Falcon 10(MER)**
ES 57, Landivisiau  
 32  
101  
129  
133  
143  
185  

**Dassault**
**Falcon 20G Guardian**
25 Flottille,  
 Papeete &  
 Tontouta  
48  
65  
72  
77  
80  

**Dassault**
**Falcon 50 SURMAR**
24 Flottille,  
 Lorient/Lann Bihoué  
 7  
30  
36  
132  

**Dassault**
**Rafale-M**
12 Flottille,  
 Landivisiau;  
AMD-BA, Istres;  
CEV, Istres  

| | |
|---|---|
| M01 | CEV |
| M02 | CEV |
| 1 | CEV |
| 2 | 12F |
| 3 | 12F |
| 4 | 12F |
| 5 | 12F |
| 6 | 12F |
| 7 | 12F |
| 8 | 12F |
| 9 | 12F |
| 10 | 12F |

**Dassault**
**Super Etendard**
11 Flottille, Landivisiau;  
17 Flottille, Landivisiau;  
CEV, Cazaux & Istres  

| | |
|---|---|
| 1 | 17F |
| 2 | 11F |
| 3 | 11F |
| 4 | 11F |
| 6 | 17F |
| 8 | 17F |
| 10 | 11F |
| 11 | 17F |
| 12 | 11F |
| 13 | 17F |
| 14 | 17F |
| 15 | 17F |
| 16 | 11F |
| 17 | 11F |
| 18 | 17F |
| 19 | 11F |
| 23 | 17F |
| 24 | 11F |
| 25 | 17F |
| 28 | 11F |
| 30 | 11F |
| 31 | 17F |
| 32 | 11F |
| 33 | 11F |
| 35 | 11F |
| 37 | 11F |
| 38 | 11F |
| 39 | 11F |
| 41 | 11F |
| 43 | 11F |
| 44 | 17F |
| 45 | 17F |
| 46 | 17F |
| 47 | 11F |
| 48 | 17F |
| 49 | 17F |
| 50 | 11F |
| 51 | 17F |
| 52 | 17F |
| 55 | 11F |
| 57 | 17F |
| 59 | 17F |
| 61 | 17F |
| 62 | 11F |
| 64 | 11F |
| 65 | 17F |
| 66 | 11F |
| 68 | CEV |
| 69 | 11F |
| 71 | 11F |

**Embraer**
**EMB.121AN Xingu**
24 Flottille,  
 Lorient/Lann Bihoué;  
28 Flottille, Hyères  

| | |
|---|---|
| 30 | 24F |
| 47 | 24F |
| 65 | 28F |
| 67 | 24F |
| 68 | 24F |
| 71 | 28F |
| 74 | 24F |
| 79 | 28F |
| 81 | 24F |
| 85 | 28F |
| 87 | 24F |

**Eurocopter**
**SA.365/AS.565 Panther**
35 Flottille, Hyères,  
 (with detachments at  
 Cherbourg, La Rochelle  
 & Le Touquet)  
36 Flottille, Hyères  

| | | |
|---|---|---|
| 17 | SA.365N | 35F |
| 19 | SA.365N | 35F |
| 24 | SA.365N | 35F |
| 57 | SA.365N | 35F |
| 81 | SA.365N | 35F |
| 91 | SA.365N | 35F |
| 157 | SA.365N | 35F |
| 313 | SA.365F1 | 35F |

| | | |
|---|---|---|
| 318 | SA.365F1 | 35F |
| 322 | SA.365F1 | 35F |
| 355 | AS.565MA | 36F |
| 362 | AS.565MA | 35F |
| 436 | AS.565MA | 36F |
| 452 | AS.565MA | 36F |
| 453 | AS.565MA | 35F |
| 466 | AS.565MA | 36F |
| 482 | AS.565MA | 36F |
| 486 | AS.565MA | 36F |
| 488 | AS.565MA | 36F |
| 503 | AS.565MA | 35F |
| 505 | AS.565MA | 36F |
| 506 | AS.565MA | 35F |
| 507 | AS.565MA | 36F |
| 511 | AS.565MA | 36F |
| 519 | AS.565MA | 36F |
| 522 | AS.565MA | 36F |
| 524 | AS.565MA | 36F |
| 542 | AS.565MA | 36F |

**Nord 262E Frégate**
24 Flottille,
Lorient/Lann Bihoué;
28 Flottille, Hyères;
ERCE, Hyères;
ES 10, Hyères;
ES 55, Aspretto

| | |
|---|---|
| 45 | 28F |
| 46 | 28F |
| 51 | 28F |
| 53 | 28F |
| 60 | 28F |
| 63 | 28F |
| 69 | 28F |
| 70 | 28F |
| 71 | 28F |
| 72 | 28F |
| 73 | 28F |
| 75 | 28F |
| 79 | 28F |
| 100 | 28F |

**Northrop Grumman
E-2C Hawkeye**
4 Flottille,
Lorient/Lann Bihoué

| | |
|---|---|
| 1 | (165455) |
| 2 | (165456) |
| 3 | (166417) |

**Westland
Lynx HAS2(FN)/HAS4(FN)\***
31 Flottille, Hyères;
34 Flottille, Lanvéoc/Poulmic;
CEPA, Hyères;

| | |
|---|---|
| 260 | CEPA |
| 263 | 34F |
| 264 | 31F |
| 265 | 34F |
| 266 | 31F |
| 267 | 34F |
| 269 | 34F |
| 270 | 31F |
| 271 | 34F |
| 272 | 34F |
| 273 | 34F |
| 274 | 31F |
| 275 | 31F |
| 276 | 34F |
| 620 | 31F |
| 621 | 31F |
| 622 | 34F |
| 623 | 34F |

| | |
|---|---|
| 624 | 31F |
| 625 | 34F |
| 627 | 34F |
| 801* | 31F |
| 802* | 31F |
| 804* | 31F |
| 806* | 34F |
| 807* | 34F |
| 808* | 34F |
| 810* | 34F |
| 811* | 31F |
| 812* | 31F |
| 813* | 34F |
| 814* | 31F |

**Aviation Legére de l'Armée
de Terre (ALAT)**
**Cessna F.406 Caravan II**
EAAT, Rennes

| | |
|---|---|
| 0008 | ABM |
| 0010 | ABN |

**Pilatus
PC-6B/B2-H4 Turbo Porter**
1 GSALAT, Montauban

| | |
|---|---|
| 887 | MCA |
| 888 | MCB |
| 889 | MCC |
| 890 | MCD |
| 891 | MCE |

**SOCATA TBM 700**
EAAT, Rennes

| | |
|---|---|
| 99 | ABO |
| 100 | ABP |
| 115 | ABQ |
| 136 | ABR |
| 139 | ABS |
| 156 | ABT |
| 159 | ABU |
| 160 | ABV |

**French Govt
Aérospatiale
AS.350B Ecureuil**
Douanes Francaises;
Sécurité Civile*

| | |
|---|---|
| F-ZBBN | AS.350B* |
| F-ZBDV | AS.350BA |
| F-ZBEA | AS.350B-1* |
| F-ZBFC | AS.350B-1* |
| F-ZBFD | AS.350B-1* |
| F-ZBFH | AS.350BA |
| F-ZBFT | AS.350B-2* |

**Aérospatiale
AS.355F-1 Twin Ecureuil**
Douanes Francaises

| | |
|---|---|
| F-ZBAC | (5026) |
| F-ZBEF | (5236) |
| F-ZBEJ | (5003) |
| F-ZBEK | (5298) |
| F-ZBEL | (5299) |

**Beech
Super King Air B200**
Sécurité Civile

| | |
|---|---|
| F-ZBEM | |
| F-ZBFJ | 98 |
| F-ZBFK | 96 |
| F-ZBMB | B97 |

**Canadair CL-415**
Sécurité Civile

| | |
|---|---|
| C-GILN | 44 |
| F-ZBEU | 42 |
| F-ZBFN | 33 |
| F-ZBFP | 31 |
| F-ZBFS | 32 |
| F-ZBFV | 37 |
| F-ZBFW | 38 |
| F-ZBFX | 34 |
| F-ZBFY | 35 |

**Cessna F.406 Caravan II**
Douanes Francaises

| | |
|---|---|
| F-ZBAB | (0025) |
| F-ZBBB | (0039) |
| F-ZBCE | (0042) |
| F-ZBCF | (0077) |
| F-ZBCG | (0066) |
| F-ZBCH | (0075) |
| F-ZBCI | (0070) |
| F-ZBCJ | (0074) |
| F-ZBEP | (0006) |
| F-ZBES | (0017) |
| F-ZBFA | (0001) |
| F-ZBGA | (0086) |
| F-ZBGD | (0090) |

**Conair Firecat\*/
Turbo Firecat**
Sécurité Civile

| | |
|---|---|
| F-ZBAA | 22 |
| F-ZBAP | 12 |
| F-ZBAU* | T2 |
| F-ZBAZ | 01 |
| F-ZBCZ | 23 |
| F-ZBEH | 20 |
| F-ZBET | 15 |
| F-ZBEW | 11 |
| F-ZBEY | 07 |
| F-ZBMA | 24 |

**Dassault Falcon 20**
AVDEF, Nimes/Garons

| | |
|---|---|
| F-GPAA | Falcon 20ECM |
| F-GPAB | Falcon 20E |
| F-GPAD | Falcon 20E |

**De Havilland Canada
DHC-8Q-402MR**
Sécurité Civile

| | |
|---|---|
| F-ZBMC | 73 |
| F-ZBMD | 74 |

**Eurocopter
EC.145**
Sécurité Civile
F-ZBPA
F-ZBPB
F-ZBPD
F-ZBPE
F-ZBPF
F-ZBPG
F-ZBPH
F-ZBPI
F-ZBPJ
F-ZBPK
F-ZBPL
F-ZBPM
F-ZBPN
F-ZBPO
F-ZBPP
F-ZBPQ
F-ZBPR
F-ZBPS
F-ZBPT

| | |
|---|---|
| F-ZBPU | |
| F-ZBPV | |
| F-ZBPW | |
| F-ZBPX | |
| F-ZBPY | |
| F-ZBPZ | |
| F-ZBQA | |
| F-ZBQB | |
| F-ZBQC | |
| F-ZBQD | |
| F-ZBQE | |
| F-ZBQF | |

**GERMANY**
**Luftwaffe, Marineflieger**
**Airbus A.310-304/MRTT\***
1/FBS, Köln-Bonn

| | |
|---|---|
| 10+21 | |
| 10+22 | |
| 10+23 | |
| 10+24\* | |
| 10+25\* | |
| 10+26\* | |
| 10+27\* | |

**Canadair**
**CL601-1A Challenger**
3/FBS, Köln-Bonn

| | |
|---|---|
| 12+02 | |
| 12+03 | |
| 12+04 | |
| 12+05 | |
| 12+06 | |
| 12+07 | |

**Eurofighter**
**EF.2000/EF.2000T\***
EADS, Manching;
JG-73 *Steinhoff*, Laage;
JG-74 *Molders*,
 Neuberg/Donau
TsLw-1, Kaufbeuren;
WTD-61, Ingolstadt

| | |
|---|---|
| 30+02\* | JG-73 |
| 30+03\* | JG-73 |
| 30+04\* | JG-73 |
| 30+05\* | JG-73 |
| 30+06 | JG-73 |
| 30+07 | TsLw-1 |
| 30+08 | JG-73 |
| 30+09 | JG-73 |
| 30+10\* | JG-73 |
| 30+11 | JG-73 |
| 30+12 | JG-73 |
| 30+13 | |
| 30+14\* | JG-73 |
| 30+15 | |
| 30+16 | |
| 30+17\* | JG-73 |
| 30+18 | |
| 30+19 | |
| 30+20\* | |
| 30+21 | |
| 30+22 | |
| 30+23 | |
| 30+24\* | |
| 30+25 | |
| 30+26 | |
| 30+27\* | |
| 98+03\* | EADS |
| 98+29 | WTD-61 |
| 98+30 | WTD-61 |
| 98+31\* | TsLw-1 |

**McD F-4F Phantom**
Fluglehrzentrum F-4F,
 Hopsten;
JG-71 *Richthofen*,
 Wittmundhaven;
JG-74 *Molders*, Neuburg/
 Donau;
TsLw-1, Kaufbeuren;
WTD-61, Ingolstadt

| | |
|---|---|
| 37+01 | FIZ F-4F |
| 37+03 | JG-71 |
| 37+04 | TsLw-1 |
| 37+11 | FIZ F-4F |
| 37+13 | JG-74 |
| 37+14 | TsLw-1 |
| 37+15 | WTD-61 |
| 37+16 | WTD-61 |
| 37+22 | JG-71 |
| 37+26 | JG-71 |
| 37+28 | JG-71 |
| 37+32 | JG-71 |
| 37+39 | FIZ F-4F |
| 37+48 | JG-71 |
| 37+55 | JG-71 |
| 37+61 | JG-74 |
| 37+63 | JG-71 |
| 37+65 | JG-71 |
| 37+71 | JG-74 |
| 37+75 | FIZ F-4F |
| 37+76 | JG-71 |
| 37+77 | JG-71 |
| 37+78 | JG-71 |
| 37+79 | JG-71 |
| 37+81 | JG-74 |
| 37+82 | JG-71 |
| 37+83 | FIZ F-4F |
| 37+84 | JG-71 |
| 37+85 | JG-71 |
| 37+86 | JG-71 |
| 37+87 | JG-71 |
| 37+88 | FIZ F-4F |
| 37+89 | JG-71 |
| 37+92 | JG-74 |
| 37+93 | FIZ F-4F |
| 37+94 | JG-74 |
| 37+96 | JG-74 |
| 37+98 | JG-71 |
| 38+00 | JG-71 |
| 38+01 | JG-71 |
| 38+02 | JG-74 |
| 38+03 | FIZ F-4F |
| 38+05 | FIZ F-4F |
| 38+06 | JG-74 |
| 38+07 | JG-71 |
| 38+09 | JG-74 |
| 38+10 | JG-74 |
| 38+12 | JG-71 |
| 38+13 | WTD-61 |
| 38+14 | JG-71 |
| 38+16 | JG-74 |
| 38+17 | JG-74 |
| 38+18 | JG-74 |
| 38+20 | FIZ F-4F |
| 38+24 | JG-74 |
| 38+26 | JG-74 |
| 38+27 | JG-71 |
| 38+28 | JG-71 |
| 38+29 | JG-74 |
| 38+30 | JG-74 |
| 38+31 | JG-74 |
| 38+32 | FIZ F-4F |
| 38+33 | JG-74 |
| 38+36 | JG-71 |
| 38+37 | FIZ F-4F |
| 38+39 | JG-74 |

| | |
|---|---|
| 38+40 | JG-71 |
| 38+42 | JG-71 |
| 38+43 | FIZ F-4F |
| 38+44 | JG-71 |
| 38+45 | JG-71 |
| 38+46 | JG-71 |
| 38+48 | JG-71 |
| 38+49 | JG-71 |
| 38+50 | FIZ F-4F |
| 38+53 | JG-74 |
| 38+54 | JG-71 |
| 38+55 | JG-71 |
| 38+56 | JG-71 |
| 38+57 | JG-74 |
| 38+58 | JG-71 |
| 38+60 | FIZ F-4F |
| 38+61 | FIZ F-4F |
| 38+62 | FIZ F-4F |
| 38+64 | JG-71 |
| 38+66 | FIZ F-4F |
| 38+67 | JG-71 |
| 38+68 | JG-74 |
| 38+69 | FIZ F-4F |
| 38+70 | JG-74 |
| 38+73 | FIZ F-4F |
| 38+74 | JG-71 |
| 38+75 | JG-71 |

**Panavia**
**Tornado Strike/**
**Trainer[1]/ECR[2]**
AkG-51 *Immelmann*,
 Schleswig/Jagel;
EADS, Manching;
GAFTTC, Holloman AFB,
 USA;
JbG-31 *Boelcke*,
 Nörvenich;
JbG-32, Lechfeld;
JbG-33, Büchel;
TsLw-1, Kaufbeuren;
WTD-61, Ingolstadt

| | |
|---|---|
| 43+01[1] | JbG-31 |
| 43+02[1] | AkG-51 |
| 43+07[1] | AkG-51 |
| 43+08[1] | JbG-32 |
| 43+10[1] | |
| 43+13 | EADS |
| 43+15[1] | |
| 43+17[1] | |
| 43+18 | JbG-31 |
| 43+20 | JbG-31 |
| 43+23[1] | JbG-33 |
| 43+25 | JbG-31 |
| 43+27 | JbG-31 |
| 43+28 | JbG-32 |
| 43+29[1] | JbG-31 |
| 43+31[1] | JbG-31 |
| 43+32 | JbG-31 |
| 43+33[1] | JbG-32 |
| 43+34 | TsLw-1 |
| 43+35[1] | AkG-51 |
| 43+37[1] | JbG-32 |
| 43+38 | JbG-31 |
| 43+41 | JbG-31 |
| 43+42[1] | GAFTTC |
| 43+43[1] | JbG-31 |
| 43+45[1] | JbG-32 |
| 43+46 | AkG-51 |
| 43+48 | AkG-51 |
| 43+52 | JbG-31 |
| 43+53 | JbG-33 |
| 43+54 | JbG-31 |
| 43+57 | GAFTTC |

| Reg. | Unit | Reg. | Unit | Reg. | Unit |
|---|---|---|---|---|---|
| 43+58 | JbG-33 | 44+63 | JbG-33 | 45+51 | AkG-51 |
| 43+59 | TsLw-1 | 44+64 | AkG-51 | 45+52 | JbG-33 |
| 43+60 | | 44+65 | AkG-51 | 45+53 | JbG-33 |
| 43+62 | JbG-33 | 44+66 | | 45+54 | GAFTTC |
| 43+63 | JbG-32 | 44+68 | AkG-51 | 45+55 | GAFTTC |
| 43+64 | | 44+69 | AkG-51 | 45+56 | JbG-31 |
| 43+65 | AkG-51 | 44+70 | JbG-31 | 45+57 | AkG-51 |
| 43+67 | | 44+71 | JbG-31 | 45+59 | JbG-31 |
| 43+70 | JbG-33 | 44+72[1] | AkG-51 | 45+61[1] | GAFTTC |
| 43+71 | JbG-32 | 44+73[1] | GAFTTC | 45+60[1] | AkG-51 |
| 43+72 | | 44+75[1] | JbG-31 | 45+64 | JbG-31 |
| 43+73 | AkG-51 | 44+76 | JbG-31 | 45+66 | |
| 43+75 | GAFTTC | 44+77 | JbG-31 | 45+67 | AkG-51 |
| 43+76 | | 44+78 | JbG-31 | 45+68 | JbG-31 |
| 43+77 | GAFTTC | 44+79 | JbG-33 | 45+69 | JbG-33 |
| 43+78 | TsLw-1 | 44+80 | JbG-31 | 45+70[1] | JbG-31 |
| 43+79 | AkG-51 | 44+81 | GAFTTC | 45+71 | JbG-32 |
| 43+81 | AkG-51 | 44+83 | JbG-33 | 45+72 | JbG-32 |
| 43+82 | AkG-51 | 44+85 | JbG-33 | 45+73[1] | GAFTTC |
| 43+85 | JbG-33 | 44+86 | AkG-51 | 45+74 | TsLw-1 |
| 43+86 | JbG-33 | 44+87 | AkG-51 | 45+76 | AkG-51 |
| 43+87 | AkG-51 | 44+88 | AkG-51 | 45+77[1] | JbG-31 |
| 43+90[1] | | 44+89 | JbG-32 | 45+78 | JbG-33 |
| 43+91[1] | GAFTTC | 44+90 | AkG-51 | 45+79 | JbG-31 |
| 43+92[1] | JbG-31 | 44+91 | JbG-33 | 45+81 | JbG-31 |
| 43+94[1] | JbG-33 | 44+92 | | 45+82 | JbG-31 |
| 43+96 | AkG-51 | 44+94 | JbG-33 | 45+84 | AkG-51 |
| 43+97[1] | AkG-51 | 44+95 | | 45+85 | AkG-51 |
| 43+98 | AkG-51 | 44+96 | JbG-31 | 45+86 | JbG-33 |
| 44+00 | JbG-31 | 44+97 | AkG-51 | 45+87 | JbG-33 |
| 44+01[1] | JbG-33 | 45+00 | | 45+88 | JbG-31 |
| 44+02 | GAFTTC | 45+01 | GAFTTC | 45+89 | AkG-51 |
| 44+04 | AkG-51 | 45+02 | JbG-31 | 45+90 | JbG-31 |
| 44+06 | AkG-51 | 45+03 | GAFTTC | 45+91 | AkG-51 |
| 44+07 | JbG-31 | 45+04 | JbG-33 | 45+92 | JbG-31 |
| 44+08 | | 45+06 | AkG-51 | 45+93 | AkG-51 |
| 44+09 | JbG-33 | 45+07 | JbG-33 | 45+94 | JbG-33 |
| 44+11 | JbG-33 | 45+08 | JbG-33 | 45+95 | JbG-31 |
| 44+12 | GAFTTC | 45+09 | JbG-33 | 45+98 | GAFTTC |
| 44+13 | TsLw-1 | 45+10 | JbG-32 | 45+99[1] | GAFTTC |
| 44+15 | AkG-51 | 45+11 | JbG-31 | 46+00[1] | GAFTTC |
| 44+16[1] | JbG-31 | 45+12[1] | | 46+01 | GAFTTC |
| 44+17 | AkG-51 | 45+13[1] | | 46+02 | JbG-33 |
| 44+19 | JbG-31 | 45+14[1] | JbG-31 | 46+04[1] | GAFTTC |
| 44+20[1] | GAFTTC | 45+15[1] | GAFTTC | 46+05[1] | AkG-51 |
| 44+21 | JbG-31 | 45+16[1] | JbG-32 | 46+07[1] | GAFTTC |
| 44+23 | JbG-33 | 45+17 | GAFTTC | 46+08[1] | GAFTTC |
| 44+26 | JbG-33 | 45+19 | JbG-33 | 46+09[1] | GAFTTC |
| 44+27 | JbG-33 | 45+20 | AkG-51 | 46+10 | WTD-61 |
| 44+29 | JbG-31 | 45+21 | JbG-33 | 46+11 | JbG-33 |
| 44+30 | JbG-31 | 45+22 | JbG-31 | 46+12 | |
| 44+32 | JbG-31 | 45+23 | JbG-31 | 46+13 | |
| 44+33 | JbG-33 | 45+24 | JbG-33 | 46+14 | AkG-51 |
| 44+34 | AkG-51 | 45+25 | JbG-31 | 46+15 | |
| 44+35 | JbG-31 | 45+28 | JbG-31 | 46+18 | JbG-33 |
| 44+37[1] | | 45+30 | AkG-51 | 46+19 | JbG-33 |
| 44+38[1] | GAFTTC | 45+31 | JbG-33 | 46+20 | AkG-51 |
| 44+39[1] | GAFTTC | 45+33 | AkG-51 | 46+21 | AkG-51 |
| 44+41 | JbG-31 | 45+34 | JbG-33 | 46+22 | AkG-51 |
| 44+42 | AkG-51 | 45+35 | | 46+23[2] | JbG-32 |
| 44+43 | JbG-31 | 45+36 | JbG-31 | 46+24[2] | JbG-32 |
| 44+44 | | 45+37 | JbG-33 | 46+25[2] | JbG-32 |
| 44+46 | JbG-33 | 45+38 | JbG-32 | 46+26[2] | JbG-32 |
| 44+49 | GAFTTC | 45+39 | JbG-31 | 46+27[2] | JbG-32 |
| 44+50 | AkG-51 | 45+40 | AkG-51 | 46+28[2] | JbG-32 |
| 44+52 | JbG-31 | 45+41 | JbG-32 | 46+29[2] | JbG-32 |
| 44+54 | JbG-33 | 45+42 | JbG-31 | 46+30[2] | JbG-32 |
| 44+55 | | 45+43 | JbG-32 | 46+31[2] | JbG-32 |
| 44+57 | JbG-31 | 45+44 | | 46+32[2] | JbG-32 |
| 44+58 | JbG-31 | 45+45 | JbG-31 | 46+33[2] | JbG-32 |
| 44+59 | GAFTTC | 45+46 | JbG-33 | 46+34[2] | JbG-32 |
| 44+60 | GAFTTC | 45+47 | TsLw-1 | 46+35[2] | JbG-32 |
| 44+61 | AkG-51 | 45+49 | | 46+36[2] | JbG-32 |
| 44+62 | JbG-31 | 45+50 | JbG-33 | 46+37[2] | JbG-32 |

# Germany

| | |
|---|---|
| 46+38[2] | JbG-32 |
| 46+39[2] | JbG-32 |
| 46+40[2] | WTD-61 |
| 46+41[2] | JbG-32 |
| 46+43[2] | JbG-32 |
| 46+44[2] | JbG-32 |
| 46+45[2] | JbG-32 |
| 46+46[2] | JbG-32 |
| 46+47[2] | JbG-32 |
| 46+48[2] | JbG-32 |
| 46+49[2] | JbG-32 |
| 46+50[2] | JbG-32 |
| 46+51[2] | JbG-32 |
| 46+52[2] | JbG-32 |
| 46+53[2] | JbG-32 |
| 46+54[2] | GAFTTC |
| 46+55[2] | JbG-32 |
| 46+56[2] | JbG-32 |
| 46+57[2] | JbG-32 |
| 98+59 | WTD-61 |
| 98+60 | WTD-61 |
| 98+77 | WTD-61 |
| 98+79[2] | WTD-61 |

**Transall C-160D**
LTG-61, Landsberg;
LTG-62, Wunstorf;
LTG-63, Hohn;
WTD-61, Ingolstadt

| | |
|---|---|
| 50+06 | LTG-63 |
| 50+07 | LTG-61 |
| 50+08 | LTG-63 |
| 50+09 | LTG-62 |
| 50+10 | LTG-62 |
| 50+17 | LTG-62 |
| 50+29 | LTG-63 |
| 50+33 | LTG-61 |
| 50+34 | LTG-63 |
| 50+35 | LTG-62 |
| 50+36 | LTG-62 |
| 50+37 | LTG-62 |
| 50+38 | LTG-62 |
| 50+40 | LTG-61 |
| 50+41 | LTG-62 |
| 50+42 | LTG-62 |
| 50+44 | LTG-61 |
| 50+45 | LTG-63 |
| 50+46 | LTG-62 |
| 50+47 | LTG-61 |
| 50+48 | LTG-62 |
| 50+49 | LTG-63 |
| 50+50 | LTG-62 |
| 50+51 | LTG-61 |
| 50+52 | LTG-62 |
| 50+53 | LTG-61 |
| 50+54 | LTG-62 |
| 50+55 | LTG-62 |
| 50+56 | LTG-63 |
| 50+57 | LTG-62 |
| 50+58 | LTG-62 |
| 50+59 | LTG-63 |
| 50+60 | LTG-62 |
| 50+61 | LTG-63 |
| 50+62 | LTG-62 |
| 50+64 | LTG-61 |
| 50+65 | LTG-62 |
| 50+66 | LTG-61 |
| 50+67 | LTG-63 |
| 50+68 | LTG-61 |
| 50+69 | LTG-61 |
| 50+70 | LTG-62 |
| 50+71 | LTG-63 |
| 50+72 | LTG-63 |

| | |
|---|---|
| 50+73 | LTG-61 |
| 50+74 | LTG-61 |
| 50+75 | LTG-63 |
| 50+76 | LTG-63 |
| 50+77 | LTG-63 |
| 50+78 | LTG-62 |
| 50+79 | LTG-62 |
| 50+81 | LTG-62 |
| 50+82 | LTG-62 |
| 50+83 | LTG-62 |
| 50+84 | LTG-61 |
| 50+85 | LTG-63 |
| 50+86 | LTG-61 |
| 50+87 | LTG-63 |
| 50+88 | LTG-61 |
| 50+89 | LTG-62 |
| 50+90 | LTG-62 |
| 50+91 | LTG-62 |
| 50+92 | LTG-61 |
| 50+93 | LTG-62 |
| 50+94 | LTG-63 |
| 50+95 | LTG-63 |
| 50+96 | LTG-61 |
| 50+97 | LTG-62 |
| 50+98 | LTG-61 |
| 50+99 | LTG-61 |
| 51+00 | LTG-62 |
| 51+01 | LTG-62 |
| 51+02 | WTD-61 |
| 51+03 | LTG-62 |
| 51+04 | LTG-61 |
| 51+05 | LTG-62 |
| 51+06 | LTG-63 |
| 51+07 | LTG-62 |
| 51+08 | WTD-61 |
| 51+09 | LTG-63 |
| 51+10 | LTG-63 |
| 51+11 | LTG-62 |
| 51+12 | LTG-63 |
| 51+13 | LTG-63 |
| 51+14 | LTG-62 |
| 51+15 | LTG-61 |

**Dornier Do.228/Do.228LM***
MFG-3, Nordholz

| | |
|---|---|
| 57+01* | |
| 57+02* | |
| 57+03 | |
| 57+04* | |

**Lockheed
P-3C Orion**
MFG-3, Nordholz

| | |
|---|---|
| 60+01 | |
| 60+02 | |
| 60+04 | |
| 60+05 | |
| 60+06 | |
| 60+07 | |
| 60+08 | |
| 98+01 | |

**Breguet Br.1150 Atlantic
*Elint**
MFG-3, Nordholz

| | |
|---|---|
| 61+03* | |
| 61+04 | |
| 61+05 | |
| 61+06* | |
| 61+09 | |
| 61+10 | |
| 61+11 | |
| 61+12 | |
| 61+19* | |

61+20

**Eurocopter
AS.532U-2 Cougar**
3/FBS, Berlin-Tegel

| | |
|---|---|
| 82+01 | |
| 82+02 | |
| 82+03 | |

**Westland
Lynx Mk88/
Super Lynx Mk88A***
MFG-3, Nordholz

| | |
|---|---|
| 83+02* | |
| 83+03* | |
| 83+04* | |
| 83+05* | |
| 83+06* | |
| 83+07* | |
| 83+09* | |
| 83+10* | |
| 83+11* | |
| 83+12* | |
| 83+13* | |
| 83+15* | |
| 83+17 | |
| 83+18* | |
| 83+19* | |
| 83+20* | |
| 83+21* | |
| 83+22* | |
| 83+23* | |
| 83+24* | |
| 83+25* | |
| 83+26* | |

**Westland
Sea King HAS41**
MFG-5, Kiel-Holtenau

| | |
|---|---|
| 89+50 | |
| 89+51 | |
| 89+52 | |
| 89+53 | |
| 89+54 | |
| 89+55 | |
| 89+56 | |
| 89+57 | |
| 89+58 | |
| 89+60 | |
| 89+61 | |
| 89+62 | |
| 89+63 | |
| 89+64 | |
| 89+65 | |
| 89+66 | |
| 89+67 | |
| 89+68 | |
| 89+69 | |
| 89+70 | |
| 89+71 | |

**NH Industries
NH.90**

| | |
|---|---|
| 98+90 | |
| 98+91 | |

**Heeresfliegertruppe
Eurocopter
AS.665 Tiger**
WTD-61, Ingolstadt

| | |
|---|---|
| 74+05 | |
| 74+06 | |
| 74+07 | |
| 74+08 | |

| Serial | Unit | Serial | Unit | Serial | Unit |
|---|---|---|---|---|---|
| 74+09 | | 84+41 | HFWS | HFWS, Bückeburg; | |
| 74+10 | | 84+42* | MTHR-25 | KHR-26, Roth; | |
| 74+11 | | 84+43 | MTHR-25 | KHR-36, Fritzlar; | |
| 74+12 | | 84+44 | MTHR-25 | TsLw-3, Fassberg; | |
| 74+13 | | 84+45* | MTHR-25 | WTD-61, Ingolstadt | |
| 74+14 | | 84+46 | MTHR-15 | 86+01 | |
| 74+15 | | 84+47 | MTHR-25 | 86+02 | KHR-36 |
| 98+12 | | 84+48 | HFWS | 86+03 | HFWS |
| 98+13 | | 84+49 | HFWS | 86+04 | KHR-36 |
| 98+14 | | 84+50 | HFWS | 86+05 | HFWS |
| 98+23 | | 84+51* | MTHR-25 | 86+06 | HFWS |
| 98+25 | | 84+52* | MTHR-25 | 86+07 | HFWS |
| 98+26 | | 84+53 | MTHR-25 | 86+08 | HFWS |
| 98+27 | | 84+54 | MTHR-25 | 86+09 | HFWS |
| | | 84+55 | MTHR-25 | 86+10 | HFVAS-100 |
| **Eurocopter EC.135P-1** | | 84+57 | HFWS | 86+11 | HFVAS-300 |
| HFWS, Bückeburg | | 84+58 | MTHR-25 | 86+12 | HFWS |
| 82+51 | | 84+59 | MTHR-25 | 86+13 | HFWS |
| 82+52 | | 84+60 | MTHR-25 | 86+14 | HFVAS-100 |
| 82+53 | | 84+62* | MTHR-25 | 86+15 | |
| 82+54 | | 84+63 | MTHR-25 | 86+16 | HFWS |
| 82+55 | | 84+64* | MTHR-25 | 86+17 | HFVS-910 |
| 82+56 | | 84+65 | MTHR-25 | 86+18 | KHR-26 |
| 82+57 | | 84+66* | MTHR-25 | 86+19 | HFWS |
| 82+59 | | 84+67* | MTHR-15 | 86+20 | HFWS |
| 82+60 | | 84+68 | MTHR-15 | 86+21 | HFVAS-100 |
| 82+61 | | 84+69 | MTHR-15 | 86+22 | HFVAS-100 |
| 82+62 | | 84+70 | MTHR-15 | 86+23 | TsLw-3 |
| 82+63 | | 84+71 | MTHR-15 | 86+24 | HFVS-910 |
| 82+64 | | 84+72 | MTHR-15 | 86+25 | HFVAS-100 |
| 82+65 | | 84+73* | MTHR-15 | 86+26 | HFVS-910 |
| | | 84+74 | MTHR-15 | 86+27 | KHR-26 |
| **Sikorsky/VFW** | | 84+75 | MTHR-15 | 86+28 | HFWS |
| **CH-53G/CH-53GS*** | | 84+76 | HFWS | 86+29 | HFVS-910 |
| HFWS, Bückeburg; | | 84+77 | MTHR-15 | 86+30 | KHR-26 |
| MTHR-15, Rheine-Bentlage; | | 84+78 | HFWS | 86+31 | |
| MTHR-25, Laupheim; | | 84+79* | MTHR-15 | 86+32 | KHR-26 |
| TsLw-3, Fassberg; | | 84+80 | MTHR-15 | 86+33 | KHR-26 |
| WTD-61, Ingolstadt | | 84+82 | MTHR-15 | 86+34 | HFUS-1 |
| 84+01* | WTD-61 | 84+83 | MTHR-15 | 86+35 | KHR-26 |
| 84+02 | WTD-61 | 84+84 | MTHR-15 | 86+36 | HFVAS-100 |
| 84+05 | HFWS | 84+85* | MTHR-25 | 86+37 | |
| 84+06 | MTHR-15 | 84+86 | MTHR-15 | 86+38 | KHR-36 |
| 84+09 | TsLw-3 | 84+87 | MTHR-15 | 86+39 | HFWS |
| 84+10 | HFWS | 84+88 | MTHR-15 | 86+41 | HFVAS-100 |
| 84+11 | HFWS | 84+89 | MTHR-15 | 86+42 | KHR-26 |
| 84+12 | MTHR-15 | 84+90 | MTHR-15 | 86+43 | |
| 84+13 | HFWS | 84+91* | MTHR-25 | 86+44 | HFWS |
| 84+14 | HFWS | 84+92 | MTHR-15 | 86+45 | |
| 84+15* | MTHR-25 | 84+94 | | 86+46 | HFWS |
| 84+16 | HFWS | 84+95 | MTHR-25 | 86+47 | HFVAS-100 |
| 84+17 | MTHR-25 | 84+96 | MTHR-25 | 86+48 | HFVAS-100 |
| 84+18 | HFWS | 84+97 | MTHR-25 | 86+49 | KHR-36 |
| 84+19 | TsLw-3 | 84+98* | MTHR-15 | 86+50 | KHR-36 |
| 84+21 | HFWS | 84+99 | MTHR-15 | 86+51 | HFVS-910 |
| 84+22 | MTHR-15 | 85+00* | HFWS | 86+52 | |
| 84+23 | | 85+01 | MTHR-25 | 86+53 | HFVAS-100 |
| 84+24 | MTHR-15 | 85+02 | MTHR-15 | 86+54 | |
| 84+25* | | 85+03 | MTHR-15 | 86+55 | HFVAS-300 |
| 84+26 | MTHR-15 | 85+04 | MTHR-15 | 86+56 | KHR-36 |
| 84+27 | HFWS | 85+05 | MTHR-15 | 86+57 | |
| 84+28 | MTHR-25 | 85+06 | MTHR-25 | 86+58 | KHR-36 |
| 84+29 | MTHR-15 | 85+07* | HFWS | 86+59 | HFVAS-100 |
| 84+30* | MTHR-15 | 85+08 | MTHR-15 | 86+60 | HFWS |
| 84+31 | MTHR-15 | 85+10* | | 86+61 | KHR-26 |
| 84+32 | MTHR-25 | 85+11 | MTHR-25 | 86+62 | HFVS-910 |
| 84+33 | | 85+12* | MTHR-15 | 86+63 | KHR-26 |
| 84+34 | MTHR-15 | | | 86+64 | KHR-26 |
| 84+35 | | **MBB Bo.105P** | | 86+65 | KHR-26 |
| 84+36 | WTD-61 | HFR-35, Mendig; | | 86+66 | HFVS-910 |
| 84+37 | HFWS | HFUS-1, Holzdorf; | | 86+67 | HFVAS-100 |
| 84+38 | MTHR-25 | HFVAS-100, Celle; | | 86+68 | KHR-36 |
| 84+39 | MTHR-15 | HFVAS-300, Mendig; | | 86+69 | KHR-26 |
| 84+40 | MTHR-25 | HFVS-910, Bückeburg; | | 86+70 | HFVAS-100 |

| | |
|---|---|
| 86+71 | KHR-36 |
| 86+72 | HFVAS-300 |
| 86+73 | KHR-36 |
| 86+74 | KHR-36 |
| 86+75 | KHR-36 |
| 86+76 | KHR-26 |
| 86+77 | HFUS-1 |
| 86+78 | HFVAS-300 |
| 86+79 | HFVAS-300 |
| 86+80 | |
| 86+81 | KHR-36 |
| 86+83 | TsLw-3 |
| 86+84 | KHR-26 |
| 86+85 | HFUS-1 |
| 86+86 | HFVAS-100 |
| 86+87 | |
| 86+88 | |
| 86+89 | HFUS-1 |
| 86+90 | KHR-26 |
| 86+91 | KHR-26 |
| 86+92 | KHR-36 |
| 86+93 | HFVS-910 |
| 86+94 | KHR-26 |
| 86+95 | HFUS-1 |
| 86+96 | KHR-26 |
| 86+97 | KHR-36 |
| 86+98 | HFVAS-300 |
| 86+99 | TsLw-3 |
| 87+00 | KHR-26 |
| 87+01 | KHR-26 |
| 87+02 | KHR-26 |
| 87+03 | TsLw-3 |
| 87+04 | HFVAS-300 |
| 87+06 | KHR-36 |
| 87+07 | KHR-26 |
| 87+08 | KHR-26 |
| 87+09 | HFWS |
| 87+10 | KHR-26 |
| 87+11 | KHR-36 |
| 87+12 | KHR-36 |
| 87+13 | KHR-36 |
| 87+14 | KHR-36 |
| 87+15 | KHR-36 |
| 87+16 | HFVAS-100 |
| 87+17 | KHR-36 |
| 87+18 | HFVAS-100 |
| 87+19 | KHR-36 |
| 87+20 | KHR-26 |
| 87+21 | TsLw-3 |
| 87+22 | |
| 87+23 | HFVAS-100 |
| 87+24 | |
| 87+25 | KHR-26 |
| 87+26 | HFUS-1 |
| 87+27 | HFVAS-100 |
| 87+28 | HFUS-1 |
| 87+29 | HFVS-910 |
| 87+30 | HFVAS-300 |
| 87+31 | |
| 87+32 | HFWS |
| 87+33 | KHR-26 |
| 87+34 | KHR-26 |
| 87+35 | KHR-26 |
| 87+36 | HFWS |
| 87+37 | KHR-26 |
| 87+38 | KHR-36 |
| 87+39 | KHR-36 |
| 87+41 | KHR-36 |
| 87+42 | KHR-36 |
| 87+43 | KHR-36 |
| 87+44 | KHR-36 |
| 87+45 | HFUS-1 |
| 87+46 | KHR-36 |
| 87+47 | HFWS |

| | |
|---|---|
| 87+48 | HFVAS-100 |
| 87+49 | HFVAS-100 |
| 87+50 | KHR-26 |
| 87+51 | HFVAS-100 |
| 87+52 | HFUS-1 |
| 87+53 | KHR-26 |
| 87+55 | HFVS-910 |
| 87+56 | TsLw-3 |
| 87+57 | KHR-26 |
| 87+58 | HFWS |
| 87+59 | KHR-36 |
| 87+60 | KHR-36 |
| 87+61 | KHR-36 |
| 87+62 | HFWS |
| 87+63 | HFWS |
| 87+64 | HFWS |
| 87+65 | KHR-36 |
| 87+66 | KHR-36 |
| 87+67 | HFVAS-100 |
| 87+68 | HFWS |
| 87+69 | KHR-26 |
| 87+70 | HFVAS-300 |
| 87+71 | KHR-26 |
| 87+72 | HFVAS-300 |
| 87+73 | HFWS |
| 87+74 | KHR-36 |
| 87+75 | KHR-26 |
| 87+76 | HFVAS-300 |
| 87+77 | |
| 87+78 | |
| 87+79 | |
| 87+80 | HFUS-1 |
| 87+81 | TsLw-3 |
| 87+82 | |
| 87+83 | |
| 87+84 | HFVS-910 |
| 87+85 | HFVAS-300 |
| 87+86 | KHR-26 |
| 87+87 | HFVAS-300 |
| 87+88 | KHR-26 |
| 87+89 | KHR-36 |
| 87+90 | HFWS |
| 87+91 | HFVAS-300 |
| 87+92 | KHR-26 |
| 87+94 | KHR-26 |
| 87+95 | KHR-26 |
| 87+96 | KHR-26 |
| 87+97 | KHR-26 |
| 87+98 | KHR-26 |
| 87+99 | KHR-36 |
| 88+01 | KHR-36 |
| 88+02 | KHR-36 |
| 88+03 | KHR-36 |
| 88+04 | KHR-36 |
| 88+05 | HFVS-910 |
| 88+06 | KHR-36 |
| 88+07 | HFVAS-100 |
| 88+08 | KHR-36 |
| 88+09 | HFR-35 |
| 88+10 | HFVS-910 |
| 88+11 | KHR-36 |
| 88+12 | HFVAS-100 |

## GHANA
**Ghana Air Force**
**Fokker**
F-28 Fellowship 3000
VIP Flight, Accra
G-530

**Grumman**
**G.1159A Gulfstream III**
VIP Flight, Accra
G-540

## GREECE
**Elliniki Polemiki Aeroporía**
**Dassault Mirage 2000**
331 MAPK/114 PM,
Tanagra;
332 MAPK/114 PM, Tanagra

**Mirage 2000BG**

| | |
|---|---|
| 201 | 331 MAPK |
| 202 | 332 MAPK |
| 204 | 332 MAPK |

**Mirage 2000EG**

| | |
|---|---|
| 210 | 332 MAPK |
| 212 | 332 MAPK |
| 213 | 331 MAPK |
| 216 | 332 MAPK |
| 217 | 331 MAPK |
| 218 | 332 MAPK |
| 219 | 331 MAPK |
| 220 | 331 MAPK |
| 221 | 331 MAPK |
| 222 | 332 MAPK |
| 226 | 332 MAPK |
| 228 | 332 MAPK |
| 230 | 332 MAPK |
| 231 | 331 MAPK |
| 232 | 332 MAPK |
| 233 | 331 MAPK |
| 234 | 332 MAPK |
| 235 | 331 MAPK |
| 236 | 332 MAPK |
| 237 | 331 MAPK |
| 239 | 331 MAPK |
| 240 | 332 MAPK |
| 241 | 331 MAPK |
| 242 | 332 MAPK |
| 243 | 331 MAPK |
| 245 | 331 MAPK |

**Mirage 2000-5 (two-seat)**

| | |
|---|---|
| 505 | 331/332 MAPK |
| 506 | 331/332 MAPK |
| 507 | 331/332 MAPK |
| 508 | 331/332 MAPK |
| 509 | 331/332 MAPK |

**Mirage 2000-5**

| | |
|---|---|
| 511 | 331/332 MAPK |
| 514 | 331/332 MAPK |
| 511 | 331/332 MAPK |
| 527 | 331/332 MAPK |
| 547 | 331/332 MAPK |
| 548 | 331/332 MAPK |
| 549 | 331/332 MAPK |
| 550 | 331/332 MAPK |
| 551 | 331/332 MAPK |
| 552 | 331/332 MAPK |
| 553 | 331/332 MAPK |
| 554 | 331/332 MAPK |
| 555 | 331/332 MAPK |

**Embraer**
**ERJ-135BJ Legacy/ERJ.
145H/ERJ.135LR**
356 MTM/112 PM, Elefsís;
380 Mira/112 PM, Elefsís

| | | |
|---|---|---|
| 135L-484 | ERJ-135BJ | 356 MTM |
| 145-209 | ERJ-135LR | 356 MTM |
| 145-374 | ERJ-145H | 380 Mira |
| 145-671 | ERJ-145H | 380 Mira |
| 145-729 | ERJ-145H | 380 Mira |
| 145-757 | ERJ-145H | 380 Mira |

**Gulfstream Aerospace**
**Gulfstream V**
356 MTM/112 PM, Elefsís
678

**Lockheed**
**C-130H Hercules**
356 MTM/112 PM, Elefsís
*ECM
741*
742
743
744
745
746
747*
749
751
752

**Lockheed**
**F-16C/F-16D***
**Fighting Falcon**
330 Mira/111 PM,
  Nea Ankhialos;
334 Mira/115PM, Souda;
340 Mira/115PM, Souda;
341 Mira/111 PM,
  Nea Ankhialos;
343 Mira/115PM, Souda;
346 MAPK/110 PM, Larissa;
347 Mira/111 PM,
  Nea Ankhialos

| | |
|---|---|
| 046 | 341 Mira |
| 047 | 347 Mira |
| 048 | 341 Mira |
| 049 | 347 Mira |
| 050 | 341 Mira |
| 051 | 347 Mira |
| 052 | 341 Mira |
| 053 | 347 Mira |
| 054 | 341 Mira |
| 055 | 347 Mira |
| 056 | 341 Mira |
| 057 | 347 Mira |
| 058 | 341 Mira |
| 059 | 347 Mira |
| 060 | 341 Mira |
| 061 | 347 Mira |
| 062 | 341 Mira |
| 063 | 347 Mira |
| 064 | 341 Mira |
| 065 | 347 Mira |
| 066 | 347 Mira |
| 067 | 347 Mira |
| 068 | 341 Mira |
| 069 | 347 Mira |
| 070 | 341 Mira |
| 071 | 347 Mira |
| 072 | 341 Mira |
| 073 | 347 Mira |
| 074 | 347 Mira |
| 075 | 341 Mira |
| 076 | 341 Mira |
| 077* | 341 Mira |
| 078* | 347 Mira |
| 079* | 347 Mira |
| 080* | 347 Mira |
| 081* | 347 Mira |
| 082* | 341 Mira |
| 083* | 347 Mira |
| 084* | 341 Mira |
| 110 | 330 Mira |
| 111 | 330 Mira |
| 112 | 346 MAPK |
| 113 | 330 Mira |
| 114 | 346 MAPK |
| 115 | 330 Mira |
| 116 | 330 Mira |

| | |
|---|---|
| 117 | 330 Mira |
| 118 | 346 MAPK |
| 119 | 330 Mira |
| 120 | 346 MAPK |
| 121 | 330 Mira |
| 122 | 346 MAPK |
| 124 | 346 MAPK |
| 125 | 330 Mira |
| 126 | 346 MAPK |
| 127 | 330 Mira |
| 128 | 346 MAPK |
| 129 | 330 Mira |
| 130 | 346 MAPK |
| 132 | 346 MAPK |
| 133 | 330 Mira |
| 134 | 346 MAPK |
| 136 | 346 MAPK |
| 138 | 346 MAPK |
| 139 | 330 Mira |
| 140 | 346 MAPK |
| 141 | 330 Mira |
| 143 | 330 Mira |
| 144* | 330 Mira |
| 145* | 330 Mira |
| 146* | 346 MAPK |
| 147* | 330 Mira |
| 148* | 346 MAPK |
| 149* | 330 Mira |
| 500 | 343 Mira |
| 501 | 334/340 Mira |
| 502 | 334/340 Mira |
| 503 | 343 Mira |
| 504 | 334/340 Mira |
| 505 | 343 Mira |
| 506 | 334/340 Mira |
| 507 | 334/340 Mira |
| 508 | 334/340 Mira |
| 509 | 334/340 Mira |
| 510 | 334/340 Mira |
| 511 | 334/340 Mira |
| 512 | 334/340 Mira |
| 513 | 343 Mira |
| 514 | 343 Mira |
| 515 | 334/340 Mira |
| 516 | 334/340 Mira |
| 517 | 334/340 Mira |
| 518 | 334/340 Mira |
| 519 | 334/340 Mira |
| 520 | 334/340 Mira |
| 521 | 334/340 Mira |
| 522 | 334/340 Mira |
| 523 | 334/340 Mira |
| 524 | 334/340 Mira |
| 525 | 334/340 Mira |
| 526 | 334/340 Mira |
| 527 | 334/340 Mira |
| 528 | 334/340 Mira |
| 529 | 334/340 Mira |
| 530 | 334/340 Mira |
| 531 | 334/340 Mira |
| 532 | 334/340 Mira |
| 533 | 340 Mira |
| 534 | 340 Mira |
| 535 | 334/340 Mira |
| 536 | 340 Mira |
| 537 | 334/340 Mira |
| 538 | 334/340 Mira |
| 539 | 334/340 Mira |
| 600* | 334/340 Mira |
| 601* | 334/340 Mira |
| 602* | 334/340 Mira |
| 603* | 334/340 Mira |
| 604* | 334/340 Mira |
| 605* | 334/340 Mira |

| | |
|---|---|
| 606* | 334/340 Mira |
| 607* | 334/340 Mira |
| 608* | 334/340 Mira |
| 609* | 334/340 Mira |
| 610* | 340 Mira |
| 611* | 334/340 Mira |
| 612* | 334/340 Mira |
| 613* | 334/340 Mira |
| 614* | 334/340 Mira |
| 615* | 334/340 Mira |
| 616* | 334/340 Mira |
| 617* | 334/340 Mira |
| 618* | 334/340 Mira |
| 619* | 334/340 Mira |

**HUNGARY**
**Magyar Honvédseg Repülö**
**Csapatai**
**Antonov An-26**
89 VSD, Szolnok
110
405
406
407
603

**Mikoyan**
**MiG-29/29UB***
59 HRO, Kecskemét
01
03
04
05
06
07
08
09
10
11
12
14
15
16
18
19
20
21
23
24*
25*
26*
27*
28*
29*

**SAAB 39C/39D Gripen***
59 HRO, Kecskemét
30
31
32
33
34
35
36
37
38
39
40
41
42*
43*

**ISRAEL**

**Heyl ha'Avir**

**Boeing 707**

| | | |
|---|---|---|
| 120 | Sqn, Tel Aviv | |
| 120 | RC-707 | |
| 128 | RC-707 | |
| 137 | RC-707 | |
| 140 | KC-707 | |
| 242 | VC-707 | |
| 248 | KC-707 | |
| 250 | KC-707 | |
| 255 | EC-707 | |
| 260 | KC-707 | |
| 264 | RC-707 | |
| 272 | VC-707 | |
| 275 | KC-707 | |
| 290 | KC-707 | |

**Lockheed**

**C-130 Hercules**

103 Sqn & 131 Sqn, Tel Aviv

| | |
|---|---|
| 102 | C-130H |
| 106 | C-130H |
| 208 | C-130E |
| 305 | C-130E |
| 309 | C-130E |
| 310 | C-130E |
| 313 | C-130E |
| 314 | C-130E |
| 316 | C-130E |
| 420 | KC-130H |
| 427 | C-130H |
| 428 | C-130H |
| 435 | C-130H |
| 436 | C-130H |
| 522 | KC-130H |
| 545 | KC-130H |

**ITALY**

**Aeronautica Militare Italiana**

**Aeritalia G222/C-27J**

9ª Brigata Aerea,
Pratica di Mare:
14° Stormo/8° Gruppo;
RSV, Pratica di Mare

**G222AAA**

| | | |
|---|---|---|
| CSX62144 | RS-44 | RSV |

**G222RM**

| | | |
|---|---|---|
| MM62139 | 14-20 | 8 |
| MM62140 | 14-21 | 8 |
| MM62141 | 14-22 | 8 |

**G222TCM**

| | | |
|---|---|---|
| MM62125 | 14-24 | 8 |
| MM62152 | RS-45 | RSV |
| MM62153X | RS-46 | RSV |

**G222VS**

| | |
|---|---|
| MM62107 | 8 |

**C-27J**

| | |
|---|---|
| MMCSX62127 | Alenia |
| MMCSX62216 | Alenia |

**Aeritalia-EMB AMX/AMX-T***

32° Stormo, Amendola:
13° Gruppo &
101° Gruppo;
51° Stormo, Istrana:
103° Gruppo &
132° Gruppo;
RSV, Pratica di Mare

| | |
|---|---|
| MMX595 | Alenia |
| MMX596 | Alenia |
| MMX597 | Alenia |
| MMX599 | Alenia |
| MM7089 | |

| | | |
|---|---|---|
| MM7090 | | |
| MM7092 | RS-14 | RSV |
| MM7093 | | |
| MM7094 | 3-37 | |
| MM7096 | | |
| MM7097 | 3-36 | |
| MM7098 | 3-35 | |
| MM7099 | | |
| MM7100 | 32-66 | 101 |
| MM7101 | | |
| MM7103 | | |
| MM7104 | 51-26 | 103 |
| MM7106 | 3-25 | |
| MM7107 | | |
| MM7110 | | |
| MM7111 | | |
| MM7115 | 2-12 | |
| MM7116 | 32-11 | 13 |
| MM7117 | 3-34 | |
| MM7118 | 2-11 | |
| MM7119 | | |
| MM7120 | | |
| MM7122 | 3-32 | |
| MM7123 | | |
| MM7124 | 51-15 | 103 |
| MM7125 | RS-11 | RSV |
| MM7126 | | |
| MM7127 | 3-24 | |
| MM7128 | | |
| MM7131 | 52-43 | 132 |
| MM7132 | 51-12 | 103 |
| MM7133 | 51-30 | 132 |
| MM7134 | 51-07 | 103 |
| MM7135 | 51-32 | 132 |
| MM7138 | | |
| MM7139 | 51-24 | 103 |
| MM7141 | | |
| MM7142 | 51-37 | 132 |
| MM7143 | 51-21 | 103 |
| MM7144 | 51-41 | 132 |
| MM7145 | 51-44 | 132 |
| MM7146 | | |
| MM7147 | 32-04 | 13 |
| MM7148 | 51-50 | 132 |
| MM7149 | | |
| MM7150 | | |
| MM7151 | 51-27 | 103 |
| MM7152 | 51-03 | 103 |
| MM7154 | | |
| MM7155 | 32-05 | 13 |
| MM7156 | | |
| MM7157 | | |
| CSX7158 | RS-12 | RSV |
| MM7159 | 51-11 | 103 |
| MM7160 | 32-14 | 13 |
| MM7161 | 2-21 | |
| MM7162 | 51-01 | 103 |
| MM7163 | 32-23 | 13 |
| MM7164 | 51-34 | 132 |
| MM7165 | 51-45 | 132 |
| MM7166 | 32-02 | 13 |
| MM7167 | 51-37 | 132 |
| MM7168 | 51-30 | 132 |
| MM7169 | 32-26 | 13 |
| MM7170 | 51-35 | 132 |
| MM7171 | | |
| MM7172 | 51-42 | 132 |
| MM7173 | | |
| MM7174 | 51-25 | 103 |
| MM7175 | | |
| MM7176 | 51-46 | 132 |
| MM7178 | 32-24 | 13 |
| MM7179 | 51-47 | 132 |
| MM7180 | 32-20 | 13 |

| | | |
|---|---|---|
| MM7182 | 51-52 | 132 |
| MM7183 | 32-22 | 13 |
| MM7184 | 51-54 | 132 |
| MM7185 | 51-55 | 132 |
| MM7186 | 51-05 | 103 |
| MM7189 | | |
| MM7190 | 32-17 | 13 |
| MM7191 | 32-01 | 13 |
| MM7192 | 51-23 | 103 |
| MM7193 | | |
| MM7194 | 32-07 | 13 |
| MM7195 | | |
| MM7196 | 32-13 | 13 |
| MM7197 | 32-21 | 13 |
| MM7198 | | |
| MM55024* | 15 | RSV |
| MM55025* | RS-16 | RSV |
| MM55026* | 32-43 | 101 |
| MM55027* | | |
| MM55029* | 32-50 | 101 |
| MM55030* | 32-41 | 101 |
| MM55031* | 32-40 | 101 |
| MM55034* | RS-18 | RSV |
| MM55035* | | |
| MM55036* | 32-51 | 101 |
| MM55037* | 32-64 | 101 |
| MM55039* | 32-54 | 101 |
| MM55041* | 32-55 | 101 |
| MM55042* | 32-56 | 101 |
| MM55043* | 32-65 | 101 |
| MM55044* | 32-57 | 101 |
| MM55046* | 32-47 | 101 |
| MM55047* | 32-45 | 101 |
| MM55048* | 32-44 | 101 |
| MM55049* | 32-46 | 101 |
| MM55050* | 32-43 | 101 |
| MM55051* | 32-42 | 101 |

**Aermacchi**

**MB339A/MB339CD***

36° Stormo, Gioia del Colle:
12° Gruppo;
51° Stormo, Istrana:
651° SC;
61° Stormo, Lecce:
212° Gruppo &
213° Gruppo;
Aermacchi, Venegono;
Frecce Tricolori [FT]
(313° Gruppo), Rivolto
(MB339A/PAN);
RSV, Pratica di Mare

| | | |
|---|---|---|
| MMX606* | | RSV |
| MM54440 | 61-00 | |
| MM54441 | 61-71 | |
| MM54442 | 61-112 | |
| MM54443 | 61-50 | |
| MM54445 | 61-25 | |
| MM54446 | 61-01 | |
| MM54447 | 61-02 | |
| MM54451 | 61-116 | |
| MM54452 | | |
| MM54453 | 61-05 | |
| MM54456 | 61-10 | |
| MM54457 | 61-11 | |
| MM54458 | 61-12 | |
| MM54459 | 61-13 | |
| MM54462 | 61-16 | |
| MM54463 | 61-17 | |
| MM54465 | 51-77 | |
| MM54467 | 61-23 | |
| MM54468 | 61-24 | |
| MM54471 | 61-27 | |
| MM54472 | 61-30 | |

| | | | |
|---|---|---|---|
| MM54473 | | [FT] | |
| MM54475 | 1 | [FT] | |
| MM54477 | | [FT] | |
| MM54478 | | [FT] | |
| MM54479 | | [FT] | |
| MM54480 | | [FT] | |
| MM54482 | | [FT] | |
| MM54483 | 61-102 | | |
| MM54484 | 61-101 | | |
| MM54485 | 2 | [FT] | |
| MM54486 | 5 | [FT] | |
| MM54487 | 10 | [FT] | |
| MM54488 | 61-32 | | |
| MM54489 | 61-33 | | |
| MM54490 | 61-34 | | |
| MM54491 | 51-76 | | |
| MM54492 | 61-36 | | |
| MM54493 | 61-37 | | |
| MM54494 | 51-75 | | |
| MM54496 | 61-42 | | |
| MM54498 | 61-44 | | |
| MM54499 | 61-45 | | |
| MM54500 | 9 | [FT] | |
| MM54503 | 61-51 | | |
| MM54504 | 61-52 | | |
| MM54505 | 4 | [FT] | |
| MM54506 | 51-74 | | |
| MM54507 | 61-55 | | |
| MM54508 | 61-56 | | |
| MM54509 | 61-57 | | |
| MM54510 | 61-60 | | |
| MM54511 | 61-61 | | |
| MM54512 | 61-62 | | |
| MM54514 | 61-64 | | |
| MM54515 | 61-65 | | |
| MM54516 | 61-66 | | |
| MM54517 | 6 | [FT] | |
| MM54518 | 61-70 | | |
| MM54532 | | | |
| MM54533 | 61-72 | | |
| MM54534 | 61-73 | | |
| MM54535 | 61-74 | | |
| MM54536 | 8 | [FT] | |
| MM54537 | | | |
| MM54538 | 61-75 | | |
| MM54539 | 61-76 | | |
| MM54541 | 61-100 | | |
| MM54542 | | [FT] | |
| MM54543 | 3 | [FT] | |
| MM54545 | 61-84 | | |
| MM54546 | 8 | [FT] | |
| MM54547 | 7 | [FT] | |
| MM54548 | 61-90 | | |
| MM54549 | 61-107 | | |
| MM54550 | 61-110 | | |
| MM54551 | 0 | [FT] | |
| MM55052 | | [FT] | |
| MM55053 | 61-114 | | |
| MM55054 | 61-15 | | |
| MM55055 | 61-20 | | |
| MM55058 | 61-41 | | |
| MM55059 | 61-26 | | |
| MM55062* | 61-128 | | |
| MM55063* | RS-27 | RSV | |
| MM55064* | 61-130 | | |
| MM55065* | 36-02 | | |
| MM55066* | 36-03 | | |
| MM55067* | 36-07 | | |
| MM55068* | 61-134 | | |
| MM55069* | 36-01 | | |
| MM55070* | 36-12 | | |
| MM55072* | 36-05 | | |
| MM55073* | 61-141 | | |
| MM55074* | 61-142 | | |

| | | |
|---|---|---|
| MM55075* | 61-143 | |
| MM55076* | 36-04 | |
| MM55077* | RS-28 | RSV |
| MM55078* | RS-29 | RSV |
| MM55079* | | |
| MM55080* | 61- | |
| MM55081* | | |
| MM55082* | 61- | |
| CSX55083* | RS-30 | RSV |
| MM55084* | 61- | |
| MM55085* | 61- | |
| MM55086* | 61-156 | |
| MM55087* | 61-167 | |
| MM55088* | 61-157 | |
| MM55089* | | |
| MM55090* | | |
| MM55091* | | |

**Aermacchi M346**
Aermacchi, Venegono
MMCSX615
CMX616

**Airbus A.319CJ-115X**
31° Stormo,
  Roma-Ciampino:
  306° Gruppo
MM62174
MM62209
MM62243

**Boeing 707-328B/-3F5C***
9ª Brigata Aerea,
  Pratica di Mare:
  8° Gruppo;

| | | |
|---|---|---|
| MM62148 | 14-01 | |
| MM62149 | 14-02 | |
| MM62150* | 14-03 | |
| MM62151* | 14-04 | |

**Breguet Br.1150 Atlantic**
41° Stormo, Catania:
  88° Gruppo

| | |
|---|---|
| MM40108 | 41-70 |
| MM40109 | 41-71 |
| MM40110 | 41-72 |
| MM40111 | 41-73 |
| MM40113 | 41-74 |
| MM40114 | 41-76 |
| MM40115 | 41-77 |
| MM40116 | 41-01 |
| MM40117 | 41-02 |
| MM40118 | 41-03 |
| MM40119 | 41-04 |
| MM40120 | 41-05 |
| MM40121 | 41-06 |
| MM40122 | 41-07 |
| MM40123 | 41-10 |
| MM40124 | 41-11 |
| MM40125 | 41-12 |

**Dassault Falcon 50**
31° Stormo,
  Roma-Ciampino:
  93° Gruppo
MM62020
MM62021
MM62026
MM62029

**Dassault Falcon 900EX**
31° Stormo,
  Roma-Ciampino:
  93° Gruppo

MM62171
MM62172
MM62210

**Eurofighter EF.2000/EF.2000B***
4° Stormo, Grosseto:
  9° Gruppo & 20° Gruppo;
Alenia, Torino/Caselle;
RSV, Pratica di Mare

| | | |
|---|---|---|
| MMX602 | RS-01 | RSV |
| MMX603 | | Alenia |
| MMX614* | | Alenia |
| MM7235 | 4-6 | 9 |
| MM7271 | 4-20 | 20 |
| MM7271 | 4-5 | 9 |
| MM7272 | | RSV |
| MM7273 | | Alenia |
| CSX55092* | | Alenia |
| MM55093* | 4-1 | 9 |
| MM55094* | 4-3 | 9 |
| MM55095* | 4-23 | 20 |
| MM55096* | 4-4 | 9 |
| MM55097* | 4-24 | 20 |
| MM55098* | | |
| MM55099* | | |
| MM55100* | | |
| MM55101* | | |

**Lockheed C-130J/C-130J-30 Hercules II**
46ª Brigata Aerea, Pisa:
  2° Gruppo & 50° Gruppo

**C-130J**

| | | |
|---|---|---|
| MM62175 | 46-40 | 2 |
| MM62176 | 46-41 | 2 |
| MM62177 | 46-42 | 2 |
| MM62178 | 46-43 | 2 |
| MM62179 | 46-44 | 2 |
| MM62180 | 46-45 | 2 |
| MM62181 | 46-46 | 50 |
| MM62182 | 46-47 | 50 |
| MM62183 | 46-48 | 50 |
| MM62184 | 46-49 | 50 |
| MM62185 | 46-50 | 50 |
| MM62186 | 46-51 | 50 |

**C-130J-30**

| | | |
|---|---|---|
| MM62187 | 46-53 | 50 |
| MM62188 | 46-54 | 50 |
| MM62189 | 46-55 | 50 |
| MM62190 | 46-56 | 50 |
| MM62191 | 46-57 | 50 |
| MM62192 | 46-58 | 50 |
| MM62193 | 46-59 | 50 |
| MM62194 | 46-60 | 50 |
| MM62195 | 46-61 | 50 |
| MM62196 | 46-62 | 50 |

**Lockheed (GD) F-16A-ADF/F-16B***
5° Stormo, Cervia:
  23° Gruppo
37° Stormo, Trapani:
  18° Gruppo

| | |
|---|---|
| MM7236 | 18 |
| MM7238 | 23 |
| MM7239 | 23 |
| MM7240 | |
| MM7241 | |
| MM7242 | 18 |
| MM7243 | 23 |
| MM7244 | 23 |
| MM7245 | 23 |

| | | |
|---|---|---|
| MM7246 | | 18 |
| MM7247 | | 18 |
| MM7248 | | 18 |
| MM7249 | | 18 |
| MM7250 | | 18 |
| MM7251 | | 23 |
| MM7252 | | 23 |
| MM7253 | | 18 |
| MM7254 | | 23 |
| MM7255 | | 18 |
| MM7256 | | 18 |
| MM7257 | | |
| MM7258 | | 18 |
| MM7259 | | 23 |
| MM7260 | | 18 |
| MM7261 | | 18 |
| MM7262 | | 23 |
| MM7263 | | 18 |
| MM7264 | | 18 |
| MM7265 | | 18 |
| MM7266* | | 18 |
| MM7267* | | 18 |
| MM7268* | | 23 |
| MM7269* | | 23 |

**Panavia**
**Tornado Strike/**
**Trainer¹/ECR²**
6° Stormo, Ghedi:
  102° Gruppo &
  154° Gruppo;
50° Stormo, Piacenza:
  155° Gruppo;
156° Gruppo Autonomo,
  Gioia del Colle;
RSV, Pratica di Mare

| | | |
|---|---|---|
| MM7002 | 6-10 | 154 |
| MM7003 | 6-23 | 154 |
| MM7004 | 36-36 | 156 |
| MM7005² | 36-43 | 156 |
| MM7006 | 6-31 | 102 |
| MM7007 | 36-37 | 156 |
| MM7008 | | |
| MM7009 | 6-09 | 154 |
| MM7011 | 6-13 | 154 |
| MM7013 | 36-40 | 156 |
| MM7014 | | |
| MM7015 | | RSV |
| MM7016 | 36-45 | 156 |
| MM7018 | 6-46 | 102 |
| MM7019² | 50-05 | 155 |
| MM7020² | 50-21 | 155 |
| MM7021² | 50-01 | 155 |
| MM7022 | | |
| MM7023 | 36-31 | 156 |
| MM7024 | 36-41 | 156 |
| MM7025 | 6-43 | 102 |
| MM7026 | 6-44 | 102 |
| MM7027² | 50-51 | 155 |
| MM7028 | | |
| MM7029 | 6-22 | 154 |
| MM7030² | 50-04 | 155 |
| MM7031 | 6-21 | 154 |
| MM7033 | 50-50 | 155 |
| MM7034 | | |
| MM7035 | 36-47 | 156 |
| MM7036² | 50-.. | 155 |
| MM7037 | 6-47 | 102 |
| MM7038 | 6-37 | 102 |
| MM7039 | 6-02 | 154 |
| CMX7040 | RS-01 | RSV |
| MM7041 | 6-41 | 102 |
| MM7042 | 36-57 | 156 |
| MM7043 | | |
| MM7044 | 36-51 | 156 |
| MM7046² | 6-06 | 154 |
| MM7047² | 50-43 | 155 |
| MM7048 | 6-16 | 154 |
| MM7049 | 6-34 | 102 |
| MM7050 | 36-44 | 156 |
| MM7051 | 50-45 | 155 |
| MM7052 | | |
| MM7053² | 50-07 | 155 |
| MM7054² | 50-40 | 155 |
| MM7055 | 50-42 | 155 |
| MM7056 | 36-50 | 156 |
| MM7057 | 36-54 | 156 |
| MM7058 | 6-11 | 154 |
| MM7059 | 50-47 | 155 |
| MM7061 | 6-01 | 154 |
| MM7062² | 50-44 | 155 |
| MM7063 | 6-26 | 154 |
| MM7064 | | |
| MM7065 | 6-25 | 154 |
| MM7066 | | |
| MM7067 | | |
| CSX7068² | | |
| Alenia | | |
| MM7070² | 50-46 | 155 |
| MM7071 | 6-12 | 154 |
| MM7072 | 6-30 | 102 |
| MM7073² | 36-42 | 156 |
| MM7075 | 36-53 | 156 |
| MM7078 | 50-02 | 155 |
| CMX7079² | | Alenia |
| MM7080 | 6-33 | 102 |
| MM7081 | | |
| MM7082² | 6-14 | 154 |
| MM7083 | 6-37 | 102 |
| MM7084 | 6-36 | 102 |
| CMX7085 | 36-50 | Alenia |
| MM7086 | 36-35 | 156 |
| MM7087 | 6-36 | 102 |
| MM7088 | 6-18 | 154 |
| MM55000¹ | 6-51 | 102 |
| MM55001¹ | 6-42 | 102 |
| MM55002¹ | 6-52 | 102 |
| MM55003¹ | 6-.. | 154 |
| MM55004¹ | 6-53 | 102 |
| MM55005¹ | 6-57 | 102 |
| MM55006¹ | 6-44 | 102 |
| MM55007¹ | 36-55 | 156 |
| MM55008¹ | 6-45 | 102 |
| MM55009¹ | 36-56 | 156 |
| MM55010¹ | 6-42 | 102 |
| MM55011¹ | | |

**Piaggio**
**P-180AM Avanti**
9ª Brigata Aerea,
  Pratica di Mare:
  71° Gruppo;
36° Stormo, Gioia del Colle:
  636ª SC;
RSV, Pratica di Mare

| | | |
|---|---|---|
| MM62159 | | 636 |
| MM62160 | 54 | RSV |
| MM62161 | | 71 |
| MM62162 | | 71 |
| MM62163 | | 71 |
| CSX62164 | | RSV |
| MM62199 | | RSV |
| MM62200 | 9-01 | 71 |
| MM62201 | | 71 |
| MM62202 | | 71 |
| MM62203 | | 71 |
| MM62204 | 9-02 | 71 |
| MM62205 | | 71 |
| MM62206 | | 71 |

**Aviazione dell'Esercito**
**Dornier Do.228-212**
28° Gruppo Squadrone
  Cavalleria dell'Aria,
  Viterbo

| | |
|---|---|
| MM62156 | E.I.101 |
| MM62157 | E.I.101 |
| MM62158 | E.I.101 |

**Guardia di Finanza**
**Aérospatiale**
**ATR.42-400MP**
2° Gruppo EM,
  Pratica di Mare

| | |
|---|---|
| MM62165 | GF-13 |
| MM62166 | GF-14 |

**Marina Militare Italiana**
**McDonnell Douglas**
**AV-8B/TAV-8B Harrier II+**
Gruppo Aerei Imbarcarti,
  Taranto/Grottaglie
**AV-8B**

| | |
|---|---|
| MM7199 | 1-03 |
| MM7200 | 1-04 |
| MM7201 | 1-05 |
| MM7212 | 1-06 |
| MM7213 | 1-07 |
| MM7214 | 1-08 |
| MM7215 | 1-09 |
| MM7217 | 1-11 |
| MM7218 | 1-12 |
| MM7219 | 1-13 |
| MM7220 | 1-14 |
| MM7221 | 1-15 |
| MM7222 | 1-16 |
| MM7223 | 1-18 |
| MM7224 | 1-19 |

**TAV-8B**

| | |
|---|---|
| MM55032 | 1-01 |
| MM55033 | 1-02 |

**Italian Govt**
**Dassault Falcon 900**
Italian Govt/Soc. CAI,
  Roma/Ciampino
I-DIES
I-FICV
I-NUMI

**IVORY COAST**
**Grumman**
**G.1159C Gulfstream IV**
Ivory Coast Govt, Abidjan
TU-VAD

**JAPAN**
**Japan Air Self Defence**
**Force**
**Boeing 747-47C**
701st Flight Sqn, Chitose
20-1101
20-1102

**JORDAN**
**Al Quwwat al Jawwiya**
**al Malakiya al Urduniya**
**Extra EA-300S**
*Royal Jordanian Falcons,*
  *Amman*
JY-RNA
JY-RNC

JY-RND
JY-RNE
JY-RNG
JY-RNL

**Lockheed C-130H Hercules**
3 Sqn, Al Matar AB/Amman
344
345
346
347

**Jordanian Govt**
**Airbus A.340-211**
Jordanian Govt, Amman
JY-ABH

**Boeing 737-7BC**
Jordanian Govt, Amman
VP-BFA

**Canadair**
**CL.604 Challenger**
Jordanian Govt, Amman
JY-ONE
JY-TWO

**Lockheed**
**L.1011 TriStar 500**
Jordanian Govt, Amman
JY-HKJ

**KAZAKHSTAN**
**Boeing 767-2DKER**
Govt of Kazakhstan, Almaty
UN-B6701

**Tupolev Tu-154B-2**
Govt of Kazakhstan, Almaty
UN-85464

**KENYA**
**Kenyan Air Force**
**Fokker 70ER**
308

**KUWAIT**
**Al Quwwat al Jawwiya**
**al Kuwaitiya**
**Lockheed**
**L100-30 Hercules**
41 Sqn, Kuwait International
KAF 323
KAF 324
KAF 325

**Kuwaiti Govt**
**Airbus A.300C4-620**
Kuwaiti Govt, Safat
9K-AHI

**Airbus A.310-308**
Kuwaiti Govt, Safat
9K-ALD

**Airbus A.320-212**
Kuwaiti Govt, Safat
9K-AKD

**Boeing 747-469**
Kuwaiti Govt, Safat
9K-ADE

**Gulfstream Aerospace**
**Gulfstream V**
Kuwaiti Govt/Kuwait
Airways, Safat
9K-AJD
9K-AJE
9K-AJF

**KYRGYZSTAN**
**Tupolev Tu-134A-3**
Govt of Kyrgyzstan, Bishkek
EX-65119

**Tupolev Tu-154B/Tu-154M**
Govt of Kyrgyzstan, Bishkek
EX-85294  Tu-154B
EX-85718  Tu-154M
EX-85762  Tu-154M

**LITHUANIA**
**Karines Oro Pajegos**
**Antonov An-26RV**
Transporto Eskadrile,
Siauliai-Zokniai
03
04
05

**LET 410 Turbolet**
Transporto Eskadrile,
Siauliai-Zokniai
01
02

**Mil Mi-8**
Sraigtasparniu Eskadrile,
Panevezys/Pajuostis
02      Mi-8T
09      Mi-8T
10      Mi-8T
11      Mi-8PS
14      Mi-8T
20      Mi-8T
21      Mi-8MTV-1
22      Mi-8MTV-1
23      Mi-8T

**LUXEMBOURG**
**NATO**
**Boeing 707TCA (CT-49A)**
NAEW&CF, Geilenkirchen
LX-N19997
LX-N19999
LX-N20000
LX-N20199

**Boeing E-3A**
NAEW&CF, Geilenkirchen
LX-N90442
LX-N90443
LX-N90444
LX-N90445
LX-N90446
LX-N90447
LX-N90448
LX-N90449
LX-N90450
LX-N90451
LX-N90452
LX-N90453
LX-N90454
LX-N90455
LX-N90456
LX-N90458

LX-N90459

**MACEDONIA**
**Macedonian Govt**
**Bombardier Lear 60**
Macedonian Govt, Skopje
Z3-MKD

**MALAYSIA**
**Royal Malaysian Air Force/**
**Tentera Udara Diraja**
**Malaysia**
**Boeing 737-7H6**
2 Sqn, Simpang
M53–01

**Bombardier**
**BD.700-1A10 Global**
**Express**
2 Sqn, Simpang
M48-02

**Dassault Falcon 900**
2 Sqn, Simpang
M37-01

**Lockheed**
**C-130 Hercules**
14 Sqn, Labuan;
20 Sqn, Subang
M30-01 C-130H(MP)  20 Sqn
M30-02 C-130H      20 Sqn
M30-03 C-130H      14 Sqn
M30-04 C-130H-30   20 Sqn
M30-05 C-130H      14 Sqn
M30-06 C-130H      14 Sqn
M30-07 C-130T      20 Sqn
M30-08 C-130H(MP)20 Sqn
M30-09 C-130H(MP)20 Sqn
M30-10 C-130H-30   20 Sqn
M30-11 C-130H-30   20 Sqn
M30-12 C-130H-30   20 Sqn
M30-14 C-130H-30   20 Sqn
M30-15 C-130H-30   20 Sqn
M30-16 C-130H-30   20 Sqn

**MALTA**
**Bombardier**
**Learjet 60**
. Govt of Malta, Luqa
9H-AEE

**MEXICO**
**Fuerza Aérea Mexicana**
**Boeing 757-225**
8° Grupo Aéreo, Mexico City
TP-01  (XC-UJM)

**MOROCCO**
**Force Aérienne Royaume**
**Marocaine/ Al Quwwat al**
**Jawwiya al Malakiya**
**Marakishiya**
**Airtech**
**CN.235M-100**
Escadrille de Transport,
Rabat
023      CNA-MA
024      CNA-MB
025      CNA-MC
026      CNA-MD
027      CNA-ME
028      CNA-MF
031      CNA-MG

**CAP-231/CAP-232**
*Marche Verte*
**CAP-231**

| | |
|---|---|
| 09 | CN-ABL |
| 22 | CN-ABM |
| 23 | CN-ABN |
| 24 | CN-ABO |

**CAP-232**

| | |
|---|---|
| 28 | CNA-BP |
| 29 | CN-ABQ |
| 31 | CN-ABR |
| 36 | CNA-BS |
| 37 | CNA-BT |
| 41 | CN-ABU |
| 42 | CN-ABV |
| 43 | CN-ABW |
| 44 | CN-ABX |

**Lockheed**
**C-130H Hercules**
Escadrille de Transport,
  Rabat

| | |
|---|---|
| 4535 | CN-AOA |
| 4551 | CN-AOC |
| 4581 | CN-AOE |
| 4583 | CN-AOF |
| 4713 | CN-AOG |
| 4717 | CN-AOH |
| 4733 | CN-AOI |
| 4738 | CN-AOJ |
| 4739 | CN-AOK |
| 4742 | CN-AOL |
| 4875 | CN-AOM |
| 4876 | CN-AON |
| 4877 | CN-AOO |
| 4888 | CN-AOP |
| 4892 | CN-AOQ |
| 4907 | CN-AOR |
| 4909 | CN-AOS |
| 4940 | CN-AOT |

**Govt of Morocco**
**Cessna 560 Citation V**
Govt of Morocco, Rabat
CNA-NW

**Dassault Falcon 50**
Govt of Morocco, Rabat
CN-ANO

**Grumman**
**G.1159 Gulfstream IITT/**
**G.1159A Gulfstream III**
Govt of Morocco, Rabat

| | |
|---|---|
| CNA-NL | Gulfstream IITT |
| CNA-NU | Gulfstream III |
| CNA-NV | Gulfstream III |

**NAMIBIA**
  **Dassault Falcon 900B**
  Namibian Govt, Windhoek
  V5-NAM

**NETHERLANDS**
  **Koninklijke Luchtmacht**
  **Agusta-Bell AB.412SP**
  303 Sqn, Leeuwarden
  R-01
  R-02
  R-03

  **Boeing-Vertol**
  **CH-47D Chinook**
  298 Sqn, Soesterberg

| | |
|---|---|
| D-101 | |
| D-102 | |
| D-103 | |
| D-106 | |
| D-661 | |
| D-662 | |
| D-663 | |
| D-664 | |
| D-665 | |
| D-666 | |
| D-667 | |

**Eurocopter**
**AS.532U-2 Cougar**
300 Sqn, Gilze-Rijen

| | |
|---|---|
| S-400 | |
| S-419 | |
| S-433 | |
| S-438 | |
| S-440 | |
| S-441 | |
| S-442 | |
| S-444 | |
| S-445 | |
| S-447 | |
| S-450 | |
| S-453 | |
| S-454 | |
| S-456 | |
| S-457 | |
| S-458 | |
| S-459 | |

**Fokker 50**
334 Sqn, Eindhoven
U-05
U-06

**Fokker 60UTA-N**
334 Sqn, Eindhoven
U-01
U-02
U-03
U-04

**General Dynamics**
**F-16**
TGp/306/311/312/313 Sqns,
  Volkel;
322/323 Sqns, Leeuwarden

| | | |
|---|---|---|
| J-001 | F-16AM | 312 Sqn |
| J-002 | F-16AM | 322 Sqn |
| J-003 | F-16AM | 311 Sqn |
| J-004 | F-16AM | 311 Sqn |
| J-005 | F-16AM | 312 Sqn |
| J-006 | F-16AM | 306 Sqn |
| J-008 | F-16AM | 322 Sqn |
| J-009 | F-16AM | 323 Sqn |
| J-010 | F-16AM | 322 Sqn |
| J-011 | F-16AM | 312 Sqn |
| J-013 | F-16AM | 322 Sqn |
| J-014 | F-16AM | 322 Sqn |
| J-015 | F-16AM | 313 Sqn |
| J-016 | F-16AM | 312 Sqn |
| J-017 | F-16AM | 323 Sqn |
| J-018 | F-16AM | 323 Sqn |
| J-019 | F-16AM | 323 Sqn |
| J-020 | F-16AM | 313 Sqn |
| J-021 | F-16AM | 312 Sqn |
| J-055 | F-16AM | 306 Sqn |
| J-057 | F-16AM | 323 Sqn |
| J-058 | F-16AM | 313 Sqn |
| J-060 | F-16AM | 313 Sqn |
| J-061 | F-16AM | 312 Sqn |

| | | |
|---|---|---|
| J-062 | F-16AM | 322 Sqn |
| J-063 | F-16AM | 322 Sqn |
| J-064 | F-16BM | 322 Sqn |
| J-065 | F-16BM | 313 Sqn |
| J-066 | F-16BM | 323 Sqn |
| J-067 | F-16BM | 313 Sqn |
| J-068 | F-16BM | 306 Sqn |
| J-135 | F-16AM | 311 Sqn |
| J-136 | F-16AM | 313 Sqn |
| J-137 | F-16AM | 322 Sqn |
| J-138 | F-16AM | 313 Sqn |
| J-139 | F-16AM | 311 Sqn |
| J-141 | F-16AM | 313 Sqn |
| J-142 | F-16AM | 312 Sqn |
| J-143 | F-16AM | 313 Sqn |
| J-144 | F-16AM | 322 Sqn |
| J-145 | F-16AM | 313 Sqn |
| J-146 | F-16AM | 323 Sqn |
| J-192 | F-16AM | 311 Sqn |
| J-193 | F-16AM | 311 Sqn |
| J-194 | F-16AM | 323 Sqn |
| J-196 | F-16AM | 323 Sqn |
| J-197 | F-16AM | 312 Sqn |
| J-198 | F-16AM | 322 Sqn |
| J-199 | F-16AM | 311 Sqn |
| J-201 | F-16AM | 322 Sqn |
| J-202 | F-16AM | 323 Sqn |
| J-203 | F-16AM | 323 Sqn |
| J-204 | F-16AM | 323 Sqn |
| J-205 | F-16AM | 322 Sqn |
| J-207 | F-16AM | 322 Sqn |
| J-208 | F-16BM | 306 Sqn |
| J-209 | F-16BM | 313 Sqn |
| J-210 | F-16BM | 323 Sqn |
| J-211 | F-16BM | 322 Sqn |
| J-254 | F-16AM | 311 Sqn |
| J-255 | F-16AM | 312 Sqn |
| J-257 | F-16AM | 312 Sqn |
| J-267 | F-16BM | 306 Sqn |
| J-270 | F-16BM | 306 Sqn |
| J-360 | F-16AM | 323 Sqn |
| J-362 | F-16AM | 323 Sqn |
| J-363 | F-16AM | 311 Sqn |
| J-364 | F-16AM | 312 Sqn |
| J-365 | F-16AM | 312 Sqn |
| J-366 | F-16AM | 313 Sqn |
| J-367 | F-16AM | 322 Sqn |
| J-368 | F-16BM | 306 Sqn |
| J-369 | F-16BM | 306 Sqn |
| J-508 | F-16AM | 313 Sqn |
| J-509 | F-16AM | 313 Sqn |
| J-510 | F-16AM | 322 Sqn |
| J-511 | F-16AM | 313 Sqn |
| J-512 | F-16AM | 313 Sqn |
| J-513 | F-16AM | 323 Sqn |
| J-514 | F-16AM | 313 Sqn |
| J-515 | F-16AM | 323 Sqn |
| J-516 | F-16AM | 322 Sqn |
| J-616 | F-16AM | 322 Sqn |
| J-617 | F-16AM | 311 Sqn |
| J-619 | F-16AM | 311 Sqn |
| J-620 | F-16AM | 323 Sqn |
| J-622 | F-16AM | 323 Sqn |
| J-623 | F-16AM | 323 Sqn |
| J-624 | F-16AM | 322 Sqn |
| J-627 | F-16AM | 323 Sqn |
| J-628 | F-16AM | 313 Sqn |
| J-630 | F-16AM | 311 Sqn |
| J-631 | F-16AM | 323 Sqn |
| J-632 | F-16AM | 322 Sqn |
| J-633 | F-16AM | 322 Sqn |
| J-635 | F-16AM | 312 Sqn |
| J-636 | F-16AM | 312 Sqn |
| J-637 | F-16AM | 311 Sqn |

| | | |
|---|---|---|
| J-638 | F-16AM | 311 Sqn |
| J-640 | F-16AM | 312 Sqn |
| J-641 | F-16AM | 311 Sqn |
| J-642 | F-16AM | 312 Sqn |
| J-643 | F-16AM | 322 Sqn |
| J-644 | F-16AM | 322 Sqn |
| J-646 | F-16AM | 311 Sqn |
| J-647 | F-16AM | 311 Sqn |
| J-648 | F-16AM | 311 Sqn |
| J-649 | F-16BM | 322 Sqn |
| J-652 | F-16BM | 306 Sqn |
| J-655 | F-16BM | 306 Sqn |
| J-656 | F-16BM | 306 Sqn |
| J-657 | F-16BM | 306 Sqn |
| J-864 | F-16AM | 313 Sqn |
| J-866 | F-16AM | 312 Sqn |
| J-867 | F-16AM | 313 Sqn |
| J-868 | F-16AM | 322 Sqn |
| J-869 | F-16AM | 322 Sqn |
| J-870 | F-16AM | 313 Sqn |
| J-871 | F-16AM | 312 Sqn |
| J-872 | F-16AM | 323 Sqn |
| J-873 | F-16AM | 322 Sqn |
| J-874 | F-16AM | 312 Sqn |
| J-875 | F-16AM | 323 Sqn |
| J-876 | F-16AM | 322 Sqn |
| J-877 | F-16AM | 322 Sqn |
| J-878 | F-16AM | 313 Sqn |
| J-879 | F-16AM | 306 Sqn |
| J-881 | F-16AM | 323 Sqn |
| J-882 | F-16BM | 323 Sqn |
| J-884 | F-16BM | 312 Sqn |
| J-885 | F-16BM | 312 Sqn |

**Grumman**
**G-1159C Gulfstream IV**
334 Sqn, Eindhoven
V-11

**Lockheed**
**C-130H-30 Hercules**
334 Sqn, Eindhoven
G-273
G-275

**MDH**
**AH-64D Apache Longbow**
301 Sqn, Gilze-Rijen
Q-01
Q-02
Q-03
Q-04
Q-05
Q-06
Q-07
Q-08
Q-09
Q-10
Q-11
Q-12
Q-13
Q-14
Q-15
Q-16
Q-17
Q-18
Q-19
Q-21
Q-22
Q-23
Q-24
Q-25
Q-26
Q-27
Q-28
Q-29
Q-30

**McDonnell Douglas**
**DC-10*/KDC-10**
334 Sqn, Eindhoven
T-235
T-255* (on odrer)
T-264

**Pilatus PC-7**
**Turbo Trainer**
131 EMVO Sqn,
  Woensdrecht
L-01
L-02
L-03
L-04
L-05
L-06
L-07
L-08
L-09
L-10
L-11
L-12
L-13

**Sud Alouette III**
300 Sqn, Soesterberg
A-247
A-275
A-292
A-301

**Marine Luchtvaart Dienst**
**Beech**
**Super King Air 200**
OVALK, Maastricht
PH-SBK

**Westland SH-14D Lynx**
MARHELI (7 Sqn &
  860 Sqn), De Kooij
(7 Sqn operates
  860 Sqn aircraft
  on loan)
261
262
264
265
267
268
269
270
271
274
276
277
279
280
281
283

**Netherlands Govt**
**Fokker 70**
Dutch Royal Flight, Schiphol
PH-KBX

**NEW ZEALAND**
**Royal New Zealand Air Force**
**Boeing 757-2K2**
40 Sqn, Whenuapai
NZ7571
NZ7572

**Lockheed**
**C-130H Hercules**
40 Sqn, Whenuapai
NZ7001
NZ7002
NZ7003
NZ7004
NZ7005

**Lockheed**
**P-3K Orion**
5 Sqn, Whenuapai
NZ4201
NZ4202
NZ4203
NZ4204
NZ4205
NZ4206

**NIGERIA**
**Federal Nigerian Air Force**
**Lockheed**
**C-130H/C-130H-30***
**Hercules**
88 MAG, Lagos
NAF-910
NAF-912
NAF-913
NAF-917*
NAF-918*

**Nigerian Govt**
**Boeing 727-2N6**
Federal Govt of Nigeria,
  Lagos
5N-FGN [001]

**Boeing 737-7N6**
Federal Govt of Nigeria,
  Lagos
5N-FGT

**Dassault Falcon 900**
Federal Govt of Nigeria,
  Lagos
5N-FGE
5N-FGO

**Grumman**
**G.1159A Gulfstream III**
Federal Govt of Nigeria,
  Lagos
5N-FGP

**Gulfstream Aerospace**
**Gulfstream V**
Federal Govt of Nigeria,
  Lagos
5N-FGS

**NORWAY**
**Luftforsvaret**
**Bell 412SP**
339 Skv, Bardufoss;
720 Skv, Rygge

| | |
|---|---|
| 139 | 339 Skv |
| 140 | 720 Skv |
| 141 | 720 Skv |
| 142 | 720 Skv |
| 143 | 339 Skv |
| 144 | 339 Skv |

| 145 | 720 Skv |
|---|---|
| 146 | 339 Skv |
| 147 | 720 Skv |
| 148 | 339 Skv |
| 149 | 339 Skv |
| 161 | 339 Skv |
| 162 | 339 Skv |
| 163 | 720 Skv |
| 164 | 720 Skv |
| 165 | 720 Skv |
| 166 | 720 Skv |
| 167 | 720 Skv |
| 194 | 720 Skv |

**Dassault**
**Falcon 20 ECM**
717 Skv, Rygge
041
053
0125

**General Dynamics**
**F-16 MLU**
331 Skv, Bodø (*r/w/bl*);
332 Skv, Rygge (*y/bk*);
338 Skv, Ørland

| 272 | F-16A | 332 Skv |
|---|---|---|
| 273 | F-16A | 332 Skv |
| 275 | F-16A | 338 Skv |
| 276 | F-16A | 338 Skv |
| 277 | F-16A | 332 Skv |
| 279 | F-16A | 338 Skv |
| 281 | F-16A | 332 Skv |
| 282 | F-16A | 338 Skv |
| 284 | F-16A | 338 Skv |
| 285 | F-16A | 338 Skv |
| 286 | F-16A | 338 Skv |
| 288 | F-16A | 338 Skv |
| 289 | F-16A | 332 Skv |
| 291 | F-16A | 338 Skv |
| 292 | F-16A | 338 Skv |
| 293 | F-16A | 338 Skv |
| 295 | F-16A | 338 Skv |
| 297 | F-16A | 338 Skv |
| 298 | F-16A | 338 Skv |
| 299 | F-16A | 338 Skv |
| 302 | F-16B | 332 Skv |
| 304 | F-16B | 338 Skv |
| 305 | F-16B | 338 Skv |
| 306 | F-16B | 332 Skv |
| 658 | F-16A | 338 Skv |
| 659 | F-16A | 338 Skv |
| 660 | F-16A | 331 Skv |
| 661 | F-16A | 338 Skv |
| 662 | F-16A | 332 Skv |
| 663 | F-16A | 331 Skv |
| 664 | F-16A | 331 Skv |
| 665 | F-16A | 332 Skv |
| 666 | F-16A | |
| 667 | F-16A | 331 Skv |
| 668 | F-16A | 331 Skv |
| 669 | F-16A | 331 Skv |
| 670 | F-16A | 331 Skv |
| 671 | F-16A | 331 Skv |
| 672 | F-16A | 331 Skv |
| 673 | F-16A | 331 Skv |
| 674 | F-16A | 331 Skv |
| 675 | F-16A | 331 Skv |
| 677 | F-16A | 331 Skv |
| 678 | F-16A | 331 Skv |
| 680 | F-16A | 331 Skv |
| 681 | F-16A | 338 Skv |
| 682 | F-16A | 331 Skv |
| 683 | F-16A | 331 Skv |

| 686 | F-16A | 331 Skv |
|---|---|---|
| 687 | F-16A | 331 Skv |
| 688 | F-16A | 331 Skv |
| 689 | F-16B | 332 Skv |
| 690 | F-16B | 338 Skv |
| 691 | F-16B | 338 Skv |
| 692 | F-16B | 332 Skv |
| 693 | F-16B | 338 Skv |
| 711 | F-16B | 338 Skv |

**Lockheed**
**C-130H Hercules**
335 Skv, Gardermoen
952
953
954
955
956
957

**Lockheed P-3C Orion**
333 Skv, Andøya
3296
3297
3298
3299

**Lockheed P-3N Orion**
333 Skv, Andøya
4576
6603

**Northrop F-5A**
Eye of the Tiger
  Project, Rygge
130
131
133
134
896
902

**Northrop F-5B**
Eye of the Tiger
  Project, Rygge
136
243
244
387
906
907
908
909

**Westland**
**Sea King Mk 43/**
**Mk 43A/Mk 43B**
330 Skv:
  A Flt, Bodø;
  B Flt, Banak;
  C Flt, Ørland;
  D Flt, Sola

| 060 | Mk 43 |
|---|---|
| 062 | Mk 43 |
| 066 | Mk 43 |
| 069 | Mk 43 |
| 070 | Mk 43 |
| 071 | Mk 43B |
| 072 | Mk 43 |
| 073 | Mk 43 |
| 074 | Mk 43 |
| 189 | Mk 43A |
| 322 | Mk 43B |
| 329 | Mk 43B |

| 330 | Mk 43B |
|---|---|

**Kystvakt (Coast Guard)**
**Westland Lynx Mk86**
337 Skv, Bardufoss
207
216
228
232
237
350

**OMAN**
**Royal Air Force of Oman**
**BAC 1-11/485GD**
4 Sqn, Seeb
551
552
553

**Lockheed**
**C-130H Hercules**
4 Sqn, Seeb
501
502
503

**Omani Govt**
**Airbus A320-233**
Govt of Oman, Seeb
A4O-AA

**Boeing 747-430**
Govt of Oman, Seeb
A4O-OMN

**Boeing 747SP-27**
Govt of Oman, Seeb
A4O-SO

**Grumman**
**G.1159C Gulfstream IV**
Govt of Oman, Seeb
A4O-AB
A4O-AC

**PAKISTAN**
**Pakistan Fiza'ya**
**Boeing 707-340C**
68-19635 12 Sqn
68-19866 12 Sqn

**Pakistani Govt**
**Boeing 737-33A**
Govt of Pakistan, Karachi
AP-BEH

**PERU**
**Fuerza Aérea Peruana**
**Douglas DC-8-62AF**
370 (OB-1372)

**POLAND**
**Siły Powietrzne RP**
**Antonov An-26**
13 ELTR, Krakow/Balice
1310
1402
1403
1406
1407
1508
1509
1602

1603
1604

**CASA 295M**
13 ELTR, Krakow/Balice
011
012
013
014
015
016
017
018

**Mikoyan MiG-29A/UB***
1 ELT, Minsk/Mazowiecki;
41 ELT, Malbork

| | |
|---|---|
| 01 | 41 ELT |
| 02 | 41 ELT |
| 04* | 41 ELT |
| 06 | 41 ELT |
| 08 | 41 ELT |
| 10 | 41 ELT |
| 11 | 41 ELT |
| 13 | 41 ELT |
| 15* | 1 ELT |
| 18 | 41 ELT |
| 19 | 41 ELT |
| 22 | 41 ELT |
| 24 | 41 ELT |
| 26* | 41 ELT |
| 28* | 1 ELT |
| 32 | 41 ELT |
| 38 | 1 ELT |
| 40 | 1 ELT |
| 42* | 1 ELT |
| 48* | 41 ELT |
| 54 | 1 ELT |
| 56 | 1 ELT |
| 59 | 1 ELT |
| 64* | 1 ELT |
| 65 | 1 ELT |
| 66 | 1 ELT |
| 67 | 1 ELT |
| 70 | 1 ELT |
| 77 | 1 ELT |
| 83 | 1 ELT |
| 89 | 1 ELT |
| 92 | 1 ELT |
| 105 | 1 ELT |
| 108 | 1 ELT |
| 111 | 1 ELT |
| 114 | 1 ELT |
| 115 | 1 ELT |
| 128 | 41 ELT |
| 300 | 41 ELT |
| 310 | 41 ELT |
| 314 | 41 ELT |
| 315 | 41 ELT |
| 408* | 41 ELT |
| 800 | 41 ELT |
| 5115 | 41 ELT |

**PZL M28 Bryza**
13 ELTR, Balice;
36 SPLT, Warszawa;
LGPR, Bydgoszcz

| | | |
|---|---|---|
| 0203 | M28B-1 | 13 ELTR |
| 0204 | M28B-1 | 13 ELTR |
| 0205 | M28TD | 36 SPLT |
| 0206 | M28TD | 36 SPLT |
| 0207 | M28TD | 13 ELTR |
| 0208 | M28TD | 13 ELTR |
| 0209 | M28TD | 13 ELTR |
| 0210 | M28TD | 13 ELTR |
| 0723 | M28RL | LGPR |
| 1003 | M28TD | 13 ELTR |

**Tupolev Tu-154M**
36 SPLT, Warszawa
101
102

**Yakovlev Yak-40**
36 SPLT, Warszawa
034
040
041
042
044
045
047
048

**Lotnictwo Marynarki
Wojennej**
**PZL M28 Bryza**
28 EL, Gdynia/Babie Doly;
29 EL, Cewice/Siemirowice

| | | |
|---|---|---|
| 0404 | M28B-E | 28 EL |
| 0405 | M28B-E | 28 EL |
| 0810 | M28B-1R | PZL |
| 1006 | M28B-1R | 29 EL |
| 1007 | M28B-1 | 28 EL |
| 1008 | M28B-1R | 29 EL |
| 1017 | M28B-1R | 29 EL |
| 1022 | M28B-1R | 29 EL |
| 1114 | M28B-1R | 29 EL |
| 1115 | M28B-1R | 29 EL |
| 1116 | M28B-1R | 29 EL |
| 1117 | M28B-1 | 28 EL |
| 1118 | M28B-1 | 28 EL |

**PORTUGAL**
**Força Aérea Portuguesa**
**Aérospatiale**
**SA.330C Puma**
Esq 711, Lajes;
Esq 751, Montijo

| | |
|---|---|
| 19502 | Esq 751 |
| 19503 | Esq 751 |
| 19504 | Esq 751 |
| 19505 | Esq 751 |
| 19506 | Esq 751 |
| 19509 | Esq 751 |
| 19511 | Esq 711 |
| 19512 | Esq 751 |
| 19513 | Esq 711 |

**Aérospatiale**
**TB-30 Epsilon**
Esq 101, Beja
11401
11402
11403
11404
11405
11406
11407
11409
11410
11411
11413
11414
11415
11416
11417
11418

**CASA**
**212A/212ECM* Aviocar**
Esq 401, Sintra;
Esq 502, Sintra;
Esq 711, Lajes

| | |
|---|---|
| 16503 | Esq 502 |
| 16504 | Esq 502 |
| 16505 | Esq 502 |
| 16506 | Esq 502 |
| 16507 | Esq 502 |
| 16508 | Esq 502 |
| 16509 | Esq 502 |
| 16510 | Esq 401 |
| 16512 | Esq 401 |
| 16513 | Esq 711 |
| 16514 | Esq 711 |
| 16517 | Esq 711 |
| 16521* | Esq 401 |
| 16524* | Esq 401 |

**CASA 212-300MP Aviocar**
Esq 401, Sintra
17201
17202

**D-BD Alpha Jet**
Esq 103, Beja;
Esq 301, Beja
15201
15202
15204
15205
15206
15208
15209
15210
15211
15213
15214
15215
15216
15217
15218
15219
15220
15221
15222
15223
15224
15225
15226
15227
15228
15229
15230
15231
15232
15233
15235
15236
15237
15238
15239
15240
15241
15242
15243
15244
15246
15247
15250

**Dassault**
**Falcon 50**
Esq 504, Lisbon/Montijo
17401
17402
17403

**EHI EH-101**
Esq 711, Lajes;
Esq 751, Montijo
19601    Esq 751
19602    Esq 751
19603    Esq 751
19604    Esq 751
19605
19606
19607
19608
19609
19610
19611
19612

**Lockheed**
**C-130H/C-130H-30* Hercules**
Esq 501, Lisbon/Montijo
16801*
16802*
16803
16804
16805
16806*

**Lockheed (GD)**
**F-16**
(MLU aircraft are marked
with a *)
Esq 201, Monte Real
| 15101 | F-16A | Esq 201 |
|---|---|---|
| 15102 | F-16A | Esq 201 |
| 15103 | F-16A | Esq 201 |
| 15104 | F-16A* | Esq 201 |
| 15105 | F-16A | Esq 201 |
| 15106 | F-16A | Esq 201 |
| 15107 | F-16A | Esq 201 |
| 15108 | F-16A | Esq 201 |
| 15109 | F-16A | Esq 201 |
| 15110 | F-16A | Esq 201 |
| 15111 | F-16A | Esq 201 |
| 15112 | F-16A | Esq 201 |
| 15113 | F-16A | Esq 201 |
| 15114 | F-16A | Esq 201 |
| 15115 | F-16A | Esq 201 |
| 15116 | F-16A | Esq 201 |
| 15117 | F-16A | Esq 201 |
| 15118 | F-16B | Esq 201 |
| 15119 | F-16B | Esq 201 |
| 15120 | F-16B | Esq 201 |
| 15121 | F-16A* | Esq 201 |
| 15122 | F-16A | |
| 15123 | F-16A | |
| 15124 | F-16A | |
| 15125 | F-16A | |
| 15126 | F-16A | |
| 15127 | F-16A | |
| 15128 | F-16A | |
| 15129 | F-16A | |
| 15130 | F-16A | |
| 15131 | F-16A | |
| 15132 | F-16A | |
| 15133 | F-16A* | Esq 201 |
| 15134 | F-16A | |
| 15135 | F-16A | |
| 15136 | F-16A | |
| 15137 | F-16A | |

| 15138 | F-16A* | Esq 201 |
|---|---|---|
| 15139 | F-16B* | Esq 201 |
| 15140 | F-16B | |
| 15141 | F-16A | |

**Lockheed**
**P-3C/P-3P Orion**
Esq 601, Lisbon/Montijo
14801    P-3P
14803    P-3P
14804    P-3P
14805    P-3P
14807    P-3C
14808    P-3C
14809    P-3C
14810    P-3C
14811    P-3C

**Marinha**
**Westland**
**Super Lynx Mk 95**
Esq de Helicopteros,
 Lisbon/Montijo
19201
19202
19203
19204
19205

**QATAR**
**Airbus A.310-304**
Qatari Govt, Doha
A7-AAF

**Airbus A.319CJ-133**
Qatari Govt, Doha
A7-HHJ

**Airbus A.320-232**
Qatari Govt, Doha
A7-AAG

**Airbus A.330-202**
Qatari Govt, Doha
A7-HJJ

**Airbus A.340-211/-541***
Qatari Govt, Doha
A7-HHH*
A7-HHK

**ROMANIA**
**Fortele Aeriene Romania**
**Antonov An-26**
Escadrilla 902,
 Bucharest/Otopeni
801
808
809
810

**Lockheed**
**C-130B Hercules**
Escadrilla 901,
 Bucharest/Otopeni
5927
5930
6150
6166

**Romanian Govt**
**Boeing 707-3K1C**
Romanian Govt,
 Bucharest/Otopeni

YR-ABB

**RUSSIA**
**Voenno-Vozdushniye Sily**
**Rossiski Federatsii**
**(Russian Air Force)**
**Sukhoi Su-27**
TsAGI, Gromov Flight
 Institute, Zhukovsky
595     Su-27P
597     Su-30
598     Su-27P

**Russian Govt**
**Ilyushin Il-62M**
Russian Govt, Moscow
RA-86466
RA-86467
RA-86468
RA-86536
RA-86537
RA-86539
RA-86540
RA-86553
RA-86554
RA-86559
RA-86561
RA-86710
RA-86711
RA-86712

**Ilyushin Il-96-300**
Russian Govt, Moscow
RA-96012
RA-96016

**Tupolev Tu-134A**
Russian Govt, Moscow
RA-65904

**Tupolev Tu-154M**
Russian Govt, Moscow;
Open Skies*
RA-85629
RA-85631
RA-85645
RA-85655*
RA-85659
RA-85666
RA-85843

**SAUDI ARABIA**
**Al Quwwat al Jawwiya**
**as Sa'udiya**
**BAe 125-800/-800B***
1 Sqn, Riyadh
HZ-105
HZ-109*
HZ-110*

**Boeing 737-7DP/-8DP***
1 Sqn, Riyadh
HZ-101
HZ-102*
**Boeing**
**E-3A/KE-3A/RE-3A Sentry**
18 Sqn, Riyadh;
19 Sqn, Riyadh
| 1801 | E-3A | 18 Sqn |
|---|---|---|
| 1802 | E-3A | 18 Sqn |
| 1803 | E-3A | 18 Sqn |
| 1804 | E-3A | 18 Sqn |
| 1805 | E-3A | 18 Sqn |
| 1811 | KE-3A | 18 Sqn |

| | | |
|---|---|---|
| 1812 | KE-3A | 18 Sqn |
| 1813 | KE-3A | 18 Sqn |
| 1814 | KE-3A | 18 Sqn |
| 1815 | KE-3A | 18 Sqn |
| 1816 | KE-3A | 18 Sqn |
| 1818 | KE-3A | 18 Sqn |
| 1901 | RE-3A | 19 Sqn |

**Lockheed**
**C-130/L.100 Hercules**
1 Sqn, Prince Sultan AB;
4 Sqn, Jeddah;
16 Sqn, Prince Sultan AB;
32 Sqn, Prince Sultan AB

| | | |
|---|---|---|
| 111 | VC-130H | 1 Sqn |
| 112 | VC-130H | 1 Sqn |
| 451 | C-130E | 4 Sqn |
| 452 | C-130E | 4 Sqn |
| 455 | C-130E | 4 Sqn |
| 461 | C-130H | 4 Sqn |
| 462 | C-130H | 4 Sqn |
| 463 | C-130H | 4 Sqn |
| 464 | C-130H | 4 Sqn |
| 465 | C-130H | 4 Sqn |
| 466 | C-130H | 4 Sqn |
| 467 | C-130H | 4 Sqn |
| 468 | C-130H | 4 Sqn |
| 471 | C-130H-30 | 4 Sqn |
| 472 | C-130H | 4 Sqn |
| 473 | C-130H | 4 Sqn |
| 474 | C-130H | 4 Sqn |
| 475 | C-130H | 4 Sqn |
| 1601 | C-130H | 16 Sqn |
| 1602 | C-130H | 16 Sqn |
| 1603 | C-130H | 16 Sqn |
| 1604 | C-130H | 16 Sqn |
| 1605 | C-130H | 16 Sqn |
| 1606 | C-130E | 16 Sqn |
| 1607 | C-130E | 16 Sqn |
| 1608 | C-130E | 16 Sqn |
| 1609 | C-130E | 16 Sqn |
| 1611 | C-130E | 16 Sqn |
| 1614 | C-130H | 16 Sqn |
| 1615 | C-130H | 16 Sqn |
| 1618 | C-130H | 16 Sqn |
| 1619 | C-130H | 16 Sqn |
| 1622 | C-130H-30 | 16 Sqn |
| 1623 | C-130H-30 | 16 Sqn |
| 1624 | C-130H | 16 Sqn |
| 1625 | C-130H | 16 Sqn |
| 1626 | C-130H | 16 Sqn |
| 3201 | KC-130H | 32 Sqn |
| 3202 | KC-130H | 32 Sqn |
| 3203 | KC-130H | 32 Sqn |
| 3204 | KC-130H | 32 Sqn |
| 3205 | KC-130H | 32 Sqn |
| 3206 | KC-130H | 32 Sqn |
| 3207 | KC-130H | 32 Sqn |
| HZ-114 | VC-130H | 1 Sqn |
| HZ-115 | VC-130H | 1 Sqn |
| HZ-116 | VC-130H | 1 Sqn |
| HZ-117 | L.100-30 | 1 Sqn |
| HZ-128 | L.100-30 | 1 Sqn |
| HZ-129 | L.100-30 | 1 Sqn |

**Saudi Govt**
**Airbus A.340-211**
Royal Embassy of Saudi
Arabia, Riyadh
HZ-124

**Boeing 747-3G1**
Saudi Royal Flight, Jeddah
HZ-HM1A

**Boeing 747SP-68**
Saudi Govt, Jeddah;
Saudi Royal Flight, Jeddah
HZ-AIF      Govt
HZ-AIJ      Royal Flight
HZ-HM1B    Royal Flight

**Boeing 757-23A**
Saudi Govt, Jeddah
HZ-HMED

**Boeing MD-11**
Saudi Royal Flight, Jeddah
HZ-AFA1
HZ-HM7

**Canadair**
**CL.604 Challenger**
Saudi Royal Flight, Jeddah
HZ-AFA2

**Cessna 550 Citation II**
1 Sqn, Riyadh
HZ-133
HZ-134

**Dassault Falcon 900**
Saudi Govt, Jeddah
HZ-AFT
HZ-AFZ

**Grumman**
**G.1159A Gulfstream III**
Armed Forces Medical
Services, Riyadh;
Saudi Govt, Jeddah
HZ-AFN      Govt
HZ-AFR      Govt
HZ-MS3      AFMS

**Grumman**
**G.1159C Gulfstream IV**
Armed Forces Medical
Services, Riyadh;
Saudi Govt, Jeddah
HZ-AFU      Govt
HZ-AFV      Govt
HZ-AFW      Govt
HZ-AFX      Govt
HZ-AFY      Govt
HZ-MS4      AFMS

**Gulfstream Aerospace**
**Gulfstream V**
Armed Forces Medical
Services, Riyadh
HZ-MS5
HZ-MS5A

**Lockheed**
**C-130H/L.100 Hercules**
Armed Forces Medical
Services, Riyadh
HZ-MS6      L.100-30
HZ-MS7      C-130H
HZ-MS8      C-130H-30
HZ-MS09     L.100-30
HZ-MS019    C-130H

**Lockheed**
**L.1011 TriStar 500**
Saudi Royal Flight, Jeddah
HZ-HM5
HZ-HM6

**SINGAPORE**
**Republic of Singapore**
**Air Force**
**Boeing**
**KC-135R Stratotanker**
112 Sqn, Changi;
750
751
752
753

**Lockheed**
**C-130 Hercules**
122 Sqn, Paya Lebar

| | |
|---|---|
| 720 | KC-130B |
| 721 | KC-130B |
| 724 | KC-130B |
| 725 | KC-130B |
| 730 | C-130H |
| 731 | C-130H |
| 732 | C-130H |
| 733 | C-130H |
| 734 | KC-130H |
| 735 | C-130H |

**SLOVAKIA**
**Slovenské Vojenske**
**Letectvo**
**Aero L-39 Albatros**
1 SLK/2 Letka, Sliač [SL]

| | |
|---|---|
| 0111 | L-39C |
| 1701 | L-39ZA |
| 1725 | L-39ZA |
| 1730 | L-39ZA |
| 4701 | L-39ZA |
| 4703 | L-39ZA |
| 4707 | L-39ZA |
| 4711 | L-39ZA |
| 5301 | L-39C |

**Antonov An-24V**
SDoLt/1 Dopravná
Roj, Malacky
2903
5605

**Antonov An-26**
SDoLt/1 Dopravná
Roj, Malacky
2506
3208

**LET 410 Turbolet**
1 SLK/3 Letka, Sliač [SL];
SDoLt/2 Dopravná
Roj, Malacky

| | | |
|---|---|---|
| 0730 | L-410UVP | SDoLt |
| 0927 | L-410T | 1 SLK |
| 0930 | L-410T | SDoLt |
| 1133 | L-410T | |
| 1521 | L-410FG | SDoLt |
| 2311 | L-410UVP | SDoLt |
| 2421 | L-410UVP | SDoLt |

**Mikoyan MiG-29A/UB***
1 SLK/1 Letka, Sliač [SL]
0619
0820
0921
1303*
2123
3709
3911
4401*

# Slovakia – Spain

5113
5304*
5515
5817
6124
6425
6526
6627
6728
7501
8003
8605
9308

**Mil M-17**
3 Vrtulnikové Letecké
Kridlo/2 Letka, Prešov
0807
0808
0812
0820
0821
0823
0824
0826
0827
0841
0842
0844
0845
0846
0847

**Mil Mi-24**
3 Vrtulnikové Letecké
Kridlo/1 Letka, Prešov

| 0100 | Mi-24D |
| 0101 | Mi-24D |
| 0149 | Mi-24D |
| 0150 | Mi-24D |
| 0215 | Mi-24D |
| 0222 | Mi-24D |
| 0223 | Mi-24D |
| 0704 | Mi-24V |
| 0707 | Mi-24V |
| 0708 | Mi-24V |
| 0786 | Mi-24V |
| 0787 | Mi-24V |
| 0813 | Mi-24V |
| 0814 | Mi-24V |
| 0832 | Mi-24V |
| 0833 | Mi-24V |
| 0927 | Mi-24V |
| 4009 | Mi-24D |
| 6040 | Mi-24DU |

**Slovak Govt
Tupolev Tu-154M**
Slovak Govt,
Bratislava/Ivanka
OM-BYO
OM-BYR

**Yakovlev Yak-40**
Slovak Govt,
Bratislava/Ivanka
OM-BYE
OM-BYL

**SLOVENIA**
**Slovene Army**
**LET 410UVP-E**
LTO, Brnik
L4-01

**Pilatus PC-9M**
1/2/3 OSBL, Cerklje
L9-51
L9-53
L9-61
L9-62
L9-63
L9-64
L9-65
L9-66
L9-67
L9-68
L9-69

**SOUTH AFRICA**
**South African Air Force/
Suid Afrikaanse Lugmag**
**Boeing 707**
60 Sqn, Waterkloof

| 1415 | 328C |
| 1417 | 328C |
| 1419 | 328C |
| 1423 | 344C |

**Boeing 737-7ED**
21 Sqn, Waterkloof
ZS-RSA

**Dassault Falcon 900**
21 Sqn, Waterkloof
ZS-NAN

**Lockheed
C-130B/C-130BZ* Hercules**
28 Sqn, Waterkloof
401
402*
403
404
405*
406*
407*
408*
409*

**SPAIN**
**Ejército del Aire**
**Airbus A.310-304**
Grupo 45, Torrejón

| T.22-1 | 45-50 |
| T.22-2 | 45-51 |

**Airtech
CN.235M-10 (T.19A)/
CN.235M-100 (T.19B)**
Ala 35, Getafe

| T.19A-01 | 35-60 |
| T.19A-02 | 35-61 |
| T.19B-03 | 35-21 |
| T.19B-04 | 35-22 |
| T.19B-05 | 35-23 |
| T.19B-06 | 35-24 |
| T.19B-07 | 35-25 |
| T.19B-08 | 35-26 |
| T.19B-09 | 35-27 |
| T.19B-10 | 35-28 |
| T.19B-11 | 35-29 |
| T.19B-12 | 35-30 |
| T.19B-13 | 35-31 |
| T.19B-14 | 35-32 |
| T.19B-15 | 35-33 |
| T.19B-16 | 35-34 |
| T.19B-17 | 35-35 |
| T.19B-18 | 35-36 |
| T.19B-19 | 35-37 |
| T.19B-20 | 35-38 |

**Boeing 707**
47 Grupo Mixto, Torrejón

| TK.17-1 | 331B | 47-01 |
| T.17-2 | 331B | 45-11 |
| T.17-3 | 368C | 45-12 |
| TM.17-4 | 351C | 408-21 |

**CASA 101EB Aviojet**
Grupo 54, Torrejón;
Grupo de Escuelas de
Matacán (74);
AGA, San Javier (79);
*Patrulla Aguila*, San Javier*

| E.25-01 | 79-01 [6]* |
| E.25-05 | 79-05 |
| E.25-06 | 79-06 [5]* |
| E.25-07 | 79-07 [7]* |
| E.25-08 | 79-08 [4]* |
| E.25-09 | 79-09 |
| E.25-10 | 79-10 |
| E.25-11 | 79-11 |
| E.25-12 | 79-12 |
| E.25-13 | 79-13 |
| E.25-14 | 79-14 |
| E.25-15 | 79-15 |
| E.25-16 | 79-16 |
| E.25-17 | 74-40 |
| E.25-18 | 74-42 |
| E.25-19 | 79-19 |
| E.25-20 | 79-20 |
| E.25-21 | 79-21 [1]* |
| E.25-23 | 79-23 [5]* |
| E.25-24 | 79-24 |
| E.25-25 | 79-25 |
| E.25-26 | 79-26 [3]* |
| E.25-27 | 79-27 [4]* |
| E.25-28 | 79-28 [2]* |
| E.25-29 | 74-45 |
| E.25-31 | 79-31 |
| E.25-33 | 74-02 |
| E.25-34 | 79-34 |
| E.25-35 | 54-20 |
| E.25-37 | 79-37 |
| E.25-38 | 79-38 |
| E.25-40 | 79-40 |
| E.25-41 | 74-41 |
| E.25-43 | 74-43 |
| E.25-44 | 79-44 |
| E.25-45 | 79-45 |
| E.25-46 | 79-46 |
| E.25-47 | 79-47 |
| E.25-48 | 79-48 |
| E.25-49 | 79-49 |
| E.25-50 | 79-33 |
| E.25-51 | 74-07 |
| E.25-52 | 79-34 |
| E.25-53 | 74-09 |
| E.25-54 | 79-35 |
| E.25-55 | 54-21 |
| E.25-56 | 74-11 |
| E.25-57 | 74-12 |
| E.25-59 | 74-13 |
| E.25-61 | 54-22 |
| E.25-62 | 79-17 |
| E.25-63 | 74-17 |
| E.25-64 | 79-18 |
| E.25-65 | 79-95 |
| E.25-66 | 74-20 |
| E.25-67 | 74-21 |
| E.25-68 | 74-22 |
| E.25-69 | 79-97 |

| | |
|---|---|
| E.25-71 | 74-25 |
| E.25-72 | 74-26 |
| E.25-73 | 79-98 |
| E.25-74 | 74-28 |
| E.25-75 | 74-29 |
| E.25-76 | 74-30 |
| E.25-78 | 79-02 |
| E.25-79 | 79-39 |
| E.25-80 | 79-03 |
| E.25-81 | 74-34 |
| E.25-83 | 74-35 |
| E.25-84 | 79-04 |
| E.25-86 | 79-32 [5]* |
| E.25-87 | 79-29 |
| E.25-88 | 74-39 |

**CASA 212 Aviocar**
**212 (XT.12)/**
**212A (T.12B)/**
**212B (TR.12A)/**
**212D (TE.12B)/**
**212DE (TM.12D)/**
**212E (T.12C)/**
**212S (D.3A)/**
**212S1 (D.3B)/**
**212-200 (T.12D)/**
**212-200 (TR.12D)**
Ala 37, Villanubla;
47 Grupo Mixto, Torrejón;
CLAEX, Torrejón (54);
Ala 72, Alcantarilla;
Grupo Esc, Matacán (74);
AGA (Ala 79), San Javier;
403 Esc, Getafe;
801 Esc, Palma/
Son San Juan;
803 Esc, Cuatro Vientos;
INTA, Torrejón

| | |
|---|---|
| D.3A-1 | (801 Esc) |
| D.3A-2 | (803 Esc) |
| D.3B-3 | (803 Esc) |
| D.3B-4 | (801 Esc) |
| D.3B-5 | (801 Esc) |
| D.3B-6 | (801 Esc) |
| D.3B-7 | (803 Esc) |
| D.3B-8 | (801 Esc) |
| TR.12A-4 | 403-02 |
| TR.12A-5 | 403-03 |
| TR.12A-6 | 403-04 |
| TR.12A-8 | 403-06 |
| T.12B-9 | 74-83 |
| TE.12B-10 | 74-85 |
| T.12B-12 | 74-82 |
| T.12B-15 | 37-02 |
| T.12B-16 | 74-71 |
| T.12B-17 | 37-03 |
| T.12B-18 | |
| T.12B-19 | 46-32 |
| T.12B-20 | 37-04 |
| T.12B-21 | 46-05 |
| T.12B-22 | 37-06 |
| T.12B-23 | 72-01 |
| T.12B-24 | 54-12 |
| T.12B-25 | 74-72 |
| T.12B-26 | 72-02 |
| T.12B-28 | 72-03 |
| T.12B-29 | 37-08 |
| T.12B-30 | 74-73 |
| T.12B-31 | |
| T.12B-33 | 72-04 |
| T.12B-34 | 74-74 |
| T.12B-36 | 37-10 |
| T.12B-37 | 72-05 |
| T.12B-39 | 74-75 |

| | |
|---|---|
| TE.12B-40 | 74-84 |
| TE.12B-41 | 79-94 |
| T.12C-43 | 46-50 |
| T.12C-44 | 37-50 |
| T.12B-46 | 74-76 |
| T.12B-47 | 72-06 |
| T.12B-48 | 37-11 |
| T.12B-49 | 72-07 |
| T.12B-52 | 46-35 |
| T.12B-53 | 46-36 |
| T.12B-54 | 46-37 |
| T.12B-56 | |
| T.12B-57 | 72-08 |
| T.12C-59 | 37-51 |
| T.12C-60 | 37-52 |
| T.12C-61 | 47-11 |
| T.12B-63 | 37-14 |
| T.12B-64 | |
| T.12B-65 | 74-80 |
| T.12B-67 | 74-81 |
| T.12B-70 | 37-17 |
| T.12B-71 | 37-18 |
| TM.12D-72 | 47-12 |
| TM.12D-74 | 54-11 |
| T.12D-75 | 403-07 |
| TR.12D-76 | 37-60 |
| TR.12D-77 | 37-61 |
| TR.12D-78 | 37-62 |
| TR.12D-79 | 37-63 |
| TR.12D-80 | 37-64 |
| TR.12D-81 | 37-65 |

**CASA 295**
Ala 35, Getafe;

| | |
|---|---|
| T.21-01 | 35-39 |
| T.21-02 | 35-40 |
| T.21-03 | 35-41 |
| T.21-04 | 35-42 |
| T.21-05 | 35-43 |
| T.21-06 | 35-44 |
| T.21-07 | 35-45 |
| T.21-08 | 35-46 |
| T.21-09 | 35-47 |

**Cessna 560 Citation VI**
403 Esc, Getafe

| | |
|---|---|
| TR.20-01 | 403-11 |
| TR.20-02 | 403-12 |

**Dassault Falcon 20D/E/F**
47 Grupo Mixto, Torrejón

| | | |
|---|---|---|
| TM.11-1 | 20E | 47-21 |
| TM.11-2 | 20D | 47-22 |
| TM.11-3 | 20D | 47-23 |
| TM.11-4 | 20E | 408-12 |

**Dassault Falcon 900/900B***
Grupo 45, Torrejón

| | |
|---|---|
| T.18-1 | 45-40 |
| T.18-2 | 45-41 |
| T.18-3* | 45-42 |
| T.18-4* | 45-43 |
| T.18-5* | 45-44 |

**Eurofighter**
**EF.2000/EF.2000B***
Ala 11, Morón;
CASA, Getafe

| | |
|---|---|
| CE.16-01* | 11-70 |
| CE.16-02* | 11-71 |
| CE.16-03* | 11-72 |
| CE.16-04* | 11-73 |
| CE.16-05* | 11-74 |
| CE.16-06* | 11-75 |

| | |
|---|---|
| C.16-20 | 11-91 |
| C.16-21 | 11-01 |
| C.16-22 | 11-02 |
| C.16-23 | 11-03 |
| C.16-24 | 11-04 |

**Fokker**
**F.27M Friendship 400MPA**
802 Esc, Gando, Las Palmas

| | |
|---|---|
| D.2-01 | 802-10 |
| D.2-02 | 802-11 |
| D.2-03 | |

**Lockheed**
**C-130H/C-130H-30/**
**KC-130H Hercules**
311 Esc/312 Esc (Ala 31),
Zaragoza

| | | |
|---|---|---|
| TL.10-01 | C-130H-30 | 31-01 |
| T.10-02 | C-130H | 31-02 |
| T.10-03 | C-130H | 31-03 |
| T.10-04 | C-130H | 31-04 |
| TK.10-5 | KC-130H | 31-50 |
| TK.10-6 | KC-130H | 31-51 |
| TK.10-07 | KC-130H | 31-52 |
| T.10-8 | C-130H | 31-05 |
| T.10-9 | C-130H | 31-06 |
| T.10-10 | C-130H | 31-07 |
| TK.10-11 | KC-130H | 31-53 |
| TK.10-12 | KC-130H | 31-54 |

**Lockheed**
**P-3A/P-3B/P-3M Orion**
Grupo 22, Morón

| | | |
|---|---|---|
| P.3-01 | P-3A | 22-21 |
| P.3-08 | P-3B | 22-31* |
| P.3-09 | P-3M | 22-32* |
| P.3-10 | P-3B | 22-33* |
| P.3-11 | P-3B | 22-34* |
| P.3-12 | P-3B | 22-35* |

**McDonnell Douglas**
**F-18 Hornet**
Ala 12, Torrejón;
Ala 15, Zaragoza;
Esc 462, Gran Canaria
**EF-18A/EF-18B* Hornet**

| | |
|---|---|
| CE.15-1 | 15-70* |
| CE.15-2 | 15-71* |
| CE.15-3 | 15-72* |
| CE.15-4 | 15-73* |
| CE.15-5 | 15-74* |
| CE.15-6 | 15-75* |
| CE.15-7 | 15-76* |
| CE.15-8 | 12-71* |
| CE.15-9 | 15-77* |
| CE.15-10 | 12-73* |
| CE.15-11 | 12-74* |
| CE.15-12 | 12-75* |
| C.15-13 | 12-01 |
| C.15-14 | 15-01 |
| C.15-15 | 15-02 |
| C.15-16 | 15-03 |
| C.15-18 | 15-05 |
| C.15-20 | 15-07 |
| C.15-21 | 15-08 |
| C.15-22 | 15-09 |
| C.15-23 | 15-10 |
| C.15-24 | 15-11 |
| C.15-25 | 15-12 |
| C.15-26 | 15-13 |
| C.15-27 | 15-14 |
| C.15-28 | 15-15 |
| C.15-29 | 15-16 |

| | |
|---|---|
| C.15-30 | 15-17 |
| C.15-31 | 15-18 |
| C.15-32 | 15-19 |
| C.15-33 | 15-20 |
| C.15-34 | 15-21 |
| C.15-35 | 15-22 |
| C.15-36 | 15-23 |
| C.15-37 | 15-24 |
| C.15-38 | 15-25 |
| C.15-39 | 15-26 |
| C.15-40 | 15-27 |
| C.15-41 | 15-28 |
| C.15-43 | 15-30 |
| C.15-45 | 12-02 |
| C.15-46 | 12-03 |
| C.15-46 | 12-04 |
| C.15-47 | 15-31 |
| C.15-48 | 12-06 |
| C.15-49 | 12-07 |
| C.15-50 | 12-08 |
| C.15-51 | 12-09 |
| C.15-52 | 12-10 |
| C.15-53 | 12-11 |
| C.15-54 | 12-12 |
| C.15-55 | 12-13 |
| C.15-56 | 12-14 |
| C.15-57 | 12-15 |
| C.15-58 | 12-16 |
| C.15-59 | 12-17 |
| C.15-60 | 12-18 |
| C.15-61 | 12-19 |
| C.15-62 | 12-20 |
| C.15-64 | 12-22 |
| C.15-65 | 12-23 |
| C.15-66 | 12-24 |
| C.15-67 | 15-33 |
| C.15-68 | 12-26 |
| C.15-69 | 12-27 |
| C.15-70 | 12-28 |
| C.15-72 | 12-30 |

**F/A-18A Hornet**

| | |
|---|---|
| C.15-73 | 46-01 |
| C.15-74 | 46-02 |
| C.15-75 | 46-03 |
| C.15-77 | 46-05 |
| C.15-78 | 46-06 |
| C.15-79 | 46-07 |
| C.15-80 | 21-08 |
| C.15-81 | 11-09 |
| C.15-82 | 46-10 |
| C.15-83 | 46-11 |
| C.15-84 | 46-12 |
| C.15-85 | 46-13 |
| C.15-86 | 46-14 |
| C.15-87 | 46-15 |
| C.15-88 | 46-16 |
| C.15-89 | 46-17 |
| C.15-90 | 46-18 |
| C.15-91 | 46-19 |
| C.15-92 | 46-20 |
| C.15-93 | 46-21 |
| C.15-94 | 46-22 |
| C.15-95 | 46-23 |
| C.15-96 | 46-24 |

**Arma Aérea de l'Armada Española**
**BAe/McDonnell Douglas**
**EAV-8B/EAV-8B+/TAV-8B Harrier II**
Esc 009, Rota
**EAV-8B**

| | |
|---|---|
| VA.1A-15 | 01-903 |
| VA.1A-18 | 01-906 |
| VA.1A-19 | 01-907 |
| VA.1A-21 | 01-909 |
| VA.1A-22 | 01-911 |
| VA.1A-23 | |
| VA.1B-24 | 01-914 |

**EAV-8B+**

| | |
|---|---|
| VA.1B-25 | 01-915 |
| VA.1B-26 | 01-912 |
| VA.1B-27 | 01-916 |
| VA.1B-28 | 01-917 |
| VA.1B-29 | 01-918 |
| VA.1B-30 | 01-919 |
| VA.1B-31 | 01-920 |
| VA.1B-34 | 01-921 |
| VA.1B-35 | 01-923 |
| VA.1B-36 | 01-924 |
| VA.1B-37 | 01-925 |
| VA.1B-38 | 01-926 |
| VA.1B-39 | 01-927 |

**TAV-8B**

| | |
|---|---|
| VAE.1A-33 | 01-922 |

**Cessna 550 Citation 2**
Esc 004, Rota

| | |
|---|---|
| U.20-1 | 01-405 |
| U.20-2 | 01-406 |
| U.20-3 | 01-407 |

# SUDAN
**Dassault Falcon 50**
Sudanese Govt, Khartoum
ST-PSR

**Dassault Falcon 900B**
Sudanese Govt, Khartoum
ST-PSA

# SWEDEN
**Svenska Flygvapnet**
**Grumman**
**G.1159C Gulfstream 4 (Tp.102A/S.102B Korpen/Tp.102C)**
Flottiljer 17M, Stockholm/Bromma & Malmslätt
**Tp.102A**

| | |
|---|---|
| 102001 | 021 |

**S.102B Korpen**

| | |
|---|---|
| 102002 | 022 |
| 102003 | 023 |

**Tp.102C**

| | |
|---|---|
| 102004 | 024 |

**Lockheed**
**C-130H Hercules (Tp.84)**
Flottiljer 7, Såtenäs

| | |
|---|---|
| 84001 | 841 |
| 84002 | 842 |
| 84003 | 843 |
| 84004 | 844 |
| 84005 | 845 |
| 84006 | 846 |
| 84007 | 847 |
| 84008 | 848 |

**Rockwell**
**Sabreliner-40 (Tp.86)**
FMV, Malmslätt

| | |
|---|---|
| 86001 | 861 |

**SAAB JAS 39 Gripen**
Flottiljer 4, Östersund/Frösön;
Flottiljer 7, Såtenäs [G];
Flottiljer 10, Ängelholm;
Flottiljer 17, Ronneby/Kallinge;
Flottiljer 21, Luleå/Kallax
FMV, Malmslätt

**JAS 39**

| | | |
|---|---|---|
| 39-5 | 55 | FMV |

**JAS 39A**

| | | |
|---|---|---|
| 39101 | 51 | FMV |
| 39103 | 103 | FMV |
| 39104 | 04 | F7 |
| 39106 | 106 | F10 |
| 39107 | 107 | F7 |
| 39109 | 09 | F7 |
| 39110 | 10 | F7 |
| 39112 | 112 | F7 |
| 39113 | 13 | F7 |
| 39114 | 14 | F7 |
| 39115 | 15 | F7 |
| 39116 | 16 | SAAB |
| 39117 | 17 | F7 |
| 39118 | 18 | SAAB |
| 39119 | 19 | F7 |
| 39120 | 120 | F21 |
| 39121 | 121 | F7 |
| 39122 | 122 | F7 |
| 39123 | 123 | F7 |
| 39124 | 124 | F7 |
| 39125 | 125 | F4 |
| 39126 | 126 | F17 |
| 39127 | 127 | F7 |
| 39128 | 128 | F7 |
| 39129 | 129 | F7 |
| 39131 | 131 | F7 |
| 39132 | 132 | F7 |
| 39133 | 133 | F7 |
| 39134 | 134 | F7 |
| 39135 | 135 | F17 |
| 39136 | 36 | F17 |
| 39137 | 137 | F10 |
| 39138 | 138 | F17 |
| 39139 | 139 | F17 |
| 39140 | 140 | F17 |
| 39141 | 41 | F17 |
| 39142 | 42 | F21 |
| 39143 | 43 | F17 |
| 39144 | 44 | F10 |
| 39145 | 145 | F7 |
| 39146 | 146 | F7 |
| 39147 | 147 | F17 |
| 39148 | 148 | F17 |
| 39149 | 149 | F7 |
| 39150 | 150 | F7 |
| 39151 | 151 | F7 |
| 39152 | 152 | F17 |
| 39153 | 153 | F7 |
| 39154 | 154 | F7 |
| 39155 | 155 | F17 |
| 39157 | 157 | F17 |
| 39158 | 158 | F17 |
| 39159 | 159 | F7 |
| 39160 | 160 | F7 |
| 39161 | 161 | F7 |
| 39162 | 162 | F7 |
| 39163 | 163 | F17 |
| 39164 | 164 | F17 |
| 39166 | 166 | F17 |
| 39167 | 167 | F17 |
| 39168 | 168 | F10 |
| 39169 | 169 | F17 |
| 39170 | 170 | F17 |
| 39171 | 171 | F17 |
| 39172 | 172 | F17 |
| 39173 | 173 | F17 |

| | | |
|---|---|---|
| 39174 | 174 | F17 |
| 39175 | 175 | F17 |
| 39176 | 176 | F7 |
| 39177 | 177 | F17 |
| 39178 | 178 | F17 |
| 39179 | 179 | F7 |
| 39180 | 180 | F17 |
| 39181 | 181 | F7 |
| 39182 | 182 | F7 |
| 39183 | 183 | F7 |
| 39185 | 185 | FMV |
| 39186 | 186 | F17 |
| 39187 | 187 | F17 |
| 39188 | 188 | F7 |
| 39189 | 189 | F17 |
| 39190 | 190 | F17 |
| 39191 | 191 | F17 |
| 39192 | 192 | F7 |
| 39193 | 193 | F21 |
| 39194 | 194 | F21 |
| 39195 | 195 | F21 |
| 39196 | 196 | F21 |
| 39197 | 197 | F21 |
| 39198 | 198 | F21 |
| 39199 | 199 | F21 |
| 39200 | 200 | F21 |
| 39201 | 201 | F21 |
| 39202 | 202 | FMV |
| 39203 | 203 | F21 |
| 39204 | 204 | F21 |
| 39205 | 205 | F21 |
| 39206 | 206 | F21 |

**JAS 39B**

| | | |
|---|---|---|
| 39800 | 58 | FMV |
| 39801 | 801 | F7 |
| 39802 | 802 | SAAB |
| 39803 | 803 | F7 |
| 39804 | 804 | F7 |
| 39805 | 805 | F21 |
| 39806 | 806 | F17 |
| 39807 | 807 | F7 |
| 39808 | 808 | F17 |
| 39809 | 809 | F21 |
| 39810 | | |
| 39811 | 811 | FMV |
| 39812 | 812 | F7 |
| 39813 | 813 | FMV |
| 39814 | 814 | FMV |

**JAS 39C**

| | | |
|---|---|---|
| 39-6 | 6 | FMV |
| 39208 | 208 | SAAB |
| 39209 | 209 | FMV |
| 39210 | 210 | FMV |
| 39211 | 211 | SAAB |
| 39212 | 212 | F17 |
| 39213 | 213 | FMV |
| 39214 | | |
| 39215 | 215 | FMV |
| 39216 | 216 | F17 |
| 39217 | 217 | F17 |
| 39218 | | |
| 39219 | 219 | F17 |
| 39220 | | |
| 39221 | 221 | F17 |
| 39222 | | |
| 39223 | | |
| 39224 | 224 | F17 |
| 39225 | 225 | F17 |
| 39226 | 226 | F17 |
| 39227 | 227 | SAAB |
| 39228 | 228 | FMV |
| 39229 | 229 | FMV |
| 39230 | | |
| 39231 | 231 | FMV |

| | | |
|---|---|---|
| 39232 | 232 | FMV |
| 39233 | 233 | FMV |
| 39246 | 246 | |
| 39247 | | |
| 39248 | | |
| 39249 | | |
| 39250 | | |
| 39251 | | |
| 39252 | | |
| 39253 | | |
| 39254 | | |
| 39255 | | |
| 39256 | | |
| 39257 | | |
| 39258 | | |

**JAS 39D**

| | | |
|---|---|---|
| 39815 | 815 | SAAB |
| 39816 | | |
| 39817 | | |
| 39818 | | |
| 39821 | | |
| 39822 | 822 | SAAB |
| 39823 | 823 | SAAB |
| 39824 | | |
| 39825 | | |

**SAAB
SF.340 (OS.100 &
Tp.100C)/SF.340AEW&C
(S.100B & S.100D)
Argus**
Flottiljer 17, Ronneby/
  Kallinge;
Flottiljer 17M, Malmslätt;
Flottiljer 21, Luleå/
  Kallax

**OS.100**

| | | |
|---|---|---|
| 100001 | 001 | F17M |

**S.100B**

| | | |
|---|---|---|
| 100002 | 002 | F17M |
| 100005 | 005 | F17M |
| 100006 | 006 | F17M |
| 100007 | 007 | F17M |

**Tp.100C**

| | | |
|---|---|---|
| 100008 | 008 | F17 |
| 100009 | 009 | F21 |

**S.100D**

| | | |
|---|---|---|
| 100003 | 003 | F17M |
| 100004 | 004 | F17M |

**Försvarsmaktens
Helikopterflottilj
Aérospatiale
AS.332M-1 Super Puma
(Hkp.10)**
1.HkpSkv, Lycksele &
  Östersund/Frösön
2.HkpSkv, Berga, Goteborg/
Säve, & Ronneby/Kallinge;

| | | |
|---|---|---|
| 10402 | 92 | 2.HkpSkv |
| 10403 | 93 | 1.HkpSkv |
| 10405 | 95 | 2.HkpSkv |
| 10406 | 96 | 2.HkpSkv |
| 10407 | 97 | 1.HkpSkv |
| 10408 | 98 | 2.HkpSkv |
| 10410 | 90 | 2.HkpSkv |
| 10411 | 88 | 1.HkpSkv |
| 10412 | 89 | 1.HkpSkv |

**MBB Bo.105CBS (Hkp.9A)**
1.HkpSkv, Boden

| | |
|---|---|
| 09201 | 01 |
| 09202 | 02 |
| 09203 | 03 |
| 09204 | 04 |
| 09205 | 05 |
| 09206 | 06 |
| 09207 | 07 |
| 09208 | 08 |
| 09209 | 09 |
| 09210 | 10 |
| 09211 | 11 |
| 09212 | 12 |
| 09213 | 13 |
| 09214 | 14 |
| 09215 | 15 |
| 09216 | 16 |
| 09217 | 17 |
| 09218 | 18 |
| 09219 | 19 |
| 09220 | 20 |
| 09221 | 90 |

**Vertol/Kawasaki-Vertol 107**
2.HkpSkv, Berga,
  Goteborg/Säve,
  & Ronneby/Kallinge;
FMV (Flygvapnet),
  Malmslätt

**Vertol 107-II-15 (Hkp.4B)**

| | | |
|---|---|---|
| 04061 | 61 | 2.HkpSkv |
| 04063 | 63 | 2.HkpSkv |
| 04064 | 64 | 2.HkpSkv |

**Kawasaki-Vertol
KV.107-II-16 (Hkp.4C)**

| | | |
|---|---|---|
| 04065 | 65 | 2.HkpSkv |
| 04067 | 67 | 2.HkpSkv |
| 04068 | 68 | 2.HkpSkv |
| 04069 | 69 | 2.HkpSkv |
| 04070 | 70 | 2.HkpSkv |
| 04071 | 71 | 2.HkpSkv |
| 04072 | 72 | FMV |

**Vertol 107-II-15 (Hkp.4D)**

| | | |
|---|---|---|
| 04073 | 73 | 2.HkpSkv |
| 04074 | 74 | 2.HkpSkv |
| 04075 | 75 | 2.HkpSkv |
| 04076 | 76 | 2.HkpSkv |

**SWITZERLAND
Schweizerische Flugwaffe**
(Most aircraft are pooled
centrally. Some carry unit
badges but these rarely
indicate actual operators.)
Aérospatiale
AS.332M-1/AS.532UL
Super Puma
Lufttransport Staffel 3
  (LtSt 3), Dübendorf;
Lufttransport Staffel 4
  (LtSt 4), Dübendorf;
Lufttransport Staffel 5
  (LtSt 5), Payerne;
Lufttransport Staffel 6
  (LtSt 6), Alpnach;
Lufttransport Staffel 8
  (LtSt 8), Alpnach
Detachments at Emmen,
  Meiringen & Sion
**AS.332M-1**
T-311
T-312
T-313
T-314
T-315
T-316
T-317
T-318

# Switzerland

T-319
T-320
T-321
T-322
T-323
T-324
T-325
**AS.532UL**
T-331
T-332
T-333
T-334
T-335
T-336
T-337
T-338
T-339
T-340
T-341
T-342

**Aérospatiale**
**SA.365N Dauphin**
Gruppe Transport
 Flugzeuge, Dübendorf
T-771

**Beechcraft**
**Super King Air 350C**
Koordinationsstelle für
 Luftaufnahmen,
 Dübendorf
T-721

**Cessna 560 Citation VI**
Gruppe Transport
 Flugzeuge, Dübendorf
T-784

**Dassault Falcon 50**
Gruppe Transport
 Flugzeuge, Dübendorf
T-783

**Gates Learjet 35A**
Gruppe Transport
 Flugzeuge, Dübendorf
T-781

**McDonnell Douglas**
**F/A-18 Hornet**
Flieger Staffel 11 (FlSt 11),
 Meiringen;
Escadrille d'Aviation 17
 (EdAv 17), Payerne;
Flieger Staffel 18 (FlSt 18),
 Payerne
**F/A-18C**
J-5001
J-5002
J-5003
J-5004
J-5005
J-5006
J-5007
J-5008
J-5009
J-5010
J-5011
J-5012
J-5013
J-5014
J-5015
J-5016

J-5017
J-5018
J-5019
J-5020
J-5021
J-5022
J-5023
J-5024
J-5025
J-5026
**F/A-18D**
J-5232
J-5233
J-5234
J-5235
J-5236
J-5237
J-5238

**Northrop F-5 Tiger II**
Armasuisse, Emmen;
Escadrille d'Aviation 6
 (EdAv 6), Sion;
Flieger Staffel 8 (FlSt 8),
 Meiringen;
Flieger Staffel 11 (FlSt 11),
 Meiringen;
Flieger Staffel 19 (FlSt 19),
 Sion;
Instrumentation Flieger
 Staffel 14 (InstruFlSt 14),
 Dübendorf;
*Patrouille Suisse*, Emmen
(*P. Suisse*)
**F-5E**
J-3001
J-3008     InstruFlSt 14
J-3015
J-3024
J-3025
J-3043
J-3044
J-3049
J-3054
J-3055
J-3058
J-3060
J-3062
J-3063
J-3066
J-3067
J-3068
J-3069
J-3070
J-3072
J-3073
J-3074
J-3075
J-3076
J-3077
J-3079
J-3080     *P. Suisse*
J-3081     *P. Suisse*
J-3082     *P. Suisse*
J-3083     *P. Suisse*
J-3084     *P. Suisse*
J-3085     *P. Suisse*
J-3086     *P. Suisse*
J-3087     *P. Suisse*
J-3088     *P. Suisse*
J-3089     *P. Suisse*
J-3090     *P. Suisse*
J-3091     *P. Suisse*
J-3092

J-3093
J-3094
J-3095     *P. Suisse*
J-3096
J-3097
J-3098
**F-5F**
J-3201
J-3202
J-3203
J-3204
J-3205
J-3206
J-3207
J-3208
J-3209
J-3210
J-3211
J-3212

**Pilatus**
**PC.6B/B2-H2 Turbo Porter**
Lufttransport Staffel 5
 (LtSt 5), Emmen
V-612
V-613
V-614
V-616
V-617
V-618
V-619
V-620
V-622
V-623
V-631
V-632
V-633
V-634
V-635

**Pilatus PC-7**
**Turbo Trainer**
Pilotenschule, Emmen
A-902
A-903
A-904
A-906
A-907
A-908
A-909
A-910
A-911
A-912
A-913
A-914
A-915
A-916
A-917
A-918
A-919
A-922
A-923
A-924
A-925
A-926
A-927
A-928
A-929
A-930
A-931
A-932
A-933
A-934
A-935

| | | | |
|---|---|---|---|
| A-936 | | 88-0021 | Öncel Filo |
| A-937 | **Lockheed** | 88-0024 | 142 Filo |
| A-938 | **C-130E Hercules** | 88-0025 | 141 Filo |
| A-939 | 222 Filo, Erkilet | 88-0026 | 142 Filo |
| A-940 | 01468     12-468 | 88-0027 | Öncel Filo |
| A-941 | 01947 | 88-0028 | 191 Filo |
| | 13186     12-186 | 88-0029 | 142 Filo |
| **Pilatus PC-9** | 13187 | 88-0030 | 191 Filo |
| Zielfligerstaffel 12, Sion | 13188     12-188 | 88-0031 | Öncel Filo |
| C-401 | 13189 | 88-0032 | Öncel Filo |
| C-402 | 73-991 | 88-0033 | 141 Filo |
| C-405 | | 88-0034 | 141 Filo |
| C-406 | **Transall C-160D** | 88-0035 | 141 Filo |
| C-407 | 221 Filo, Erkilet | 88-0036 | 141 Filo |
| C-408 | 69-019 | 88-0037 | 141 Filo |
| C-409 | 69-020 | 89-0022 | 141 Filo |
| C-410 | 021 | 89-0023 | 141 Filo |
| C-411 | 69-023 | 89-0024 | 141 Filo |
| C-412 | 69-024 | 89-0025 | 141 Filo |
| | 69-026 | 89-0026 | 141 Filo |
| **SYRIA** | 69-027 | 89-0027 | 141 Filo |
| **Dassault Falcon 900** | 69-028     12-028 | 89-0028 | 141 Filo |
| Govt of Syria, Damascus | 69-029 | 89-0030 | 141 Filo |
| YK-ASC | 69-031 | 89-0031 | Öncel Filo |
| | 69-032 | 89-0032 | 141 Filo |
| **TANZANIA** | 69-033 | 89-0034 | 162 Filo |
| **Gulfstream G550** | 034 | 89-0035 | 162 Filo |
| Tanzanian Govt, | 035     12-035 | 89-0036 | 162 Filo |
| Dar-es-Salaam | 036 | 89-0037 | 162 Filo |
| 5H-ONE | 69-038 | 89-0038 | 162 Filo |
| | 69-040 | 89-0039 | 162 Filo |
| **THAILAND** | | 89-0040 | 162 Filo |
| **Airbus A.310-324** | **TUSAS-GD F-16C/F-16D\*** | 89-0041 | 162 Filo |
| Royal Flight, Bangkok | **Fighting Falcon** | 89-0042\* | Öncel Filo |
| L.13-1/34   (HS-TYQ) [44-444] | 4 AJÜ, Mürted: | 89-0043\* | 162 Filo |
| |   141 Filo, 142 Filo | 89-0044\* | 162 Filo |
| **TUNISIA** |   & 143/Öncel Filo; | 89-0045\* | 182 Filo |
| **Boeing 737-7HJ** | 5 AJÜ, Merzifon: | 90-0001 | 162 Filo |
| Govt of Tunisia, Tunis |   151 Filo & 152 Filo; | 90-0004 | 162 Filo |
| TS-IOO | 6 AJÜ, Bandirma: | 90-0005 | 162 Filo |
| |   161 Filo & 162 Filo; | 90-0006 | 162 Filo |
| **TURKEY** | 8 AJÜ, Diyarbakir: | 90-0007 | 162 Filo |
| **Türk Hava Kuvvetleri** |   181 Filo & 182 Filo; | 90-0008 | 162 Filo |
| **Boeing** | 9 AJÜ, Balikesir: | 90-0009 | 162 Filo |
| **KC-135R Stratotanker** |   191 Filo & 192 Filo | 90-0010 | 162 Filo |
| 101 Filo, Incirlik | 86-0066    Öncel Filo | 90-0011 | 162 Filo |
| 00325 | 86-0068    Öncel Filo | 90-0012 | 161 Filo |
| 00326 | 86-0069    Öncel Filo | 90-0013 | 161 Filo |
| 23539 | 86-0070    Öncel Filo | 90-0014 | 162 Filo |
| 23563 | 86-0071    Öncel Filo | 90-0016 | 161 Filo |
| 23567 | 86-0072    Öncel Filo | 90-0017 | 161 Filo |
| 57-2609 | 86-0192\*    Öncel Filo | 90-0018 | 161 Filo |
| 80110 | 86-0193\*    Öncel Filo | 90-0019 | 161 Filo |
| | 86-0194\*    Öncel Filo | 90-0020 | 162 Filo |
| **Cessna 650 Citation VII** | 86-0195\*    Öncel Filo | 90-0021 | 161 Filo |
| 212 Filo, Ankara/Etimesgut | 86-0196\*    Öncel Filo | 90-0022\* | 161 Filo |
| 004 | 87-0002\*    Öncel Filo | 90-0023\* | 161 Filo |
| 005 | 87-0003\*    Öncel Filo | 90-0024\* | 161 Filo |
| | 87-0009    Öncel Filo | 91-0001 | 161 Filo |
| **Grumman** | 87-0010    Öncel Filo | 91-0002 | 161 Filo |
| **G.1159C Gulfstream IV** | 87-0011    Öncel Filo | 91-0003 | 161 Filo |
| 211 Filo, Ankara/Etimesgut | 87-0013    Öncel Filo | 91-0004 | 161 Filo |
| 003 | 87-0014    Öncel Filo | 91-0005 | 161 Filo |
| TC-ATA | 87-0015    Öncel Filo | 91-0006 | 161 Filo |
| TC-GAP | 87-0016    Öncel Filo | 91-0007 | 161 Filo |
| | 87-0017    Öncel Filo | 91-0008 | 141 Filo |
| | 87-0018    Öncel Filo | 91-0010 | 141 Filo |
| **Lockheed** | 87-0019    Öncel Filo | 91-0011 | 141 Filo |
| **C-130B Hercules** | 87-0020    Öncel Filo | 91-0012 | 141 Filo |
| 222 Filo, Erkilet | 87-0021    Öncel Filo | 91-0013 | 192 Filo |
| 3496     (23496) | 88-0013\*    Öncel Filo | 91-0014 | 141 Filo |
| 10960 | 88-0014\*    141 Filo | 91-0015 | 182 Filo |
| 10963 | 88-0015\*    141 Filo | 91-0016 | 182 Filo |
| 70527 | 88-0019    Öncel Filo | 91-0017 | 182 Filo |
| 80736 | 88-0020    Öncel Filo | | |

## Turkey – United Arab Emirates

| | | | | | |
|---|---|---|---|---|---|
| 91-0018 | 182 Filo | 93-0692* | 151 Filo | 76520 | Il-76T |
| 91-0019 | 182 Filo | 93-0693* | 152 Filo | 76531 | Il-76MD |
| 91-0020 | 182 Filo | 93-0694* | | 76534 | Il-76MD |
| 91-0022* | 141 Filo | 93-0695* | 192 Filo | 76535 | Il-76MD |
| 91-0024* | 141 Filo | 93-0696* | 192 Filo | 76559 | Il-76MD |
| 92-0001 | 182 Filo | 94-0071 | 192 Filo | 76564 | Il-76MD |
| 92-0002 | 182 Filo | 94-0072 | 191 Filo | 76565 | Il-76MD |
| 92-0003 | 162 Filo | 94-0073 | 191 Filo | 76566 | Il-76MD |
| 92-0004 | 182 Filo | 94-0074 | 191 Filo | 76580 | Il-76MD |
| 92-0005 | 191 Filo | 94-0075 | 191 Filo | 76585 | Il-76MD |
| 92-0006 | 182 Filo | 94-0076 | 191 Filo | 76596 | Il-76MD |
| 92-0007 | 182 Filo | 94-0077 | 191 Filo | 76597 | Il-76MD |
| 92-0008 | 191 Filo | 94-0078 | 191 Filo | 76598 | Il-76MD |
| 92-0009 | 191 Filo | 94-0079 | 191 Filo | 76601 | Il-76MD |
| 92-0010 | 182 Filo | 94-0080 | 191 Filo | 76618 | Il-76MD |
| 92-0011 | 182 Filo | 94-0082 | 191 Filo | 76633 | Il-76MD |
| 92-0012 | 182 Filo | 94-0083 | 191 Filo | 76645 | Il-76MD |
| 92-0013 | 182 Filo | 94-0084 | 191 Filo | 76647 | Il-76MD |
| 92-0014 | 182 Filo | 94-0085 | 191 Filo | 76654 | Il-76MD |
| 92-0015 | 182 Filo | 94-0086 | 191 Filo | 76657 | Il-76MD |
| 92-0016 | 182 Filo | 94-0087 | 191 Filo | 76661 | Il-76MD |
| 92-0017 | 182 Filo | 94-0088 | | 76665 | Il-76MD |
| 92-0018 | 182 Filo | 94-0089 | 152 Filo | 76683 | Il-76MD |
| 92-0019 | 181 Filo | 94-0090 | 152 Filo | 76697 | Il-76MD |
| 92-0020 | 181 Filo | 94-0091 | 152 Filo | 76698 | Il-76MD |
| 92-0021 | 181 Filo | 94-0092 | | 76699 | Il-76MD |
| 92-0022* | 181 Filo | 94-0093 | | 76767 | Il-76MD |
| 92-0023* | 181 Filo | 94-0094 | 152 Filo | 76822 | Il-76MD |
| 92-0024* | 182 Filo | 94-0095 | 152 Filo | 78820 | Il-76MD |
| 93-0001 | 181 Filo | 94-0096 | 152 Filo | 86915 | Il-76MD |
| 93-0003 | 181 Filo | 94-0105* | 191 Filo | 86922 | Il-76MD |
| 93-0004 | 181 Filo | 94-0106* | 191 Filo | 86923 | Il-76MD |
| 93-0005 | 181 Filo | 94-0107* | 191 Filo | UR-76413 | Il-76MD |
| 93-0006 | 181 Filo | 94-0108* | 152 Filo | UR-76537 | Il-76MD |
| 93-0007 | 181 Filo | 94-0109* | 152 Filo | UR-76624 | Il-76MD |
| 93-0008 | 181 Filo | 94-0110* | 152 Filo | UR-76677 | Il-76MD |
| 93-0009 | 181 Filo | 94-1557* | 152 Filo | UR-76697 | Il-76MD |
| 93-0010 | 181 Filo | 94-1558* | Öncel Filo | UR-76699 | Il-76MD |
| 93-0011 | 181 Filo | 94-1559* | 152 Filo | | |
| 93-0012 | 181 Filo | 94-1560* | 151 Filo | **Ilyushin Il-62M** | |
| 93-0013 | 181 Filo | 94-1561* | 191 Filo | Govt of Ukraine, Kiev | |
| 93-0014 | 181 Filo | 94-1562* | 192 Filo | UR-86527 | |
| 93-0658 | | 94-1563* | 192 Filo | UR-86528 | |
| 93-0659 | 151 Filo | 94-1564* | 191 Filo | | |
| 93-0660 | 152 Filo | | | **UNITED ARAB EMIRATES** | |
| 93-0661 | 151 Filo | **Turkish Govt** | | **United Arab Emirates Air** | |
| 93-0663 | 151 Filo | **Airbus A.319CJ-115** | | **Force** | |
| 93-0664 | | Turkish Govt, Ankara | | *Abu Dhabi* | |
| 93-0665 | 152 Filo | TC-ANA | | **Lockheed** | |
| 93-0667 | 151 Filo | | | **C-130H/L.100-30*** | |
| 93-0668 | | **TURKMENISTAN** | | **Hercules** | |
| 93-0669 | 151 Filo | **BAe 1000B** | | 1211 | |
| 93-0670 | 151 Filo | Govt of Turkmenistan, | | 1212 | |
| 93-0671 | | Ashkhabad | | 1213 | |
| 93-0672 | 152 Filo | EZ-B021 | | 1214 | |
| 93-0673 | Öncel Filo | | | 1215* | |
| 93-0674 | 192 Filo | **Boeing 757-23A** | | 1216* | |
| 93-0675 | 192 Filo | Govt of Turkmenistan, | | *Dubai* | |
| 93-0676 | 192 Filo | Ashkhabad | | 311* | |
| 93-0677 | 192 Filo | EZ-A010 | | 312* | |
| 93-0678 | 192 Filo | | | | |
| 93-0679 | 192 Filo | **UGANDA** | | **United Arab Emirates Air** | |
| 93-0680 | 192 Filo | **Grumman** | | **Navy** | |
| 93-0681 | 192 Filo | **G.1159C Gulfstream IV** | | **Gates LearJet 35A** | |
| 93-0682 | 192 Filo | Govt of Uganda, | | Abu Dhabi | |
| 93-0683 | 192 Filo | Entebbe | | 800 | |
| 93-0684 | 192 Filo | 5X-UEF | | 801 | |
| 93-0685 | 192 Filo | | | | |
| 93-0686 | 192 Filo | **UKRAINE** | | **UAE Govt** | |
| 93-0687 | 192 Filo | **Ukrainian Air Force** | | **Airbus A.319CJ-113X** | |
| 93-0688 | 192 Filo | **Ilyushin** | | Dubai Air Wing | |
| 93-0689 | 192 Filo | **Il-76MD/Il-76T/Il-76TD** | | A6-ESH | |
| 93-0690 | 192 Filo | 321 TAP, Uzin | | | |
| 93-0691* | | 76413 | Il-76TD | **Antonov AN-124** | |

UAE Govt
UR-ZYD

**Boeing
737-2W8/7F0/7Z5/8AJ/8EC/
8EX**
Govt of Abu Dhabi;
Govt of Dubai

| | | |
|---|---|---|
| A6-AIN | 7Z5 | Abu Dhabi |
| A6-AUH | 8EX | Dubai |
| A6-DAS | 7Z5 | Abu Dhabi |
| A6-ESJ | 2W8 | Dubai |
| A6-HEH | 8AJ | Dubai |
| A6-HRS | 7F0 | Dubai |
| A6-LIW | 7Z5 | Dubai |
| A6-MRM | 8EC | Dubai |

**Boeing
747-2B4BF/422/48E/4F6**
Dubai Air Wing;

Govt of Abu Dhabi

| | | |
|---|---|---|
| A6-GDP | 2B4BF | Dubai |
| A6-HRM | 422 | Dubai |
| A6-MMM | 422 | Dubai |
| A6-UAE | 48E | Dubai |
| A6-YAS | 4F6 | Abu Dhabi |

**Boeing
747SP-31/
747SP-Z5\***
Govt of Dubai
A6-SMR
A6-ZSN\*
**Boeing 767-341ER**
Govt of Abu Dhabi
A6-SUL

**Dassault Falcon 900**
Govt of Abu Dhabi
A6-AUH

**Grumman
G.1159C Gulfstream IV**
Dubai Air Wing
A6-HHH

**YEMEN**
  **Boeing 747SP-27**
  Govt of Yemen, Sana'a
  7O-YMN

**YUGOSLAVIA**
  **Dassault Falcon 50**
  Govt of Yugoslavia,
    Belgrade
  YU-BNA

Finnish Air Force Gates Learjet 35A LJ-1 from Rissala was a visitor to RIAT 2005.

French Navy Super Etendard M No 47 is flown by 11 Flottille at Landivisiau.

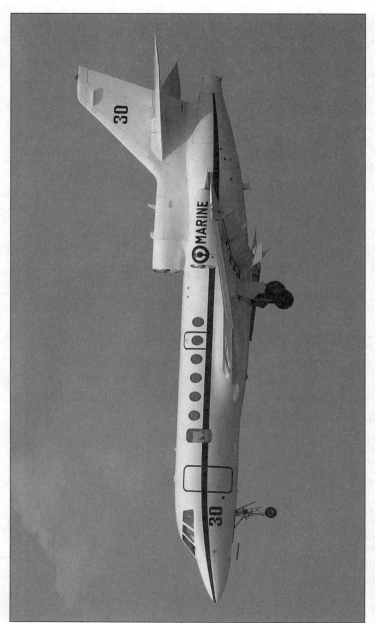

Falcon 50M 30 SURMAR operated by French Navy 24 Flotille at Lorient/Lann Bihoué.

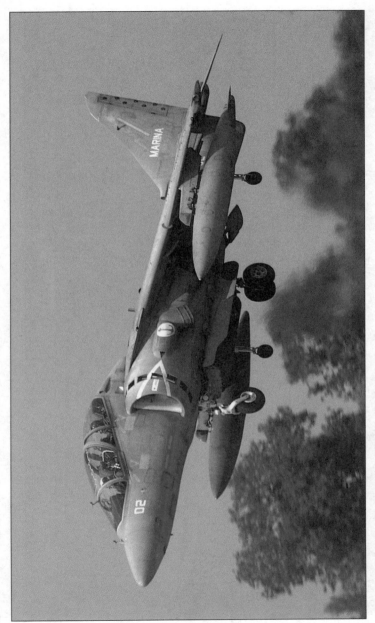

Italian Navy McDonnell Douglas Harrier II+ TAV-8B MM55033 of 1-02 from Taranto.

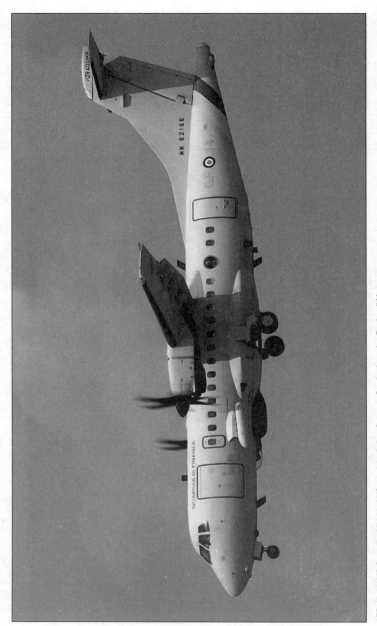

ATR-42-400MP Surveiller MM 62166/G-14 of the Italian Customs Service based at Pratica di Mare.

Royal Netherlands AF AH-64D Apache Q-21 flown by 301 Squadron at Gilze-Rijen.

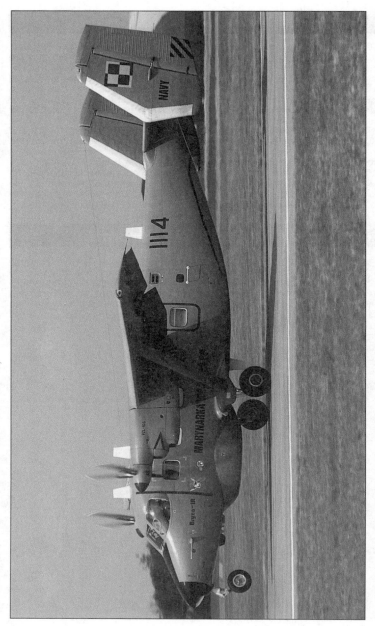

This Polish Navy PZL M-28 Bryza-1R 1114 is flown by 29 EL at Cewice/Siemirowice.

# US Military Aircraft Markings

All USAF aircraft have been allocated a fiscal year (FY) number since 1921. Individual aircraft are given a serial according to the fiscal year in which they are ordered. The numbers commence at 0001 and are prefixed with the year of allocation. For example F-15C Eagle 84-001 (84-0001) was the first aircraft ordered in 1984. The fiscal year (FY) serial is carried on the technical data block which is usually stencilled on the left-hand side of the aircraft just below the cockpit. The number displayed on the fin is a corruption of the FY serial. Most tactical aircraft carry the fiscal year in small figures followed by the last three or four digits of the serial in large figures. Large transport and tanker aircraft such as C-130s and KC-135s sometimes display a five-figure number commencing with the last digit of the appropriate fiscal year and four figures of the production number. An example of this is KC-135R 58-0128 which displays 80128 on its fin.

USN serials follow a straightforward numerical sequence which commenced, for the present series, with the allocation of 00001 to an SB2C Helldiver by the Bureau of Aeronautics in 1940. Numbers in the 166000 series are presently being issued. They are usually carried in full on the rear fuselage of the aircraft.

# UK-based USAF Aircraft

The following aircraft are normally based in the UK. They are listed in numerical order of type with individual aircraft in serial number order, as depicted on the aircraft. The number in brackets is either the alternative presentation of the five-figure number commencing with the last digit of the fiscal year, or the fiscal year where a five-figure serial is presented on the aircraft. Where it is possible to identify the allocation of aircraft to individual squadrons by means of colours carried on fin or cockpit edge, this is also provided.

| Notes | Type | | | | Notes | Type | | |
|---|---|---|---|---|---|---|---|---|
| | **McDonnell Douglas** | | | | | 86-0164 | F-15C | y |
| | **F-15C Eagle/F-15D Eagle/** | | | | | 86-0165 | F-15C | y [493rd FS] |
| | **F-15E Strike Eagle** | | | | | 86-0166 | F-15C | y |
| | LN:48th FW, RAF Lakenheath: | | | | | 86-0167 | F-15C | y |
| | 92nd FS blue/white | | | | | 86-0171 | F-15C | y |
| | 493rd FS black/yellow | | | | | 86-0172 | F-15C | y |
| | 494th FS red/white | | | | | 86-0174 | F-15C | y |
| 00-3000 | F-15E | r | | | | 86-0175 | F-15C | y |
| 00-3001 | F-15E | r | | | | 86-0176 | F-15C | y |
| 00-3002 | F-15E | r | | | | 86-0178 | F-15C | y |
| 00-3003 | F-15E | r | | | | 86-0182 | F-15D | y |
| 00-3004 | F-15E | r | | | | 91-0301 | F-15E | bl |
| 01-2000 | F-15E | r | | | | 91-0302 | F-15E | bl |
| 01-2001 | F-15E | m | [48th OG] | | | 91-0303 | F-15E | bl |
| 01-2002 | F-15E | r | [494th FS] | | | 91-0304 | F-15E | bl |
| 01-2003 | F-15E | r | | | | 91-0306 | F-15E | r |
| 01-2004 | F-15E | r | | | | 91-0307 | F-15E | bl |
| 83-0018 | F-15C | y | | | | 91-0308 | F-15E | bl |
| 84-0001 | F-15C | y | | | | 91-0309 | F-15E | bl |
| 84-0004 | F-15C | y | | | | 91-0310 | F-15E | r |
| 84-0009 | F-15C | y | | | | 91-0311 | F-15E | bl |
| 84-0010 | F-15C | y | | | | 91-0312 | F-15E | bl |
| 84-0014 | F-15C | y | | | | 91-0313 | F-15E | m |
| 84-0015 | F-15C | y | | | | 91-0314 | F-15E | r |
| 84-0019 | F-15C | y | | | | 91-0315 | F-15E | r |
| 84-0027 | F-15C | y | | | | 91-0316 | F-15E | r |
| 84-0044 | F-15D | y | | | | 91-0317 | F-15E | r |
| 86-0147 | F-15C | y | | | | 91-0318 | F-15E | r |
| 86-0154 | F-15C | y | | | | 91-0320 | F-15E | r |
| 86-0156 | F-15C | y | | | | 91-0321 | F-15E | bl |
| 86-0159 | F-15C | y | | | | 91-0324 | F-15E | r |
| 86-0160 | F-15C | y | | | | 91-0326 | F-15E | r |
| 86-0163 | F-15C | y | | | | 91-0329 | F-15E | bl |

| Type | | | Notes | Type | | Notes |
|------|------|------|-------|------|------|-------|
| 91-0331 | F-15E | r | | 40476 (FY84) | MC-130H* | |
| 91-0332 | F-15E | bl | | 61699 (FY86) | MC-130H* | |
| 91-0334 | F-15E | r | | 70023 (FY87) | MC-130H* | |
| 91-0335 | F-15E | r | | 70126 (FY87) | MC-130H* | |
| 91-0602 | F-15E | r | | 80192 (FY88) | MC-130H* | |
| 91-0603 | F-15E | r | | 80193 (FY88) | MC-130H* | |
| 91-0604 | F-15E | r | | 80194 (FY88) | MC-130H* | |
| 91-0605 | F-15E | bl | | 90280 (FY89) | MC-130H* | |
| 92-0364 | F-15E | r | | 90282 (FY89) | MC-130H* | |
| 96-0201 | F-15E | bl | | 95825 (FY69) | MC-130P | |
| 96-0202 | F-15E | bl | | 95826 (FY69) | MC-130P | |
| 96-0204 | F-15E | bl | | 95828 (FY69) | MC-130P | |
| 96-0205 | F-15E | bl | | 95831 (FY69) | MC-130P | |
| 97-0217 | F-15E | bl | | 95832 (FY69) | MC-130P | |
| 97-0218 | F-15E | m | [48th FW] | | | |
| 97-0219 | F-15E | bl | | **Boeing KC-135R** | | |
| 97-0220 | F-15E | bl | | **Stratotanker** | | |
| 97-0221 | F-15E | bl | [492nd FS] | 351st ARS/100th ARW, | | |
| 97-0222 | F-15E | bl | | RAF Mildenhall [D] (r/w/bl) | | |
| 98-0131 | F-15E | bl | | 00351 (FY60) | | |
| 98-0132 | F-15E | bl | | 10292 (FY61) | | |
| 98-0133 | F-15E | bl | | 10299 (FY61) | | |
| 98-0134 | F-15E | bl | | 10314 (FY61) | | |
| 98-0135 | F-15E | bl | | 14830 (FY64) | | |
| | | | | 23505 (FY62) | | |

**Sikorsky MH-53M**
21st SOS/352nd SOG,
   RAF Mildenhall
01630 (FY70)
14994 (FY67)
31649 (FY73)
31652 (FY73)
95784 (FY69)
95795 (FY69)
95796 (FY69)

**Lockheed C-130 Hercules**
352nd SOG, RAF Mildenhall:
   7th SOS* & 67th SOS,
37814 (FY63)   C-130E

23538 (FY62)
23541 (FY62)
23551 (FY62)
23561 (FY62)
23562 (FY62)
23573 (FY62)
23575 (FY62)
37987 (FY63)
38871 (FY63)
38884 (FY63)
71474 (FY57)
72605 (FY57)
80001 (FY58)
80128 (FY58)

Boeing E-3B Mercury 164406 is from VQ-4 of the US Navy at Tinker AFB, Oklahoma.

These aircraft are normally based in Western Europe with the USAFE. They are shown in numerical order of type designation, with individual aircraft in serial number order as carried on the aircraft. Fiscal year (FY) details are also provided if necessary. The unit allocation and operating bases are given for most aircraft.

| Notes | Type | | | Notes | Type | | |
|---|---|---|---|---|---|---|---|
| | **Fairchild** | | | | 89-2001 | AV m | [31st FW] |
| | **A-10A Thunderbolt II** | | | | 89-2009 | AV gn | |
| | **SP:** 52nd FW, Spangdahlem, | | | | 89-2011 | AV pr | |
| | Germany: | | | | 89-2016 | AV gn | [16th AF] |
| | 81st FS yellow | | | | 89-2018 | AV gn | |
| | 80-0281 | y | | | 89-2023 | AV gn | |
| | 81-0945 | y | | | 89-2024 | AV gn | |
| | 81-0948 | y | | | 89-2026 | AV gn | |
| | 81-0951 | y | | | 89-2029 | AV pr | |
| | 81-0952 | y | [81st FS] | | 89-2030 | AV pr | |
| | 81-0954 | y | | | 89-2035 | AV gn | [555th FS] |
| | 81-0956 | y | | | 89-2038 | AV gn | |
| | 81-0962 | y | | | 89-2039 | AV gn | |
| | 81-0963 | y | | | 89-2041 | AV gn | |
| | 81-0966 | y | | | 89-2044 | AV gn | |
| | 81-0976 | y | | | 89-2046 | AV pr | |
| | 81-0978 | y | | | 89-2047 | AV pr | |
| | 81-0980 | y | | | 89-2049 | AV pr | [USAFE] |
| | 81-0983 | y | | | 89-2057 | AV gn | |
| | 81-0984 | y | | | 89-2068 | AV gn | |
| | 81-0985 | y | | | 89-2102 | AV gn | |
| | 81-0988 | y | | | 89-2118 | AV pr | |
| | 81-0991 | y | | | 89-2137 | AV pr | [31st OG] |
| | 81-0992 | m | [52nd OG] | | 89-2178* | AV pr | |
| | 82-0649 | y | | | 90-0709 | AV pr | |
| | 82-0650 | y | | | 90-0772 | AV gn | |
| | 82-0654 | y | | | 90-0773 | AV gn | |
| | 82-0656 | y | | | 90-0777* | AV pr | |
| | | | | | 90-0795* | AV gn | |
| | **Beech C-12D Super King Air** | | | | 90-0796* | AV pr | |
| | US Embassy Flight, Budapest, | | | | 90-0800* | AV gn | |
| | Hungary | | | | 90-0813 | SP r | |
| | FY83 | | | | 90-0818 | SP r | |
| | 30495 | | | | 90-0827 | SP r | |
| | | | | | 90-0828 | SP r | |
| | **Lockheed (GD)** | | | | 90-0829 | SP r | [22nd FS] |
| | **F-16C/F-16D*** | | | | 90-0831 | SP r | |
| | **AV:** 31st FW, Aviano, Italy: | | | | 90-0833 | SP r | |
| | 510th FS purple/white | | | | 90-0843* | SP r | |
| | 555th FS green/yellow | | | | 90-0846* | SP bl | |
| | **SP:** 52nd FW, Spangdahlem, | | | | 91-0336 | SP r | |
| | Germany: | | | | 91-0337 | SP r | |
| | 22nd FS red/white | | | | 91-0338 | SP r | |
| | 23rd FS blue/white | | | | 91-0339 | SP r | |
| | 87-0350 | AV gn | | | 91-0340 | SP r | |
| | 87-0351 | AV m | [31st OSS] | | 91-0341 | SP r | |
| | 87-0355 | AV pr | | | 91-0342 | SP r | |
| | 87-0359 | AV gn | | | 91-0343 | SP r | |
| | 88-0413 | AV pr | [510th FS] | | 91-0344 | SP r | |
| | 88-0425 | AV gn | | | 91-0351 | SP r | |
| | 88-0435 | AV gn | | | 91-0352 | SP m | [52nd FW] |
| | 88-0443 | AV pr | | | 91-0391 | SP r | |
| | 88-0444 | AV pr | | | 91-0402 | SP bl | |
| | 88-0446 | AV gn | | | 91-0403 | SP bl | |
| | 88-0491 | AV pr | | | 91-0405 | SP bl | |
| | 88-0525 | AV pr | | | 91-0406 | SP bl | |
| | 88-0526 | AV gn | | | 91-0407 | SP bl | |
| | 88-0529 | AV pr | | | 91-0408 | SP r | |
| | 88-0532 | AV gn | | | 91-0409 | SP bl | |
| | 88-0535 | AV gn | | | 91-0410 | SP bl | |
| | 88-0541 | AV pr | | | 91-0412 | SP bl | |

| Type | | Notes |
|---|---|---|
| 91-0414 | SP *bl* | |
| 91-0416 | SP *bl* | [52nd OG] |
| 91-0417 | SP *bl* | |
| 91-0418 | SP *bl* | |
| 91-0419 | SP *bl* | |
| 91-0420 | SP *bl* | |
| 91-0421 | SP *bl* | |
| 91-0464* | SP *r* | |
| 91-0472* | SP *bl* | |
| 91-0474* | SP *bl* | |
| 91-0481* | SP *bl* | |
| 92-3915 | SP *bl* | |
| 92-3918 | SP *bl* | |
| 96-0080 | SP *bl* | [23rd FS] |
| 96-0081 | SP *bl* | |
| 96-0082 | SP *bl* | |
| 96-0083 | SP *bl* | |

**Grumman**
**C-20H Gulfstream IV**
76th AS/86th AW, Ramstein,
  Germany
*FY90*
00300
*FY92*
20375

**Gates C-21A**
**Learjet**
76th AS/86th AW, Ramstein,
  Germany
*FY84*
40068
40081
40082
40083
40084
40085
40086
40087
40108
40109
40110
40111
40112

| Type | | Notes |
|---|---|---|

**Gulfstream Aerospace**
**C-37A Gulfstream V**
309th AS/86th AW, Chievres,
  Belgium
*FY01*
10076

**Boeing C-40B**
76th AS/86th AW, Ramstein,
  Germany
*FY01*
10040

**Sikorsky HH-60G**
**Blackhawk**
56th RQS/85th Wing, Keflavik,
  Iceland [IS]
26109 (FY88)
26205 (FY89)
26206 (FY89)
26208 (FY89)
26212 (FY89)

**Lockheed C-130E**
**Hercules**
37th AS/86th AW, Ramstein,
  Germany [RS] (*bl/w*)

| | | |
|---|---|---|
| 01260 | (FY70) | |
| 01264 | (FY70) | |
| 01271 | (FY70) | |
| 01274 | (FY70) | [86th AW] |
| 10935 | (FY68) | |
| 10947 | (FY68) | |
| 17681 | (FY64) | |
| 21835 | (FY62) | |
| 37825 | (FY63) | |
| 37865 | (FY63) | |
| 37879 | (FY63) | |
| 37885 | (FY63) | |
| 37887 | (FY63) | |
| 37897 | (FY63) | |
| 40502 | (FY64) | |
| 40527 | (FY64) | |

# European based US Navy Aircraft

| Type | | Notes |
|---|---|---|

**Beech UC-12M**
**Super King Air**
NAF Rota, Spain
3839 (163839)     Rota
3842 (163842)     Rota

**Fairchild C-26D**
NAF Naples, Italy;
NAF Sigonella, Italy
900528     Naples
900530     Sigonella
900531     Naples
910502     Sigonella

**Grumman C-20A**
**Gulfstream III**
CinCUSNFE
NAF Sigonella, Italy
830500

| Type | | Notes |
|---|---|---|

**Sikorsky MH-53E**
**Sea Stallion**
HC-4, NAF Sigonella, Italy
162504     [HC-40]
162513
162514     [HC-50]
163055     [HC-45]
163057     [HC-41]
163065     [HC-43]
164864     [HC-00]

| Notes | Type | | |
|---|---|---|---|
| | **Bell UH-1H Iroquois** | | |
| | Combat Manoeuvre Training Centre, Hohenfels | | |
| | *FY72* | | |
| | 21569 | | |
| | 21636 | | |
| | *FY73* | | |
| | 21668 | | |
| | *FY74* | | |
| | 22330 | | |
| | 22355 | | |
| | 22370 | | |
| | 22410 | | |
| | 22448 | | |
| | 22465 | | |
| | | | |
| | **Beech C-12 Huron** | | |
| | 'A' Co, 2nd Btn, 228th Avn Reg't, Heidelberg; | | |
| | HQ/USEUCOM, Stuttgart; | | |
| | 'E' Co, 1st Btn, 214th Avn Reg't, Vicenza, Italy; | | |
| | 1st Military Intelligence Btn, Wiesbaden; | | |
| | 'B' Co, 1st Btn, 214th Avn Reg't, Wiesbaden | | |
| | *FY84* | | |
| | 40156 | C-12U | B/1-214th Avn |
| | 40157 | C-12U | E/1-214th Avn |
| | 40158 | C-12U | B/1-214th Avn |
| | 40160 | C-12U | E/1-214th Avn |
| | 40161 | C-12U | B/1-214th Avn |
| | 40162 | C-12U | B/1-214th Avn |
| | 40163 | C-12U | HQ/USEUCOM |
| | 40165 | C-12U | B/1-214th Avn |
| | 40180 | C-12U | HQ/USEUCOM |
| | *FY94* | | |
| | 40315 | C-12R | A/2-228th Avn |
| | 40316 | C-12R | A/2-228th Avn |
| | 40318 | C-12R | A/2-228th Avn |
| | 40319 | C-12R | A/2-228th Avn |
| | *FY95* | | |
| | 50091 | C-12R | A/2-228th Avn |
| | *FY85* | | |
| | 50147 | RC-12K | 1st MIB |
| | 50148 | RC-12K | 1st MIB |
| | 50149 | RC-12K | 1st MIB |
| | 50150 | RC-12K | 1st MIB |
| | 50152 | RC-12K | 1st MIB |
| | 50153 | RC-12K | 1st MIB |
| | 50155 | RC-12K | 1st MIB |
| | | | |
| | **Beech C-12J Huron** | | |
| | HQ/USEUCOM, Stuttgart | | |
| | *FY86* | | |
| | 60079 | | |
| | | | |
| | **Cessna UC-35A Citation V** | | |
| | 214th Avn Reg't, Wiesbaden | | |
| | *FY95* | | |
| | 50123 | | |
| | 50124 | | |
| | *FY97* | | |
| | 70101 | | |
| | 70102 | | |

| Notes | Type | | |
|---|---|---|---|
| | 70105 | | |
| | *FY99* | | |
| | 90102 | | |
| | | | |
| | **Boeing-Vertol CH-47D Chinook** | | |
| | 'F' Co, 159th Avn Reg't Giebelstadt | | |
| | *FY87* | | |
| | 70072 | | |
| | 70073 | | |
| | *FY88* | | |
| | 80099 | | |
| | 80100 | | |
| | 80101 | | |
| | 80102 | | |
| | 80103 | | |
| | 80104 | | |
| | 80106 | | |
| | *FY89* | | |
| | 90138 | | |
| | 90139 | | |
| | 90140 | | |
| | 90141 | | |
| | 90142 | | |
| | 90143 | | |
| | 90144 | | |
| | 90145 | | |
| | | | |
| | **Sikorsky H-60 Black Hawk** | | |
| | 2nd Btn, 1st Avn Reg't, Ansbach; | | |
| | 45th Medical Co, Ansbach; | | |
| | 'B' Co, 5th Btn, 158th Avn Reg't, Aviano; | | |
| | 'A' Co, 127th Divisional Avn Support Btn, Bad Kreuznach; | | |
| | 357th Avn Det/SHAPE, Chievres; | | |
| | 'B' Co, 70th Transportation Reg't, Coleman Barracks; | | |
| | 'C' Co, 1st Btn, 214th Avn Reg't, Coleman Barracks; | | |
| | 'A' Co, 3rd Btn, 158th Avn Reg't, Giebelstadt; | | |
| | 'B' Co, 3rd Btn, 158th Avn Reg't, Giebelstadt; | | |
| | 'A' Co, 5th Btn, 158th Avn Reg't, Giebelstadt; | | |
| | 'C' Co, 5th Btn, 158th Avn Reg't, Giebelstadt; | | |
| | 2nd Btn, 501st Avn Reg't, Hanau; | | |
| | 'B' Co, 7th Btn, 159th AVIM, Illesheim; | | |
| | 236th Medical Co (HA), Landstuhl; | | |
| | 6th Avn Co, Vicenza, Italy; | | |
| | 159th Medical Co, Wiesbaden | | |
| | *FY82* | | |
| | 23675 | UH-60A | 45th Med Co |
| | 23685 | UH-60A | 159th Med Co |
| | 23692 | UH-60A | A/3-158th Avn |
| | 23693 | UH-60A | 45th Med Co |
| | 23729 | UH-60A | 159th Med Co |
| | 23735 | UH-60A | 236th Med Co |
| | 23737 | UH-60A | 159th Med Co |
| | 23738 | UH-60A | 159th Med Co |
| | 23745 | UH-60A | 236th Med Co |
| | 23750 | UH-60A | 159th Med Co |
| | 23751 | UH-60A | 159th Med Co |
| | 23752 | UH-60A | 236th Med Co |

| Type | | | Notes |
|---|---|---|---|
| 23753 | UH-60A | 159th Med Co | |
| 23754 | UH-60A | 45th Med Co | |
| 23755 | UH-60A | 236th Med Co | |
| 23756 | UH-60A | 159th Med Co | |
| 23757 | UH-60A | C/1-214th Avn | |
| *FY83* | | | |
| 23854 | UH-60A | A/5-158th Avn | |
| 23855 | UH-60A | C/1-214th Avn | |
| 23868 | UH-60A | C/1-214th Avn | |
| 23869 | UH-60A | C/1-214th Avn | |
| *FY84* | | | |
| 23951 | UH-60A | 45th Med Co | |
| 23970 | UH-60A | C/5-158th Avn | |
| 23975 | UH-60A | C/5-158th Avn | |
| *FY85* | | | |
| 24391 | UH-60A | 45th Med Co | |
| *FY86* | | | |
| 24498 | UH-60A | 2-501st Avn | |
| 24530 | UH-60A | 2-501st Avn | |
| 24531 | UH-60A | 45th Med Co | |
| 24532 | UH-60A | 236th Med Co | |
| 24538 | UH-60A | C/1-214th Avn | |
| 24550 | UH-60A | 236th Med Co | |
| 24551 | UH-60A | C/1-214th Avn | |
| 24552 | UH-60A | 159th Med Co | |
| 24554 | UH-60A | C/5-158th Avn | |
| 24555 | UH-60A | | |
| *FY87* | | | |
| 24579 | UH-60A | A/5-158th Avn | |
| 24581 | UH-60A | 159th Med Co | |
| 24583 | UH-60A | 357th Avn Det | |
| 24584 | UH-60A | 357th Avn Det | |
| 24589 | UH-60A | C/1-214th Avn | |
| 24621 | UH-60A | C/1-214th Avn | |
| 24628 | UH-60A | 159th Med Co | |
| 24634 | UH-60A | 159th Med Co | |
| 24642 | UH-60A | C/1-214th Avn | |
| 24643 | UH-60A | C/1-214th Avn | |
| 24644 | UH-60A | 45th Med Co | |
| 24645 | UH-60A | 45th Med Co | |
| 24647 | UH-60A | C/1-214th Avn | |
| 24650 | UH-60A | | |
| 24656 | UH-60A | 159th Med Co | |
| 26001 | UH-60A | 45th Med Co | |
| 26002 | UH-60A | 159th Med Co | |
| 26003 | UH-60A | B/5-158th Avn | |
| 26004 | UH-60A | 45th Med Co | |
| *FY88* | | | |
| 26019 | UH-60A | C/1-214th Avn | |
| 26020 | UH-60A | 236th Med Co | |
| 26021 | UH-60A | B/5-158th Avn | |
| 26023 | UH-60A | 236th Med Co | |
| 26025 | UH-60A | C/1-214th Avn | |
| 26026 | UH-60A | B/5-158th Avn | |
| 26027 | UH-60A | C/1-214th Avn | |
| 26028 | UH-60A | C/5-158th Avn | |
| 26031 | UH-60A | 236th Med Co | |
| 26034 | UH-60A | 159th Med Co | |
| 26037 | UH-60A | B/7-159th AVIM | |
| 26038 | UH-60A | A/5-158th Avn | |
| 26039 | UH-60A | 45th Med Co | |
| 26040 | UH-60A | 236th Med Co | |
| 26041 | UH-60A | A/5-158th Avn | |
| 26042 | UH-60A | A/5-158th Avn | |
| 26045 | UH-60A | 45th Med Co | |
| 26050 | UH-60A | 159th Med Co | |
| 26051 | UH-60A | A/5-158th Avn | |
| 26052 | UH-60A | B/5-158th Avn | |
| 26053 | UH-60A | A/5-158th Avn | |

| Type | | | Notes |
|---|---|---|---|
| 26054 | UH-60A | 236th Med Co | |
| 26055 | UH-60A | 236th Med Co | |
| 26056 | UH-60A | A/5-158th Avn | |
| 26058 | UH-60A | 159th Med Co | |
| 26063 | UH-60A | B/5-158th Avn | |
| 26067 | UH-60A | B/5-158th Avn | |
| 26068 | UH-60A | 236th Med Co | |
| 26071 | UH-60A | 2-501st Avn | |
| 26072 | UH-60A | 236th Med Co | |
| 26075 | UH-60A | 159th Med Co | |
| 26077 | UH-60A | C/5-158th Avn | |
| 26080 | UH-60A | 236th Med Co | |
| 26085 | UH-60A | 236th Med Co | |
| 26086 | UH-60A | 236th Med Co | |
| *FY89* | | | |
| 26138 | UH-60A | 159th Med Co | |
| 26142 | UH-60A | 2-501st Avn | |
| 26145 | UH-60A | B/5-158th Avn | |
| 26146 | UH-60A | 159th Med Co | |
| 26151 | UH-60A | 159th Med Co | |
| 26153 | UH-60A | C/1-214th Avn | |
| 26164 | UH-60A | C/5-158th Avn | |
| 26165 | UH-60A | C/1-214th Avn | |
| *FY95* | | | |
| 26621 | UH-60L | 2-1st Avn | |
| 26628 | UH-60L | 2-1st Avn | |
| 26629 | UH-60L | 2-1st Avn | |
| 26630 | UH-60L | 2-1st Avn | |
| 26631 | UH-60L | 2-1st Avn | |
| 26632 | UH-60L | 2-1st Avn | |
| 26633 | UH-60L | 2-1st Avn | |
| 26635 | UH-60L | 2-1st Avn | |
| 26636 | UH-60L | 2-1st Avn | |
| 26637 | UH-60L | 2-1st Avn | |
| 26638 | UH-60L | 2-1st Avn | |
| 26639 | UH-60L | 2-1st Avn | |
| 26640 | UH-60L | 2-1st Avn | |
| 26641 | UH-60L | B/3-158th Avn | |
| 26642 | UH-60L | B/3-158th Avn | |
| 26643 | UH-60L | B/3-158th Avn | |
| 26644 | UH-60L | 2-1st Avn | |
| 26645 | UH-60L | A/3-158th Avn | |
| 26646 | UH-60L | 2-1st Avn | |
| 26647 | UH-60L | 2-1st Avn | |
| 26648 | UH-60L | 2-1st Avn | |
| 26649 | UH-60L | B/3-158th Avn | |
| 26650 | UH-60L | A/3-158th Avn | |
| 26651 | UH-60L | B/3-158th Avn | |
| 26652 | UH-60L | B/3-158th Avn | |
| 26653 | UH-60L | A/3-158th Avn | |
| 26654 | UH-60L | A/3-158th Avn | |
| 26655 | UH-60L | A/3-158th Avn | |
| *FY96* | | | |
| 26674 | UH-60L | B/3-158th Avn | |
| 26675 | UH-60L | A/3-158th Avn | |
| 26676 | UH-60L | B/3-158th Avn | |
| 26677 | UH-60L | B/3-158th Avn | |
| 26678 | UH-60L | B/3-158th Avn | |
| 26679 | UH-60L | B/3-158th Avn | |
| 26680 | UH-60L | B/3-158th Avn | |
| 26681 | UH-60L | B/3-158th Avn | |
| 26682 | UH-60L | B/3-158th Avn | |
| 26683 | UH-60L | A/3-158th Avn | |
| 26684 | UH-60L | A/3-158th Avn | |
| 26685 | UH-60L | A/3-158th Avn | |
| 26686 | UH-60L | A/3-158th Avn | |
| 26687 | UH-60L | A/3-158th Avn | |
| 26688 | UH-60L | A/3-158th Avn | |
| 26689 | UH-60L | A/3-158th Avn | |

# US Army Europe

| Type | | |
|---|---|---|
| 26690 | UH-60L | A/3-158th Avn |
| 26691 | UH-60L | A/3-158th Avn |
| 26692 | UH-60L | A/3-158th Avn |
| *FY97* | | |
| 26762 | UH-60L | A/3-158th Avn |
| 26763 | UH-60L | 2-501st Avn |
| 26765 | UH-60L | A/3-158th Avn |
| 26766 | UH-60L | 2-501st Avn |
| 26767 | UH-60L | A/3-158th Avn |
| *FY98* | | |
| 26795 | UH-60L | 2-501st Avn |
| 26796 | UH-60L | 2-501st Avn |
| 26797 | UH-60L | 2-501st Avn |
| 26798 | UH-60L | 2-501st Avn |
| 26799 | UH-60L | 2-501st Avn |
| 26800 | UH-60L | 2-501st Avn |
| 26801 | UH-60L | 2-501st Avn |
| 26802 | UH-60L | 2-501st Avn |
| 26813 | UH-60L | 2-501st Avn |
| 26814 | UH-60L | 2-501st Avn |
| *FY01* | | |
| 26878 | UH-60L | B/3-158th Avn |
| 26880 | UH-60L | B/3-158th Avn |
| 26884 | UH-60L | B/3-158th Avn |
| 26885 | UH-60L | B/3-158th Avn |
| 26886 | UH-60L | B/3-158th Avn |
| 26889 | UH-60L | B/3-158th Avn |
| *FY02* | | |
| 26970 | UH-60L | B/3-158th Avn |
| *FY03* | | |
| 26992 | UH-60L | B/3-158th Avn |

## MDH AH-64 Apache
3rd Btn, 1st Avn Reg't, Illesheim;
2nd Btn, 6th Cavalry Reg't, Illesheim;
6th Btn, 6th Cavalry Reg't, Illesheim

### AH-64A
*FY86*

| | | |
|---|---|---|
| 68940 | 3-1st Avn | |
| 68942 | 3-1st Avn | |
| 68943 | 3-1st Avn | |
| 68946 | 3-1st Avn | |
| 68948 | 3-1st Avn | |
| 68951 | 3-1st Avn | |
| 68952 | 3-1st Avn | |
| 68955 | 3-1st Avn | |
| 68956 | 3-1st Avn | |
| 68957 | 3-1st Avn | |
| 68959 | 3-1st Avn | |
| 68960 | 3-1st Avn | |
| 68961 | 3-1st Avn | |
| 68981 | 3-1st Avn | |
| 69026 | 3-1st Avn | |
| 69030 | 3-1st Avn | |
| 69032 | 3-1st Avn | |

| Type | |
|---|---|
| 69037 | 3-1st Avn |
| 69048 | 3-1st Avn |
| *FY87* | |
| 70443 | 3-1st Avn |
| 70503 | 3-1st Avn |

### AH-64D
*FY96*

| | |
|---|---|
| 05007 | 2-6th Cav |
| 05009 | 6-6th Cav |
| 05011 | 2-6th Cav |
| 05015 | 2-6th Cav |
| 05018 | 2-6th Cav |
| 05020 | 2-6th Cav |
| 05021 | 2-6th Cav |
| 05022 | 2-6th Cav |
| *FY99* | |
| 05101 | 2-6th Cav |
| 05109 | 2-6th Cav |
| 05114 | 2-6th Cav |
| 05120 | 2-6th Cav |
| 05143 | 2-6th Cav |
| *FY00* | |
| 05175 | 6-6th Cav |
| 05178 | 2-6th Cav |
| 05190 | 2-6th Cav |
| 05199 | 6-6th Cav |
| 05200 | 6-6th Cav |
| 05204 | 6-6th Cav |
| 05205 | 6-6th Cav |
| 05206 | 6-6th Cav |
| 05207 | 6-6th Cav |
| 05208 | 6-6th Cav |
| 05209 | 6-6th Cav |
| 05210 | 6-6th Cav |
| 05212 | 6-6th Cav |
| 05213 | 6-6th Cav |
| 05214 | 6-6th Cav |
| 05215 | 6-6th Cav |
| 05216 | 2-6th Cav |
| 05217 | 6-6th Cav |
| 05218 | 6-6th Cav |
| 05220 | 6-6th Cav |
| 05225 | 6-6th Cav |
| 05226 | 6-6th Cav |
| 05231 | 6-6th Cav |
| 05232 | 6-6th Cav |
| *FY01* | |
| 05233 | 2-6th Cav |
| 05243 | 2-6th Cav |
| 05250 | 2-6th Cav |
| 05253 | 2-6th Cav |
| 05273 | 6-6th Cav |
| 05274 | 2-6th Cav |
| 05284 | 2-6th Cav |

# US based USAF Aircraft

The following aircraft are normally based in the USA but are likely to be seen visiting the UK from time to time. The presentation is in numerical order of the type, commencing with the B-1B and concluding with the C-141. The aircraft are listed in numerical progression by the serial actually carried externally. Fiscal year information is provided, together with details of mark variations and in some cases operating units. Where base-code letter information is carried on the aircrafts' tails, this is detailed with the squadron/base data; for example the 7th Wing's B-1B 60105 carries the letters DY on its tail, thus identifying the Wing's home base as Dyess AFB, Texas.

| Type | | | Notes | Type | | | Notes |
|------|---|---|-------|------|---|---|--------|
| **Rockwell B-1B Lancer** | | | | 60115 | 28th BW | | |
| 7th BW, Dyess AFB, Texas [DY]: | | | | 60116 | 28th BW | | |
| 9th BS (*y/bk*), 13th BS (*r*) | | | | 60117 | 7th BW | *bl/w* | |
| & 28th BS (*bl/w*); | | | | 60118 | 28th BW | | |
| 28th BW, Ellsworth AFB, | | | | 60119 | 7th BW | *bl/w* | |
| South Dakota [EL]: | | | | 60120 | 7th BW | *y/bk* | |
| 34th BS (*bk/r*) & 37th BS (*bk/y*); | | | | 60121 | 28th BW | *bk/y* | |
| 419th FLTS/412th TW, Edwards AFB, | | | | 60122 | 7th BW | *r* | |
| California [ED] | | | | 60123 | 7th BW | *y/bk* | |
| *FY84* | | | | 60124 | 7th BW | *y/bk* | |
| 40049 | 412th TW | | | 60125 | 28th BW | | |
| *FY85* | | | | 60126 | 7th BW | *bl/w* | |
| 50059 | 7th BW | *bl/w* | | 60127 | 28th BW | *bk/y* | |
| 50060 | 28th BW | | | 60129 | 28th BW | | |
| 50061 | 7th BW | *bl/w* | | 60130 | 7th BW | *bl/w* | |
| 50064 | 7th BW | *y/bk* | | 60132 | 7th BW | *bl/w* | |
| 50065 | 7th BW | *bl/w* | | 60133 | 7th BW | *y/bk* | |
| 50066 | 28th BW | | | 60134 | 28th BW | *bk/r* | |
| 50068 | 412th TW | | | 60135 | 7th BW | *bl/w* | |
| 50069 | 7th BW | | | 60136 | 7th BW | *bl/w* | |
| 50072 | 7th BW | *y/bk* | | 60137 | 7th BW | | |
| 50073 | 7th BW | | | 60138 | 28th BW | *bk/y* | |
| 50074 | 7th BW | *r* | | 60139 | 28th BW | *bk/y* | |
| 50075 | 412th TW | | | 60140 | 7th BW | *y/bk* | |
| 50077 | 28th BW | | | | | | |
| 50079 | 28th BW | | | **Northrop B-2 Spirit** | | | |
| 50080 | 7th BW | *bl/w* | | 419th FLTS/412th TW, Edwards AFB, | | | |
| 50081 | 28th BW | *bk/y* | | California [ED]; | | | |
| 50083 | 28th BW | *bk/y* | | 509th BW, Whiteman AFB, | | | |
| 50084 | 28th BW | | | Missouri [WM]: | | | |
| 50085 | 28th BW | *bk/y* | | 325th BS, 393rd BS & 715th BS | | | |
| 50087 | 28th BW | *bk/y* | | (Names are given where known. | | | |
| 50088 | 7th BW | *y/bk* | | Each begins *Spirit of ...* ) | | | |
| 50089 | 7th BW | *bl/w* | | *FY90* | | | |
| 50090 | 7th BW | | | 00040 | 509th BW | *Alaska* | |
| 50091 | 28th BW | *bk/y* | | 00041 | 509th BW | *Hawaii* | |
| *FY86* | | | | *FY92* | | | |
| 60093 | 28th BW | | | 20700 | 509th BW | *Florida* | |
| 60094 | 28th BW | | | *FY82* | | | |
| 60095 | 28th BW | | | 21066 | 509th BW | *America* | |
| 60097 | 7th BW | | | 21067 | 509th BW | *Arizona* | |
| 60098 | 7th BW | *bl/w* | | 21068 | 412th TW | *New York* | |
| 60099 | 28th BW | *bk/y* | | 21069 | 509th BW | *Indiana* | |
| 60100 | 7th BW | | | 21070 | Northrop | *Ohio* | |
| 60101 | 7th BW | *bl/w* | | 21071 | 509th BW | *Mississippi* | |
| 60102 | 28th BW | | | *FY93* | | | |
| 60103 | 7th BW | *y/bk* | | 31085 | 509th BW | *Oklahoma* | |
| 60104 | 28th BW | *bk/y* | | 31086 | 509th BW | *Kitty Hawk* | |
| 60105 | 7th BW | *bl/w* | | 31087 | 509th BW | *Pennsylvania* | |
| 60107 | 7th BW | *y/bk* | | 31088 | 509th BW | *Louisiana* | |
| 60108 | 7th BW | *y/bk* | | *FY88* | | | |
| 60109 | 7th BW | | | 80328 | 509th BW | *Texas* | |
| 60110 | 7th BW | *y/bk* | | 80329 | 509th BW | *Missouri* | |
| 60111 | 28th BW | | | 80330 | 509th BW | *California* | |
| 60112 | 7th BW | *y/bk* | | 80331 | 509th BW | *South Carolina* | |
| 60113 | 28th BW | *bk/y* | | 80332 | 509th BW | *Washington* | |

| Notes | Type | | | |
|---|---|---|---|---|
| | *FY89* | | | |
| | 90127 | 509th BW | *Kansas* | |
| | 90128 | 509th BW | *Nebraska* | |
| | 90129 | 509th BW | *Georgia* | |
| | | | | |
| | **Lockheed U-2** | | | |
| | 9th RW, Dyess AFB, Texas [BB]: | | | |
| | 1st RS, 5th RS | | | |
| | & 99th RS (*bk/r*); | | | |
| | Lockheed, Palmdale; | | | |
| | Warner Robins | | | |
| | Air Logistics Centre [WR] | | | |
| | *FY68* | | | |
| | 68-10329 | U-2S | 9th RW | |
| | 68-10331 | U-2S | 9th RW | |
| | 68-10336 | U-2S | WR ALC | |
| | 68-10337 | U-2S | 9th RW | |
| | *FY80* | | | |
| | 80-1064 | TU-2S | 9th RW | |
| | 80-1065 | TU-2S | 9th RW | |
| | 80-1066 | U-2S | 9th RW | |
| | 80-1067 | U-2S | Lockheed | |
| | 80-1068 | U-2S | 9th RW | |
| | 80-1069 | U-2S | 9th RW | |
| | 80-1070 | U-2S | 9th RW | |
| | 80-1071 | U-2S | 9th RW | |
| | 80-1073 | U-2S | 9th RW | |
| | 80-1074 | U-2S | 9th RW | |
| | 80-1076 | U-2S | 9th RW | |
| | 80-1077 | U-2S | 9th RW | |
| | 80-1078 | TU-2S | 9th RW | |
| | 80-1079 | U-2S | 9th RW | |
| | 80-1080 | U-2S | 9th RW | |
| | 80-1081 | U-2S | 9th RW | |
| | 80-1083 | U-2S | 9th RW | |
| | 80-1084 | U-2S | 9th RW | |
| | 80-1085 | U-2S | 9th RW | |
| | 80-1086 | U-2S | 9th RW | |
| | 80-1087 | U-2S | 9th RW | |
| | 80-1089 | U-2S | 9th RW | |
| | 80-1090 | U-2S | 9th RW | |
| | 80-1091 | TU-2S | 9th RW | |
| | 80-1092 | U-2S | 9th RW | |
| | 80-1093 | U-2S | 9th RW | |
| | 80-1094 | U-2S | 9th RW | |
| | 80-1096 | U-2S | 9th RW | |
| | 80-1099 | U-2S | 9th RW | |
| | | | | |
| | **Boeing E-3 Sentry** | | | |
| | 552nd ACW, Tinker AFB, | | | |
| | Oklahoma [OK]: | | | |
| | 960th AACS (*w*), 963rd AACS (*bk*), | | | |
| | 964th AACS (*r*), 965th AACS (*y*) | | | |
| | & 966th AACS (*bl*); | | | |
| | 961st AACS/18th Wg, Kadena AB, | | | |
| | Japan [ZZ] (*or*); | | | |
| | 962nd AACS/3rd Wg, Elmendorf AFB, | | | |
| | Alaska [AK] (*gn*); | | | |
| | *FY80* | | | |
| | 00137 | E-3C | *r* | |
| | 00138 | E-3C | *y* | |
| | 00139 | E-3C | *gn* | |
| | *FY81* | | | |
| | 10004 | E-3C | *m* | |
| | 10005 | E-3C | *w* | |
| | *FY71* | | | |
| | 11407 | E-3B | *r* | |
| | 11408 | E-3B | *bl* | |
| | *FY82* | | | |
| | 20006 | E-3C | *r* | |
| | 20007 | E-3C | *w* | |

| Notes | Type | | | |
|---|---|---|---|---|
| | *FY83* | | | |
| | 30008 | E-3C | *bk* | |
| | 30009 | E-3C | *or* | |
| | *FY73* | | | |
| | 31674 | JE-3C | Boeing | |
| | 31675 | E-3B | *gn* | |
| | *FY75* | | | |
| | 50556 | E-3B | *w* | |
| | 50557 | E-3B | *bl* | |
| | 50558 | E-3B | *r* | |
| | 50559 | E-3B | *w* | |
| | 50560 | E-3B | *w* | |
| | *FY76* | | | |
| | 61604 | E-3B | *r* | |
| | 61605 | E-3B | *m* | |
| | 61606 | E-3B | *r* | |
| | 61607 | E-3B | *r* | |
| | *FY77* | | | |
| | 70351 | E-3B | *or* | |
| | 70352 | E-3B | *r* | |
| | 70353 | E-3B | *y* | |
| | 70355 | E-3B | *r* | |
| | 70356 | E-3B | *w* | |
| | *FY78* | | | |
| | 80576 | E-3B | *r* | |
| | 80577 | E-3B | *w* | |
| | 80578 | E-3B | *or* | |
| | *FY79* | | | |
| | 90001 | E-3B | *bl* | |
| | 90002 | E-3B | *r* | |
| | 90003 | E-3B | *m* | |
| | | | | |
| | **Boeing E-4B** | | | |
| | 1st ACCS/55th Wg, Offutt AFB, | | | |
| | Nebraska [OF] | | | |
| | 31676 | (FY73) | | |
| | 31677 | (FY73) | | |
| | 40787 | (FY74) | | |
| | 50125 | (FY75) | | |
| | | | | |
| | **Lockheed C-5 Galaxy** | | | |
| | 60th AMW, Travis AFB, California: | | | |
| | 21st AS (*bk/gd*) & 22nd AS (*bk/bl*); | | | |
| | 56th AS/97th AMW, Altus AFB, | | | |
| | Oklahoma (*r/y*); | | | |
| | 137th AS/105th AW, Stewart AFB, | | | |
| | New York (*bl*); | | | |
| | 155th AS/164th AW, Memphis, | | | |
| | Tennessee ANG(*r*); | | | |
| | 68th AS/433rd AW AFRC, Kelly AFB, | | | |
| | Texas; | | | |
| | 436th AW, Dover AFB, Delaware: | | | |
| | 3rd AS (*y/r*) & 9th AS (*y/bl*); | | | |
| | 337th AS/439th AW AFRC, Westover | | | |
| | ARB, Massachusetts (*bl/r*); | | | |
| | 445th AW AFRC, Wright- | | | |
| | Patterson AFB, Ohio (*si*): | | | |
| | 89th AS & 356th AS | | | |
| | *FY70* | | | |
| | 00445 | C-5A | 433rd AW | |
| | 00446 | C-5A | 433rd AW | |
| | 00447 | C-5A | 439th AW | *bl/r* |
| | 00448 | C-5A | 439th AW | *bl/r* |
| | 00449 | C-5A | 164th AW | *r* |
| | 00451 | C-5A | 433rd AW | |
| | 00452 | C-5A | 97th AMW | *r/y* |
| | 00453 | C-5A | 433rd AW | |
| | 00454 | C-5A | 164th AW | *r* |
| | 00455 | C-5A | 105th AW | *bl* |
| | 00456 | C-5A | 433rd AW | |
| | 00457 | C-5A | 445th AW | *y* |
| | 00459 | C-5A | 97th AMW | *r/y* |

| Type | | | Notes |
|------|------|------|-------|
| 00460 | C-5A | 105th AW | bl |
| 00461 | C-5A | 436th AW | y |
| 00462 | C-5A | 97th AMW | r/y |
| 00463 | C-5A | 97th AMW | r/y |
| 00464 | C-5A | 105th AW | bl |
| 00465 | C-5A | 97th AMW | r/y |
| 00466 | C-5A | 433rd AW | |
| 00467 | C-5A | 97th AMW | r/y |
| **FY83** | | | |
| 31285 | C-5B | 436th AW | y/r |
| **FY84** | | | |
| 40059 | C-5B | 436th AW | |
| 40060 | C-5B | 60th AMW | bk/bl |
| 40061 | C-5B | 436th AW | y |
| 40062 | C-5B | 60th AMW | bk/gd |
| **FY85** | | | |
| 50001 | C-5B | 436th AW | m |
| 50002 | C-5B | 60th AMW | bk/gd |
| 50003 | C-5B | 436th AW | y |
| 50004 | C-5B | LMTAS | |
| 50005 | C-5B | 436th AW | y |
| 50006 | C-5B | 60th AMW | bk/gd |
| 50007 | C-5B | 436th AW | y/bl |
| 50008 | C-5B | 60th AMW | bk/gd |
| 50009 | C-5B | 436th AW | y |
| 50010 | C-5B | 60th AMW | bk/gd |
| **FY86** | | | |
| 60011 | C-5B | 436th AW | y/bl |
| 60012 | C-5B | 60th AMW | bk/bl |
| 60013 | C-5B | 436th AW | y |
| 60014 | C-5B | 60th AMW | bk/bl |
| 60015 | C-5B | 436th AW | y/r |
| 60016 | C-5B | 60th AMW | bk/bl |
| 60017 | C-5B | 436th AW | y |
| 60018 | C-5B | 60th AMW | bk/gd |
| 60019 | C-5B | 436th AW | y |
| 60020 | C-5B | 436th AW | y |
| 60021 | C-5B | 60th AMW | bk/gd |
| 60022 | C-5B | 60th AMW | bk/bl |
| 60023 | C-5B | 436th AW | y |
| 60024 | C-5B | 60th AMW | bk/bl |
| 60025 | C-5B | 436th AW | y |
| 60026 | C-5B | 60th AMW | bk/gd |
| **FY87** | | | |
| 70027 | C-5B | 436th AW | y/bl |
| 70028 | C-5B | 60th AMW | bk/bl |
| 70029 | C-5B | 436th AW | y |
| 70030 | C-5B | 60th AMW | bk/bl |
| 70031 | C-5B | 436th AW | y |
| 70032 | C-5B | 60th AMW | bk/bl |
| 70033 | C-5B | 436th AW | y |
| 70034 | C-5B | 60th AMW | bk/gd |
| 70035 | C-5B | 436th AW | y |
| 70036 | C-5B | 60th AMW | bk/bl |
| 70037 | C-5B | 436th AW | y |
| 70038 | C-5B | 60th AMW | bk/bl |
| 70039 | C-5B | 436th AW | y |
| 70040 | C-5B | 60th AMW | bk/gd |
| 70041 | C-5B | 436th AW | y |
| 70042 | C-5B | 60th AMW | bk/gd |
| 70043 | C-5B | 436th AW | y/bl |
| 70044 | C-5B | 60th AMW | bk/gd |
| 70045 | C-5B | 436th AW | y |
| **FY68** | | | |
| 80211 | C-5A | 439th AW | bl/r |
| 80212 | C-5A | 105th AW | bl |
| 80213 | C-5C | 60th AMW | bk/bl |
| 80214 | C-5A | 433rd AW | |
| 80215 | C-5A | 445th AW | si |
| 80216 | C-5C | 60th AMW | bk/gd |
| 80217 | C-5A | 97th AMW | r/y |
| 80219 | C-5A | 439th AW | bl/r |

| Type | | | Notes |
|------|------|------|-------|
| 80220 | C-5A | 433rd AW | |
| 80221 | C-5A | 433rd AW | |
| 80222 | C-5A | 439th AW | bl/r |
| 80223 | C-5A | 433rd AW | |
| 80224 | C-5A | 105th AW | bl |
| 80225 | C-5A | 105th AW | bl |
| 80226 | C-5A | 105th AW | bl |
| **FY69** | | | |
| 90001 | C-5A | 105th AW | bl |
| 90002 | C-5A | 433rd AW | |
| 90003 | C-5A | 439th AW | bl/r |
| 90005 | C-5A | 439th AW | bl/r |
| 90006 | C-5A | 433rd AW | |
| 90007 | C-5A | 433rd AW | |
| 90008 | C-5A | 105th AW | bl |
| 90009 | C-5A | 105th AW | bl |
| 90010 | C-5A | 97th AMW | r/y |
| 90011 | C-5A | 439th AW | bl/r |
| 90012 | C-5A | 105th AW | bl |
| 90013 | C-5A | 439th AW | bl/r |
| 90014 | C-5A | 433rd AW | |
| 90015 | C-5A | 105th AW | bl |
| 90016 | C-5A | 433rd AW | |
| 90017 | C-5A | 439th AW | bl/r |
| 90018 | C-5A | 164th AW | r |
| 90019 | C-5A | 439th AW | bl/r |
| 90020 | C-5A | 439th AW | bl/r |
| 90021 | C-5A | 105th AW | bl |
| 90022 | C-5A | 439th AW | bl/r |
| 90023 | C-5A | 105th AW | bl |
| 90024 | C-5A | 436th AW | y |
| 90025 | C-5A | 164th AW | r |
| 90026 | C-5A | 433rd AW | |
| 90027 | C-5A | 439th AW | bl/r |

**Boeing E-8 J-STARS**
116th ACW, Robins AFB,
  Georgia [WR]:
    12th ACCS (gn), 16th ACCS (bk),
    128th ACS/Georgia ANG (r)
    & 330th CTS (y);
Grumman, Melbourne, Florida

| Type | | | Notes |
|------|------|------|-------|
| **FY00** | | | |
| 02000 | E-8C | 116th ACW | |
| **FY90** | | | |
| 00175 | E-8A | Grumman | |
| **FY01** | | | |
| 12005 | E-8C | 116th ACW | |
| **FY02** | | | |
| 29111 | E-8C | 116th ACW | |
| **FY92** | | | |
| 23289 | E-8C | 116th ACW | m |
| 23290 | E-8C | 116th ACW | bk |
| **FY93** | | | |
| 30597 | E-8C | 116th ACW | gn |
| 31097 | E-8C | 116th ACW | gn |
| **FY94** | | | |
| 40284 | E-8C | 116th ACW | gn |
| 40285 | E-8C | 116th ACW | bk |
| **FY95** | | | |
| 50121 | E-8C | 116th ACW | r |
| 50122 | E-8C | 116th ACW | r |
| **FY96** | | | |
| 60042 | E-8C | 116th ACW | bk |
| 60043 | E-8C | 116th ACW | |
| **FY86** | | | |
| 60416 | TE-8A | 116th ACW | y |
| 60417 | TE-8A | 116th ACW | y |
| **FY97** | | | |
| 70100 | E-8C | 116th ACW | r |
| 70200 | E-8C | 116th ACW | bk |
| 70201 | E-8C | 116th ACW | r |

| Notes | Type | | | |
|---|---|---|---|---|
| | *FY99* | | | |
| | 90006 | E-8C | 116th ACW | *gn* |
| | **McDonnell Douglas** | | | |
| | **C-9 Nightingale** | | | |
| | 932nd AW AFRC, Scott AFB, | | | |
| | Illinois | | | |
| | *FY67* | | | |
| | 22584 | C-9A | | |
| | *FY73* | | | |
| | 31681 | C-9C | | |
| | 31682 | C-9C | | |
| | 31683 | C-9C | | |
| | **McDonnell Douglas** | | | |
| | **KC-10A Extender** | | | |
| | 60th AMW, Travis AFB, California: | | | |
| | 6th ARS (*bk/bl*) & 9th ARS (*bk/r*); | | | |
| | 305th AMW, McGuire AFB, | | | |
| | New Jersey: | | | |
| | 2nd ARS (*bl/r*) & 32nd ARS (*bl*) | | | |
| | *FY82* | | | |
| | 20191 | 60th AMW | bk/bl | |
| | 20192 | 60th AMW | bk/r | |
| | 20193 | 60th AMW | bk/bl | |
| | *FY83* | | | |
| | 30075 | 60th AMW | bk/r | |
| | 30076 | 60th AMW | bk/bl | |
| | 30077 | 60th AMW | bk/r | |
| | 30078 | 60th AMW | bk/bl | |
| | 30079 | 305th AMW | bl/r | |
| | 30080 | 60th AMW | bk/bl | |
| | 30081 | 305th AMW | bl | |
| | 30082 | 305th AMW | bl | |
| | *FY84* | | | |
| | 40185 | 60th AMW | bk/bl | |
| | 40186 | 305th AMW | bl/r | |
| | 40187 | 60th AMW | bk/bl | |
| | 40188 | 305th AMW | bl/r | |
| | 40189 | 305th AMW | bl | |
| | 40190 | 305th AMW | bl/r | |
| | 40191 | 60th AMW | bk/bl | |
| | 40192 | 305th AMW | bl | |
| | 50027 | 305th AMW | bl/r | |
| | 50028 | 305th AMW | bl/r | |
| | 50029 | 60th AMW | bk/r | |
| | 50030 | 305th AMW | bl/r | |
| | 50031 | 305th AMW | bl/r | |
| | 50032 | 305th AMW | bl/r | |
| | 50033 | 305th AMW | bl | |
| | 50034 | 305th AMW | bl/r | |
| | *FY86* | | | |
| | 60027 | 305th AMW | bl | |
| | 60028 | 305th AMW | bl/r | |
| | 60029 | 60th AMW | bk/r | |
| | 60030 | 305th AMW | bl/r | |
| | 60031 | 60th AMW | bk/r | |
| | 60032 | 60th AMW | bk/r | |
| | 60033 | 60th AMW | bk/r | |
| | 60034 | 60th AMW | bk/r | |
| | 60035 | 305th AMW | bl | |
| | 60036 | 305th AMW | bl | |
| | 60037 | 60th AMW | bk/r | |
| | 60038 | 60th AMW | bk/r | |
| | *FY87* | | | |
| | 70117 | 60th AMW | bk/r | |
| | 70118 | 60th AMW | bk/bl | |
| | 70119 | 60th AMW | bk/r | |
| | 70120 | 305th AMW | bl | |
| | 70121 | 305th AMW | bl | |
| | 70122 | 305th AMW | bl/r | |
| | 70123 | 305th AMW | bl | |
| | 70124 | 305th AMW | bl/r | |

| Notes | Type | | | |
|---|---|---|---|---|
| | *FY79* | | | |
| | 90433 | 305th AMW | bl | |
| | 90434 | 305th AMW | bl/r | |
| | 91710 | 305th AMW | bl/r | |
| | 91711 | 305th AMW | bl | |
| | 91712 | 305th AMW | bl/r | |
| | 91713 | 305th AMW | bl | |
| | 91946 | 60th AMW | bk/bl | |
| | 91947 | 305th AMW | bl | |
| | 91948 | 60th AMW | bk/bl | |
| | 91949 | 305th AMW | bl/r | |
| | 91950 | 60th AMW | bk/bl | |
| | 91951 | 60th AMW | bk/bl | |
| | **Boeing** | | | |
| | **C-17 Globemaster III** | | | |
| | 15th AW, Hickam AFB, | | | |
| | Hawaii: 535th AS; | | | |
| | 62nd AW, McChord AFB, | | | |
| | Washington (*gn*): | | | |
| | 4th AS, 7th AS,8th AS | | | |
| | & 10th AS; | | | |
| | 58th AS/97th AMW, Altus AFB, | | | |
| | Oklahoma (*r/y*); | | | |
| | 172nd AW, Jackson Int'l | | | |
| | Airport, Mississippi ANG: | | | |
| | 183rd AS (*bl/gd*); | | | |
| | 305th AMW, McGuire AFB, | | | |
| | New Jersey (*bl*): | | | |
| | 6th AS & 13th AS; | | | |
| | 417th FLTS/412th TW, Edwards AFB, | | | |
| | California [ED]; | | | |
| | 437th AW, Charleston AFB, | | | |
| | South Carolina (*y/bl*): | | | |
| | 14th AS, 15th AS, | | | |
| | 16th AS & 17th AS; | | | |
| | 452nd AMW AFRC, March ARB, | | | |
| | California (*or/y*): | | | |
| | 729th AS | | | |
| | *FY00* | | | |
| | 00171 | C-17A | 62nd AW | gn |
| | 00172 | C-17A | 62nd AW | gn |
| | 00173 | C-17A | 62nd AW | gn |
| | 00174 | C-17A | 62nd AW | gn |
| | 00175 | C-17A | 62nd AW | gn |
| | 00176 | C-17A | 437th AW | y/bl |
| | 00177 | C-17A | 437th AW | y/bl |
| | 00178 | C-17A | 62nd AW | gn |
| | 00179 | C-17A | 62nd AW | gn |
| | 00180 | C-17A | 62nd AW | gn |
| | 00181 | C-17A | 62nd AW | gn |
| | 00182 | C-17A | 62nd AW | gn |
| | 00183 | C-17A | 62nd AW | gn |
| | 00184 | C-17A | 62nd AW | gn |
| | 00185 | C-17A | 62nd AW | gn |
| | *FY90* | | | |
| | 00532 | C-17A | 97th AMW | r/y |
| | 00533 | C-17A | 62nd AW | gn |
| | 00534 | C-17A | 437th AW | y/bl |
| | 00535 | C-17A | 62nd AW | gn |
| | *FY01* | | | |
| | 10186 | C-17A | 62nd AW | gn |
| | 10187 | C-17A | 62nd AW | gn |
| | 10188 | C-17A | 437th AW | y/bl |
| | 10189 | C-17A | 437th AW | y/bl |
| | 10190 | C-17A | 437th AW | y/bl |
| | 10191 | C-17A | 437th AW | y/bl |
| | 10192 | C-17A | 437th AW | y/bl |
| | 10193 | C-17A | 437th AW | y/bl |
| | 10194 | C-17A | 437th AW | y/bl |
| | 10195 | C-17A | 437th AW | y/bl |
| | 10197 | C-17A | 437th AW | y/bl |
| | *FY02* | | | |

| Type | | | Notes | | Type | | | Notes |
|------|--|--|-------|--|------|--|--|-------|
| 21098 | C-17A | 437th AW | y/bl | | 55142 | C-17A | 452nd AMW | or/y |
| 21099 | C-17A | 437th AW | y/bl | | 55143 | C-17A | 452nd AMW | or/y |
| 21100 | C-17A | 437th AW | y/bl | | 55144 | C-17A | 452nd AMW | or/y |
| 21101 | C-17A | 437th AW | y/bl | | 55145 | C-17A | 452nd AMW | or/y |
| 21102 | C-17A | 437th AW | y/bl | | 55146 | | | |
| 21103 | C-17A | 62nd AW | gn | | 55147 | | | |
| 21104 | C-17A | 62nd AW | gn | | 55148 | | | |
| 21105 | C-17A | 62nd AW | gn | | 55149 | | | |
| 21106 | C-17A | 62nd AW | gn | | 55150 | | | |
| 21107 | C-17A | 62nd AW | gn | | *FY96* | | | |
| 21108 | C-17A | 62nd AW | gn | | 60001 | C-17A | 437th AW | y/bl |
| 21109 | C-17A | 62nd AW | gn | | 60002 | C-17A | 437th AW | y/bl |
| 21110 | C-17A | 62nd AW | gn | | 60003 | C-17A | 62nd AW | gn |
| 21111 | C-17A | 62nd AW | gn | | 60004 | C-17A | 437th AW | y/bl |
| 21112 | C-17A | 172nd AW | bl/gd | | 60005 | C-17A | 437th AW | y/bl |
| *FY92* | | | | | 60006 | C-17A | 437th AW | y/bl |
| 23291 | C-17A | 62nd AW | gn | | 60007 | C-17A | 437th AW | y/bl |
| 23292 | C-17A | 437th AW | y/bl | | 60008 | C-17A | 437th AW | y/bl |
| 23293 | C-17A | 437th AW | y/bl | | *FY87* | | | |
| 23294 | C-17A | 97th AMW | r/y | | 70025 | C-17A | 412th TW | |
| *FY93* | | | | | *FY97* | | | |
| 30599 | C-17A | 97th AMW | r/y | | 70041 | C-17A | 437th AW | y/bl |
| 30600 | C-17A | 62nd AW | gn | | 70042 | C-17A | 437mth AW | y/bl |
| 30601 | C-17A | 437th AW | y/bl | | 70043 | C-17A | 437th AW | y/bl |
| 30602 | C-17A | 97th AMW | r/y | | 70044 | C-17A | 437th AW | y/bl |
| 30603 | C-17A | 97th AMW | r/y | | 70045 | C-17A | 437th AW | y/bl |
| 30604 | C-17A | 437th AW | y/bl | | 70046 | C-17A | 437th AW | y/bl |
| *FY03* | | | | | 70047 | C-17A | 437th AW | y/bl |
| 33113 | C-17A | 172nd AW | bl/gd | | 70048 | C-17A | 437th AW | y/bl |
| 33114 | C-17A | 172nd AW | bl/gd | | *FY98* | | | |
| 33115 | C-17A | 172nd AW | bl/gd | | 80049 | C-17A | 62nd AW | gn |
| 33116 | C-17A | 172nd AW | bl/gd | | 80050 | C-17A | 62nd AW | gn |
| 33117 | C-17A | 172nd AW | bl/gd | | 80051 | C-17A | 97th AMW | r/y |
| 33118 | C-17A | 172nd AW | bl/gd | | 80052 | C-17A | 62nd AW | gn |
| 33119 | C-17A | 172nd AW | bl/gd | | 80053 | C-17A | 97th AMW | r/y |
| 33120 | C-17A | 62nd AW | gn | | 80054 | C-17A | 437th AW | y/bl |
| 33121 | C-17A | 412th TW | | | 80055 | C-17A | 62nd AW | gn |
| 33122 | C-17A | 62nd AW | gn | | 80056 | C-17A | 62nd AW | gn |
| 33123 | C-17A | 62nd AW | gn | | 80057 | C-17A | 62nd AW | y/bl |
| 33124 | C-17A | 62nd AW | gn | | *FY88* | | | |
| 33125 | C-17A | 305th AMW | bl | | 80265 | C-17A | 97th AMW | r/y |
| 33126 | C-17A | 305th AMW | bl | | 80266 | C-17A | 437th AW | y/bl |
| 33127 | C-17A | 305th AMW | bl | | *FY99* | | | |
| *FY94* | | | | | 90058 | C-17A | 62nd AW | gn |
| 40065 | C-17A | 437th AW | y/bl | | 90059 | C-17A | 62nd AW | gn |
| 40066 | C-17A | 437th AW | y/bl | | 90060 | C-17A | 62nd AW | gn |
| 40067 | C-17A | 437th AW | y/bl | | 90061 | C-17A | 62nd AW | gn |
| 40068 | C-17A | 437th AW | y/bl | | 90062 | C-17A | 62nd AW | gn |
| 40069 | C-17A | 437th AW | y/bl | | 90063 | C-17A | 62nd AW | gn |
| 40070 | C-17A | 437th AW | y/bl | | 90064 | C-17A | 62nd AW | gn |
| *FY04* | | | | | 90165 | C-17A | 62nd AW | gn |
| 44128 | C-17A | 305th AMW | bl | | 90166 | C-17A | 62nd AW | gn |
| 44129 | C-17A | 305th AMW | bl | | 90167 | C-17A | 62nd AW | gn |
| 44130 | C-17A | 305th AMW | bl | | 90168 | C-17A | 62nd AW | gn |
| 44131 | C-17A | 305th AMW | bl | | 90169 | C-17A | 62nd AW | gn |
| 44132 | C-17A | 305th AMW | bl | | 90170 | C-17A | 62nd AW | gn |
| 44133 | C-17A | 305th AMW | bl | | *FY89* | | | |
| 44134 | C-17A | 305th AMW | bl | | 91189 | C-17A | 97th AMW | r/y |
| 44135 | C-17A | 305th AMW | bl | | 91190 | C-17A | 97th AMW | r/y |
| 44136 | C-17A | 305th AMW | bl | | 91191 | C-17A | 437th AW | y/bl |
| 44137 | C-17A | 305th AMW | bl | | 91192 | C-17A | 437th AW | y/bl |
| 44138 | C-17A | 452nd AMW | or/y | | | | | |
| *FY95* | | | | | **Grumman** | | | |
| 50102 | C-17A | 437th AW | y/bl | | **C-20 Gulfstream III/IV** | | | |
| 50103 | C-17A | 437th AW | y/bl | | 89th AW, Andrews AFB, Maryland: | | | |
| 50104 | C-17A | 97th AMW | r/y | | 99th AS; | | | |
| 50105 | C-17A | 437th AW | y/bl | | OSAC/PAT, US Army, Andrews AFB, | | | |
| 50106 | C-17A | 437th AW | y/bl | | Maryland; | | | |
| 50107 | C-17A | 437th AW | y/bl | | Pacific Flight Detachment, | | | |
| *FY05* | | | | | Hickam AFB, Hawaii | | | |
| 55139 | C-17A | 452nd AMW | or/y | | **C-20B Gulfstream III** | | | |
| 55140 | C-17A | 452nd AMW | or/y | | *FY86* | | | |
| 55141 | C-17A | 452nd AMW | or/y | | 60201 | 89th AW | | |

| Notes | Type | | |
|---|---|---|---|
| | 60202 | 89th AW | |
| | 60203 | 89th AW | |
| | 60204 | 89th AW | |
| | 60206 | 89th AW | |
| | 60403 | 89th AW | |

**C-20C Gulfstream III**
*FY85*

| | | |
|---|---|---|
| 50049 | 89th AW | |
| 50050 | 89th AW | |

**C-20E Gulfstream III**
*FY87*

| | | |
|---|---|---|
| 70139 | Pacific Flt Det | |
| 70140 | OSAC/PAT | |

**C-20F Gulfstream IV**
*FY91*

| | | |
|---|---|---|
| 10108 | OSAC/PAT | |

**Boeing VC-25A**
89th AW, Andrews AFB, Maryland
*FY82*

28000

*FY92*

29000

**Boeing C-32**
1st AS/89th AW, Andrews AFB,
  Maryland;
486th FLTS/46th TW, Eglin AFB,
  Florida & McGuire AFB,
  New Jersey
*FY00*

| | | |
|---|---|---|
| 09001 | C-32B | 486th FLTS |

*FY02*

| | | |
|---|---|---|
| 24452 | C-32B | 486th FLTS |
| 25001 | C-32B | 486th FLTS |

*FY98*

| | | |
|---|---|---|
| 80001 | C-32A | 89th AW |
| 80002 | C-32A | 89th AW |

*FY99*

| | | |
|---|---|---|
| 90003 | C-32A | 89th AW |
| 90004 | C-32A | 89th AW |

**Gulfstream Aerospace
C-37A Gulfstream V**
6th AMW, MacDill AFB, Florida:
  310th AS;
15th ABW, Hickam AFB, Hawaii:
  65th AS;
89th AW, Andrews AFB, Maryland:
  99th AS;
OSAC/PAT, US Army, Andrews AFB,
  Maryland
*FY01*

| | | |
|---|---|---|
| 10028 | 6th AMW | |
| 10029 | 6th AMW | |
| 10030 | 6th AMW | |
| 10065 | 15th ABW | |

*FY02*

| | | |
|---|---|---|
| 21863 | OSAC/PAT | |

*FY04*

| | | |
|---|---|---|
| 41778 | OSAC/PAT | |

*FY97*

| | | |
|---|---|---|
| 70400 | 89th AW | |
| 70401 | 89th AW | |

*FY99*

| | | |
|---|---|---|
| 90402 | 89th AW | |
| 90404 | 89th AW | |

**IAI C-38A Astra**
201st AS/113th FW, DC ANG,
  Andrews AFB, Maryland
*FY94*

41569

41570

**Boeing C-40**
15th ABW, Hickam AFB, Hawaii:
  65th AS;
86th AW, Ramstein,
  Germany:
  76th AS;
89th AW, Andrews AFB, Maryland:
  1st AS;
201st AS/113th FW, DC ANG,
  Andrews AFB, Maryland
*FY01*

| | | |
|---|---|---|
| 10005 | C-40B | 89th AW |
| 10015 | C-40B | 15th ABW |
| 10040 | C-40B | 86th AW |
| 10041 | C-40B | 89th AW |

*FY02*

| | | |
|---|---|---|
| 20042 | C-40B | 89th AW |
| 20201 | C-40C | 201st AS |
| 20202 | C-40C | 201st AS |
| 20203 | C-40C | 201st AS |
| 20204 | C-40C | 201st AS |

**Boeing T-43A**
562nd FTS/12th FTW, Randolph
  AFB, Texas [RA] (*bk/y*)
*FY71*

11404

*FY72*

20288

*FY73*

31150
31151
31152
31153
31154
31156

**Boeing B-52H Stratofortress**
2nd BW, Barksdale AFB,
  Louisiana [LA]:
  11th BS (*gd*), 20th BS (*bl*)
  & 96th BS (*r*);
23rd BS/5th BW, Minot AFB,
  North Dakota [MT] (*r/y*);
49th TES/53rd TEG, Barksdale AFB,
  Louisiana [OT];
93rd BS/917th Wg AFRC,
  Barksdale AFB,
  Louisiana [BD] (*y/bl*);
419th FLTS/412th TW Edwards AFB,
  California [ED]
*FY60*

| | | |
|---|---|---|
| 00001 | 2nd BW | r |
| 00002 | 2nd BW | gd |
| 00003 | 93rd BS | y/bl |
| 00004 | 5th BW | r/y |
| 00005 | 5th BW | r/y |
| 00007 | 5th BW | r/y |
| 00008 | 2nd BW | r |
| 00009 | 5th BW | r/y |
| 00010 | 2nd BW | r |
| 00011 | 2nd BW | gd |
| 00012 | 2nd BW | r |
| 00013 | 2nd BW | r |
| 00014 | 2nd BW | bl |
| 00015 | 5th BW | r/y |
| 00016 | 2nd BW | r |
| 00017 | 2nd BW | gd |
| 00018 | 5th BW | r/y |
| 00019 | 2nd BW | r |
| 00020 | 2nd BW | bl |

| Type | | | Notes |
|------|------|------|-------|
| 00022 | 2nd BW | r | |
| 00023 | 5th BW | r/y | |
| 00024 | 5th BW | r/y | |
| 00025 | 2nd BW | bl | |
| 00026 | 5th BW | r/y | |
| 00028 | 2nd BW | r | |
| 00029 | 5th BW | r/y | |
| 00030 | 2nd BW | bl | |
| 00031 | 53rd TEG | | |
| 00032 | 2nd BW | gd | |
| 00033 | 5th BW | r/y | |
| 00034 | 5th BW | r/y | |
| 00035 | 2nd BW | gd | |
| 00036 | 419th FLTS | | |
| 00037 | 2nd BW | r | |
| 00038 | 2nd BW | gd | |
| 00041 | 93rd BS | y/bl | |
| 00042 | 93rd BS | y/bl | |
| 00043 | 2nd BW | bl | |
| 00044 | 5th BW | r/y | |
| 00045 | 93rd BS | y/bl | |
| 00046 | 2nd BW | bl | |
| 00047 | 5th BW | r/y | |
| 00048 | 2nd BW | r | |
| 00049 | 412th TW | | |
| 00050 | 412th TW | | |
| 00051 | 5th BW | r/y | |
| 00052 | 2nd BW | r | |
| 00053 | 2nd BW | r | |
| 00054 | 2nd BW | gd | |
| 00055 | 5th BW | r/y | |
| 00056 | 5th BW | r/y | |
| 00057 | 2nd BW | gd | |
| 00058 | 2nd BW | gd | |
| 00059 | 2nd BW | | |
| 00060 | 5th BW | r/y | |
| 00061 | 2nd BW | gd | |
| 00062 | 2nd BW | bl | |
| FY61 | | | |
| 10001 | 5th BW | r/y | |
| 10002 | 2nd BW | bl | |
| 10003 | 2nd BW | bl | |
| 10004 | 2nd BW | bl | |
| 10005 | 5th BW | r/y | |
| 10006 | 2nd BW | gd | |
| 10007 | 5th BW | r/y | |
| 10008 | 93rd BS | y/bl | |
| 10009 | 2nd BW | r | |
| 10010 | 2nd BW | bl | |
| 10011 | 2nd BW | gd | |
| 10012 | 2nd BW | r | |
| 10013 | 2nd BW | r | |
| 10014 | 5th BW | r/y | |
| 10015 | 2nd BW | gd | |
| 10016 | 2nd BW | gd | |
| 10017 | 2nd BW | bl | |
| 10018 | 5th BW | r/y | |
| 10019 | 2nd BW | gd | |
| 10020 | 2nd BW | gd | |
| 10021 | 93rd BS | y/bl | |
| 10022 | 93rd BS | y/bl | |
| 10023 | 2nd BW | bl | |
| 10024 | 2nd BW | r | |
| 10027 | 5th BW | r/y | |
| 10028 | 2nd BW | gd | |
| 10029 | 93rd BS | y/bl | |
| 10031 | 2nd BW | gd | |
| 10032 | 93rd BS | y/bl | |
| 10034 | 5th BW | r/y | |
| 10035 | 5th BW | r/y | |
| 10036 | 2nd BW | gd | |
| 10038 | 2nd BW | gd | |
| 10039 | 2nd BW | gd | |

| Type | | | Notes |
|------|------|------|-------|
| 10040 | 5th BW | r/y | |

**Lockheed F-117A Nighthawk**
49th FW, Holloman AFB,
  New Mexico [HO]:
  8th FS (y) & 9th FS (r)
53rd Wg, Nellis AFB,
  Nevada [OT] (gy/w);
445th FLTS/412th TW, Edwards AFB,
  California [ED]

| 79-783 | (79-10783) | ED | |
| 79-784 | (79-10784) | ED | |
| 80-786 | (80-0786) | HO | r |
| 80-787 | (80-0787) | HO | y |
| 80-788 | (80-0788) | HO | |
| 80-789 | (80-0789) | HO | r |
| 80-790 | (80-0790) | HO | r |
| 80-791 | (80-0791) | HO | y |
| 81-794 | (81-10794) | HO | y |
| 81-795 | (81-10795) | HO | y |
| 81-796 | (81-10796) | HO | r [49th OG] |
| 81-797 | (81-10797) | HO | r |
| 81-798 | (81-10798) | HO | r [49th FW] |
| 82-799 | (82-0799) | HO | r |
| 82-800 | (82-0800) | HO | y [8th FS] |
| 82-801 | (82-0801) | HO | |
| 82-802 | (82-0802) | HO | y |
| 82-803 | (82-0803) | HO | y |
| 82-804 | (82-0804) | HO | y |
| 82-805 | (82-0805) | HO | r |
| 83-807 | (83-0807) | HO | r |
| 83-808 | (83-0808) | HO | r |
| 84-809 | (84-0809) | HO | r [9th FS] |
| 84-810 | (84-0810) | HO | r |
| 84-811 | (84-0811) | HO | r |
| 84-812 | (84-0812) | HO | |
| 84-824 | (84-0824) | HO | r |
| 84-825 | (84-0825) | HO | y |
| 84-826 | (84-0826) | HO | r |
| 84-827 | (84-0827) | HO | y |
| 84-828 | (84-0828) | HO | r |
| 85-813 | (85-0813) | HO | r |
| 85-814 | (85-0814) | HO | r |
| 85-816 | (85-0816) | HO | y [49th FW] |
| 85-817 | (85-0817) | HO | y |
| 85-818 | (85-0818) | HO | y |
| 85-819 | (85-0819) | HO | y [49th FW] |
| 85-820 | (85-0820) | HO | r |
| 85-829 | (85-0829) | HO | r |
| 85-830 | (85-0830) | HO | r |
| 85-831 | (85-0831) | ED | |
| 85-832 | (85-0832) | HO | y |
| 85-833 | (85-0833) | HO | r |
| 85-834 | (85-0834) | HO | y |
| 85-835 | (85-0835) | OT | |
| 85-836 | (85-0836) | HO | r |
| 86-821 | (86-0821) | HO | r |
| 86-822 | (86-0822) | HO | |
| 86-823 | (86-0823) | HO | r |
| 86-837 | (86-0837) | HO | y |
| 86-838 | (86-0838) | HO | y |
| 86-839 | (86-0839) | HO | y |
| 86-840 | (86-0840) | HO | r |
| 88-841 | (88-0841) | HO | r [9th FS] |
| 88-842 | (88-0842) | HO | y |
| 88-843 | (88-0843) | HO | y |

**Lockheed C-130 Hercules**
1st SOS/353rd SOG, Kadena AB,
  Japan;
3rd Wg, Elmendorf AFB,
  Alaska [AK]:
  517th AS (w);

# C-130

4th SOS/16th SOW, Hurlburt Field,
  Florida;
7th SOS/352nd SOG,
  RAF Mildenhall, UK;
8th SOS/16th SOW, Duke Field,
  Florida;
9th SOS/16th OG, Eglin AFB, Florida;
15th SOS/16th SOW, Hurlburt Field,
  Florida;
16th SOS/16th SOW, Hurlburt Field,
  Florida;
17th SOS/353rd SOG, Kadena AB,
  Japan;
37th AS/86th AW, Ramstein AB,
  Germany [RS] (bl/w);
39th RQS/920th RQW AFRC,
  Patrick AFB, Florida [FL];
41st ECS/55th Wg, Davis-Monthan
  AFB, Arizona [DM] (bl);
43rd AW, Pope AFB,
  North Carolina [FT]:
  2nd AS (gn/bl) & 41st AS (gn/or);
43rd ECS/55th Wg, Davis-Monthan
  AFB, Arizona [DM] (r);
53rd WRS/403rd AW AFRC,
  Keesler AFB, Missouri;
58th SOW, Kirtland AFB,
  New Mexico:
  550th SOS;
67th SOS/352nd SOG,
  RAF Mildenhall, UK;
71st RQS/347th Wg, Moody AFB,
  Georgia [MY] (bl);
79th RQS/55th Wg, Davis-Monthan
  AFB, Arizona [DM];
95th AS/440th AW AFRC,
  General Mitchell ARS,
  Wisconsin (w/r);
96th AS/934th AW AFRC,
  Minneapolis/St Paul,
  Minnesota (pr);
102nd RQS/106th RQW, Suffolk Field,
  New York ANG [LI];
105th AS/118th AW, Nashville,
  Tennessee ANG (r);
109th AS/133rd AW,
  Minneapolis/St Paul,
  Minnesota ANG [MN] (pr/bk);
115th AS/146th AW,
  Channel Island ANGS,
  California ANG [CI] (gn);
122nd FS/159th FW,
  NAS New Orleans,
  Louisiana ANG [JZ];
130th AS/130th AW, Yeager Int'l
  Airport, Charleston
  West Virginia ANG [WV] (pr/y);
130th RQS/129th RQW, Moffet Field,
  California ANG [CA] (bl);
135th AS/135th AW, Martin State
  Airport, Maryland ANG [MD] (bk/y);
139th AS/109th AW, Schenectady,
  New York ANG [NY];
142nd AS/166th AW,
  New Castle County Airport,
  Delaware ANG [DE] (bl);
143rd AS/143rd AW, Quonset,
  Rhode Island ANG [RI] (r);
144th AS/176th CW, Kulis ANGB,
  Alaska ANG (bk/y);
154th TS/189th AW, Little Rock,
  Arkansas ANG (r);
156th AS/145th AW, Charlotte,

North Carolina ANG [NC] (bl);
157th FS/169th FW, McEntire ANGS,
  South Carolina ANG [SC];
158th AS/165th AW, Savannah,
  Georgia ANG (r);
159th FS/125th FW, Jacksonville,
  Florida ANG;
164th AS/179th AW, Mansfield,
  Ohio ANG [OH] (bl);
165th AS/123rd AW, Standiford Field,
  Kentucky ANG [KY];
167th AS/167th AW, Martinsburg,
  West Virginia ANG [WV] (r);
169th AS/182nd AW, Peoria,
  Illinois ANG [IL];
171st AS/191st AW, Selfridge ANGB,
  Michigan ANG (y/bk);
180th AS/139th AW,
  Rosencrans Memorial Airport,
  Missouri ANG [XP] (y);
181st AS/136th AW, NAS Dallas,
  Texas ANG (bl/w);
185th AS/137th AW, Will Rogers World
  Airport, Oklahoma ANG [OK] (bl);
187th AS/153rd AW, Cheyenne,
  Wyoming ANG [WY]; (y)
189th AS/124th Wg, Boise,
  Idaho ANG [ID];
192nd AS/152nd AW, Reno,
  Nevada ANG [NV] (w);
193rd SOS/193rd SOW, Harrisburg,
  Pennsylvania ANG [PA];
198th AS/156th AW, San Juan,
  Puerto Rico ANG;
204th AS/154th Wg, Hickam AFB,
  Hawaii ANG [HH];
210th RQS/176th CW, Kulis ANGB,
  Alaska ANG [AK];
314th AW, Little Rock AFB,
  Arkansas:
  48th AS (y), 53rd AS (bk)
  & 62nd AS (bl);
317th AG, Dyess AFB, Texas:
  39th AS (r) & 40th AS (bl);
327th AS/913th AW AFRC,
  NAS Willow Grove,
  Pennsylvania (bk);
328th AS/914th AW AFRC,
  Niagara Falls,
  New York [NF] (bl);
357th AS/908th AW AFRC,
  Maxwell AFB, Alabama (bl);
374th AW, Yokota AB,
  Japan [YJ]: 36th AS (r);
412th TW Edwards AFB,
  California:
  452nd FLTS [ED];
463rd AG Little Rock AFB,
  Arkansas [LK]:
  50th AS (r) & 61st AS (gn);
645th Materiel Sqn, Palmdale,
  California [D4];
700th AS/94th AW AFRC,
  Dobbins ARB,
  Georgia [DB] (bl);
711th SOS/919th SOW AFRC,
  Duke Field, Florida;
731st AS/302nd AW AFRC,
  Peterson AFB,
  Colorado (pr/w);
757th AS/910th AW AFRC,
  Youngstown ARS,
  Ohio [YO] (bl);

| Type | | | Notes | Type | | | Notes |
|------|--|--|-------|------|--|--|-------|
| 758th AS/911th AW AFRC, | | | | 11235 | C-130H | 165th AS | |
| Pittsburgh ARS, | | | | 11236 | C-130H | 165th AS | |
| Pennsylvania (*bk/y*); | | | | 11237 | C-130H | 165th AS | |
| 773rd AS/910th AW AFRC, | | | | 11238 | C-130H | 165th AS | |
| Youngstown ARS, | | | | 11239 | C-130H | 165th AS | |
| Ohio [YO] (*r*); | | | | *FY01* | | | |
| 815th AS/403rd AW AFRC, | | | | 11461 | C-130J | 115th AS | gn |
| Keesler AFB, | | | | 11462 | C-130J | 115th AS | gn |
| Missouri [KT] (*r*); | | | | *FY91* | | | |
| LMTAS, Marietta, | | | | 11651 | C-130H | 165th AS | |
| Georgia | | | | 11652 | C-130H | 165th AS | |
| *FY90* | | | | 11653 | C-130H | 165th AS | |
| 00162 | MC-130P | 15th SOS | | *FY61* | | | |
| 00163 | AC-130U | 4th SOS | | 12358 | C-130E | 154th TS | r |
| 00164 | AC-130U | 4th SOS | | 12367 | C-130E | 314th AW | bl |
| 00165 | AC-130U | 4th SOS | | 12369 | C-130E | 198th AS | |
| 00166 | AC-130U | 4th SOS | | 12370 | C-130E | 463rd AG | gn |
| 00167 | AC-130U | 4th SOS | | 12372 | C-130E | 115th AS | gn |
| *FY80* | | | | *FY64* | | | |
| 00320 | C-130H | 158th AS | r | 14852 | HC-130P | 71st RQS | bl |
| 00321 | C-130H | 158th AS | r | 14853 | HC-130P | 71st RQS | bl |
| 00322 | C-130H | 158th AS | r | 14854 | MC-130P | 9th SOS | |
| 00323 | C-130H | 158th AS | r | 14855 | HC-130P | 39th RQS | |
| 00324 | C-130H | 158th AS | r | 14858 | MC-130P | 58th SOW | |
| 00325 | C-130H | 158th AS | r | 14859 | C-130E | 16th SOW | |
| 00326 | C-130H | 158th AS | r | 14860 | HC-130P | 79th RQS | |
| 00332 | C-130H | 158th AS | r | 14861 | WC-130H | 53rd WRS | |
| *FY90* | | | | 14862 | EC-130H | 645th MS | |
| 01057 | C-130H | 142nd AS | bl | 14863 | HC-130P | 71st RQS | bl |
| 01058 | C-130H | 204th AS | | 14864 | HC-130P | 39th RQS | |
| *FY70* | | | | 14865 | HC-130P | 71st RQS | bl |
| 01260 | C-130E | 37th AS | bl/w | 14866 | WC-130H | 53rd WRS | |
| 01261 | C-130E | 43rd AW | gn/bl | 17681 | C-130E | 37th AS | bl/w |
| 01264 | C-130E | 37th AS | bl/w | *FY91* | | | |
| 01265 | C-130E | 43rd AW | gn/bl | 19141 | C-130H | 96th AS | pr |
| 01266 | C-130E | 43rd AW | gn/bl | 19142 | C-130H | 96th AS | pr |
| 01267 | C-130E | 43rd AW | gn/or | 19143 | C-130H | 96th AS | pr |
| 01270 | C-130E | 43rd AW | gn/bl | 19144 | C-130H | 96th AS | pr |
| 01271 | C-130E | 37th AS | bl/w | *FY82* | | | |
| 01274 | C-130E | 37th AS | bl/w | 20054 | C-130H | 144th AS | bk/y |
| 01275 | C-130E | 43rd AW | gn/bl | 20055 | C-130H | 144th AS | bk/y |
| *FY90* | | | | 20056 | C-130H | 144th AS | bk/y |
| 01791 | C-130H | 164th AS | bl | 20057 | C-130H | 144th AS | bk/y |
| 01792 | C-130H | 164th AS | bl | 20058 | C-130H | 144th AS | bk/y |
| 01793 | C-130H | 164th AS | bl | 20059 | C-130H | 144th AS | bk/y |
| 01794 | C-130H | 164th AS | bl | 20060 | C-130H | 144th AS | bk/y |
| 01795 | C-130H | 164th AS | bl | 20061 | C-130H | 144th AS | bk/y |
| 01796 | C-130H | 164th AS | bl | *FY02* | | | |
| 01797 | C-130H | 164th AS | bl | 20314 | C-130J | 314th AW | y |
| 01798 | C-130H | 164th AS | bl | *FY92* | | | |
| *FY00* | | | | 20253 | AC-130U | 4th SOS | |
| 01934 | EC-130J | LMTAS | | 20547 | C-130H | 463rd AG | r |
| *FY90* | | | | 20548 | C-130H | 463rd AG | r |
| 02103 | HC-130N | 210th RQS | | 20549 | C-130H | 463rd AG | r |
| 09107 | C-130H | 757th AS | bl | 20550 | C-130H | 463rd AG | r |
| 09108 | C-130H | 757th AS | bl | 20551 | C-130H | 463rd AG | r |
| *FY81* | | | | 20552 | C-130H | 463rd AG | r |
| 10626 | C-130H | 700th AS | bl | 20553 | C-130H | 463rd AG | r |
| 10627 | C-130H | 700th AS | bl | 20554 | C-130H | 463rd AG | r |
| 10628 | C-130H | 700th AS | bl | 21094 | LC-130H | 139th AS | |
| 10629 | C-130H | 700th AS | bl | 21095 | LC-130H | 139th AS | |
| 10630 | C-130H | 700th AS | bl | *FY72* | | | |
| 10631 | C-130H | 700th AS | bl | 21288 | C-130E | 374th AW | r |
| *FY68* | | | | 21289 | C-130E | 374th AW | r |
| 10935 | C-130E | 37th AS | bl/w | 21290 | C-130E | 374th AW | r |
| 10941 | C-130E | 43rd AW | gn/bl | 21291 | C-130E | 314th AW | bk |
| 10947 | C-130E | 37th AS | bl/w | 21292 | C-130E | 463rd AG | gn |
| 10948 | C-130E | 463rd AG | gn | 21293 | C-130E | 463rd AG | gn |
| *FY91* | | | | 21294 | C-130E | 463rd AG | gn |
| 11231 | C-130H | 165th AS | | 21295 | C-130E | 314th AW | bl |
| 11232 | C-130H | 165th AS | | 21296 | C-130E | 314th AW | bk |
| 11233 | C-130H | 165th AS | | 21299 | C-130E | 374th AW | r |
| 11234 | C-130H | 165th AS | | | | | |

# C-130

| Notes | Type | | | | Notes | Type | | | |
|---|---|---|---|---|---|---|---|---|---|
| | *FY02* | | | | | | 23284 | C-130H | 328th AS | bl |
| | 21434 | C-130J | 143rd AS | r | | 23285 | C-130H | 328th AS | bl |
| | *FY92* | | | | | 23286 | C-130H | 328th AS | bl |
| | 21451 | C-130H | 156th AS | bl | | 23287 | C-130H | 328th AS | bl |
| | 21452 | C-130H | 169th AS | bl | | 23288 | C-130H | 328th AS | bl |
| | 21453 | C-130H | 156th AS | bl | | *FY02* | | | |
| | 21454 | C-130H | 156th AS | bl | | 28155 | C-130J | 815th AS | r |
| | *FY02* | | | | | *FY83* | | | |
| | 21463 | C-130J | 115th AS | gn | | 30486 | C-130H | 139th AS | |
| | 21464 | C-130J | 115th AS | gn | | 30487 | C-130H | 139th AS | |
| | *FY92* | | | | | 30488 | C-130H | 139th AS | |
| | 21531 | C-130H | 187th AS | | | 30489 | C-130H | 139th AS | |
| | 21532 | C-130H | 187th AS | | | 30490 | LC-130H | 139th AS | |
| | 21533 | C-130H | 187th AS | | | 30491 | LC-130H | 139th AS | |
| | 21534 | C-130H | 187th AS | | | 30492 | LC-130H | 139th AS | |
| | 21535 | C-130H | 187th AS | | | 30493 | LC-130H | 139th AS | |
| | 21536 | C-130H | 187th AS | | | *FY93* | | | |
| | 21537 | C-130H | 187th AS | | | 31036 | C-130H | 463rd AG | r |
| | 21538 | C-130H | 187th AS | | | 31037 | C-130H | 463rd AG | r |
| | *FY62* | | | | | 31038 | C-130H | 463rd AG | r |
| | 21784 | C-130E | 154th TS | r | | 31039 | C-130H | 463rd AG | r |
| | 21786 | C-130E | 314th AW | | | 31040 | C-130H | 463rd AG | r |
| | 21787 | C-130E | 154th TS | r | | 31041 | C-130H | 463rd AG | r |
| | 21788 | C-130E | 154th TS | r | | 31096 | LC-130H | 139th AS | |
| | 21789 | C-130E | 314th AW | bk | | *FY83* | | | |
| | 21791 | MC-130E | 17th SOS | | | 31212 | MC-130H | 15th SOS | |
| | 21792 | C-130E | 463rd AG | gn | | *FY93* | | | |
| | 21793 | C-130E | 115th AS | gn | | 31455 | C-130H | 156th AS | bl |
| | 21798 | C-130E | 314th AW | bk | | 31456 | C-130H | 156th AS | bl |
| | 21799 | C-130E | 317th AG | | | 31457 | C-130H | 156th AS | bl |
| | 21801 | C-130E | 154th TS | r | | 31458 | C-130H | 156th AS | bl |
| | 21804 | C-130E | 314th AW | bl | | 31459 | C-130H | 156th AS | bl |
| | 21806 | C-130E | 317th AG | | | 31561 | C-130H | 156th AS | bl |
| | 21808 | C-130E | 314th AW | bk | | 31562 | C-130H | 156th AS | bl |
| | 21810 | C-130E | 314th AW | bl | | 31563 | C-130H | 156th AS | bl |
| | 21811 | C-130E | 317th AG | | | *FY73* | | | |
| | 21816 | C-130E | 314th AW | bl | | 31580 | EC-130H | 43rd ECS | r |
| | 21817 | C-130E | 189th AS | | | 31581 | EC-130H | 43rd ECS | r |
| | 21820 | C-130E | 171st AS | y/bk | | 31582 | C-130H | 317th AG | r |
| | 21823 | C-130E | 43rd AW | | | 31583 | EC-130H | 43rd ECS | r |
| | 21824 | C-130E | 154th TS | r | | 31584 | EC-130H | 43rd ECS | r |
| | 21829 | C-130E | 171st AS | y/bk | | 31585 | EC-130H | 41st ECS | bl |
| | 21832 | HC-130P | 79th RQS | | | 31586 | EC-130H | 41st ECS | bl |
| | 21833 | C-130E | 115th AS | gn | | 31587 | EC-130H | 55th Wg | |
| | 21834 | C-130E | 374th AW | r | | 31588 | EC-130H | 41st ECS | bl |
| | 21835 | C-130E | 37th AS | bl/w | | 31590 | EC-130H | 43rd ECS | r |
| | 21836 | HC-130P | 79th RQS | | | 31592 | EC-130H | 41st ECS | bl |
| | 21837 | C-130E | 189th AS | | | 31594 | EC-130H | 41st ECS | bl |
| | 21842 | C-130E | 171st AS | y/bk | | 31595 | EC-130H | 43rd ECS | r |
| | 21843 | MC-130E | 711th SOS | | | 31597 | C-130H | 317th AG | r |
| | 21844 | C-130E | 314th AW | | | 31598 | C-130H | 317th AG | r |
| | 21846 | C-130E | 189th AS | | | *FY93* | | | |
| | 21847 | C-130E | 43rd AW | | | 32041 | C-130H | 169th AS | |
| | 21848 | C-130E | 314th AW | bk | | 32042 | C-130H | 169th AS | |
| | 21850 | C-130E | 314th AW | bk | | 32104 | HC-130N | 210th RQS | |
| | 21851 | C-130E | 43rd AW | | | 32105 | HC-130N | 210th RQS | |
| | 21852 | C-130E | 327th AS | bk | | 32106 | HC-130N | 210th RQS | |
| | 21855 | C-130E | 43rd AW | | | 37311 | C-130H | 731st AS | pr/w |
| | 21856 | C-130E | 374th AW | r | | 37312 | C-130H | 169th AS | |
| | 21857 | C-130E | 16th SOW | r | | 37313 | C-130H | 731st AS | pr/w |
| | 21858 | C-130E | 171st AS | y/bk | | 37314 | C-130H | 731st AS | pr/w |
| | 21859 | C-130E | 122nd FS | | | *FY63* | | | |
| | 21862 | C-130E | 171st AS | y/bk | | 37764 | C-130E | 463rd AG | gn |
| | 21863 | EC-130E | | | | 37767 | C-130E | 314th AW | bl |
| | 21864 | C-130E | 317th AG | | | 37769 | C-130E | 327th AS | bk |
| | *FY92* | | | | | 37770 | C-130E | 43rd AW | |
| | 23021 | C-130H | 773rd AS | r | | 37776 | C-130E | 327th AS | bk |
| | 23022 | C-130H | 773rd AS | r | | 37781 | C-130E | 463rd AG | gn |
| | 23023 | C-130H | 773rd AS | r | | 37782 | C-130E | 43rd AW | |
| | 23024 | C-130H | 773rd AS | r | | *gn/or* | | | |
| | 23281 | C-130H | 328th AS | bl | | 37784 | C-130E | 314th AW | bl |
| | 23282 | C-130H | 328th AS | bl | | 37785 | MC-130E | 711th SOS | |
| | 23283 | C-130H | 328th AS | bl | | 37786 | C-130E | 171st AS | y/bk |

| Type | | | Notes | | Type | | | Notes |
|------|------|------|-------|---|------|------|------|-------|
| 37790 | C-130E | 374th AW | r | | *FY03* | | | |
| 37791 | C-130E | 314th AW | bl | | 38154 | C-130J | 815th AS | r |
| 37792 | C-130E | 171st AS | y/bk | | *FY63* | | | |
| 37796 | C-130E | 314th AW | bk | | 39810 | C-130E | 71st RQS | bl |
| 37800 | C-130E | 171st AS | y/bk | | 39812 | C-130E | 314th AW | bk |
| 37804 | C-130E | 314th AW | bl | | 39813 | C-130E | 171st AS | y/bk |
| 37809 | C-130E | 463rd AG | gn | | 39814 | C-130E | 314th AW | bl |
| 37811 | C-130E | 143rd AS | r | | 39815 | C-130E | 198th AS | |
| 37812 | C-130E | 171st AS | y/bk | | 39816 | EC-130E | 193rd SOS | |
| 37814 | C-130E | 67th SOS | | | *FY84* | | | |
| 37815 | C-130E | 193rd SOS | | | 40204 | C-130H | 700th AS | bl |
| 37816 | C-130E | 193rd SOS | | | 40205 | C-130H | 700th AS | bl |
| 37817 | C-130E | 43rd AW | | | 40206 | C-130H | 142nd AS | bl |
| 37818 | C-130E | 169th AS | | | 40207 | C-130H | 142nd AS | bl |
| 37819 | C-130E | 374th AW | r | | 40208 | C-130H | 142nd AS | bl |
| 37821 | C-130E | 374th AW | r | | 40209 | C-130H | 142nd AS | bl |
| 37823 | C-130E | 43rd AW | | | 40210 | C-130H | 142nd AS | bl |
| 37824 | C-130E | 143rd AS | r | | 40212 | C-130H | 142nd AS | bl |
| 37825 | C-130E | 37th AS | bl/w | | 40213 | C-130H | 142nd AS | bl |
| 37828 | EC-130E | 193rd SOS | | | 40476 | MC-130H | 7th SOS | |
| 37829 | C-130E | 314th AW | bk | | *FY64* | | | |
| 37830 | C-130E | 314th AW | bk | | 40498 | C-130E | 43rd AW | gn/bl |
| 37831 | C-130E | 171st AS | y/bk | | 40502 | C-130E | 37th AS | bl/w |
| 37832 | C-130E | 314th AW | bk | | 40504 | C-130E | 43rd AW | gn/bl |
| 37833 | C-130E | 327th AS | bk | | 40510 | C-130E | 198th AS | |
| 37834 | C-130E | 327th AS | bk | | 40512 | C-130E | 314th AW | |
| 37835 | C-130E | 314th AW | bk | | 40515 | C-130E | 198th AS | |
| 37837 | C-130E | 374th AW | r | | 40517 | C-130E | 43rd AW | gn/bl |
| 37839 | C-130E | 463rd AG | gn | | 40518 | C-130E | 463rd AG | gn |
| 37840 | C-130E | 374th AW | r | | 40519 | C-130E | 314th AW | bl |
| 37841 | C-130E | 198th AS | | | 40520 | C-130E | 157th FS | |
| 37845 | C-130E | 463rd AG | | | 40521 | C-130E | 159th FS | |
| 37846 | C-130E | 314th AW | | | 40523 | MC-130E | 8th SOS | |
| 37847 | C-130E | 154th TS | r | | 40526 | C-130E | 154th TS | r |
| 37848 | C-130E | 43rd AW | | | 40527 | C-130E | 37th AS | bl/w |
| 37850 | C-130E | 374th AW | r | | 40529 | C-130E | 43rd AW | gn/or |
| 37851 | C-130E | 198th AS | | | 40531 | C-130E | 43rd AW | gn/bl |
| 37852 | C-130E | 463rd AG | gn | | 40537 | C-130E | 43rd AW | gn/or |
| 37853 | C-130E | 43rd AW | | | 40538 | C-130E | 314th AW | bk |
| 37856 | C-130E | 463rd AG | gn | | 40540 | C-130E | 43rd AW | gn/bl |
| 37857 | C-130E | 463rd AG | gn | | 40541 | C-130E | 314th AW | bk |
| 37858 | C-130E | 43rd AW | | | 40544 | C-130E | 198th AS | |
| 37859 | C-130E | 143rd AS | r | | 40551 | MC-130E | 711th SOS | |
| 37860 | C-130E | 314th AW | bl | | 40555 | MC-130E | 711th SOS | |
| 37864 | C-130E | 314th AW | bl | | 40559 | MC-130E | 711th SOS | |
| 37865 | C-130E | 37th AS | bl/w | | 40561 | MC-130E | 711th SOS | |
| 37866 | C-130E | 314th AW | bk | | 40562 | MC-130E | 711th SOS | |
| 37867 | C-130E | 327th AS | bk | | 40565 | MC-130E | 711th SOS | |
| 37868 | C-130E | 317th AG | | | 40566 | MC-130E | 711th SOS | |
| 37871 | C-130E | 374th AW | r | | 40567 | MC-130E | 8th SOS | |
| 37872 | C-130E | 171st AS | y/bk | | 40568 | MC-130E | 8th SOS | |
| 37874 | C-130E | 314th AW | bk | | 40571 | MC-130E | 711th SOS | |
| 37876 | C-130E | 463rd AG | gn | | 40572 | MC-130E | 8th SOS | |
| 37877 | C-130E | 314th AW | | | *FY74* | | | |
| 37879 | C-130E | 37th AS | bl/w | | 41658 | C-130H | 3rd Wg | w |
| 37880 | C-130E | 314th AW | bl | | 41659 | C-130H | 3rd Wg | w |
| 37882 | C-130E | 43rd AW | | | 41660 | C-130H | 3rd Wg | w |
| 37883 | C-130E | 43rd AW | bk | | 41661 | C-130H | 3rd Wg | w |
| 37884 | C-130E | 463rd AG | gn | | 41663 | C-130H | 317th AG | bl |
| 37885 | C-130E | 37th AS | bl/w | | 41664 | C-130H | 3rd Wg | w |
| 37887 | C-130E | 37th AS | bl/w | | 41665 | C-130H | 317th AG | bl |
| 37888 | C-130E | 463rd AG | gn | | 41666 | C-130H | 317th AG | bl |
| 37889 | C-130E | 143rd AS | r | | 41667 | C-130H | 317th AG | r |
| 37890 | C-130E | 314th AW | bl | | 41668 | C-130H | 3rd Wg | w |
| 37892 | C-130E | 327th AS | bk | | 41669 | C-130H | 317th AG | bl |
| 37893 | C-130E | 314th AW | bk | | 41670 | C-130H | 317th AG | r |
| 37894 | C-130E | 463rd AG | gn | | 41671 | C-130H | 317th AG | bl |
| 37895 | C-130E | 171st AS | y/bk | | 41673 | C-130H | 317th AG | bl |
| 37896 | C-130E | 314th AW | bk | | 41674 | C-130H | 317th AG | r |
| 37897 | C-130E | 37th AS | bl/w | | 41675 | C-130H | 317th AG | r |
| 37898 | C-130E | 8th SOS | | | 41676 | C-130H | 3rd Wg | m |
| 37899 | C-130E | 314th AW | bl | | 41677 | C-130H | 317th AG | bl |
| | | | | | 41679 | C-130H | 317th AG | bl |

# C-130

| Notes | Type | | | | Notes | Type | | | |
|---|---|---|---|---|---|---|---|---|---|
| | 41680 | C-130H | 317th AG | r | | 50979 | NC-130H | 412th TW | |
| | 41682 | C-130H | 3rd Wg | w | | 50980 | WC-130H | 53rd WRS | |
| | 41684 | C-130H | 3rd Wg | w | | 50981 | HC-130P | 71st RQS | bl |
| | 41685 | C-130H | 3rd Wg | w | | 50982 | HC-130P | 71st RQS | bl |
| | 41687 | C-130H | 317th AG | r | | 50983 | MC-130P | 71st RQS | bl |
| | 41688 | C-130H | 317th AG | bl | | 50984 | WC-130H | 53rd WRS | |
| | 41689 | C-130H | 317th AG | bl | | 50985 | WC-130H | 53rd WRS | |
| | 41690 | C-130H | 3rd Wg | w | | 50986 | HC-130P | 71st RQS | bl |
| | 41691 | C-130H | 317th AG | r | | 50987 | HC-130P | 71st RQS | bl |
| | 41692 | C-130H | 3rd Wg | w | | 50988 | HC-130P | 71st RQS | bl |
| | 42061 | C-130H | 317th AG | r | | 50989 | EC-130H | 41st ECS | bl |
| | 42062 | C-130H | 3rd Wg | w | | 50991 | MC-130P | 9th SOS | |
| | 42063 | C-130H | 317th AG | bl | | 50992 | MC-130P | 17th SOS | |
| | 42065 | C-130H | 317th AG | bl | | 50993 | MC-130P | 17th SOS | |
| | 42066 | C-130H | 3rd Wg | w | | 50994 | MC-130P | 17th SOS | |
| | 42067 | C-130H | 317th AG | r | | *FY95* | | | |
| | 42069 | C-130H | 317th AG | r | | 51001 | C-130H | 109th AS | pr/bk |
| | 42070 | C-130H | 3rd Wg | w | | 51002 | C-130H | 109th AS | pr/bk |
| | 42071 | C-130H | 3rd Wg | w | | *FY85* | | | |
| | 42072 | C-130H | 317th AG | bl | | 51361 | C-130H | 181st AS | bl/w |
| | 42130 | C-130H | 317th AG | r | | 51362 | C-130H | 181st AS | bl/w |
| | 42131 | C-130H | 3rd Wg | w | | 51363 | C-130H | 181st AS | bl/w |
| | 42132 | C-130H | 317th AG | r | | 51364 | C-130H | 181st AS | bl/w |
| | 42133 | C-130H | 3rd Wg | w | | 51365 | C-130H | 181st AS | bl/w |
| | 42134 | C-130H | 317th AG | r | | 51366 | C-130H | 181st AS | bl/w |
| | *FY04* | | | | | 51367 | C-130H | 181st AS | bl/w |
| | 43142 | C-130J | 314th AW | y | | 51368 | C-130H | 181st AS | bl/w |
| | 43143 | C-130J | 314th AW | y | | *FY05* | | | |
| | 43144 | C-130J | 314th AW | y | | 53147 | C-130J | 314th AW | r |
| | *FY94* | | | | | *FY95* | | | |
| | 46701 | C-130H | 169th AS | | | 56709 | C-130H | 167th AS | r |
| | 46702 | C-130H | 167th AS | r | | 56710 | C-130H | 167th AS | r |
| | 46703 | C-130H | 169th AS | | | 56711 | C-130H | 167th AS | r |
| | 46704 | C-130H | 167th AS | r | | 56712 | C-130H | 167th AS | r |
| | 46705 | C-130H | 167th AS | r | | *FY66* | | | |
| | 46706 | C-130H | 167th AS | r | | 60212 | HC-130P | 130th RQS | bl |
| | 46707 | C-130H | 167th AS | r | | 60216 | HC-130P | 130th RQS | bl |
| | 46708 | C-130H | 167th AS | r | | 60217 | MC-130P | 9th SOS | |
| | 47310 | C-130H | 731st AS | pr/w | | 60219 | HC-130P | 130th RQS | bl |
| | 47315 | C-130H | 731st AS | pr/w | | 60220 | MC-130P | 17th SOS | |
| | 47316 | C-130H | 731st AS | pr/w | | 60221 | HC-130P | 58th SOW | |
| | 47317 | C-130H | 731st AS | pr/w | | 60222 | HC-130P | 102nd RQS | |
| | 47318 | C-130H | 731st AS | pr/w | | 60223 | MC-130P | 9th SOS | |
| | 47319 | C-130H | 731st AS | pr/w | | 60224 | HC-130P | 79th RQS | |
| | 47320 | C-130H | 731st AS | pr/w | | 60225 | MC-130P | 9th SOS | |
| | 47321 | C-130H | 731st AS | pr/w | | *FY86* | | | |
| | 48151 | C-130J | 815th AS | r | | 60410 | C-130H | 758th AS | bk/y |
| | 48152 | C-130J | 115th AS | gn | | 60411 | C-130H | 758th AS | bk/y |
| | *FY85* | | | | | 60412 | C-130H | 758th AS | bk/y |
| | 50011 | MC-130H | 15th SOS | | | 60413 | C-130H | 758th AS | bk/y |
| | 50035 | C-130H | 357th AS | bl | | 60414 | C-130H | 758th AS | bk/y |
| | 50036 | C-130H | 357th AS | bl | | 60415 | C-130H | 758th AS | bk/y |
| | 50037 | C-130H | 357th AS | bl | | 60418 | C-130H | 758th AS | bk/y |
| | 50038 | C-130H | 357th AS | bl | | 60419 | C-130H | 758th AS | bk/y |
| | 50039 | C-130H | 357th AS | bl | | *FY96* | | | |
| | 50040 | C-130H | 357th AS | bl | | 61003 | C-130H | 109th AS | pr/bk |
| | 50041 | C-130H | 773rd AS | r | | 61004 | C-130H | 109th AS | pr/bk |
| | 50042 | C-130H | 357th AS | bl | | 61005 | C-130H | 109th AS | pr/bk |
| | *FY65* | | | | | 61006 | C-130H | 109th AS | pr/bk |
| | 50962 | EC-130H | 43rd ECS | r | | 61007 | C-130H | 109th AS | pr/bk |
| | 50963 | WC-130H | 815th AS | r | | 61008 | C-130H | 109th AS | pr/bk |
| | 50964 | HC-130P | 79th RQS | | | *FY86* | | | |
| | 50966 | WC-130H | 53rd WRS | | | 61391 | C-130H | 180th AS | y |
| | 50967 | WC-130H | 53rd WRS | | | 61392 | C-130H | 180th AS | y |
| | 50968 | WC-130H | 53rd WRS | | | 61393 | C-130H | 180th AS | y |
| | 50970 | HC-130P | 39th RQS | | | 61394 | C-130H | 180th AS | y |
| | 50971 | MC-130P | 58th SOW | | | 61395 | C-130H | 180th AS | y |
| | 50973 | HC-130P | 71st RQS | bl | | 61396 | C-130H | 180th AS | y |
| | 50974 | HC-130P | 102nd RQS | | | 61397 | C-130H | 180th AS | y |
| | 50975 | MC-130P | 58th SOW | | | 61398 | C-130H | 180th AS | y |
| | 50976 | HC-130P | 39th RQS | | | 61699 | MC-130H | 7th SOS | |
| | 50977 | WC-130H | 53rd WRS | | | *FY76* | | | |
| | 50978 | HC-130P | 102nd RQS | | | 63300 | LC-130R | 139th AS | |

| Type | | | Notes | | Type | | | Notes |
|---|---|---|---|---|---|---|---|---|
| 63302 | LC-130R | 139th AS | | | 84401 | C-130H | 95th AS | w/r |
| FY96 | | | | | 84402 | C-130H | 95th AS | w/r |
| 65300 | WC-130J | 53rd WRS | | | 84403 | C-130H | 95th AS | w/r |
| 65301 | WC-130J | 53rd WRS | | | 84404 | C-130H | 95th AS | w/r |
| 65302 | WC-130J | 53rd WRS | | | 84405 | C-130H | 95th AS | w/r |
| 67322 | C-130H | 731st AS | pr/w | | 84406 | C-130H | 95th AS | w/r |
| 67323 | C-130H | 731st AS | pr/w | | 84407 | C-130H | 95th AS | w/r |
| 67324 | C-130H | 731st AS | pr/w | | FY98 | | | |
| 67325 | C-130H | 731st AS | pr/w | | 85307 | WC-130J | 53rd WRS | |
| 68153 | C-130J | 815th AS | r | | 85308 | WC-130J | 53rd WRS | |
| 68154 | C-130J | 193rd SOS | | | FY89 | | | |
| FY87 | | | | | 90280 | MC-130H | 7th SOS | |
| 70023 | MC-130H | 7th SOS | | | 90281 | MC-130H | 15th SOS | |
| 70024 | MC-130H | 15th SOS | | | 90282 | MC-130H | 7th SOS | |
| 70125 | MC-130H | 58th SOW | | | 90283 | MC-130H | 15th SOS | |
| 70126 | MC-130H | 7th SOS | | | FY79 | | | |
| 70128 | AC-130U | 4th SOS | | | 90473 | C-130H | 192nd AS | w |
| FY97 | | | | | 90474 | C-130H | 192nd AS | w |
| 71351 | C-130J | 135th AS | bk/y | | 90475 | C-130H | 192nd AS | w |
| 71352 | C-130J | 135th AS | bk/y | | 90476 | C-130H | 192nd AS | w |
| 71353 | C-130J | 135th AS | bk/y | | 90477 | C-130H | 192nd AS | w |
| 71354 | C-130J | 135th AS | bk/y | | 90478 | C-130H | 192nd AS | w |
| 71931 | EC-130J | 193rd SOS | | | 90479 | C-130H | 192nd AS | w |
| 75303 | WC-130J | 53rd WRS | | | 90480 | C-130H | 192nd AS | w |
| 75304 | WC-130J | 53rd WRS | | | FY89 | | | |
| 75305 | WC-130J | 53rd WRS | | | 90509 | AC-130U | 4th SOS | |
| 75306 | WC-130J | 53rd WRS | | | 90510 | AC-130U | 4th SOS | |
| FY87 | | | | | 90511 | AC-130U | 4th SOS | |
| 79281 | C-130H | 96th AS | pr | | 90512 | AC-130U | 4th SOS | |
| 79282 | C-130H | 95th AS | w/r | | 90513 | AC-130U | 4th SOS | |
| 79283 | C-130H | 96th AS | pr | | 90514 | AC-130U | 4th SOS | |
| 79284 | C-130H | 700th AS | bl | | 91051 | C-130H | 105th AS | r |
| 79285 | C-130H | 96th AS | pr | | 91052 | C-130H | 105th AS | r |
| 79286 | C-130H | 357th AS | bl | | 91053 | C-130H | 105th AS | r |
| 79287 | C-130H | 96th AS | pr | | 91054 | C-130H | 105th AS | r |
| 79288 | C-130H | 700th AS | bl | | 91055 | C-130H | 105th AS | r |
| FY88 | | | | | 91056 | AC-130U | LMTAS | |
| 80191 | MC-130H | 1st SOS | | | 91181 | C-130H | 105th AS | r |
| 80192 | MC-130H | 7th SOS | | | 91182 | C-130H | 105th AS | r |
| 80193 | MC-130H | 7th SOS | | | 91183 | C-130H | 105th AS | r |
| 80194 | MC-130H | 58th SOW | | | 91184 | C-130H | 105th AS | r |
| 80195 | MC-130H | 1st SOS | | | 91185 | C-130H | 105th AS | r |
| 80264 | MC-130H | 1st SOS | | | 91186 | C-130H | 105th AS | r |
| FY78 | | | | | 91187 | C-130H | 105th AS | r |
| 80806 | C-130H | 185th AS | bl | | 91188 | C-130H | 105th AS | r |
| 80807 | C-130H | 185th AS | bl | | FY99 | | | |
| 80808 | C-130H | 185th AS | bl | | 91431 | C-130J | 143rd AS | r |
| 80809 | C-130H | 185th AS | bl | | 91432 | C-130J | 143rd AS | r |
| 80810 | C-130H | 185th AS | bl | | 91433 | C-130J | 143rd AS | r |
| 80811 | C-130H | 185th AS | bl | | 91933 | EC-130J | LMTAS | |
| 80812 | C-130H | 185th AS | bl | | 95309 | WC-130J | 53rd WRS | |
| 80813 | C-130H | 185th AS | bl | | FY69 | | | |
| FY88 | | | | | 95819 | MC-130P | 9th SOS | |
| 81301 | C-130H | 130th AS | pr/y | | 95820 | MC-130P | 9th SOS | |
| 81302 | C-130H | 130th AS | pr/y | | 95821 | MC-130P | 58th SOW | |
| 81303 | C-130H | 130th AS | pr/y | | 95822 | MC-130P | 9th SOS | |
| 81304 | C-130H | 130th AS | pr/y | | 95823 | MC-130P | 9th SOS | |
| 81305 | C-130H | 130th AS | pr/y | | 95825 | MC-130P | 67th SOS | |
| 81306 | C-130H | 130th AS | pr/y | | 95826 | MC-130P | 67th SOS | |
| 81307 | C-130H | 130th AS | pr/y | | 95827 | MC-130P | 9th SOS | |
| 81308 | C-130H | 130th AS | pr/y | | 95828 | MC-130P | 67th SOS | |
| FY98 | | | | | 95829 | HC-130N | 58th SOW | |
| 81355 | C-130J | 135th AS | bk/y | | 95830 | HC-130N | 39th RQS | |
| 81356 | C-130J | 135th AS | bk/y | | 95831 | MC-130P | 67th SOS | |
| 81357 | C-130J | 135th AS | bk/y | | 95832 | MC-130P | 67th SOS | |
| 81358 | C-130J | 135th AS | bk/y | | 95833 | HC-130N | 58th SOW | |
| FY88 | | | | | 96568 | AC-130H | 16th SOS | |
| 81803 | MC-130H | 1st SOS | | | 96569 | AC-130H | 16th SOS | |
| FY98 | | | | | 96570 | AC-130H | 16th SOS | |
| 81932 | EC-130J | 193rd SOS | | | 96571 | AC-130H | 16th SOS | |
| FY88 | | | | | 96572 | AC-130H | 16th SOS | |
| 82101 | HC-130N | 102nd RQS | | | 96573 | AC-130H | 16th SOS | |
| 82102 | HC-130N | 71st RQS | bl | | 96574 | AC-130H | 16th SOS | |
| | | | | | 96575 | AC-130H | 16th SOS | |

| Notes | Type | | | |
|---|---|---|---|---|
| | 96577 | AC-130H | 16th SOS | |
| | *FY89* | | | |
| | 99101 | C-130H | 757th AS | *bl* |
| | 99102 | C-130H | 757th AS | *bl* |
| | 99103 | C-130H | 757th AS | *bl* |
| | 99104 | C-130H | 757th AS | *bl* |
| | 99105 | C-130H | 757th AS | *bl* |
| | 99106 | C-130H | 757th AS | *bl* |

**Boeing C-135**

6th AMW, MacDill AFB, Florida:
  91st ARS (*y/bl*);
15th ABW, Hickam AFB, Hawaii:
  65th AS;
18th Wg, Kadena AB, Japan [ZZ]:
  909th ARS (*w*);
19th ARG, Robins AFB, Georgia:
  99th ARS (*y/bl*);
22nd ARW, McConnell AFB, Kansas:
  344th ARS (*y/bk*), 349th ARS (*y/bl*)
  350th ARS (*y/r*) & 384th ARS (*y/pr*);
55th Wg, Offutt AFB, Nebraska [OF]:
  38th RS (*gn*), 45th RS (*bk*)
  & 343rd RS;
88th ABW, Wright-Patterson AFB, Ohio;
92nd ARW, Fairchild AFB,
  Washington:
92nd ARS (*bk*), 93rd ARS (*bl*),
  & 97th ARS (*y*);
97th AMW, Altus AFB, Oklahoma:
  54th ARS & 55th ARS (*y/r*);
100th ARW, RAF Mildenhall, UK [D]:
  351st ARS (*r/w/bl*);
106th ARS/117th ARW, Birmingham,
  Alabama ANG (*w/r*);
108th ARS/126th ARW,
  Scott AFB, Illinois ANG (*w/bl*);
108th ARW, McGuire AFB,
  New Jersey ANG:
  141st ARS (*bk/y*) &
  150th ARS (*bl*);
116th ARS/141st ARW, Fairchild AFB,
  Washington ANG (*gn/w*);
117th ARS/190th ARW, Forbes Field,
  Kansas ANG (*bl/y*);
121st ARW, Rickenbacker ANGB,
  Ohio ANG:
  145th ARS & 166th ARS (*bl*);
126th ARS/128th ARW, Mitchell Field,
  Wisconsin ANG (*w/bl*);
127th ARS/184th ARW, McConnell
  AFB, Kansas ANG;
132nd ARS/101st ARW, Bangor,
  Maine ANG (*w/gn*);
133rd ARS/157th ARW, Pease ANGB,
  New Hampshire ANG (*bl*);
136th ARS/107th ARW, Niagara Falls,
  New York ANG (*bl*);
151st ARS/134th ARW, Knoxville,
  Tennessee ANG (*w/or*);
153rd ARS/186th ARW, Meridian,
  Mississippi ANG (*bk/gd*);
168th ARS/168th ARW, Eielson AFB,
  Alaska ANG (*bl/y*);
171st ARW, Greater Pittsburgh,
  Pennsylvania ANG:
  146th ARS (*y/bk*) &
  147th ARS (*bk/y*);
173rd ARS/155th ARW, Lincoln,
  Nebraska ANG (*r/w*);
174th ARS/185th ARW, Sioux City,
  Iowa ANG (*y/bk*);
191st ARS/151st ARW, Salt Lake City,

Utah ANG (*bl/bk*);
196th ARS/163rd ARW, March ARB,
  California ANG (*bl/w*);
197th ARS/161st ARW, Phoenix,
  Arizona ANG;
203rd ARS/154th Wg, Hickam AFB,
  Hawaii ANG [HH] (*y/bk*);
319th ARW, Grand Forks AFB,
  North Dakota:
  905th ARS (*bl*), 906th ARS (*y*),
  911th ARS (*r*) & 912th ARS (*w*);
366th Wg, Mountain Home AFB,
  Idaho [MO]:
  22nd ARS (*y/gn*);
412th TW, Edwards AFB,
  California [ED]:
  452nd FLTS (*bl*);
434th ARW AFRC, Grissom AFB,
  Indiana:
  72nd ARS (*bl*) & 74th ARS (*r/w*);
452nd AMW AFRC, March ARB,
  California:
  336th ARS (*y*);
459th ARW AFRC, Andrews AFB,
  Maryland:
  756th ARS (*y/bk*);
507th ARW AFRC, Tinker AFB,
  Oklahoma:
  465th ARS (*bl/y*);
645th Materiel Sqn, Greenville, Texas;
916th ARW AFRC,
  Seymour Johnson AFB,
  North Carolina:
  77th ARS (*gn*);
927th ARW AFRC, Selfridge ANGB,
  Michigan:
  63rd ARS (*pr/w*);
939th ARW AFRC, Portland,
  Oregon:
  64th ARS (*pr/y*);
940th ARW AFRC, McClellan AFB,
  California:
  314th ARS (*or/bk*)

| Notes | Type | | | |
|---|---|---|---|---|
| | *FY60* | | | |
| | 00313 | KC-135R | 22nd ARW | |
| | 00314 | KC-135R | 927th AW | *pr/w* |
| | 00315 | KC-135R | 126th ARS | *w/bl* |
| | 00316 | KC-135R | 116th ARS | *gn/w* |
| | 00318 | KC-135R | 203rd ARS | *y/bk* |
| | 00319 | KC-135R | 22nd ARW | |
| | 00320 | KC-135R | 97th AMW | *y/r* |
| | 00321 | KC-135R | 319th ARW | *w* |
| | 00322 | KC-135R | 434th ARW | *bl* |
| | 00323 | KC-135R | 203rd ARS | *y/bk* |
| | 00324 | KC-135R | 319th ARW | |
| | 00327 | KC-135E | 191st ARS | *bl/bk* |
| | 00328 | KC-135R | 97th AMW | *y/r* |
| | 00329 | KC-135R | 203rd ARS | *y/bk* |
| | 00331 | KC-135R | 319th ARW | |
| | 00332 | KC-135R | 319th ARW | *w* |
| | 00333 | KC-135R | 92nd ARW | |
| | 00334 | KC-135R | 168th ARS | *bl/y* |
| | 00335 | KC-135T | 22nd ARW | *y/bk* |
| | 00336 | KC-135T | 92nd ARW | |
| | 00337 | KC-135T | 92nd ARW | *m* |
| | 00339 | KC-135T | 92nd ARW | *bk* |
| | 00341 | KC-135T | 121st ARW | *bl* |
| | 00342 | KC-135T | 319th ARW | *r* |
| | 00343 | KC-135T | 19th ARG | *y/bl* |
| | 00344 | KC-135T | 319th ARW | *r* |
| | 00345 | KC-135T | 319th ARW | |
| | 00346 | KC-135T | 92nd ARW | *bk* |
| | 00347 | KC-135R | 121st ARW | *bl* |

| Type | | | Notes | Type | | | Notes |
|------|---|---|-------|------|---|---|-------|
| 00348 | KC-135R | 18th Wg | w | 14831 | KC-135R | 22nd ARW | |
| 00349 | KC-135R | 916th ARW | gn | 14832 | KC-135R | 203rd ARS | y/bk |
| 00350 | KC-135R | 97th AMW | y/r | 14833 | KC-135R | 18th Wg | w |
| 00351 | KC-135R | 100th ARW | r/w/bl | 14834 | KC-135R | 434th ARW | r/w |
| 00353 | KC-135R | 22nd ARW | | 14835 | KC-135R | | |
| 00355 | KC-135R | 22nd ARW | | 14836 | KC-135R | 197th ARS | |
| 00356 | KC-135R | 22nd ARW | | 14837 | KC-135R | 92nd ARW | |
| 00357 | KC-135R | 22nd ARW | | 14838 | KC-135R | 92nd ARW | w |
| 00358 | KC-135R | 136th ARS | bl | 14839 | KC-135R | 136th ARS | bl |
| 00359 | KC-135R | 434th ARW | r/w | 14840 | KC-135R | 121st ARW | bl |
| 00360 | KC-135R | 97th AMW | y/r | 14841 | RC-135V | 55th Wg | gn |
| 00362 | KC-135R | 22nd ARW | y/r | 14842 | RC-135V | 55th Wg | gn |
| 00363 | KC-135R | 434th ARW | bl | 14843 | RC-135V | 55th Wg | gn |
| 00364 | KC-135R | 434th ARW | r/w | 14844 | RC-135V | 55th Wg | gn |
| 00365 | KC-135R | 127th ARS | | 14845 | RC-135V | 55th Wg | gn |
| 00366 | KC-135R | 22nd ARW | | 14846 | RC-135V | 55th Wg | gn |
| 00367 | KC-135R | 121st ARW | bl | 14847 | RC-135U | 55th Wg | bk |
| **FY61** | | | | 14848 | RC-135V | 55th Wg | gn |
| 10264 | KC-135R | 121st ARW | bl | 14849 | RC-135U | 55th Wg | gn |
| 10266 | KC-135R | 173rd ARS | r/w | **FY62** | | | |
| 10267 | KC-135R | 92nd ARW | y | 23498 | KC-135R | 319th ARW | y |
| 10268 | KC-135E | 940th ARW | or/bk | 23499 | KC-135R | 22nd ARW | y |
| 10270 | KC-135E | 927th ARW | pr/w | 23500 | KC-135R | 126th ARS | w/bl |
| 10271 | KC-135E | 927th ARW | pr/w | 23502 | KC-135R | 92nd ARW | |
| 10272 | KC-135R | 434th ARW | r/w | 23503 | KC-135R | 939th ARW | pr/y |
| 10275 | KC-135R | 319th ARW | | 23504 | KC-135R | 319th ARW | y |
| 10276 | KC-135R | 173rd ARS | r/w | 23505 | KC-135R | 100th ARW | r/w/bl |
| 10277 | KC-135R | 127th ARS | | 23506 | KC-135R | 133rd ARS | bl |
| 10280 | KC-135R | 452nd AMW | y | 23507 | KC-135R | 92nd ARW | |
| 10281 | KC-135E | 197th ARS | | 23508 | KC-135R | 19th ARG | y/bl |
| 10284 | KC-135R | 319th ARW | bl | 23509 | KC-135R | 916th ARW | gn |
| 10288 | KC-135R | 92nd ARW | bk | 23510 | KC-135R | 434th ARW | r/w |
| 10290 | KC-135R | 203rd ARS | y/bk | 23511 | KC-135R | 121st ARW | bl |
| 10292 | KC-135R | 100th ARW | r/w/bl | 23512 | KC-135R | 126th ARS | w/bl |
| 10293 | KC-135R | 22nd ARW | y/r | 23513 | KC-135R | 127th ARS | |
| 10294 | KC-135R | 92nd ARW | | 23514 | KC-135R | 203rd ARS | y/bk |
| 10295 | KC-135R | 319th ARW | bl | 23515 | KC-135R | 133rd ARS | bl |
| 10298 | KC-135R | 126th ARS | w/bl | 23516 | KC-135R | 197th ARS | |
| 10299 | KC-135R | 100th ARW | r/w/bl | 23517 | KC-135R | 22nd ARW | |
| 10300 | KC-135R | 319th ARW | | 23518 | KC-135R | 434th ARW | bl |
| 10302 | KC-135R | 97th AMW | y/r | 23519 | KC-135R | 22nd ARW | |
| 10303 | KC-135R | 916th ARW | gn | 23520 | KC-135R | 319th ARW | |
| 10304 | KC-135R | 97th AMW | y/r | 23521 | KC-135R | 434th ARW | r/w |
| 10305 | KC-135R | 92nd ARW | bk | 23523 | KC-135R | 19th ARG | y/bl |
| 10306 | KC-135R | 18th Wg | w | 23524 | KC-135R | 106th ARS | w/r |
| 10307 | KC-135R | 459th ARW | y/bk | 23526 | KC-135R | 173rd ARS | r/w |
| 10308 | KC-135R | 97th AMW | y/r | 23527 | KC-135E | 927th ARW | pr/w |
| 10309 | KC-135R | 126th ARS | w/bl | 23528 | KC-135R | 927th ARW | pr/w |
| 10310 | KC-135R | 133rd ARS | bl | 23529 | KC-135R | 18th Wg | w |
| 10311 | KC-135R | 22nd ARW | y | 23530 | KC-135R | 434th ARW | bl |
| 10312 | KC-135R | 97th AMW | y/r | 23531 | KC-135R | 121st ARW | bl |
| 10313 | KC-135R | 916th ARW | gn | 23533 | KC-135R | 319th ARW | bl |
| 10314 | KC-135R | 100th ARW | r/w/bl | 23534 | KC-135R | 22nd ARW | |
| 10315 | KC-135R | 18th Wg | w | 23537 | KC-135R | 22nd ARW | |
| 10317 | KC-135R | 18th Wg | w | 23538 | KC-135R | 100th ARW | r/w/bl |
| 10318 | KC-135R | 6th AMW | y/bl | 23540 | KC-135R | 6th AMW | y/bl |
| 10320 | KC-135R | 412th TW | bl | 23541 | KC-135R | 100th ARW | r/w/bl |
| 10321 | KC-135R | 18th Wg | w | 23542 | KC-135R | 916th ARW | gn |
| 10323 | KC-135R | 18th Wg | w | 23543 | KC-135R | 459th ARW | y/bk |
| 10324 | KC-135R | 452nd AMW | y | 23544 | KC-135R | 319th ARW | |
| 10327 | KC-135R | 92nd ARW | bl | 23545 | KC-135R | 22nd ARW | |
| 10330 | EC-135E | 412th TW | bl | 23546 | KC-135R | 6th AMW | y/bl |
| 12662 | RC-135S | 55th Wg | bk | 23547 | KC-135R | 133rd ARS | bl |
| 12663 | RC-135S | 55th Wg | bk | 23548 | KC-135R | 6th AMW | y/bl |
| 12666 | NC-135W | 645th MS | | 23549 | KC-135R | 97th AMW | y/r |
| 12667 | WC-135W | 55th Wg | bk | 23550 | KC-135R | 197th ARS | |
| 12669 | C-135C | 412th TW | bl | 23551 | KC-135R | 100th ARW | r/w/bl |
| 12670 | OC-135B | 55th Wg | | 23552 | KC-135R | 97th AMW | y/r |
| 12672 | OC-135B | 55th Wg | | 23553 | KC-135R | 97th AMW | y/r |
| **FY64** | | | | 23554 | KC-135R | 19th ARG | y/bl |
| 14828 | KC-135R | 319th ARW | w | 23556 | KC-135R | 459th ARW | y/bk |
| 14829 | KC-135R | 319th ARW | | 23557 | KC-135R | 927th ARW | pr/w |
| 14830 | KC-135R | 100th ARW | r/w/bl | 23558 | KC-135R | 939th ARW | pr/y |

## C-135

| Notes | Type | | | Notes | Type | | |
|---|---|---|---|---|---|---|---|
| | 23559 KC-135R | 22nd ARW | gy/si | | 38029 KC-135R | 126th ARS | w/bl |
| | 23561 KC-135R | 100th ARW | r/w/bl | | 38030 KC-135R | 203rd ARS | y/bk |
| | 23562 KC-135R | 100th ARW | r/w/bl | | 38031 KC-135R | 6th AMW | y/bl |
| | 23564 KC-135R | 97th AMW | y/r | | 38032 KC-135R | 434th ARW | bl |
| | 23565 KC-135R | 92nd ARW | y/bl | | 38033 KC-135R | 92nd ARW | bk |
| | 23566 KC-135E | 116th ARS | gn/w | | 38034 KC-135R | 97th MW | y/r |
| | 23568 KC-135R | 97th AMW | y/r | | 38035 KC-135R | 106th ARS | w/r |
| | 23569 KC-135R | 19th ARG | y/bl | | 38036 KC-135R | 136th ARS | bl |
| | 23571 KC-135R | 168th ARS | bl/y | | 38037 KC-135R | 6th AMW | y/bl |
| | 23572 KC-135R | 127th ARS | | | 38038 KC-135R | 133rd ARS | bl |
| | 23573 KC-135R | 100th ARW | r/w/bl | | 38039 KC-135R | 507th ARW | bl/y |
| | 23575 KC-135R | 100th ARW | r/w/bl | | 38040 KC-135R | 6th AMW | y/bl |
| | 23576 KC-135R | 133rd ARS | bl | | 38041 KC-135R | 434th ARW | bl |
| | 23577 KC-135R | 916th ARW | gn | | 38043 KC-135R | 168th ARS | bl/y |
| | 23578 KC-135R | 18th Wg | w | | 38044 KC-135R | 927th ARW | pr/w |
| | 23580 KC-135R | 927th ARW | pr/w | | 38045 KC-135R | 319th ARW | |
| | 23582 WC-135C | 55th Wg | bk | | 38050 NKC-135B | 412th TW | bl |
| | 24125 RC-135W | 55th Wg | gn | | 38058 KC-135D | 117th ARS | bl/y |
| | 24126 C-135B | 108th ARW | bk/y | | 38059 KC-135D | 117th ARS | bl/y |
| | 24127 RC-135W | 55th Wg | | | 38060 KC-135D | 117th ARS | bl/y |
| | 24128 RC-135S | 55th Wg | | | 38061 KC-135D | 117th RS | bl/y |
| | 24129 TC-135W | 55th Wg | gn | | 38871 KC-135R | 319th ARW | y |
| | 24130 RC-135W | 55th Wg | gn | | 38872 KC-135R | 136th ARS | bl |
| | 24131 RC-135W | 55th Wg | gn | | 38873 KC-135R | 92nd ARW | |
| | 24132 RC-135W | 55th Wg | gn | | 38874 KC-135R | 6th AMW | y/bl |
| | 24133 TC-135S | 55th Wg | bk | | 38875 KC-135R | 127th ARS | |
| | 24134 RC-135W | 55th Wg | gn | | 38876 KC-135R | 168th ARS | bl/y |
| | 24135 RC-135W | 55th Wg | gn | | 38877 KC-135R | 97th AMW | y/r |
| | 24138 RC-135W | 55th Wg | gn | | 38878 KC-135R | 97th AMW | y/r |
| | 24139 RC-135W | 55th Wg | gn | | 38879 KC-135R | 319th ARW | |
| | FY63 | | | | 38880 KC-135R | 507th ARW | bl/y |
| | 37976 KC-135R | 319th ARW | | | 38881 KC-135R | 18th Wg | w |
| | 37977 KC-135R | 97th AMW | y/r | | 38883 KC-135R | 18th Wg | w |
| | 37978 KC-135R | 97th AMW | y/r | | 38884 KC-135R | 100th ARW | r/w/bl |
| | 37979 KC-135R | 18th Wg | w | | 38885 KC-135R | 18th Wg | w |
| | 37980 KC-135R | | | | 38886 KC-135R | 18th Wg | w |
| | 37981 KC-135R | 136th ARS | bl | | 38887 KC-135R | 97th AMW | y/r |
| | 37982 KC-135R | 22nd ARW | gy/si | | 38888 KC-135R | 92nd ARW | |
| | 37984 KC-135R | 106th ARS | w/r | | 39792 RC-135V | 55th Wg | gn |
| | 37985 KC-135R | 507th ARW | bl/y | | FY55 | | |
| | 37987 KC-135R | 100th ARW | r/w/bl | | 53132 NKC-135E | 412th TW | bl |
| | 37988 KC-135R | 173rd ARS | r/w | | 53141 KC-135E | 174th ARS | y/bk |
| | 37991 KC-135R | 173rd ARS | r/w | | 53145 KC-135E | 117th ARS | bl/y |
| | 37992 KC-135R | 121st ARS | bl | | 53146 KC-135E | 108th ARW | bk/y |
| | 37993 KC-135R | 121st ARW | m | | FY56 | | |
| | 37995 KC-135R | 22nd ARW | gy | | 63593 KC-135E | 108th ARW | bk/y |
| | 37996 KC-135R | 434th ARW | bl | | 63606 KC-135E | 132nd ARS | w/gn |
| | 37997 KC-135R | 319th ARW | bl | | 63609 KC-135E | 151st ARS | w/or |
| | 37999 KC-135R | 319th ARW | | | 63611 KC-135E | 108th ARS | w/bl |
| | 38000 KC-135R | 22nd ARW | gy/si | | 63622 KC-135E | 132nd ARS | w/gn |
| | 38002 KC-135R | 22nd ARW | gy/si | | 63626 KC-135E | 108th ARS | bk/y |
| | 38003 KC-135R | 6th AMW | y/bl | | 63630 KC-135E | 171st ARW | y/bk |
| | 38004 KC-135R | 127th ARS | | | 63631 KC-135E | 191st ARS | bl/bk |
| | 38006 KC-135R | 97th AMW | y/r | | 63638 KC-135E | 197th ARS | |
| | 38007 KC-135R | 106th ARS | w/r | | 63640 KC-135E | 132nd ARS | w/gn |
| | 38008 KC-135R | 22nd ARW | | | 63641 KC-135E | 117th ARS | bl/y |
| | 38011 KC-135R | 92nd ARW | y | | 63650 KC-135E | 174th ARS | y/bk |
| | 38012 KC-135R | 18th Wg | w | | FY57 | | |
| | 38013 KC-135R | 121st ARW | bl | | 71419 KC-135R | 19th ARG | y/bl |
| | 38014 KC-135R | 927th ARW | pr/w | | 71421 KC-135E | 174th ARS | y/bk |
| | 38015 KC-135R | 168th ARS | bl/y | | 71422 KC-135E | 927th ARW | pr/w |
| | 38017 KC-135R | 97th AMW | y/r | | 71423 KC-135E | 108th ARW | bk/y |
| | 38018 KC-135R | 173rd ARS | r/w | | 71425 KC-135E | 151st ARS | w/or |
| | 38019 KC-135R | 97th AMW | y/r | | 71426 KC-135E | 117th ARS | bl/y |
| | 38020 KC-135R | 6th AMW | y/bl | | 71427 KC-135E | 127th ARS | |
| | 38021 KC-135R | 6th AMW | y/bl | | 71428 KC-135R | 196th ARS | bl/w |
| | 38022 KC-135R | 22nd ARW | m | | 71429 KC-135R | 196th ARS | bl/w |
| | 38023 KC-135R | 197th ARS | | | 71430 KC-135R | 133rd ARS | bl |
| | 38024 KC-135R | 452nd AMW | y | | 71431 KC-135E | 108th ARW | bk/y |
| | 38025 KC-135R | 319th ARW | w | | 71432 KC-135R | 106th ARS | w/r |
| | 38026 KC-135R | 319th ARW | y | | 71433 KC-135E | 151st ARS | w/or |
| | 38027 KC-135R | 97th AMW | y/r | | 71434 KC-135E | 174th ARS | y/bk |
| | 38028 KC-135R | 168th ARS | bl/y | | 71435 KC-135R | 18th Wg | w |

| Type | | | Notes | Type | | | Notes |
|---|---|---|---|---|---|---|---|
| 71436 | KC-135R | 196th ARS | bl/w | 72605 | KC-135R | 100th ARW | r/w/bl |
| 71437 | KC-135R | 916th ARW | gn | 72606 | KC-135R | 116th ARS | gn/w |
| 71438 | KC-135R | 939th ARW | pr/y | 72608 | KC-135E | 174th ARS | y/bk |
| 71439 | KC-135R | 319th ARW | bl | *FY58* | | | |
| 71440 | KC-135R | 319th ARW | r | 80001 | KC-135R | 100th ARW | r/w/bl |
| 71441 | KC-135R | 108th ARS | w/bl | 80003 | KC-135R | 108th ARS | w/bl |
| 71443 | KC-135E | 132nd ARS | w/gn | 80004 | KC-135R | 153rd ARS | bk/gd |
| 71445 | KC-135E | 108th ARW | bk/y | 80005 | KC-135E | 117th ARS | bl/y |
| 71447 | KC-135E | 174th ARS | y/bk | 80006 | KC-135R | 108th ARS | w/bl |
| 71448 | KC-135E | 132nd ARS | w/gn | 80008 | KC-135R | 133rd ARS | bl |
| 71450 | KC-135E | 132nd ARS | w/gn | 80009 | KC-135R | 126th ARS | w/bl |
| 71451 | KC-135R | 196th ARS | bl/w | 80010 | KC-135R | 153rd ARS | bk/gd |
| 71452 | KC-135E | 197th ARS | | 80011 | KC-135R | 22nd ARW | |
| 71453 | KC-135R | 106th ARS | w/r | 80012 | KC-135R | 191st ARS | bl/bk |
| 71454 | KC-135R | 319th ARW | w | 80013 | KC-135E | 117th ARS | bl/y |
| 71455 | KC-135E | 151st ARS | w/or | 80014 | KC-135E | 117th ARS | bl/y |
| 71456 | KC-135R | 927th ARW | pr/w | 80015 | KC-135R | 939th ARW | pr/y |
| 71458 | KC-135E | 108th ARS | w/bl | 80016 | KC-135R | 92nd ARW | bk |
| 71459 | KC-135E | 939th ARW | pr/y | 80017 | KC-135E | 132nd ARS | w/gn |
| 71460 | KC-135E | 117th ARS | bl/y | 80018 | KC-135R | 22nd ARW | y |
| 71461 | KC-135E | 173rd ARS | r/w | 80020 | KC-135E | 171st ARW | y/bk |
| 71462 | KC-135R | 121st ARW | bl | 80021 | KC-135R | 127th ARS | |
| 71463 | KC-135E | 117th ARS | bl/y | 80023 | KC-135R | 136th ARS | bl |
| 71464 | KC-135R | 108th ARW | bk/y | 80024 | KC-135E | 108th ARS | bl |
| 71465 | KC-135E | 151st ARS | w/or | 80027 | KC-135R | 319th ARW | y |
| 71468 | KC-135E | 452nd AMW | y | 80030 | KC-135R | 106th ARS | w/r |
| 71469 | KC-135R | 121st ARW | bl | 80032 | KC-135E | 108th ARS | bl |
| 71471 | KC-135E | 132nd ARS | w/gn | 80034 | KC-135R | 319th ARW | |
| 71472 | KC-135R | 434th ARW | bl | 80035 | KC-135R | 22nd ARW | y |
| 71473 | KC-135R | 19th ARG | y/bl | 80036 | KC-135R | 92nd ARW | bk |
| 71474 | KC-135R | 100th ARW | r/w/bl | 80037 | KC-135E | 171st ARW | bk/y |
| 71475 | KC-135R | 197th ARS | | 80038 | KC-135R | 916th ARW | gn |
| 71478 | KC-135E | 151st ARS | w/or | 80040 | KC-135E | 108th ARS | bl |
| 71479 | KC-135R | 459th ARW | y/bk | 80041 | KC-135E | 927th ARW | pr/w |
| 71480 | KC-135E | 108th ARS | w/bl | 80042 | KC-135T | 22nd ARW | |
| 71483 | KC-135R | 319th ARW | | 80043 | KC-135E | 191st ARS | bl/bk |
| 71484 | KC-135R | 108th ARW | | 80044 | KC-135E | 108th ARW | bk/y |
| 71485 | KC-135R | 151st ARS | w/or | 80045 | KC-135T | 171st ARW | y/bk |
| 71486 | KC-135R | 197th ARS | | 80046 | KC-135T | 92nd ARW | bl |
| 71487 | KC-135R | 459th ARW | y/bk | 80047 | KC-135T | 319th ARW | |
| 71488 | KC-135R | 319th ARW | | 80049 | KC-135T | 92nd ARW | y |
| 71491 | KC-135E | 132nd ARS | w/gn | 80050 | KC-135T | 92nd ARW | bk |
| 71492 | KC-135E | 151st ARS | w/or | 80051 | KC-135R | 507th ARW | bl/y |
| 71493 | KC-135R | 92nd ARW | bk | 80052 | KC-135R | 452nd AMW | y |
| 71494 | KC-135E | 108th ARS | w/bl | 80054 | KC-135T | 171st ARW | y/bk |
| 71495 | KC-135R | 197th ARS | | 80055 | KC-135T | 18th Wg | w |
| 71496 | KC-135E | 132nd ARS | w/gn | 80056 | KC-135R | 153rd ARS | bk/gd |
| 71497 | KC-135E | 191st ARS | bl/bk | 80057 | KC-135R | 116th ARS | gn/w |
| 71499 | KC-135R | 319th ARW | r | 80058 | KC-135R | 939th ARW | pr/y |
| 71501 | KC-135E | 174th ARS | y/bk | 80059 | KC-135R | 153rd ARS | bk/gd |
| 71502 | KC-135R | 22nd ARW | | 80060 | KC-135T | 171st ARW | y/bk |
| 71503 | KC-135E | 151st ARS | w/or | 80061 | KC-135T | 22nd ARW | |
| 71504 | KC-135E | 940th ARS | or/bk | 80062 | KC-135T | 940th ARW | or/bk |
| 71505 | KC-135E | 132nd ARS | w/gn | 80063 | KC-135R | 507th ARW | bl/y |
| 71506 | KC-135R | 6th AMW | y/bl | 80065 | KC-135T | 22nd ARW | |
| 71507 | KC-135E | 108th ARW | bk/y | 80066 | KC-135R | 507th ARW | bl/y |
| 71508 | KC-135R | 203rd ARS | y/bk | 80067 | KC-135R | 116th ARS | gn/w |
| 71509 | KC-135E | 108st ARW | bk/y | 80068 | KC-135E | 108th ARS | w/bl |
| 71510 | KC-135E | 191st ARS | bl/bk | 80069 | KC-135T | 92nd ARW | bk |
| 71512 | KC-135R | 459th ARW | y/bk | 80071 | KC-135T | 22nd ARW | y/bk |
| 71514 | KC-135R | 126th ARS | w/bl | 80072 | KC-135T | 171st ARW | y/bk |
| 72589 | KC-135E | 412th TW | | 80073 | KC-135R | 106th ARS | w/r |
| 72593 | KC-135R | 121st ARW | bl | 80074 | KC-135T | 171st ARW | y/bk |
| 72594 | KC-135E | 108th ARS | w/bl | 80075 | KC-135R | 459th ARW | y/bk |
| 72595 | KC-135E | 117th ARS | bl/y | 80076 | KC-135R | 434th ARW | r/w |
| 72597 | KC-135R | 153rd ARS | bk/gd | 80077 | KC-135T | 171st ARW | y/bk |
| 72598 | KC-135R | 452nd AMW | y | 80078 | KC-135E | 108th ARW | bl |
| 72599 | KC-135R | 916th ARW | gn | 80079 | KC-135R | 507th ARW | bl/y |
| 72600 | KC-135E | 174th ARS | y/bk | 80080 | KC-135E | 174th ARS | y/bk |
| 72601 | KC-135E | 151st ARS | w/or | 80082 | KC-135R | 174th ARS | y/bk |
| 72602 | KC-135E | 108th ARW | bl | 80083 | KC-135R | 121st ARW | bl |
| 72603 | KC-135R | 452nd AMW | y | 80084 | KC-135T | 171st ARW | y/bk |
| 72604 | KC-135E | 108th ARW | bl | 80085 | KC-135R | 452nd AMW | y |

# C-135

| Notes | Type | | | | Notes | Type | | | |
|---|---|---|---|---|---|---|---|---|---|
| | 80086 | KC-135T | 92nd ARW | bk | | 91470 | KC-135T | 92nd ARW | bk |
| | 80087 | KC-135E | 108th ARW | bl | | 91471 | KC-135T | 92nd ARW | y |
| | 80088 | KC-135T | 940th ARW | or/bk | | 91472 | KC-135R | 203rd ARS | y/bk |
| | 80089 | KC-135T | 319th ARW | w | | 91473 | KC-135E | 191st ARS | bl/bk |
| | 80090 | KC-135E | 940th ARW | or/bk | | 91474 | KC-135T | 92nd ARW | bk |
| | 80092 | KC-135R | 92nd ARW | | | 91475 | KC-135R | 97th AMW | y/r |
| | 80093 | KC-135R | 92nd ARW | | | 91476 | KC-135R | 319th ARW | r |
| | 80094 | KC-135T | 92nd ARW | bk | | 91477 | KC-135E | 940th ARW | or/bk |
| | 80095 | KC-135T | 319th ARW | w | | 91478 | KC-135R | 153rd ARS | bk/gd |
| | 80098 | KC-135R | 133rd ARS | bl | | 91479 | KC-135E | 171st ARW | y/bk |
| | 80099 | KC-135T | 171st ARW | y/bk | | 91480 | KC-135T | 92nd ARW | bk |
| | 80100 | KC-135R | 92nd ARW | | | 91482 | KC-135R | 319th ARW | w |
| | 80102 | KC-135R | 939th ARW | pr/y | | 91483 | KC-135R | 121st ARW | bl |
| | 80103 | KC-135R | 92nd ARW | | | 91484 | KC-135E | 108th ARS | w/bl |
| | 80104 | KC-135R | 136th ARS | bl | | 91485 | KC-135E | 108th ARW | bl |
| | 80106 | KC-135R | 106th ARS | w/r | | 91486 | KC-135R | 22nd ARW | y |
| | 80107 | KC-135E | 116th ARS | gn/w | | 91487 | KC-135E | 108th ARS | w/bl |
| | 80108 | KC-135E | 940th ARW | or/bk | | 91488 | KC-135R | 6th AMW | y/bl |
| | 80109 | KC-135E | 153rd ARS | bk/gd | | 91489 | KC-135E | 191st ARS | bl/bk |
| | 80111 | KC-135E | 108th ARW | bk/y | | 91490 | KC-135T | 171st ARW | |
| | 80112 | KC-135T | 171st ARW | y/bk | | 91492 | KC-135R | 22nd ARW | |
| | 80113 | KC-135R | 97th AMW | y/r | | 91493 | KC-135E | 132nd ARS | w/gn |
| | 80114 | KC-135R | 92nd ARW | bl | | 91495 | KC-135R | 126th ARS | w/bl |
| | 80115 | KC-135E | 108th ARW | bl | | 91496 | KC-135E | 171st ARW | y/bk |
| | 80116 | KC-135E | 197th ARS | | | 91497 | KC-135E | 108th ARW | bl |
| | 80117 | KC-135T | 92nd ARW | bl | | 91498 | KC-135R | 127th ARS | |
| | 80118 | KC-135R | 92nd ARW | bk | | 91499 | KC-135R | 196th ARS | bl/w |
| | 80119 | KC-135R | 92nd ARW | | | 91500 | KC-135R | 197th ARS | |
| | 80120 | KC-135R | 319th ARW | | | 91501 | KC-135R | 319th ARW | |
| | 80121 | KC-135R | 507th ARW | bl/y | | 91502 | KC-135R | 319th ARW | y |
| | 80122 | KC-135R | 168th ARS | bl/y | | 91503 | KC-135E | 108th ARW | bk/y |
| | 80123 | KC-135R | 319th ARW | | | 91504 | KC-135T | 171st ARW | y/bk |
| | 80124 | KC-135R | 22nd ARW | | | 91505 | KC-135R | 196th ARS | bl/w |
| | 80125 | KC-135T | 92nd ARW | bl | | 91506 | KC-135E | 116th ARS | gn/w |
| | 80126 | KC-135R | 22nd ARW | y | | 91507 | KC-135R | 19th ARG | y/bl |
| | 80128 | KC-135R | 100th ARW | r/w/bl | | 91508 | KC-135R | 92nd ARW | bk |
| | 80129 | KC-135T | 92nd ARW | bk | | 91509 | KC-135R | 196th ARS | bl/w |
| | 80130 | KC-135R | 126th ARS | w/bl | | 91510 | KC-135T | 319th ARW | r |
| | FY59 | | | | | 91511 | KC-135R | 22nd ARW | |
| | 91444 | KC-135R | 121st ARW | bl | | 91512 | KC-135T | 940th ARW | or/bk |
| | 91445 | KC-135E | 174th ARS | y/bk | | 91513 | KC-135T | 92nd ARW | bl |
| | 91446 | KC-135R | 153rd ARS | bk/gd | | 91515 | KC-135R | 319th ARW | r |
| | 91447 | KC-135E | 927th ARW | pr/w | | 91516 | KC-135R | 196th ARS | bl/w |
| | 91448 | KC-135R | 196th ARS | bl/w | | 91517 | KC-135R | 197th ARS | |
| | 91450 | KC-135R | 196th ARS | bl/w | | 91519 | KC-135R | 116th ARS | gn/w |
| | 91451 | KC-135E | 927th ARW | pr/w | | 91520 | KC-135T | 92nd ARW | bk |
| | 91453 | KC-135R | 121st ARW | bl | | 91521 | KC-135R | 168th ARS | bl/y |
| | 91455 | KC-135R | 153rd ARS | bk/gd | | 91522 | KC-135R | 136th ARS | bl |
| | 91456 | KC-135E | 108th ARW | bk/y | | 91523 | KC-135T | 171st AMW | |
| | 91457 | KC-135E | 171st ARW | y/bk | | | | | |
| | 91458 | KC-135R | 121st ARW | bl | | **Lockheed C-141C Starlifter** | | | |
| | 91459 | KC-135R | | | | 445th AW AFRC, Wright- | | | |
| | 91460 | KC-135T | 171st ARW | | | Patterson AFB, Ohio (si): | | | |
| | 91461 | KC-135R | 168th ARS | bl/y | | 89th AS & 356th AS; | | | |
| | 91462 | KC-135T | 319th ARW | bl | | FY64 | | | |
| | 91463 | KC-135R | 173rd ARS | r/w | | 40620 | | | |
| | 91464 | KC-135T | 92nd ARW | bk | | 40637 | | | |
| | 91466 | KC-135R | 136th ARS | bl | | FY66 | | | |
| | 91467 | KC-135T | 171st ARW | bk/y | | 60177 | | | |
| | 91468 | KC-135T | 171st ARW | | | FY67 | | | |
| | 91469 | KC-135R | 459th ARW | y/bk | | 70166 | | | |

**Lockheed P-3 Orion**
CinCLANT/VP-30, NAS Jacksonville, Florida;
CinCPAC/ETD, MCBH Kaneohe Bay, Hawaii;
CNO/VP-30, NAS Jacksonville, Florida;
NASC-FS, NAS Point Mugu, California;
USNTPS, NAS Point Mugu, California;
VP-1, NAS Whidbey Island, Washington [YB];
VP-4, MCBH Kaneohe Bay, Hawaii [YD];
VP-5, NAS Jacksonville, Florida [LA];
VP-8, NAS Brunswick, Maine [LC];
VP-9, MCBH Kaneohe Bay, Hawaii [PD];
VP-10, NAS Brunswick, Maine [LD];
VP-16, NAS Jacksonville, Florida [LF];
VP-26, NAS Brunswick, Maine [LK];
VP-30, NAS Jacksonville, Florida [LL];
VP-40, NAS Whidbey Island, Washington [QE];
VP-45, NAS Jacksonville, Florida [LN];
VP-46, NAS Whidbey Island, Washington [RC];
VP-47, MCBH Kaneohe Bay, Hawaii [RD];
VP-62, NAS Jacksonville, Florida [LT];
VP-65, NAS Point Mugu, California [PG];
VP-66, NAS Willow Grove, Pennsylvania [LV];
VP-69, NAS Whidbey Island, Washington [PJ];
VP-92, NAS Brunswick, Maine [LY];
VP-94, NAS New Orleans, Louisiana [PZ];
VPU-1, NAS Brunswick, Maine;
VPU-2, MCBH Kaneohe Bay, Hawaii;
VQ-1, NAS Whidbey Island, Washington [PR];
VQ-2, NAS Whidbey Island, Washington;
VX-1, NAS Patuxent River, Maryland;
VX-20, Patuxent River, Maryland;
VX-30, NAS Point Mugu, California;
VXS-1, Patuxent River, Maryland

| Serial | Code | Type | Unit |
|---|---|---|---|
| 148889 | | UP-3A | USNTPS |
| 149676 | | VP-3A | CinCPAC |
| 150499 | [337] | NP-3D | VX-30 |
| 150521 | [341] | NP-3D | VX-30 |
| 150522 | [340] | NP-3D | VX-30 |
| 152141 | [408] | P-3A | VP-1 |
| 152150 | [150] | NP-3D | VXS-1 |
| 152165 | [404] | P-3A | VP-1 |
| 153443 | [443] | NP-3D | USNTPS |
| 154587 | [587] | NP-3D | VXS-1 |
| 154589 | [589] | NP-3D | VXS-1 |
| 156507 | [PR-507] | EP-3E | VQ-1 |
| 156509 | [LL-509] | P-3C | VP-30 |
| 156510 | [LL-510] | P-3C | VP-30 |
| 156511 | [PR-32] | EP-3E | VQ-1 |
| 156514 | [PR-514] | EP-3E | VQ-1 |
| 156515 | [515] | P-3C | VP-40 |
| 156517 | [PR-34] | EP-3E | VQ-1 |
| 156519 | [21] | EP-3E | VQ-2 |
| 156521 | [QE-521] | P-3C | VP-40 |
| 156527 | [YD-527] | P-3C | VP-4 |
| 156528 | [PR-36] | EP-3E | VQ-1 |
| 156529 | [24] | EP-3E | VQ-2 |
| 157316 | [23] | EP-3E | VQ-2 |
| 157318 | [PR-318] | EP-3E | VQ-1 |
| 157319 | [LL-319] | P-3C | VP-30 |
| 157322 | [RC-322] | P-3C | VP-46 |
| 157325 | [25] | EP-3E | VQ-2 |
| 157326 | [22] | EP-3E | VQ-2 |
| 157327 | [LL-327] | P-3C | VP-30 |
| 157329 | [329] | P-3C | VP-10 |
| 157330 | [330] | P-3C | VP-26 |
| 157331 | [LL-331] | P-3C | VP-30 |
| 158204 | [204] | NP-3C | VX-20 |
| 158206 | | P-3C | VPU-1 |
| 158210 | [210] | P-3C | VP-26 |
| 158214 | [LL-214] | P-3C | VP-30 |
| 158215 | [LL-215] | P-3C | VP-30 |
| 158222 | [LL-51] | P-3C | VP-30 |
| 158224 | [LN-224] | P-3C | VP-45 |
| 158225 | [225] | P-3C | VP-5 |
| 158563 | [LD-563] | P-3C | VP-10 |
| 158564 | [LK-564] | P-3C | VP-26 |
| 158567 | [567] | P-3C | VP-16 |
| 158568 | [357] | NP-3C | VX-30 |
| 158570 | [02] | P-3C | VX-1 |
| 158571 | [LL-571] | P-3C | VP-30 |
| 158573 | [573] | P-3C | VP-92 |
| 158574 | | P-3C | NASC-FS |
| 158912 | [912] | P-3C | VX-20 |
| 158914 | [RC-914] | P-3C | VP-46 |
| 158915 | [915] | P-3C | VP-45 |
| 158916 | [916] | P-3C | VP-40 |
| 158917 | [917] | P-3C | VP-26 |
| 158918 | [918] | P-3C | VP-40 |
| 158919 | [919] | P-3C | VP-45 |
| 158921 | [921] | P-3C | VP-40 |
| 158922 | 922] | P-3C | VP-30 |
| 158923 | [923] | P-3C | VP-47 |
| 158924 | [LA-924] | P-3C | VP-16 |
| 158925 | [LC-925] | P-3C | VP-8 |
| 158926 | [926] | P-3C | VP-30 |
| 158927 | [927] | P-3C | VP-47 |
| 158928 | | P-3C | VPU-2 |
| 158929 | [929] | P-3C | VP-16 |
| 158934 | [YB-934] | P-3C | VP-1 |
| 158935 | [LL-935] | P-3C | VP-30 |
| 159318 | [LD-318] | P-3C | VP-10 |
| 159320 | [320] | P-3C | VP-1 |
| 159322 | [LL-322] | P-3C | VP-30 |
| 159323 | [QE-323] | P-3C | VP-40 |
| 159326 | [PD-326] | P-3C | VP-9 |
| 159329 | [QE-329] | P-3C | VP-40 |
| 159503 | [LN-503] | P-3C | VP-45 |
| 159504 | | P-3C | VPU-2 |
| 159506 | [LK-506] | P-3C | VP-26 |
| 159507 | [RD-507] | P-3C | VP-47 |
| 159512 | [512] | P-3C | VP-16 |
| 159513 | [LL-513] | P-3C | VP-30 |
| 159514 | [LL-514] | P-3C | VP-30 |
| 159884 | | P-3C | VQ-2 |
| 159885 | [885] | P-3C | VP-40 |
| 159887 | | EP-3E | NASC-FS |
| 159889 | [04] | P-3C | VX-1 |
| 159894 | [PD-894] | P-3C | VP-9 |
| 160283 | [283] | P-3C | VP-9 |
| 160284 | [LT-284] | P-3C | VP-62 |
| 160285 | | P-3C | VPU-1 |
| 160287 | [LL-287] | P-3C | VP-30 |
| 160288 | | P-3C | NASC-FS |
| 160290 | [290] | P-3C | VX-20 |
| 160291 | [JA-05] | EP-3E | NASC-FS |
| 160292 | [292] | P-3C | VPU-2 |
| 160293 | | P-3C | NASC-FS |
| 160610 | [YD-610] | P-3C | VP-4 |
| 160611 | [PG-611] | P-3C | VP-65 |
| 160612 | [PR-52] | P-3C | VQ-1 |
| 160761 | [RD-761] | P-3C | VP-47 |
| 160762 | | P-3C | VPU-2 |
| 160763 | [763] | P-3C | VQ-2 |
| 160764 | [764] | EP-3E | VQ-2 |
| 160765 | [765] | P-3C | VP-5 |
| 160766 | [PD-766] | P-3C | VP-9 |
| 160767 | [LT-767] | P-3C | VP-62 |
| 160769 | [LD-769] | P-3C | VP-10 |
| 160770 | [LN-770] | P-3C | VP-45 |
| 160999 | [LL-999] | P-3C | VP-30 |

| | | | |
|---|---|---|---|
| 161001 | [PJ-001] | P-3C | VP-69 |
| 161002 | [LN-002] | P-3C | VP-45 |
| 161005 | [JA-07] | P-3C | VX-1 |
| 161006 | [006] | P-3C | VP-10 |
| 161007 | [LV-007] | P-3C | VP-66 |
| 161008 | [LL-008] | P-3C | VP-30 |
| 161009 | | P-3C | VP-10 |
| 161010 | [LL-010] | P-3C | VP-30 |
| 161011 | [LA-011] | P-3C | VP-5 |
| 161012 | [YD-012] | P-3C | VP-4 |
| 161013 | [LT-013] | P-3C | VP-62 |
| 161014 | [PG-014] | P-3C | VP-65 |
| 161121 | [121] | P-3C | VP-45 |
| 161122 | [226] | P-3C | VPU-1 |
| 161124 | [LC-124] | P-3C | VP-8 |
| 161125 | [LV-125] | P-3C | VP-66 |
| 161126 | [PR-50] | P-3C | VQ-1 |
| 161127 | [LY-127] | P-3C | VP-92 |
| 161129 | [LT-129] | P-3C | VP-62 |
| 161329 | [LT-329] | P-3C | VP-62 |
| 161331 | [LY-331] | P-3C | VP-92 |
| 161332 | [PG-332] | P-3C | VP-65 |
| 161333 | [PZ-333] | P-3C | VP-94 |
| 161334 | [PZ-334] | P-3C | VP-94 |
| 161335 | [PZ-335] | P-3C | VP-94 |
| 161336 | [LY-336] | P-3C | VP-92 |
| 161337 | [PZ-337] | P-3C | VP-94 |
| 161338 | [LA-338] | P-3C | VP-5 |
| 161339 | [339] | P-3C | VP-4 |
| 161404 | [LL-404] | P-3C | VP-30 |
| 161405 | [405] | P-3C | VP-40 |
| 161406 | [PR-406] | P-3C | VQ-1 |
| 161407 | [PG-407] | P-3C | VP-65 |
| 161408 | [PJ-408] | P-3C | VP-69 |
| 161409 | [LT-409] | P-3C | VP-62 |
| 161410 | | EP-3E | NASC-FS |
| 161411 | [LL-411] | P-3C | VP-30 |
| 161412 | [LY-412] | P-3C | VP-92 |
| 161413 | [LL-413] | P-3C | VP-30 |
| 161414 | [LA-414] | P-3C | VP-5 |
| 161415 | [LL-415] | P-3C | VP-30 |
| 161585 | | P-3C | VPU-1 |
| 161586 | [LL-586] | P-3C | VP-30 |
| 161587 | [YD-587] | P-3C | VP-4 |
| 161588 | [LL-588] | P-3C | VP-30 |
| 161589 | [589] | P-3C | VX-1 |
| 161590 | [LL-590] | P-3C | VP-30 |
| 161591 | [PZ-591] | P-3C | VP-94 |
| 161592 | [LV-592] | P-3C | VP-66 |
| 161593 | [LL-593] | P-3C | VP-30 |
| 161594 | [LL-594] | P-3C | VP-30 |
| 161595 | [LV-595] | P-3C | VP-66 |
| 161596 | [LL-596] | P-3C | VP-30 |
| 161763 | [PD-763] | P-3C | VP-9 |
| 161764 | [764] | P-3C | VP-4 |
| 161765 | [LF-765] | P-3C | VP-16 |
| 161766 | [LL-766] | P-3C | VP-30 |
| 161767 | [LD-767] | P-3C | VP-10 |
| 162314 | [RC-314] | P-3C | VP-46 |
| 162315 | [315] | P-3C | VP-40 |
| 162316 | [LD-316] | P-3C | VP-10 |
| 162317 | [PD-317] | P-3C | VP-9 |
| 162318 | [RC-318] | P-3C | VP-46 |
| 162770 | [RC-770] | P-3C | VP-46 |
| 162771 | [RD-771] | P-3C | VP-47 |
| 162772 | [QE-772] | P-3C | VP-40 |
| 162773 | [773] | P-3C | VP-26 |
| 162774 | [774] | P-3C | VX-20 |
| 162775 | [PD-775] | P-3C | VP-9 |
| 162776 | [LK-776] | P-3C | VP-26 |
| 162777 | [YD-777] | P-3C | VP-4 |
| 162778 | [778] | P-3C | VP-40 |
| 162998 | [RD-998] | P-3C | VP-47 |
| 162999 | [LD-999] | P-3C | VP-10 |

| | | | |
|---|---|---|---|
| 163000 | [000] | P-3C | VP-45 |
| 163001 | [LT-001] | P-3C | VP-62 |
| 163002 | [LT-002] | P-3C | VP-62 |
| 163003 | [LT-003] | P-3C | VP-62 |
| 163004 | [LY-004] | P-3C | VP-92 |
| 163006 | [LF-006] | P-3C | VP-16 |
| 163289 | [YB-289] | P-3C | VP-1 |
| 163290 | [LL-290] | P-3C | VP-30 |
| 163291 | [LT-291] | P-3C | VP-62 |
| 163292 | [LF-292] | P-3C | VP-16 |
| 163293 | [293] | P-3C | VP-40 |
| 163294 | [294] | P-3C | VP-16 |
| 163295 | [PJ-295] | P-3C | VP-69 |

**Boeing E-6B Mercury**
Boeing, McConnell AFB, Kansas;
VQ-3 & VQ-4, SCW-1,
Tinker AFB, Oklahoma

| | |
|---|---|
| 162782 | VQ-4 |
| 162783 | VQ-3 |
| 162784 | VQ-3 |
| 163918 | VQ-3 |
| 163919 | VQ-3 |
| 163920 | VQ-3 |
| 164386 | VQ-3 |
| 164387 | VQ-3 |
| 164388 | VQ-4 |
| 164404 | VQ-4 |
| 164405 | VQ-4 |
| 164406 | VQ-3 |
| 164407 | VQ-4 |
| 164408 | VQ-4 |
| 164409 | VQ-4 |
| 164410 | VQ-4 |

**McDonnell Douglas**
**C-9B Skytrain II/DC-9-32\***
VMR-1, Cherry Point MCAS,
North Carolina;
VR-46, Atlanta, Georgia [JS];
VR-52, Willow Grove NAS,
Pennsylvania [JT];
VR-56, Norfolk NAS,
Virginia [JU];
VR-61, Whidbey Island NAS,
Washington [RS];

| | | |
|---|---|---|
| 159113 | [RS] | VR-61 |
| 159114 | [RS] | VR-61 |
| 159115 | [JU] | VR-56 |
| 159116 | [RS] | VR-61 |
| 159117 | [JU] | VR-56 |
| 159118 | [JU] | VR-56 |
| 159119 | [JU] | VR-56 |
| 159120 | [JU] | VR-56 |
| 160046 | | VMR-1 |
| 160047 | | VMR-1 |
| 160048 | [JT] | VR-52 |
| 160049 | [JT] | VR-52 |
| 160050 | [JT] | VR-52 |
| 160051 | [JT] | VR-52 |
| 161266 | [JS] | VR-46 |
| 161529 | [JS] | VR-46 |
| 161530 | [JS] | VR-46 |
| 164606\* | [RS] | VR-61 |
| 164608\* | [RS] | VR-61 |

**Grumman C-20D Gulfstream III/**
**C-20G Gulfstream IV\***
MASD, NAF Washington, Maryland;
VR-1, NAF Washington, Maryland;
VR-48, NAF Washington, Maryland [JR];
VR-51, MCBH Kaneohe Bay, Hawaii [RG]

| | |
|---|---|
| 163691 | VR-1 |
| 163692 | VR-1 |

| | | |
|---|---|---|
| 165093* [JR] | VR-48 | |
| 165094* [JR] | VR-48 | |
| 165151* [JR] | VR-48 | |
| 165152* [RG] | VR-51 | |
| 165153* | MASD | |

**Gulfstream Aerospace**
**C-37A Gulfstream V**
VR-1, NAF Washington, Maryland;

| | | |
|---|---|---|
| 166375 | VR-1 | |
| 166376 | VR-1 | |
| 166377 | | |
| 166378 | | |
| 166379 | | |

**Boeing C-40A Clipper**
VR-57, North Island NAS,
  California [RX];
VR-58, Jacksonville NAS,
  Florida [JV];
VR-59, NAS Fort Worth JRB,
  Texas [RY]

| | | |
|---|---|---|
| 165829 | [JV] | VR-58 |
| 165830 | [RY] | VR-59 |
| 165831 | [RY] | VR-59 |
| 165832 | [JV] | VR-58 |
| 165833 | [RY] | VR-59 |
| 165834 | [JV] | VR-58 |
| 165835 | [RX] | VR-57 |
| 165836 | [RX] | VR-57 |

**Lockheed C-130 Hercules**
VR-53, NAF Washington, Maryland [AX];
VR-54, New Orleans NAS, Louisiana [CW];
VR-55, NAS Point Mugu, California [RU];
VR-62, Brunswick NAS, Maine [JW];
VR-64, NAS Willow Grove, Pennsylvania [BD];
VMGR-152, Futenma MCAS, Japan [QD];
VMGR-234, NAS Fort Worth, Texas [QH];
VMGR-252, Cherry Point MCAS,
  North Carolina [BH];
VMGRT-253, Cherry Point MCAS,
  North Carolina [GR];
VMGR-352, MCAS Miramar, California [QB];
VMGR-452, Stewart Field, New York [NY];
VX-20, Patuxent River, Maryland;
VX-30, NAS Point Mugu, California

| | | |
|---|---|---|
| 147573 [QD] | KC-130F | VMGR-152 |
| 148246 [GR] | KC-130F | VMGRT-253 |
| 148247 [QB] | KC-130F | VMGR-352 |
| 148249 [GR] | KC-130F | VMGRT-253 |
| 148891 [QD] | KC-130F | VMGR-152 |
| 148893 [401] | KC-130F | VX-30 |
| 148894 [GR] | KC-130F | VMGRT-253 |
| 148896 [GR] | KC-130F | VMGRT-253 |
| 148897 [400] | KC-130F | VX-30 |
| 148899 [QD] | KC-130F | VMGR-152 |
| 149789 [QB] | KC-130F | VMGR-352 |
| 149795 [QD] | KC-130F | VMGR-152 |
| 149799 [QD] | KC-130F | VMGR-152 |
| 149803 [GR] | KC-130F | VMGRT-253 |
| 149807 [QD] | KC-130F | VMGR-152 |
| 149808 | KC-130F | VX-20 |
| 149815 | KC-130F | VX-20 |
| 150684 [GR] | KC-130F | VMGRT-253 |
| 150686 [BH] | KC-130F | VMGR-252 |
| 150689 [QB] | KC-130F | VMGR-352 |
| 150690 [QD] | KC-130F | VMGR-152 |
| 160013 [QD] | KC-130R | VMGR-152 |
| 160014 [QD] | KC-130R | VMGR-152 |
| 160015 [QB] | KC-130R | VMGR-352 |
| 160016 [QB] | KC-130R | VMGR-352 |
| 160017 [QB] | KC-130R | VMGR-352 |
| 160018 [QD] | KC-130R | VMGR-152 |
| 160022 [QB] | KC-130R | VMGR-352 |
| 160240 [QB] | KC-130R | VMGR-352 |
| 160625 [QD] | KC-130R | VMGR-152 |
| 160626 [QD] | KC-130R | VMGR-152 |
| 160627 [QD] | KC-130R | VMGR-152 |
| 160628 [QD] | KC-130R | VMGR-152 |
| 162308 [QH] | KC-130T | VMGR-234 |
| 162309 [QH] | KC-130T | VMGR-234 |
| 162310 [QH] | KC-130T | VMGR-234 |
| 162311 [QH] | KC-130T | VMGR-234 |
| 162785 [QH] | KC-130T | VMGR-234 |
| 162786 [QH] | KC-130T | VMGR-234 |
| 163022 [QH] | KC-130T | VMGR-234 |
| 163023 [QH] | KC-130T | VMGR-234 |
| 163310 [QH] | KC-130T | VMGR-234 |
| 163311 [NY] | KC-130T | VMGR-452 |
| 163591 [NY] | KC-130T | VMGR-452 |
| 163592 [NY] | KC-130T | VMGR-452 |
| 164105 [NY] | KC-130T | VMGR-452 |
| 164106 [NY] | KC-130T | VMGR-452 |
| 164180 [NY] | KC-130T | VMGR-452 |
| 164181 [NY] | KC-130T | VMGR-452 |
| 164441 [NY] | KC-130T | VMGR-452 |
| 164442 [NY] | KC-130T | VMGR-452 |
| 164597 [NY] | KC-130T-30 | VMGR-452 |
| 164598 [QH] | KC-130T-30 | VMGR-234 |
| 164762 [CW] | C-130T | VR-54 |
| 164763 | C-130T | Blue Angels |
| 164993 [BD] | C-130T | VR-64 |
| 164994 [AX] | C-130T | VR-53 |
| 164995 [CW] | C-130T | VR-54 |
| 164996 [BD] | C-130T | VR-64 |
| 164997 [AX] | C-130T | VR-53 |
| 164998 [AX] | C-130T | VR-53 |
| 164999 [QH] | KC-130T | VMGR-234 |
| 165000 [NY] | KC-130T | VMGR-452 |
| 165158 [CW] | C-130T | VR-54 |
| 165159 [CW] | C-130T | VR-54 |
| 165160 [CW] | C-130T | VR-54 |
| 165161 [BD] | C-130T | VR-64 |
| 165162 [QH] | KC-130T | VMGR-234 |
| 165163 [QH] | KC-130T | VMGR-234 |
| 165313 [JW] | C-130T | VR-62 |
| 165314 [CW] | C-130T | VR-54 |
| 165315 [NY] | KC-130T | VMGR-452 |
| 165316 [NY] | KC-130T | VMGR-452 |
| 165348 [JW] | C-130T | VR-62 |
| 165349 [JW] | C-130T | VR-62 |
| 165350 [RU] | C-130T | VR-55 |
| 165351 [RU] | C-130T | VR-55 |
| 165352 [NY] | KC-130T | VMGR-452 |
| 165353 [NY] | KC-130T | VMGR-452 |
| 165378 [RU] | C-130T | VR-55 |
| 165379 [RU] | C-130T | VR-55 |
| 165735 [BH] | KC-130J | VMGR-252 |
| 165736 [QB] | KC-130J | VMGR-352 |
| 165737 [BH] | KC-130J | VMGR-252 |
| 165738 [BH] | KC-130J | VMGR-252 |
| 165739 [BH] | KC-130J | VMGR-252 |
| 165809 [BH] | KC-130J | VMGR-252 |
| 165957 [BH] | KC-130J | VMGR-252 |
| 166380 [BH] | KC-130J | VMGR-252 |
| 166381 [BH] | KC-130J | VMGR-252 |
| 166382 [BH] | KC-130J | VMGR-252 |
| 166472 [BH] | KC-130J | VMGR-252 |
| 166473 | KC-130J | VX-20 |
| 166511 [BH] | KC-130J | VMGR-252 |
| 166512 [QB] | KC-130J | VMGR-352 |
| 166513 [QB] | KC-130J | VMGR-352 |
| 166514 [QB] | KC-130J | VMGR-352 |
| 166762 [QB] | KC-130J | VMGR-352 |
| 166763 [QB] | KC-130J | VMGR-352 |
| 166764 [QB] | KC-130J | VMGR-352 |

166765 [QB]    KC-130J    VMGR-352

# US based US Coast Guard Aircraft

**Gulfstream Aerospace**
**C-37A Gulfstream V**
USCG, Washington DC
01

**Grumman Gulfstream IV**
USCG, Washington DC
02

**Lockheed C-130 Hercules**
USCGS Barbers Point, Hawaii;
USCGS Clearwater, Florida;
USCGS Elizabeth City, North Carolina;
USCGS Kodiak, Alaska;
USCGS Sacramento, California

| | | |
|---|---|---|
| 1500 | HC-130H | Elizabeth City |
| 1501 | HC-130H | Elizabeth City |
| 1502 | HC-130H | Elizabeth City |
| 1503 | HC-130H | Elizabeth City |
| 1504 | HC-130H | Elizabeth City |
| 1700 | HC-130H | Sacramento |
| 1701 | HC-130H | Barbers Point |
| 1702 | HC-130H | Kodiak |
| 1703 | HC-130H | Barbers Point |
| 1704 | HC-130H | Sacramento |
| 1705 | HC-130H | Clearwater |
| 1706 | HC-130H | Clearwater |
| 1707 | HC-130H | Kodiak |
| 1708 | HC-130H | Kodiak |
| 1709 | HC-130H | Kodiak |
| 1710 | HC-130H | Kodiak |
| 1711 | HC-130H | Kodiak |
| 1712 | HC-130H | Clearwater |
| 1713 | HC-130H | Barbers Point |
| 1714 | HC-130H | Barbers Point |
| 1715 | HC-130H | Sacramento |
| 1716 | HC-130H | Sacramento |
| 1717 | HC-130H | Clearwater |
| 1718 | HC-130H | Clearwater |
| 1719 | HC-130H | Barbers Point |
| 1720 | HC-130H | Clearwater |
| 1790 | HC-130H | Kodiak |
| 2001 | HC-130J | Elizabeth City |
| 2002 | HC-130J | Elizabeth City |
| 2003 | HC-130J | Elizabeth City |
| 2004 | HC-130J | Elizabeth City |
| 2005 | HC-130J | Elizabeth City |
| 2006 | HC-130J | Elizabeth City |

# Aircraft in US Government or Military Services with Civil Registrations

**BAe 125-800A (C-29A)**
Federal Aviation Administration, Oklahoma
| | |
|---|---|
| N94 | (88-0269) |
| N95 | (88-0270) |
| N96 | (88-0271) |
| N97 | (88-0272) |
| N98 | (88-0273) |
| N99 | (88-0274) |

**Canadair CL.601/CL.604\***
**Challenger**
Federal Aviation Administration, Oklahoma
N85
N86
N87
N88*

**Gates LearJet 35A**
Phoenix Aviation/Flight International/
  US Navy, Naples
N20DK
N50FN
N88JA
N118FN
N710GS

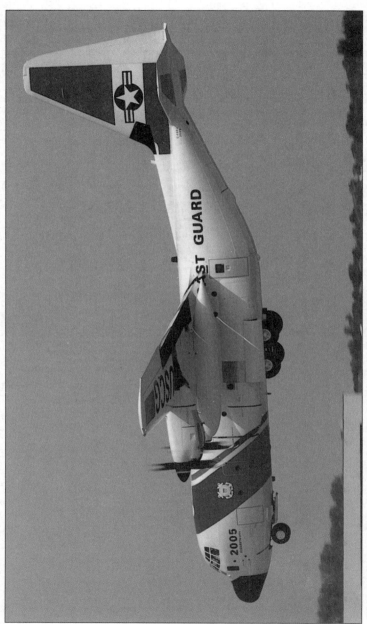

Colourful Lockheed HC-130J Hercules 2005 is flown by the US Coast Guard at CGS Elizabeth City, NC.

# Military Aviation Sites on the Internet

The list below is not intended to be a complete list of military aviation sites on the Internet. The sites listed cover Museums, Locations, Air Forces, Companies and Organisations that are mentioned elsewhere in 'Military Aircraft Markings'. Sites listed are in English or contain sufficient English to be reasonably easily understood. Each site address is believed to be correct at the time of going to press. Additions are welcome, via the usual address found at the front of the book, or via e-mail to admin@aviation-links.co.uk. An up to date copy of this list is to be found at http://www.aviation-links.co.uk/.

| NAME OF SITE | INTERNET DIAL (ALL PREFIXED 'HTTP://') |
| --- | --- |
| No 1 Sqn | www.raf.mod.uk/rafcottesmore/1sqn.html |
| No 2 Sqn | www.rafmarham.co.uk/organisation/2squadron/2squadron.htm |
| No 3 Flt | www.leuchars.raf.mod.uk/lodg3aac.htm |
| No 3 Sqn | www.raf.mod.uk/rafcottesmore/3sqn.html |
| No 4 Regiment Army Air Corps | www.4regimentaac.co.uk/ |
| No 4 Sqn | www.raf-cott.demon.co.uk/4Sqn.htm |
| No 6 Flt | www.shawbury.raf.mod.uk/6fltaac.htm |
| No 6 Sqn | www.raf.mod.uk/rafcoltishall/6squadron.html |
| No 7 Sqn | www.raf.mod.uk/rafodiham/7sqn.html |
| No 8 Sqn | www.users.globalnet.co.uk/~8sqnwad/ |
| No 9 Sqn | www.rafmarham.co.uk/organisation/9squadron/9sqn_front.htm |
| No 12 Sqn | www.loscom.org.uk/sqns/12sqn/12sqn.html |
| No 13 Sqn | www.rafmarham.co.uk/organisation/13squadron/13squadron.htm |
| No 14 Sqn | www.loscom.org.uk/sqns/14sqn/14sqn.html |
| No 15(R) Sqn | www.loscom.org.uk/sqns/xvsquadron/xvsquadron.html |
| No 16(R) Sqn | www.raf.mod.uk/rafcoltishall/16squadron.html |
| No 18 Sqn | www.raf.mod.uk/rafodiham/18sqn.html |
| No 19(R) Sqn | www.rafvalley.org/Flying/19Sqn/19Sqnindex.htm |
| No 20(R) Sqn | www.raf.mod.uk/rafwittering/squadrons.html |
| No 23 Sqn | www.users.globalnet.co.uk/~23sqnwad/ |
| No 24 Sqn | www.lyneham.raf.mod.uk/24sqn/xxiv.htm |
| No 27 Sqn | www.raf.mod.uk/rafodiham/27sqn.html |
| No 31 Sqn | www.rafmarham.co.uk/organisation/31squadron/31sqn.htm |
| No 39(1 PRU) Sqn | www.rafmarham.co.uk/organisation/39squadron/39squadron2.htm |
| No 41 Sqn | www.raf.mod.uk/rafcoltishall/41squadron.html |
| No 42(R) Sqn | www.kinloss-raf.co.uk//42sqnintro.html |
| No 43 Sqn | www.leuchars.raf.mod.uk/sqn43.htm |
| No 45(R) Sqn | www.cranwell.raf.mod.uk/Squadrons/45Sqn/45squadron.html |
| No 51 Sqn | website.lineone.net/~redgoose/ |
| No 54 Sqn | www.raf.mod.uk/rafcoltishall/54squadron.html |
| No 55(R) Sqn | www.cranwell.raf.mod.uk/Squadrons/55Sqn/55squadron.html |
| No 56(R) Sqn | www.leuchars.raf.mod.uk/sqn56.htm |
| No 70 Sqn | 70sqn.tripod.com/ |
| No 99 Sqn | www.raf.mod.uk/rafbrizenorton/squadrons/99squadron.html |
| No 101 Sqn | www.raf.mod.uk/rafbrizenorton/squadrons/101squadron.html |
| No 111 Sqn | www.leuchars.raf.mod.uk/sqn111.htm |
| No 120 Sqn | www.kinloss-raf.co.uk//120sqnintro.htm |
| No 201 Sqn | www.kinloss-raf.co.uk//201sqnintro.html |
| No 202 Sqn | www.202squadron.com/ |
| No 206 Sqn | www.kinloss.raf.mod.uk/opswing/ops206.htm |
| No 216 Sqn | www.raf.mod.uk/rafbrizenorton/squadrons/216squadron.html |
| No 617 Sqn | www.loscom.org.uk/sqns/617sqn/617sqn.html |
| No 700M NAS | www.royal-navy.mod.uk/content/1500.html |
| No 702 NAS | www.royal-navy.mod.uk/content/804.html |
| No 727 NAS | www.royal-navy.mod.uk/content/3322.html |
| No 750 NAS | www.royal-navy.mod.uk/content/805.html |

| Name of site | Internet Dial (all prefixed 'http://') |
|---|---|
| No 771 NAS | www.royal-navy.mod.uk/content/806.html |
| No 792 NAS | www.royal-navy.mod.uk/content/3907.html |
| No 814 NAS | www.royal-navy.mod.uk/content/810.html |
| No 815 NAS | www.royal-navy.mod.uk/content/811.html |
| No 820 NAS | www.royal-navy.mod.uk/content/813.html |
| No 824 NAS | www.royal-navy.mod.uk/content/1909.html |
| No 845 NAS | www.royal-navy.mod.uk/content/814.html |
| No 846 NAS | www.royal-navy.mod.uk/content/815.html |
| No 847 NAS | www.royal-navy.mod.uk/content/816.html |
| No 848 NAS | www.royal-navy.mod.uk/content/817.html |
| No 849 NAS | www.royal-navy.mod.uk/content/818.html |
| Aberdeen, Dundee and St Andrews UAS | dialspace.dial.pipex.com/town/way/gba87/adstauas/ |
| The Army Air Corps | www.army.mod.uk/armyaircorps/info.htm |
| Blue Eagles Home Page | www.deltaweb.co.uk/eagles/ |
| Cambridge University Air Squadron | www.srcf.ucam.org/cuas/ |
| Defence Helicopter Flying School | www.shawbury.raf.mod.uk/dhfs.htm |
| East Midlands UAS | www.emuas.dial.pipex.com/ |
| Fleet Air Arm | www.royal-navy.mod.uk/static/pages/145.html |
| JFACTSU | www.raf.mod.uk/jfactsu/ |
| Liverpool University Air Squadron | www.sn63.dial.pipex.com/ |
| Manchester & Salford Universities Air Sqn | www.masuas.dial.pipex.com/ |
| Ministry of Defence | www.mod.uk/ |
| Northumbrian UAS | www.castle-jcr.dus.ac/ul/ranger/ |
| Oxford University Air Sqn | users.ox.ac.uk/~ouairsqn/ |
| QinetiQ | www.qinetiq.com/ |
| RAF Benson | www.raf.mod.uk/rafbenson/index.htm |
| RAF Boulmer | www.rafboulmer.co.uk/ |
| RAF Brize Norton | www.raf.mod.uk/rafbrizenorton/ |
| RAF Church Fenton (unofficial) | www.rafchurchfenton.org.uk/ |
| RAF College Cranwell | www.cranwell.raf.mod.uk/ |
| RAF Coltishall | www.raf.mod.uk/rafcoltishall/ |
| RAF Cosford | www.raf.mod.uk/cosford/ |
| RAF Cottesmore | www.raf.mod.uk/rafcottesmore/ |
| RAF Kinloss | www.kinloss.raf.mod.uk/ |
| RAF Leuchars | www.leuchars.raf.mod.uk/ |
| RAF Lossiemouth | www.loscom.org.uk/ |
| RAF Lyneham | www.lyneham.raf.mod.uk/ |
| RAF Marham | www.rafmarham.co.uk/ |
| RAF Northolt | www.rafnortholt.com/ |
| RAF Northolt (unofficial) | www.fly.to/Northolt/ |
| RAF Odiham | www.raf.mod.uk/rafodiham/index.html |
| RAF Shawbury | www.shawbury.raf.mod.uk/ |
| RAF Valley | www.rafvalley.org/ |
| RAF Waddington | www.raf-waddington.com/ |
| RAF Wittering | www.raf.mod.uk/rafwittering/ |
| Red Arrows | www.raf.mod.uk/reds/redhome.html |
| Royal Air Force | www.raf.mod.uk/ |
| Royal Auxiliary Air Force | www.rauxaf.mod.uk/ |
| University of London Air Sqn | www.raf.mod.uk/ulas |
| Yorkshire UAS | www.yuas.dial.pipex.com/ |

**MILITARY SITES-US**

| | |
|---|---|
| Air Combat Command | www.acc.af.mil/ |
| Air Force Reserve Command | www.afrc.af.mil/ |
| Air National Guard | www.ang.af.mil/ |
| Aviano Air Base | www.aviano.af.mil/ |
| Liberty Wing Home Page (48th FW) | www.lakenheath.af.mil/ |
| NASA | www.nasa.gov/ |
| Ramstein Air Base | www.ramstein.af.mil/home.html |
| Spangdahlem Air Base | www.spangdahlem.af.mil/ |
| USAF | www.af.mil/ |
| USAF Europe | www.usafe.af.mil/ |
| USAF World Wide Web Sites | www.af.mil/sites/ |
| US Army | www.army.mil/ |
| US Marine Corps | www.usmc.mil/ |
| US Navy | www.navy.mil/ |
| US Navy Patrol Squadrons (unofficial) | www.vpnavy.com/ |

**MILITARY SITES-ELSEWHERE**

| | |
|---|---|
| Armée de l'Air | www.defense.gouv.fr/air/ |
| Aeronautica Militare | www.aeronautica.difesa.it |
| Austrian Armed Forces (in German) | www.bmlv.gv.at/ |

# Military Aviation Internet

| Name of site | Internet Dial (all prefixed 'http://') |
|---|---|
| Belgian Air Force | www.mil.be/aircomp/index.asp?LAN=E |
| Canadian Forces | www.forces.ca/ |
| Finnish Defence Force | www.mil.fi/english/ |
| Forca Aerea Portuguesa | www.emfa.pt/ |
| Frecce Tricolori | users.iol.it/gromeo/ |
| German Marine | www.deutschemarine.de/ |
| Greek Air Force | www.haf.gr/gea_uk/frame.htm |
| Irish Air Corps | www.military.ie/aircorps/index.html |
| Israeli Defence Force/Air Force | www.idf.il/ |
| Luftforsvaret | www.mil.no/ |
| Luftwaffe | www.luftwaffe.de/ |
| NATO | www.nato.int/ |
| Royal Australian Air Force | www.defence.gov.au/RAAF/ |
| Royal Danish Air Force (in Danish) | www.ftk.dk/ |
| Royal Netherlands AF | www.luchtmacht.nl/ |
| Royal New Zealand AF | www.airforce.mil.nz/ |
| Singapore Air Force | www.mindef.gov.sg/rsaf/ |
| South African AF Site (unofficial) | www.saairforce.co.za/ |
| Spanish Air Force | www.aire.org/ |
| Swedish Air Force | www.mil.se/ |
| Swedish Military Aviation (unofficial) | www.canit.se/%7Egriffon/aviation/ |
| Swiss Armed Forces | www.vbs.admin.ch/internet/e/armee/ |
| Turkish General Staff (Armed Forces) | www.tsk.mil.tr/ |

## AIRCRAFT & AERO ENGINE MANUFACTURERS

| | |
|---|---|
| BAE Systems | www.baesystems.com/ |
| Bell Helicopter Textron | www.bellhelicopter.textron.com/index.html |
| Boeing | www.boeing.com/ |
| Bombardier | www.bombardier.com/ |
| Britten-Norman | www.britten-norman.com/ |
| CFM International | www.cfm56.com/ |
| Dassault | www.dassault-aviation.com/ |
| EADS | www.eads.net/ |
| Embraer | www.embraer.com/ |
| General Electric | www.ge.com/ |
| Gulfstream Aerospace | www.gulfstream.com/ |
| Kaman Aerospace | www.kaman.com/ |
| Lockheed Martin | www.lockheedmartin.com/ |
| Lockheed Martin Aeronautics | www.lmaeronautics.com/palmdale/index.html |
| Raytheon | www.raytheon.com/rac/ |
| Rolls-Royce | www.rolls-royce.com/ |
| SAAB | www.saab.se/ |
| Sikorsky | www.sikorsky.com/ |
| Westland | www.whl.co.uk/ |

## UK AVIATION MUSEUMS

| | |
|---|---|
| Aeroventure | www.aeroventure.org.uk/ |
| Bournemouth Aviation Museum | www.aviation-museum.co.uk/ |
| Brooklands Museum | www.brooklandsmuseum.com/ |
| City of Norwich Aviation Museum | www.cnam.co.uk/ |
| Cold War Jets | www.coldwarjets.co.uk/ |
| de Havilland Aircraft Heritage Centre | www.hertsmuseums.org.uk/dehavilland/index.htm |
| Dumfries & Galloway Aviation Museum | www.dgam.co.uk/ |
| Fleet Air Arm Museum | www.fleetairarm.com/ |
| Gatwick Aviation Museum | www.gatwick-aviation-museum.co.uk/ |
| The Helicopter Museum | www.helicoptermuseum.co.uk/ |
| Imperial War Museum, Duxford | www.iwm.org.uk/duxford/ |
| Imperial War Museum, Duxford (unofficial) | dspace.dial.pipex.com/town/square/rcy85/ |
| The Jet Age Museum | www.jetagemuseum.org/ |
| Lincs Aviation Heritage Centre | freespace.virgin.net/nick.tasker/ekirkby.htm |
| Midland Air Museum | www.midlandairmuseum.co.uk/ |
| Museum of Army Flying | www.flying-museum.org.uk/ |
| Museum of Berkshire Aviation | fly.to/MuseumofBerkshireAviation/ |
| Museum of Flight, East Fortune | www.nms.ac.uk/flight/index.asp |
| Museum of Science & Industry, Manchester | www.msim.org.uk/ |
| Newark Air Museum | www.newarkairmuseum.co.uk/ |
| North East Aircraft Museum | www.neam.co.uk/ |
| RAF Manston Spitfire & Hurricane Memorial | www.spitfire-museum.com/ |
| RAF Museum, Hendon | www.rafmuseum.org.uk/ |
| Science Museum, South Kensington | www.sciencemuseum.org.uk/ |
| Yorkshire Air Museum, Elvington | www.yorkshireairmuseum.co.uk |

| Names of sites | Internet Dial (all prefixed 'http;//') |
|---|---|

## AVIATION SOCIETIES

| | |
|---|---|
| Air Britain | www.air-britain.com/ |
| Air North | www.airnorth.demon.co.uk/ |
| Cleveland Aviation Society | homepage.ntlworld.com/phillip.charlton/ cashome.html |
| East London Aviation Society | www.westrowops.co.uk/newsletter/elas.htm |
| Friends of Leeming Aviation Group | www.screamin-leeming.co.uk/ |
| Gilze-Rijen Aviation Society | www.gras-spotters.nl/ |
| Lowestoft Aviation Society | www.lowestoftaviationsociety.org/ |
| Royal Aeronautical Society | www.raes.org.uk/ |
| St Athan Aviation Group | www.westrowops.co.uk/newsletter/stamu.htm |
| Scottish Air News | www.scottishairnews.co.uk/ |
| Scramble (Dutch Aviation Society) | www.scramble.nl/ |
| Solent Aviation Society | www.solent-aviation-society.co.uk/ |
| Spitfire Society | www.spitfiresociety.demon.co.uk/ |
| The Aviation Society Manchester | www.tasmanchester.com/ |
| Ulster Aviation Society | www.d-n-a.net/users/dnetrAzQ/ |
| Wolverhampton Aviation Group | www.wolverhamptonaviationgroup.co.uk/ |

## OPERATORS OF HISTORIC AIRCRAFT

| | |
|---|---|
| The Aircraft Restoration Company | www.arc-duxford.co.uk/ |
| Battle of Britain Memorial Flight | www.bbmf.co.uk/ |
| Catalina Online | www.catalina.org.uk/ |
| De Havilland Aviation | www.dehavilland.net/ |
| Delta Jets | www.deltajets.com/ |
| Hunter Flying Club | www.hunterflyingclub.co.uk/ |
| Kennet Aircraft | www.airplane.demon.co.uk/ |
| Old Flying Machine Company | www.ofmc.co.uk/ |
| The Fighter Collection | www.fighter-collection.com/ |
| The Real Aeroplane Company | www.realaero.com/ |
| The Shuttleworth Collection | www.shuttleworth.org/ |
| The Vulcan Operating Company | www.tvoc.co.uk/ |

## SITES RELATING TO SPECIFIC TYPES OF MILITARY AIRCRAFT

| | |
|---|---|
| The 655 Maintenance & Preservation Society | www.xm655.com/ |
| The Avro Shackleton Page | www.home.aone.net.au/shack_one/ |
| B-24 Liberator | www.b24bestweb.com/ |
| EE Canberra | www.bywat.co.uk/ |
| English Electric Lightning - Vertical Reality | www.aviation-picture-hangar.co.uk/Lightning.html |
| The Eurofighter site | www.eurofighter.org/ |
| The ex FRADU Canberra Site | www.fradu-hunters.co.uk/canberra/ |
| The ex FRADU Hunter Site | www.fradu-hunters.co.uk/ |
| F-4 Phantom II Society | www.f4phantom.com/ |
| F-16: The Complete Reference | www.f-16.net/ |
| F-86 Web Page | f-86.tripod.com/ |
| F-105 Thunderchief | www.geocities.com/Pentagon/7002/ |
| The Gripen | www.gripen.com/ |
| Jet Provost Heaven | www.jetprovosts.com |
| K5083 - Home Page (Hawker Hurricane) | www3.mistral.co.uk/k5083/ |
| Lockheed C-130 Hercules | hometown.aol.com/SamC130/ |
| Lockheed SR-71 Blackbird | www.wvi.com/~lelandh/sr-71~1.htm |
| The MiG-21 Page | www.topedge.com/panels/aircraft/sites/kraft/mig.htm |
| P-3 Orion Research Group | home.wxs.nl/~p3orin/ |
| P-51 Mustang | www.p51.mustangsmustangs.com/ |
| Scramble on the Web - SAAB Viggen Database | www.scramble.nl/viggen.htm |
| Thunder & Lightnings (Postwar British Aircraft) | www.thunder-and-lightnings.co.uk/ |
| UK Apache Resource Centre | www.ukapache.com/ |
| Vulcan 558 Club | www.vulcan558club.demon.co.uk/ |
| Vulcan Restoration Trust | www.XL426.com |

## MISCELLANEOUS

| | |
|---|---|
| Aerodata | www.aerodata.biz/ |
| Aeroflight | www.netlink.co.uk/users/aeroflt/ |
| The AirNet Web Site | fly.to/AirNet/ |
| Air-Scene UK | www.f4aviation.co.uk |
| Chinese Military Aviation | www.concentric.net/~Jetfight/ |
| Demobbed: Out of Service British Military Aircraft | www.demobbed.org.uk |
| Joseph F. Baugher's US Military Serials Site | home.att.net/%7Ejbaugher/ |
| Military Aircraft Database | www.csd.uwo.ca/~pettypi/elevon/gustin_military/ |
| Military Aviation | www.crakehal.demon.co.uk/aviation/aviation.htm |
| Military Aviation Review/MAP | www.mar.co.uk/ |
| Pacific Aviation Database Organisation | www.gfiapac.co.uk/ |

## Military Aviation Internet

| | |
|---|---|
| Polish Aviation Site | aviation.pol.pl/ |
| Russian Aviation Page | aeroweb.lucia.it/~agretch/RAP.html |
| Scramble on the Web - Air Show Reports | www.scramble.nl/airshows.htm |
| The Spotter's Nest | www.spotters.it/ |
| Target Lock Military Aviation E-zine | www.targetlock.org.uk/ |
| UK Military Aircraft Serials Resource Centre | www.ukserials.com/ |
| UK Military Spotting | www.thunder-and-lightnings.co.uk/spotting/ |

USAFE F-16CJ Fighting Falcon 91-0352/SP from 22nd FS/52nd FW based at Spangdahlem, Germany.